INTRODUCTION TO

Vector Analysis

THIRD EDITION

INTRODUCTION TO *Vector Analysis*

Harry F. Davis
University of Waterloo, Canada

Arthur David Snider
University of South Florida

ALLYN AND BACON, INC. BOSTON

Library of Congress Cataloging in Publication Data

Davis, Harry F
Introduction to vector analysis.

1. *Vector analysis. I. Snider, Arthur David,*
1940– *joint author. II. Title.*

QA433.D38 1975 515′.63 74-4749

Contents

Preface

In preparing the third edition of this book, the authors had one principal goal in mind: completeness. Since the earlier editions have enjoyed a reputation for expository excellence, the revisions are mainly directed toward enhancing its comprehensiveness as a reference. With the expanded treatment of cartesian tensors, vector identities, solenoidal vectors, and curvilinear coordinates, we feel that the new edition will stand the engineer and scientist in good stead for his professional needs in this area and provide the aspiring mathematician with a firm grasp of the three-dimensional versions of the theorems of higher geometry. Accordingly, we anticipate that the present text will continue to serve the student's needs for some time after he has completed his course work in the subject.

We felt, however, that some changes in the exposition would be beneficial, and we have incorporated many suggestions that have evolved from our colleagues' experiences in the classroom. For the edification of those familiar with the earlier editions, the major modifications to be found in this version are indicated here.

First of all, we have sought to introduce each new concept geometrically, reserving analytic definitions for later in the treatment. For instance, a discussion of the physical significance of the cross product, divergence, and curl precedes a heuristic derivation of the associated formulas. We feel that this approach will aid the student in remembering the concepts, encourage him to anticipate their integral theorems, and argue favorably for their covariance properties. Thus we defer, but do not delete, the rigorous treatments.

Secondly, the machinery of cartesian tensor notation is introduced early in the text (albeit in "optional" sections, designated with an asterisk). Although the tensor *concept* is not developed until Chapter 5, we see no reason why the student should be deprived of this valuable tool in deriving vector identities. In fact, we have expanded considerably the sections on the indentities, and the student who reads the tensor sections will find proofs of all of them.

The Frenet-Serret formulas are derived in the text by exploiting the analogy with rigid-body motion; indeed, the whole treatment of curve theory has been made more heuristic and less analytic, in accordance with the philosophy stated earlier. Along the same lines, the treatment of the curl is premised on its interpretation as the vorticity of a fluid, measured by the motion of a paddle wheel. And, as we hinted above, a new section has been added on the vector potential.

The section in Chapter 4 on orthogonal curvilinear coordinates has been expanded to include heuristic derivations of the expressions for all the vector operators. Although this material is rederived rigorously in the next chapter, experience seems to indicate that most classes don't cover Chapter 5, so a broader treatment on the elementary level seemed worthwhile.

With regard to the problems: new ones have been added, and the ordering of the problems has been rearranged according to increasing difficulty. In addition, it was clear from the comments of many of the users of the previous editions that the various *Review Problems* sections in the book were being ignored; accordingly, they have been dismantled and the problems redistributed among the appropriate sections. However, the final *Review* section was left intact, in fact supplemented, and it appears at the end of the present edition. The problems therein are distinguished by being more difficult, or more involved with specific applications, or more universal in scope.

Finally, the authors of the third edition would like to express their gratitude to the reviewers for their many helpful comments and suggestions.

CHAPTER

1

Vector Algebra

1.1 DEFINITIONS

The vector concept is closely related to the geometrical idea of a *directed line segment*. Roughly speaking, a vector is a quantity which has direction as well as magnitude. It is represented by an arrow of length equal to its magnitude, pointing in the appropriate direction. Two vectors **A** and **B** are said to be equal, $\mathbf{A} = \mathbf{B}$, if they have the same length and direction.

The definition just given suffers from a lack of precision that will be rectified in the following discussion.

Let us consider two points P and Q in space. If P and Q are distinct points, there will exist one and only one line passing through them both. That part of the line between P and Q, including both P and Q as endpoints, is called a *line segment*. A line segment is said to be *directed* when the endpoints are given a definite order. The same line segment determines two directed line segments, one denoted PQ and the other QP (or $-PQ$). If P and Q coincide, PQ is said to be *degenerate*.

Two directed line segments PQ and RS are said to be equivalent if $PQSR$ is a parallelogram. A *vector* is defined to be a *collection of equivalent directed line segments*. We may represent a vector by any one of the directed line segments in the collection. Thus, we may represent a vector by giving a particular directed line segment PQ, but it is understood that the vector itself is the set of all directed line segments that are equivalent to PQ.

Thus, in Fig. 1.1, we see that PQ and RS are equivalent, so that they represent the same vector. An infinite number of other directed line segments could be used to represent this same vector.

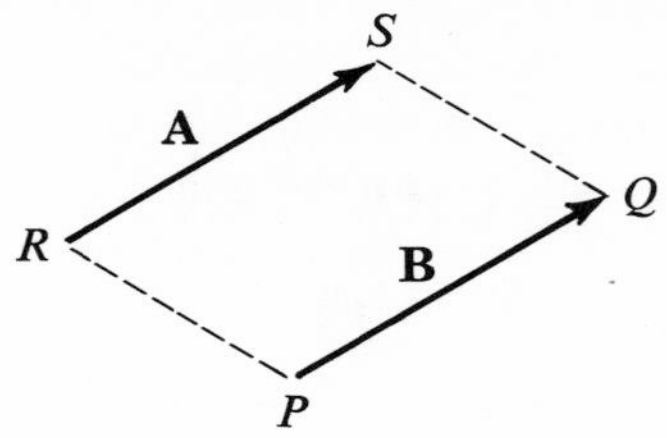

FIGURE 1.1

In this book, boldface letters are usually used to denote vectors. In the diagrams, a single directed line segment will often be drawn to represent a vector, and will be labeled by a boldface letter to denote the vector it represents. In Fig. 1.1, PQ is labeled **B** and RS is labeled **A**. Since both PQ and RS represent the same vector, we can write $\mathbf{A} = \mathbf{B}$. Notice, however, that PQ and RS are *not* the same directed line segment, since they occupy different positions in space, so we cannot write $PQ = RS$.

In this case, $\mathbf{A} = \mathbf{B}$ implies that PQ is parallel to RS, that PQ and RS have the same directed sense, and that the distance between P and Q is the same as the distance between R and S. This common distance is called the *magnitude* of the vector.

Any point (degenerate line segment) is said to represent the *zero vector* **0**. The vector **0** has zero magnitude and no defined direction. Since a direction can be ascribed only to nonzero vectors, the statement in the first paragraph of this section is technically incorrect. It ignores the exceptional zero vector.

Since the opposite sides of a parallelogram have the same magnitude, it makes perfectly good sense, within the context of elementary geometry, to say that PQ and RS have the *same* magnitude. This does not indicate how we are going to measure this magnitude. We might use centimeters or we might use inches.

Many of the quantities of physics are conveniently represented by vectors. As examples we mention force, displacement, velocity, acceleration, and magnetic field intensity. Such quantities are represented graphically by arrows of length proportional to the magnitude of the quantity, and pointing in the appropriate direction.

In some older books, what we call *directed line segments* were called *bound vectors*, and what we simply call "vectors" were called *free vectors*. The idea was that a "free vector" can be moved freely through space; provided it is always kept parallel to its initial position, and is never allowed to reverse its sense or to vary in magnitude, it does not really "change", whereas a "bound vector" could not be moved about in space. The distinction created logical difficulties for both the pure mathematician and for the physicist. For the pure mathematician, it is difficult to accept such loose terminology as "moving freely through space" in the definition of a quantity that does not fundamentally involve the idea of time or motion at all. For the physicist, the difficulty is in determining whether *force* is a bound or a free vector: in many cases, the effect produced by a force acting on a body depends not only on its magnitude and direction, but on its point of application as well; hence, force might well be regarded as a bound vector, but in deeper theoretical work this is extremely awkward. Physicists now regard force as a vector quantity (i.e., a "free" vector), recognizing nevertheless that the *effect* of a force may depend on where it is applied.

In this book, the word *scalar* is used as a synonym for *number*, until the last chapter, where only certain kinds of numerical quantities will be called *scalars*. Those quantities of physics that are characterized by numerical magnitude alone (and have nothing to do with direction) are called *scalars* or *scalar quantities*. Examples are mass, time, density, distance, temperature, and speed (as read from a speedometer).

Loosely speaking, you can think of a vector as simply an arrow, but recognize that two arrows are considered equal, from a vector viewpoint, provided they are parallel, have the same directed sense, and the same magnitude.

As I write this, I am sitting at a desk with a horizontal surface. How many vectors are there that are perpendicular to this surface, are directed upward, and have magnitude of three inches? *Only one.* There are an infinite number of directed line segments with these properties, but they are *identical* as vectors.

1.2 ADDITION AND SUBTRACTION

The *sum* $\mathbf{A} + \mathbf{B}$ of two vectors may be defined in the following way. Let the vectors be represented by arrows so placed that the terminal point of $\mathbf{A}$ coincides with the initial point of $\mathbf{B}$. Then $\mathbf{A} + \mathbf{B}$ is represented by the arrow extending from the initial point of $\mathbf{A}$ to the terminal point of $\mathbf{B}$ (Fig. 1.2). It is evident that this definition of addition is compatible with

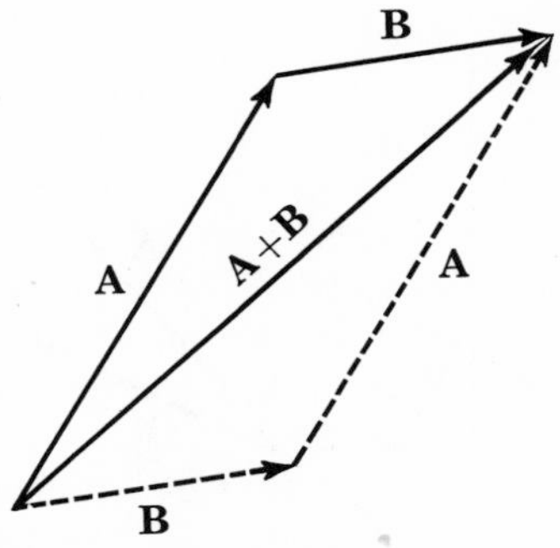

FIGURE 1.2

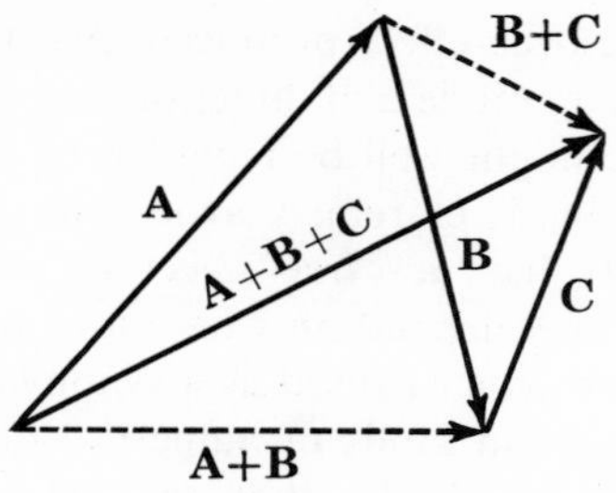

FIGURE 1.3

the definition of equality; that is, if $\mathbf{A} = \mathbf{A}'$ and $\mathbf{B} = \mathbf{B}'$, then $\mathbf{A} + \mathbf{B} = \mathbf{A}' + \mathbf{B}'$. Since opposite sides of a parallelogram are equal in magnitude and have the same direction (Fig. 1.2), vector addition is commutative, $\mathbf{A} + \mathbf{B} = \mathbf{B} + \mathbf{A}$. It is easy to see that it is also associative,

$$(\mathbf{A} + \mathbf{B}) + \mathbf{C} = \mathbf{A} + (\mathbf{B} + \mathbf{C})$$

so that there is no ambiguity in writing $\mathbf{A} + \mathbf{B} + \mathbf{C}$ without parentheses (Fig. 1.3).

If $\mathbf{B}$ is a vector, $-\mathbf{B}$ is defined to be the vector with the same magnitude as $\mathbf{B}$ but opposite direction (Fig. 1.4). Subtraction of vectors is defined by adding the negative,

$$\mathbf{A} - \mathbf{B} = \mathbf{A} + (-\mathbf{B})$$

The student who ignores this definition and simply memorizes Fig. 1.4 will inevitably confuse $\mathbf{A} - \mathbf{B}$ with $\mathbf{B} - \mathbf{A}$, which has the opposite direction.

The above definitions apply to the vector $\mathbf{0}$ if it is represented by a degenerate line segment. We have $\mathbf{0} = -\mathbf{0}$, $\mathbf{A} - \mathbf{A} = \mathbf{0}$, $\mathbf{A} + \mathbf{0} = \mathbf{A}$, $\mathbf{0} + \mathbf{A} = \mathbf{A}$, for every vector $\mathbf{A}$.

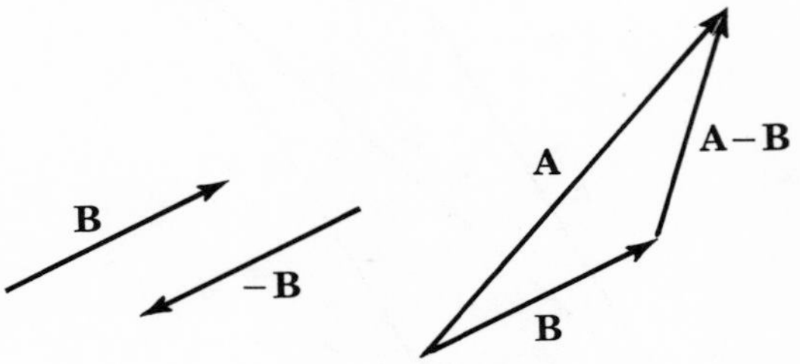

FIGURE 1.4

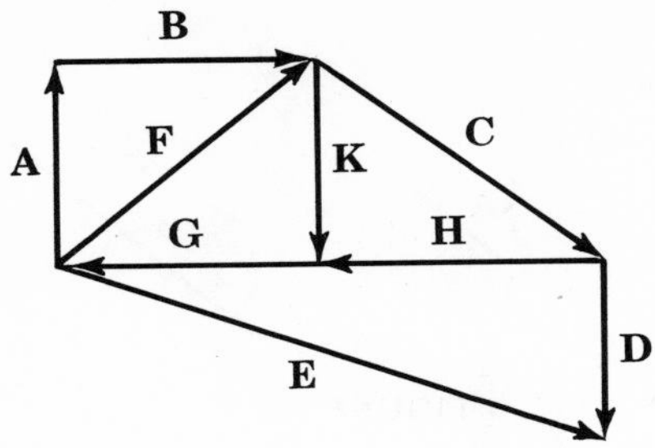

FIGURE 1.5

EXERCISES

1. If **A** and **B** are represented by arrows whose initial points coincide, what arrow represents $\mathbf{A} + \mathbf{B}$?
2. By drawing a diagram, show that if $\mathbf{A} + \mathbf{B} = \mathbf{C}$, then $\mathbf{B} = \mathbf{C} - \mathbf{A}$.
3. Is the following statement correct? If **A**, **B**, **C**, and **D** are nonzero vectors represented by arrows from the origin to the points A, B, C, D, and if $\mathbf{B} - \mathbf{A} = \mathbf{C} - \mathbf{D}$, then $ABCD$ is a parallelogram.
4. Let the sides of a regular hexagon be drawn as arrows, with the terminal point of each arrow at the initial point of the next.
   (a) If **A** and **B** are vectors represented by consecutive sides, find the other four vectors in terms of **A** and **B**.
   (b) What is the vector sum of all six vectors?

The following problems refer to Fig. 1.5:

5. Write **C** in terms of **E**, **D**, **F**.
6. Write **G** in terms of **C**, **D**, **E**, **K**.
7. Solve for **x**: $\mathbf{x} + \mathbf{B} = \mathbf{F}$.
8. Solve for **x**: $\mathbf{x} + \mathbf{H} = \mathbf{D} - \mathbf{E}$.

1.3 MULTIPLICATION OF VECTORS BY NUMBERS

The symbol $|\mathbf{A}|$ denotes the *magnitude* of the vector **A**. Although it should not be confused with $|s|$, which denotes (as usual) the absolute value of a number s, it does have many properties that are quite similar. For example, $|\mathbf{A}|$ is never negative, and $|\mathbf{A}| = 0$ if and only if $\mathbf{A} = \mathbf{0}$. Since **A** and $-\mathbf{A}$ have the same magnitude, we can always write $|\mathbf{A}| = |-\mathbf{A}|$ and $|\mathbf{A} - \mathbf{B}| = |\mathbf{B} - \mathbf{A}|$. The inequality

$$|\mathbf{A} + \mathbf{B}| \leq |\mathbf{A}| + |\mathbf{B}|$$

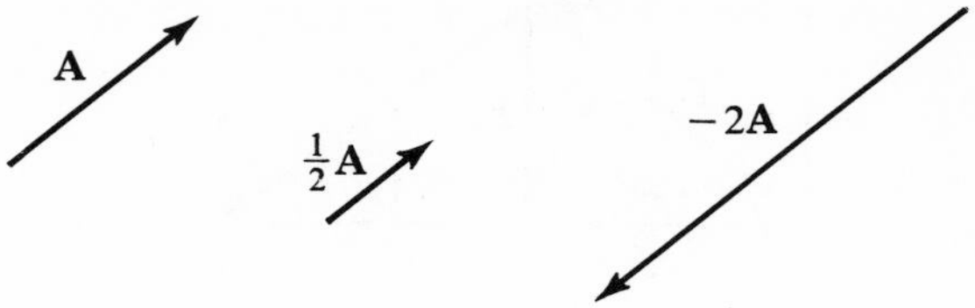

FIGURE 1.6

is the vector expression of the fact that the side of any triangle does not exceed, in length, the sum of the lengths of the other two sides (Fig. 1.2).

If s is a number and **A** is a vector, $s\mathbf{A}$ is defined to be the vector having magnitude $|s|$ times that of **A** and pointing in the same direction if s is positive or in the opposite direction if s is negative. Any vector $s\mathbf{A}$ is called a *scalar multiple* of **A** (Fig. 1.6).

Here are the fundamental properties of the operation of multiplying vectors by numbers:

$$0\mathbf{A} = \mathbf{0} \qquad 1\mathbf{A} = \mathbf{A} \qquad (-1)\mathbf{A} = -\mathbf{A} \tag{1.1}$$

$$(s + t)\mathbf{A} = s\mathbf{A} + t\mathbf{A} \tag{1.2}$$

$$s(\mathbf{A} + \mathbf{B}) = s\mathbf{A} + s\mathbf{B} \tag{1.3}$$

$$s(t\mathbf{A}) = (st)\mathbf{A} \tag{1.4}$$

EXERCISES

1. Is it ever possible to have $|\mathbf{A}| < 0$?

2. If $|\mathbf{A}| = 3$, what is $|4\mathbf{A}|$? What is $|-2\mathbf{A}|$? What can you say about $|s\mathbf{A}|$ if you know that $-2 \leq s \leq 1$?

3. If **A** is a nonzero vector, and if $s = |\mathbf{A}|^{-1}$, what is $|s\mathbf{A}|$? What is $|-s\mathbf{A}|$?

4. If **B** is a nonzero vector, and $s = |\mathbf{A}|/|\mathbf{B}|$, what can you say about $|s\mathbf{B}|$?

5. If **A** is a scalar multiple of **B**, is **B** necessarily a scalar multiple of **A**?

6. If $\mathbf{A} - \mathbf{B} = \mathbf{0}$, is it necessarily true that $\mathbf{A} = \mathbf{B}$?

7. If $|\mathbf{A}| = |\mathbf{B}|$, is it necessarily true that $\mathbf{A} = \mathbf{B}$?

8. You are given a plane in space. How many distinct vectors of unit magnitude are perpendicular to this plane?

9. How many distinct vectors exist, all having unit magnitude, perpendicular to a given line in space?

10. If **A** is a nonzero vector, how many distinct scalar multiples of **A** will have unit magnitude?

11. Let **A** and **B** be nonzero vectors represented by arrows with the same initial point to points A and B respectively. Let **C** denote the vector represented by an arrow from this same initial point to the midpoint of the line segment AB. Write **C** in terms of **A** and **B**.
12. Prove that $|\mathbf{A} - \mathbf{B}| \geq |\mathbf{A}| - |\mathbf{B}|$.
13. Find nonzero scalars a, b, and c such that $a\mathbf{A} + b(\mathbf{A} - \mathbf{B}) + c(\mathbf{A} + \mathbf{B}) = \mathbf{0}$ for every pair of vectors **A** and **B**.

1.4 CARTESIAN COORDINATES

Let us consider a cartesian coordinate system in the plane, obtained by introducing two mutually perpendicular axes, labeled x and y, with the same unit of length on both axes (Fig. 1.7). We assume that the reader is already familiar with this construction, which sets up a one-to-one correspondence between points in the plane and ordered pairs (x,y) of numbers.

Let **i** denote the unit vector parallel to the x axis, in the positive x direction, and **j** the unit vector in the positive y direction. Every vector in the plane can be written uniquely in the form

$$\mathbf{A} = A_1\mathbf{i} + A_2\mathbf{j}$$

for a suitable choice of numbers A_1 and A_2. These numbers are called the *components* of **A** in the x direction and y direction respectively; the component of a vector in a given direction is the orthogonal projection of the vector in that direction.

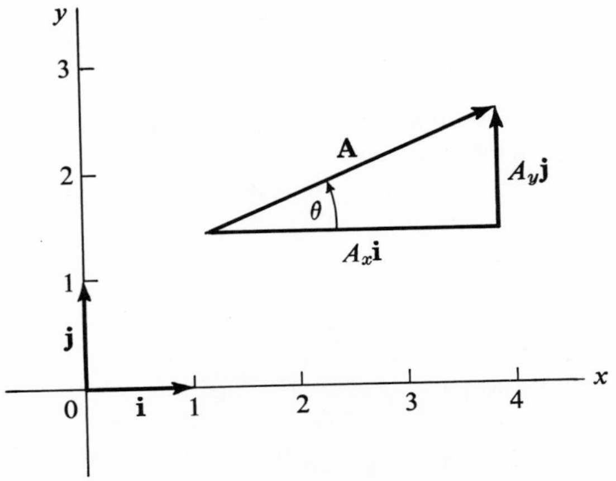

FIGURE 1.7

The magnitude of **A** can be determined from its components by using the pythagorean theorem:

$$|\mathbf{A}| = \sqrt{A_1{}^2 + A_2{}^2}$$

To determine the components of a vector, *any* directed line segment representing the vector can be used. Thus, if $P_1(x_1,y_1)$ and $P_2(x_2,y_2)$ are points in the xy plane, the vector represented by the directed line segment P_1P_2 (initial point P_1, terminal point P_2) is $(x_2 - x_1)\mathbf{i} + (y_2 - y_1)\mathbf{j}$. Any other directed line segment equivalent to P_1P_2 would give the same components.

Example 1.1 The directed line segment extending from (4,6) to (7,11) is equivalent to the directed line segment extending from (−1,3) to (2,8). Both of these directed line segments represent the vector $3\mathbf{i} + 5\mathbf{j}$.

EXERCISES

1. What is the x component of **i**?

2. What is the x component of **j**?

3. What is the magnitude of $\mathbf{i} + \mathbf{j}$?

4. What is the magnitude of $3\mathbf{i} - 4\mathbf{j}$?

5. With the axes in conventional position (Fig. 1.7), directions may be specified in geographical terms. What is the unit vector pointing west? south? northeast?

6. Vector **A** is represented by an arrow with initial point (4,2) and terminal point (5,−1). Write **A** in terms of **i** and **j**.

7. In Fig. 1.7, if $|\mathbf{A}| = 6$ and $\theta = 30°$, determine A_1 and A_2.

8. The direction of a nonzero vector in the plane can be described by giving the angle θ it makes with the positive x direction. This angle is conventionally taken to be positive in the counterclockwise sense. Write A_1 and A_2 in terms of $|\mathbf{A}|$ and this angle θ.

9. In terms of **i** and **j**, determine
(a) the unit vector at positive angle 60° with the x axis;
(b) the unit vector with $\theta = -30°$ (θ as in Exercise 6);
(c) the unit vector having the same direction as $3\mathbf{i} + 4\mathbf{j}$;
(d) the unit vectors having x components equal to $\frac{1}{2}$;
(e) the unit vectors perpendicular to the line $x + y = 0$.

10. Determine $|6\mathbf{i} + 8\mathbf{j}|$, $|-3\mathbf{i}|$, $|\mathbf{i} + s\mathbf{j}|$, $|(\cos\theta)\mathbf{i} + (\sin\theta)\mathbf{j}|$.

11. In terms of **i** and **j**, determine the vector represented by the arrow extending from the origin to the midpoint of the line segment joining (1,4) with (3,8).

1.5 SPACE VECTORS

Throughout most of this book, we shall be concerned with vectors in space. By the introduction of three mutually perpendicular axes, with the same unit of length along all three axes, we obtain the usual cartesian coordinate system. The conventional orientation of axes is shown in Fig, 1.8. Every vector can be expressed in the form $\mathbf{A} = A_1\mathbf{i} + A_2\mathbf{j} + A_3\mathbf{k}$ where **i**, **j**, and **k** are unit vectors in the positive x, y, and z directions respectively. The numbers A_1, A_2, and A_3 are the components of **A** in the x, y, and z directions respectively.

If $P_1(x_1,y_1,z_1)$, $P_2(x_2,y_2,z_2)$, and $P_3(x_3,y_3,z_3)$ are points in space, the vector represented by P_1P_2 is

$$(x_2 - x_1)\mathbf{i} + (y_2 - y_1)\mathbf{j} + (z_2 - z_1)\mathbf{k}$$

and similarly for P_2P_3 and P_1P_3. Observe that the components of P_1P_3 are given by the sums of the corresponding components of P_1P_2 and P_2P_3; e.g., in the x direction we have

$$x_3 - x_1 = (x_2 - x_1) + (x_3 - x_2)$$

Since, furthermore, P_1P_3 represents the *vector* sum of P_1P_2 and P_2P_3, we have shown that vector addition proceeds componentwise; i.e.,

$$\mathbf{A} + \mathbf{B} = (A_1 + B_1)\mathbf{i} + (A_2 + B_2)\mathbf{j} + (A_3 + B_3)\mathbf{k}$$

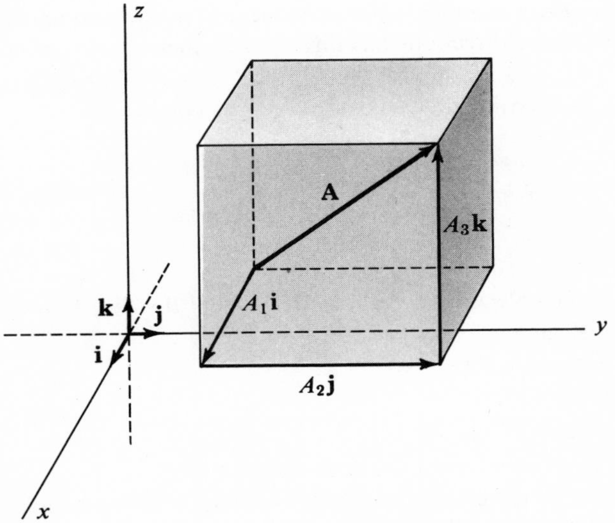

FIGURE 1.8

Similar reasoning for multiplication by a scalar shows that, in terms of components,

$$s\mathbf{A} = sA_1\mathbf{i} + sA_2\mathbf{j} + sA_3\mathbf{k}$$

The commutative and associative laws of addition for space vectors follow immediately from the expressions. These can also be verified by interpreting Figs. 1.2 and 1.3 as three-dimensional.

By a double application of the pythagorean theorem, we obtain

$$|\mathbf{A}| = \sqrt{A_1^2 + A_2^2 + A_3^2}$$

A nonzero vector in space also can be described by giving its magnitude and direction. We can describe the direction by giving three *direction angles* α, β, and γ, which are the angles between the vector and the positive x, y, and z directions respectively. Sometimes it is more convenient to give $\cos\alpha$, $\cos\beta$, and $\cos\gamma$, which are called the *direction cosines* of the vector.

The direction cosines are given by:

$$\cos\alpha = \frac{A_1}{|\mathbf{A}|} \qquad \cos\beta = \frac{A_2}{|\mathbf{A}|} \qquad \cos\gamma = \frac{A_3}{|\mathbf{A}|}$$

They are related by the identity

$$\cos^2\alpha + \cos^2\beta + \cos^2\gamma = 1$$

which shows that, if we know two direction cosines, the third is determined (except for its sign).

There is no way of telling from the direction cosines what the *magnitude* of the vector may be; the magnitude must be specified separately. For example, *any* vector parallel to the yz plane and making an angle of 45° with the positive y and z directions has direction cosines

$$\cos\alpha = 0 \qquad \cos\beta = \frac{\sqrt{2}}{2} \qquad \cos\gamma = \frac{\sqrt{2}}{2}$$

EXERCISES

In the first seven problems below let $\mathbf{A} = 3\mathbf{i} + 4\mathbf{j}$, $\mathbf{B} = 2\mathbf{i} + 2\mathbf{j} - \mathbf{k}$, and $\mathbf{C} = 3\mathbf{i} - 4\mathbf{k}$.

1. Find $|\mathbf{A}|$, $|\mathbf{B}|$, and $|\mathbf{C}|$.

2. Find $\mathbf{A} + \mathbf{B}$ and $\mathbf{A} - \mathbf{C}$.

3. Determine $|\mathbf{A} - \mathbf{C}|$.

4. For what values of s is $|s\mathbf{B}| = 1$?

5. Find the unit vector having the same direction as **A**.

6. Let **A** and **C** be represented by arrows extending from the origin.
   (a) Find the length of the line segment joining their endpoints.
   (b) This line segment is parallel to one of the coordinate planes. Which one?

7. Let α denote the angle between **A** and the positive x direction. Determine $\cos\alpha$. Generalize.
8. Determine all unit vectors perpendicular to the xz plane.
9. Compute $|\mathbf{i}+\mathbf{j}+\mathbf{k}|$.
10. Write the vector represented by P_1P_2 in terms of **i**, **j**, and **k**, given that $P_1(3,4,7)$ and $P_2(4,-1,6)$ are points in space.
11. What vector is represented by the directed line segment OP, if O is the origin and $P(x,y,z)$ is a general point in space?
12. Let $\mathbf{D}=\mathbf{i}+\mathbf{j}+\mathbf{k}$, $\mathbf{E}=\mathbf{i}+\mathbf{j}-\mathbf{k}$, and $\mathbf{F}=\mathbf{i}-\mathbf{j}$. Determine scalars s, t, and r such that $4\mathbf{i}+6\mathbf{j}-\mathbf{k}=s\mathbf{D}+t\mathbf{E}+r\mathbf{F}$.
13. What are the direction cosines of the vector $2\mathbf{i}-2\mathbf{j}+\mathbf{k}$?
14. Derive the identity $\cos^2\alpha+\cos^2\beta+\cos^2\gamma=1$.
15. Give a geometrical description of the locus of all points P for which OP represents a vector with direction cosine $\cos\alpha=\frac{1}{2}$ (O is the origin).
16. How many unit vectors are there for which $\cos\alpha=\frac{1}{2}$ and also $\cos\beta=\frac{1}{2}$? Illustrate with a diagram.
17. **A** is a vector with direction cosines $\cos\alpha$, $\cos\beta$, and $\cos\gamma$ respectively. What are the direction cosines of the reflected image of **A** in the yz plane? (Think of the yz plane as a mirror.)
18. Determine all unit vectors for which $\cos\alpha=\cos\beta=\cos\gamma$.

1.6 DIGRESSION

This section can be omitted with no loss of continuity.

A first step in solving some problems in mechanics is to choose a coordinate system. For instance, if the problem involves a particle sliding down an inclined plane, it may be convenient to take one of the axes, say the x axis, parallel to the plane, and another axis, say the z axis, perpendicular to the plane. After we have chosen a particular coordinate system, we can speak of the *position vector* of the particle. This is the vector represented by the directed line segment extending from the origin (0,0,0) to the point (x,y,z) where the particle is located, and (in terms of **i**, **j**, and **k**) it is the vector $x\mathbf{i}+y\mathbf{j}+z\mathbf{k}$. (Strictly speaking, we should not say "position vector of a particle" because this might give the false impression that it is an intrinsic property of the particle, whereas it depends on the choice of the coordinate system.)

If a particle moves from an initial position (x_1,y_1,z_1) to another position (x_2,y_2,z_2) the displacement of the particle is the vector represented by the directed line segment extending from its initial position to its final position. This vector is $(x_2-x_1)\mathbf{i}+(y_2-y_1)\mathbf{j}+(z_2-z_1)\mathbf{k}$. Notice that if the initial position vector is $\mathbf{R}_1=x_1\mathbf{i}+y_1\mathbf{j}+z_1\mathbf{k}$ and the final position vector is $\mathbf{R}_2=x_2\mathbf{i}+y_2\mathbf{j}+z_2\mathbf{k}$, the displacement is $\mathbf{R}_2-\mathbf{R}_1$. *The displacement of a particle is the final position vector minus the initial position vector.*

In Sec. 1.1 we stated that displacement is a vector quantity. This seems obvious since it is a physical quantity that can be represented by a directed line segment. Moreover, we defined the addition of vectors so that they add in the same way that displacements "add." Thus (Fig. 1.2) if a particle undergoes a displacement **A**, and then another displacement **B**, it is clear that the resultant displacement is $\mathbf{A} + \mathbf{B}$. That is, $\mathbf{A} + \mathbf{B}$ is the single displacement that produces the same net effect as the two displacements **A** and **B**. From the physicist's viewpoint, this is the reason for defining vector addition in this way.

Occasionally it is helpful to think of vectors as representing displacements, even when no physics is involved. For example, consider Exercise 5 of Sec. 1.2, where we are asked to write **C** in terms of **E**, **D**, and **F**. The answer is $\mathbf{C} = -\mathbf{F} + \mathbf{E} - \mathbf{D}$, which is clear since the net result of the three displacements $-\mathbf{F}$, **E**, and $-\mathbf{D}$ is **C**, as one can see by looking at Fig. 1.5.

Do not get the mistaken impression that when we represent a displacement by a vector **A**, the path of the particle has necessarily been straight. The directed line segment representing a displacement extends directly from the initial position to the final position, but the particle itself may have gone by way of the North Pole.

Forces are also vector quantities. This may *seem* obvious since a force is conveniently represented geometrically by a directed line segment. It is *not* so obvious, however. How do we know that forces "add" in the same way as vectors? We shall simply take the word of the physicists that they do, and let the interested reader study the matter elsewhere. If $\mathbf{F}_1$ and $\mathbf{F}_2$ are forces acting on a particle, their vector sum $\mathbf{F}_1 + \mathbf{F}_2$ is the single force that would produce the same effect, and is sometimes called the *resultant* of the two forces. In elementary physics the resultant of two or more forces is usually found in the following manner: one draws a diagram showing the forces, then systematically marks out each force, replacing it by its components along the coordinate axes. The forces along each axis are summed algebraically, so that one has a single force remaining along each of the coordinate axes. The magnitude of the resultant force **F** can then be found by the pythagorean theorem, since the axes are perpendicular. This is discussed with examples in *University Physics* by F. W. Sears and M. W. Zemansky (Addison-Wesley, 1963). The process is equivalent to writing each force in terms of **i**, **j**, and **k**, and adding them in the manner of the preceding section. In working with vectors in space, the use of the unit vectors **i**, **j**, and **k** is especially convenient, since it is hard to draw suitable diagrams.

It is rather surprising that rotations in space are *not* vector quantities. Clearly, a rotation can be represented by a directed line segment; the direction would be the axis of rotation, and the length would be the angle through which the body is rotated around that axis. But the result of two successive rotations is not represented by the vector sum of these line segments. In fact, the "sum" of two rotations is not even commutative! A body rotated through 90° about, first, the x direction, then the y direction, will achieve a final position quite different from the one resulting from the rotations performed in the other order (try this with the textbook). The proper description of rotations is discussed in *Classical Mechanics* by H. Goldstein (Addison-Wesley, 1959). (In this light, it is even more remarkable that angular *velocity* is, nonetheless, a vector quantity. We shall deal with this concept later in the book.)

Before concluding this section, we wish to mention that we have not yet given a really satisfactory general definition of *vector*. The definition we have given is based on the notion of a directed line segment. It is unsatisfactory in several ways. First of all, it is not general enough for some purposes in physics. Certain physical quantities can be represented by directed line segments only in a very superficial way. These physical quantities (we will discuss them later) have magnitude and direction, and hence should qualify to be called vector quantities, but when we change from one coordinate system to another, their components do not change in the same way as the components of a directed line segment would change under the same circumstances. In other words, such a physical quantity may be represented by a particular directed line segment only if we do not ever change from one coordinate system to another. When we change coordinates, we must use a different directed line segment. Because of this, some physicists prefer to consider a space vector as simply an ordered triple of numbers (the components), classifying various kinds of vectors according to the way these numbers change when the coordinate system is changed (Chap. 5).

On the other hand, mathematicians find the definition we have given unsatisfying for a number of reasons, not the least of which is that it is conceptually very narrow. Most mathematicians prefer not to define "vector" at all, but to give an axiomatic definition of what is meant by a "vector space." This directs attention to the fundamental properties of vector addition and multiplication by scalars. With respect to this viewpoint, there are objects that can qualify to be called "vectors" not because they have direction and magnitude but because they are manipulated algebraically in a certain manner.

Both physicists and mathematicians have occasion to deal with "vectors" in spaces that are n-dimensional, where n is greater than 3. Such spaces cannot be visualized, but are important nonetheless.

EXERCISES

1. A particle moves from (3,7,8) to (5,2,0) Write its displacement in terms of **i**, **j**, and **k**.

2. What is the position vector of a particle located at the point (1,2,9)?

3. The position vector of a moving particle at time t is $\mathbf{R} = 3\mathbf{i} + 4t^2\mathbf{j} - t^3\mathbf{k}$. Find its displacement during the time interval from $t = 1$ to $t = 3$.

4. What is the *magnitude* of the resultant of the following two displacements: 6 miles east, 8 miles north?
5. Strings are tied to a small metal ring and, by an arrangement of pulleys and weights, four forces are exerted on the ring. One force is directed upward with magnitude 3 lb, another is directed east with magnitude 6 lb, and a third is directed north with magnitude 2 lb. The ring is in equilibrium (i.e., it is not moving). What is the magnitude of the fourth force that is counterbalancing the other three?
6. The *center of mass* of a system of n particles is defined by the position vector

$$\mathbf{R}_{\text{c.m.}} = \frac{m_1\mathbf{R}_1 + m_2\mathbf{R}_2 + \cdots + m_n\mathbf{R}_n}{m_1 + m_2 + \cdots + m_n}$$

where the ith particle is located at $\mathbf{R}_i$ and has mass m_i. The *mass unbalance* of the system, measured at the position $\mathbf{R}$, is defined to be

$$m_1(\mathbf{R}_1 - \mathbf{R}) + m_2(\mathbf{R}_2 - \mathbf{R}) + \cdots + m_n(\mathbf{R}_n - \mathbf{R})$$

Show that the mass unbalance, measured at the center of mass, is zero.

1.7 SOME PROBLEMS IN GEOMETRY

To avoid circumlocution, practically everybody who works with vectors makes no distinction between vectors and directed line segments. It is easier to say "the vector **A**" than to say "the vector represented by the directed line segment **A**." When we do this, it is still important to recognize that the concept of a vector is an *abstraction* from the concept of a directed line segment, in which we ignore the actual location of the directed line segment: we say "$\mathbf{A} = \mathbf{B}$" when we really mean "the directed line segments **A** and **B** are equivalent and therefore represent the same vector." If **A** extends from (2,3,4) to (2,3,5), and if **B** extends from (3, −2,8) to (3, −2,9), then we have as vectors $\mathbf{A} = \mathbf{B}$ even though they extend from different points.

What we are saying is that two things are equal when they are really not identical but are only "equivalent" according to some definition. We are already familiar with this in elementary arithmetic. We say the fractions $\frac{2}{3}$ and $\frac{4}{6}$ are "equal" when in fact they are not identical but are only "equivalent" in a certain way. Strictly speaking, we should say that $\frac{2}{3}$ and $\frac{4}{6}$ are fractions that represent the same rational number: as fractions, they are not equal, but they represent the same rational number.

Similarly, if we have two directed line segments **A** and **B**, we may write $\mathbf{A} = \mathbf{B}$ even when the directed line segments are not equal (because they extend from different points) but are equivalent according to the definition given in Sec. 1.1.

We will not dwell on these pedantic matters. Instead, we will turn to the practical utility of vector algebra. The simplest applications are in geometry, and will be considered first.

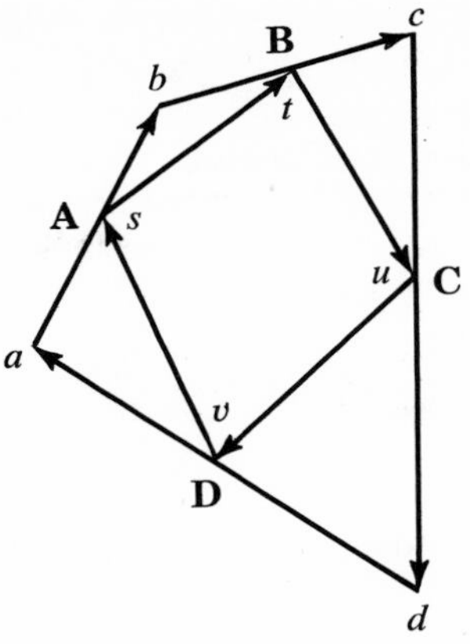

FIGURE 1.9

Example 1.2 If the midpoints of the consecutive sides of a quadrilateral are joined by line segments, is the resulting quadrilateral a parallelogram?

Let *abcd* be the quadrilateral and s, t, u, v the midpoints of its sides. In the case shown in Fig. 1.9 it certainly *appears* that *stuv* is a parallelogram. Keep in mind, however, that *abcd* need not be a plane figure: perhaps d is a point several inches above the plane containing a, b, and c. In view of this possibility, is *stuv* a parallelogram?

Solution Let the sides be made into directed line segments **A**, **B**, **C**, and **D**, as shown in Fig. 1.9. Then

$$\mathbf{A}+\mathbf{B}+\mathbf{C}+\mathbf{D}=\mathbf{0} \qquad st=\tfrac{1}{2}(\mathbf{A}+\mathbf{B}) \qquad uv=\tfrac{1}{2}(\mathbf{C}+\mathbf{D})$$

Therefore $\mathbf{A}+\mathbf{B}=-(\mathbf{C}+\mathbf{D})$ and we have

$$st=\tfrac{1}{2}(\mathbf{A}+\mathbf{B})=-\tfrac{1}{2}(\mathbf{C}+\mathbf{D})=-uv=vu$$

Thus st and vu are parallel and have the same magnitude, so *stuv* is indeed a parallelogram.

Example 1.3 Line segments are drawn from a vertex of a parallelogram to the midpoints of the opposite sides. Show that they trisect a diagonal.

Solution This problem is solved by a standard technique, using the obvious fact that if **A** and **B** are nonzero vectors that are not parallel, then $m\mathbf{A}=n\mathbf{B}$ if and only if $m=0$ and $n=0$. Write the vector **C** (Fig. 1.10) in two different ways: it is obvious that $\mathbf{C}=s(\mathbf{A}+\mathbf{B})$ for some number s, as yet unknown; we want to prove that $s=\frac{1}{3}$. Moreover, $\mathbf{C}=\mathbf{A}+t(\frac{1}{2}\mathbf{B}-\mathbf{A})$, where t is unknown. Setting equal these two expressions for **C** and rearranging terms, we obtain

$$(1-t-s)\mathbf{A}=(s-\tfrac{1}{2}t)\mathbf{B}$$

As noted above, this implies $1-t-s=0$ and $s-\frac{1}{2}t=0$. Solving, we obtain $s=\frac{1}{3}$, as desired.

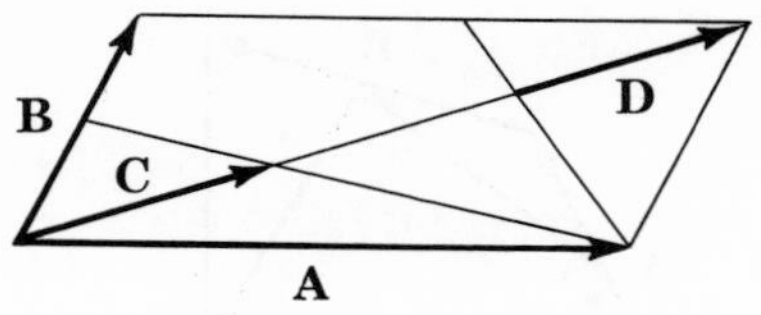

FIGURE 1.10

The reader should complete the solution as an exercise, by showing that $\mathbf{D} = \frac{1}{3}(\mathbf{A} + \mathbf{B})$.

Example 1.4 Prove that the medians of a triangle intersect at a single point.

Solution In Fig. 1.11 **R** is the vector from the corner a to the point of intersection of the medians from b and c. We must show that **R** lies along the median from a, i.e., that it is a multiple of $\mathbf{A} + \frac{1}{2}\mathbf{B}$. The condition that **R** lie along the median from c is expressed as

$$\mathbf{C} + \mathbf{R} = s(\mathbf{C} + \tfrac{1}{2}\mathbf{A})$$

for some number s, while that fact that **R** lies on the median from b implies that, for some number t,

$$\mathbf{A} - \mathbf{R} = t(\tfrac{1}{2}\mathbf{C} + \mathbf{A})$$

Equating the expressions for **R** and eliminating **B** by using the equation

$$\mathbf{A} + \mathbf{B} + \mathbf{C} = \mathbf{0}$$

we derive

$$(s + \tfrac{1}{2}t - 1)\mathbf{C} = (1 - t - \tfrac{1}{2}s)\mathbf{A}$$

As in Example 1.3, we conclude that both coefficients must vanish; thus

$$s = t = \tfrac{2}{3}$$

Using this in either equation for **R** and writing **C** in terms of **A** and **B**, we find

$$\mathbf{R} = \tfrac{2}{3}(\mathbf{A} + \tfrac{1}{2}\mathbf{B})$$

which is the expression we sought.

Example 1.5 Let θ denote the angle between two nonzero vectors **A** and **B**. Show that

$$\cos\theta = \frac{A_1B_1 + A_2B_2 + A_3B_3}{|\mathbf{A}|\,|\mathbf{B}|}$$

Solution First we introduce two new vectors having unit magnitude and making the same angle θ: $\mathbf{U} = \mathbf{A}/|\mathbf{A}|$ and $\mathbf{V} = \mathbf{B}/|\mathbf{B}|$. Thus

$$\mathbf{U} = U_1\mathbf{i} + U_2\mathbf{j} + U_3\mathbf{k} = \frac{A_1}{|\mathbf{A}|}\mathbf{i} + \frac{A_2}{|\mathbf{A}|}\mathbf{j} + \frac{A_3}{|\mathbf{A}|}\mathbf{k}$$

$$\mathbf{V} = V_1\mathbf{i} + V_2\mathbf{j} + V_3\mathbf{k} = \frac{B_1}{|\mathbf{B}|}\mathbf{i} + \frac{B_2}{|\mathbf{B}|}\mathbf{j} + \frac{B_3}{|\mathbf{B}|}\mathbf{k}$$

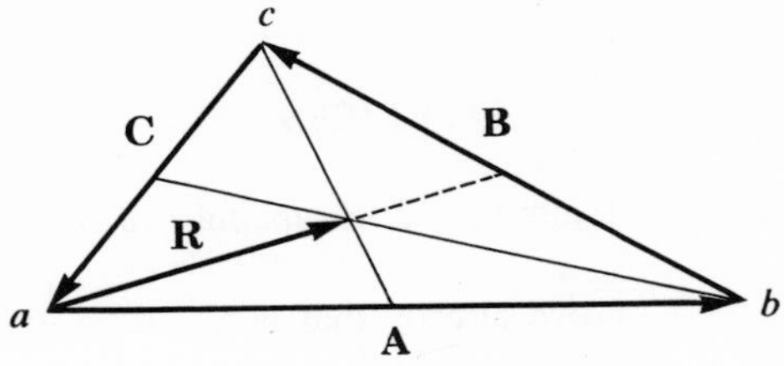

FIGURE 1.11

Let **U** and **V** be represented by arrows extending from the origin O to points U and V respectively. Then OUV is an isosceles triangle, and the length of side UV equals the positive square root of

$$|UV|^2 = (U_1 - V_1)^2 + (U_2 - V_2)^2 + (U_3 - V_3)^2$$

Expanding the right side, and using the fact that $U_1{}^2 + U_2{}^2 + U_3{}^2 = 1$, $V_1{}^2 + V_2{}^2 + V_3{}^2 = 1$, we obtain

$$|UV|^2 = 2 - 2(U_1 V_1 + U_2 V_2 + U_3 V_3)$$

Now let us consider a triangle in the plane with vertices at (0,0), $P(1,0)$, $Q(\cos\theta, \sin\theta)$ (Fig. 1.12). This triangle is congruent to OUV, and therefore $|UV| = |PQ|$. Hence

$$|UV|^2 = |PQ|^2 = (\cos\theta - 1)^2 + \sin^2\theta = 2 - 2\cos\theta$$

Comparing these two expressions for $|UV|^2$, we obtain

$$\cos\theta = U_1 V_1 + U_2 V_2 + U_3 V_3$$

Now substitute $U_1 = A_1|\mathbf{A}|$, $V_1 = B_1/|\mathbf{B}|, \ldots$, and the proof is complete. (This result is extremely important for vector analysis, as the subsequent discussion will show.)

Example 1.6 Show that the vectors $\mathbf{A} = 2\mathbf{i} - \mathbf{j} + 5\mathbf{k}$ and $\mathbf{B} = \mathbf{i} + 7\mathbf{j} + \mathbf{k}$ are perpendicular.

Solution

$$\cos\theta = \frac{2 - 7 + 5}{\sqrt{30}\sqrt{51}} = 0$$

Hence $\theta = \pm 90°$.

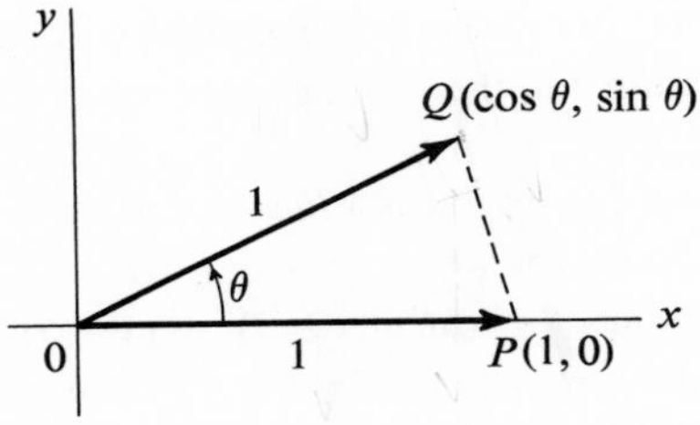

FIGURE 1.12

EXERCISES

1. Imitate the solution of Example 1.2, except instead of proving that $st = vu$, prove that $vs = ut$.
2. Using vector methods, prove directly that if two sides of a quadrilateral are parallel and equal in magnitude, the other two sides are also.
3. By vector methods, show that the line segment joining the midpoints of two sides of a triangle is parallel to the third side, and has length equal to one-half the length of the third side.
4. Show that the diagonals of a parallelogram bisect each other.
5. Construct another proof of the fact that the medians of a triangle intersect at a point, based on the following observation: if **D**, **E**, and **F** are vectors drawn from some fixed point to the corners of the triangle, then

$$\mathbf{D} + \tfrac{3}{2}[\tfrac{1}{3}(\mathbf{D} + \mathbf{E} + \mathbf{F}) - \mathbf{D}] = \tfrac{1}{2}(\mathbf{E} + \mathbf{F})$$

Verify this and interpret it geometrically. [*Hint*: The tip of the vector $\frac{1}{3}(\mathbf{D} + \mathbf{E} + \mathbf{F})$ *is* this point of intersection.]

6. Find the angle between $2\mathbf{i} + \mathbf{j} + 2\mathbf{k}$ and $3\mathbf{i} - 4\mathbf{k}$.
7. Find the angle between the x axis and $\mathbf{i} + \mathbf{j} + \mathbf{k}$.
8. Find the three angles of the triangle with vertices $(2,-1,1)$, $(1,-3,-5)$, $(3,-4,-4)$.
9. Find the angle between the xy plane and $2\mathbf{i} + 2\mathbf{j} - \mathbf{k}$. (Note that $\mathbf{k}$ is perpendicular to the xy plane.)
10. Show that $\mathbf{i} + \mathbf{j} + \mathbf{k}$ is perpendicular to the plane $x + y + z = 0$. (*Hint*: This plane passes through the origin. Show that $\mathbf{i} + \mathbf{j} + \mathbf{k}$ is perpendicular to every vector extending from the origin to a point in the plane.)

The following simple exercises are inserted here to help you to recall some of the basic ideas of analytic geometry.

11. True or false: $3x - 4y + 5z = 0$ represents a plane passing through the origin.
12. True or false: The yz plane is represented by the equation $x = 0$.
13. True or false: The locus of points for which $x = 3$ and $y = 4$ is a line parallel to the z axis whose distance from the z axis is 5.
14. True or false: $x^2 + y^2 + z^2 = 9$ is the equation of a sphere centered at the origin having radius 9.
15. Write down the equation of a sphere centered at the point (2,3,4) having radius 3.
16. Write down an equation for the cylinder concentric with the z axis having radius 2.
17. Do the equations $x = y = z$ represent a *line* or a *plane*?
18. What is the locus of points for which $x^2 + z^2 = 0$?
19. What is the locus of points for which $(x - 2)^2 + (y + 3)^2 + (z - 4)^2 = 0$?
20. What geometrical figure is represented by the equation $xyz = 0$? (Keep in mind that a product of numbers is zero if, and only if, at least one of the numbers is zero.)

21. What is the distance between the points (2,3,4) and (5,3,8)?
22. What is the distance between the point (3,8,9) and the xz plane? (Distance in such cases always means *shortest distance* or *perpendicular distance.*)
23. What is the distance between the point (0,3,0) and the cylinder $x^2 + y^2 = 4$? (I doubt you will find a formula for this in any of your books. Just use some common sense.)
24. The expression $x^2 + y^2$ gives the square of the distance between (x,y,z) and the z axis. In view of this, what figure is represented by $x^2 + y^2 = z^2$?
25. Do you know what figure is represented by the equation $(x/2)^2 + (y/3)^2 + (z/4)^2 = 1$? (If so, you know more analytic geometry than is required to read this book.)

1.8 EQUATIONS OF A LINE

The *position vector* of a point is the vector extending from the origin to the point. Thus the position vector of a point (x,y,z) is the vector $x\mathbf{i} + y\mathbf{j} + z\mathbf{k}$. This correspondence between points and vectors is the fundamental means whereby problems in analytic geometry can be studied by vector methods.

As an elementary example, let us derive the equations of a line passing through a given point (x_0,y_0,z_0) and parallel to a given nonzero vector $\mathbf{V} = a\mathbf{i} + b\mathbf{j} + c\mathbf{k}$.

Let $\mathbf{R}_0$ be the position vector of (x_0,y_0,z_0) and let $\mathbf{R}$ be the position vector of a point (x,y,z). The point (x,y,z) will lie on the desired line if and only if $\mathbf{R} - \mathbf{R}_0$ is parallel to $\mathbf{V}$ (see Fig. 1.13). A vector will be parallel to $\mathbf{V}$ if and only if it equals some scalar multiple of $\mathbf{V}$, so the condition that (x,y,z) be on the line is that $\mathbf{R} - \mathbf{R}_0 = t\mathbf{V}$ for some number t. Rewriting this as $\mathbf{R} = \mathbf{R}_0 + t\mathbf{V}$ and writing this out in terms of the components of the vectors we obtain

$$
\begin{aligned}
x &= x_0 + at \\
y &= y_0 + bt \\
z &= z_0 + ct
\end{aligned}
\tag{1.5}
$$

A point (x,y,z) is on the line through (x_0,y_0,z_0) and parallel to $\mathbf{V} = a\mathbf{i} + b\mathbf{j} + c\mathbf{k}$ if and only if its coordinates satisfy all three of the equations (1.5) for some value of the parameter t.

Equations (1.5) are called the *parametric form* of the equations of the line. The parameter t can be thought of as representing *time*; we can think of Eqs. (1.5) as giving the position of a moving particle at time t. This particle traverses a line parallel to $\mathbf{V}$ and passes through the point (x_0,y_0,z_0) at time $t = 0$.

Observe that the parametric form is not unique; for example, $\mathbf{V}$ could be replaced by any other vector having the same direction, and $\mathbf{R}_0$ could be replaced by any other point on the line.

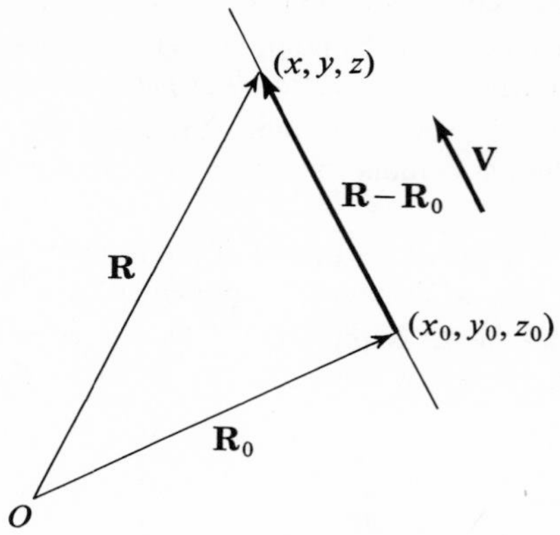

FIGURE 1.13

If all three coordinates of **V** are nonzero, this system of equations can be written in the following form, obtained by eliminating the parameter t:

$$\frac{x - x_0}{a} = \frac{y - y_0}{b} = \frac{z - z_0}{c} \tag{1.6}$$

Example 1.7 Find equations of the line passing through (2,0,4) and parallel to $2\mathbf{i} + \mathbf{j} + 3\mathbf{k}$, in both parametric and nonparametric form.

Solution Here $\mathbf{V} = 2\mathbf{i} + \mathbf{j} + 3\mathbf{k}$, so $a = 2$, $b = 1$, and $c = 3$. In parametric form the equations are

$$\begin{aligned} x &= 2 + 2t \\ y &= t \\ z &= 4 + 3t \end{aligned}$$

In nonparametric form they are

$$\frac{x - 2}{2} = y = \frac{z - 4}{3}$$

Example 1.8 Find equations of the line passing through $(0,3,-1)$ parallel to $3\mathbf{i} + 4\mathbf{k}$.

Solution In this case $b = 0$, so (1.6) would not make sense. In parametric form we have

$$\begin{aligned} x &= 3t \\ y &= 3 \\ z &= -1 + 4t \end{aligned}$$

If we now eliminate the parameter from the first and third equations we obtain

$$\frac{x}{3} = \frac{z + 1}{4} \qquad y = 3$$

This pair of equations can also be written

$$4x - 3z = 3 \qquad y = 3$$

Example 1.9 Find a unit vector parallel to the line

$$\frac{x-4}{2} = y - 3 = \frac{z+1}{2}$$

Solution By comparison with (1.6) we have $a = 2$, $b = 1$, and $c = 2$, so a vector parallel to the line is $2\mathbf{i} + \mathbf{j} + 2\mathbf{k}$. Dividing this vector by its own length we obtain a unit vector $\frac{2}{3}\mathbf{i} + \frac{1}{3}\mathbf{j} + \frac{2}{3}\mathbf{k}$. The negative of this vector is also a correct solution.

EXERCISES

1. Find parametric equations of the line passing through the origin parallel to $3\mathbf{i} + 7\mathbf{k} - 2\mathbf{j}$.
2. Find equations of the line parallel to the z axis passing through the point (1,2,3).
3. Find equations of the line perpendicular to the yz plane, passing through (1,2,3).
4. Find the two unit vectors parallel to the line

$$\frac{x-1}{3} = \frac{y+2}{4} \qquad z = 9$$

5. Find two unit vectors parallel to the line $x = 2y = 3z + 3$. These equations can be written in form (1.6) as follows:

$$x = \frac{y}{\frac{1}{2}} = \frac{z+1}{\frac{1}{3}}$$

6. Find two unit vectors parallel to the line represented by the equations $x + y = 1$, $x - 3z = 5$. [*Hint*: Rewrite in form (1.6).]
7. Find equations of the line passing through the origin and parallel to the line

$$x - 3 = \frac{y+2}{4} = 1 - z$$

8. Find equations of the line passing through the points (3,4,5) and (3,4,7).
9. Find equations of the line passing through the points (1,4,−1) and (2,2,7).
10. By vector methods, find the cosine of the angle between the lines

$$\frac{x-1}{3} = \frac{y+8}{2} = z \qquad \text{and} \qquad x = y = z$$

11. Find the angle between the two intersecting lines

$$\frac{x-1}{3} = \frac{y-3}{4} = \frac{z}{5} \qquad \text{and} \qquad \frac{x-1}{2} = 3 - y = 2z$$

12. Let A and B be two points with position vectors $\mathbf{A}$ and $\mathbf{B}$ respectively. Show that the line passing through these points may be represented by the vector equation

$$\mathbf{R} = s\mathbf{A} + t\mathbf{B} \qquad s + t = 1 \tag{1.7}$$

13. Solve Exercise 9 by making use of (1.7).

14. (*Points of Division*) When the points A, B, and P are collinear, P is said to divide the segment AB in the ratio λ when the segments AP and PB are related by

$$AP = \lambda(PB) \tag{1.8}$$

(a) For what values of λ does P lie between A and B? to the left of A? to the right of B?

(b) Show that, relative to an origin O, Eq. (1.8) can be written

$$OP = \frac{OA + \lambda(OB)}{1 + \lambda}$$

Relate this to Eq. (1.7).

(c) If P and P' divide AB internally and externally in the same numerical ratios $\pm\lambda$, show that A and B divide PP' internally and externally in the ratios $\pm(1 - \lambda)/(1 + \lambda)$.

15. Find the point(s) of intersection of the following pairs of straight lines. (*Hint*: Should you use parametric or nonparametric representation?)

(a) $\mathbf{R} = (5\mathbf{i} + 4\mathbf{j} + 5\mathbf{k})t + 7\mathbf{i} + 6\mathbf{j} + 8\mathbf{k}$ and
$\mathbf{R} = (6\mathbf{i} + 4\mathbf{j} + 6\mathbf{k})t + 8\mathbf{i} + 6\mathbf{j} + 9\mathbf{k}$

(b) $\mathbf{R} = (3\mathbf{i} + 2\mathbf{j} + \mathbf{k})t + 2\mathbf{k}$ and
$\mathbf{R} = (6\mathbf{i} + 4\mathbf{j} + 2\mathbf{k})t + 3\mathbf{i} + 2\mathbf{j} + 3\mathbf{k}$

(c) $\mathbf{R} = (3\mathbf{i} - \mathbf{j} + \mathbf{k})t$ and
$\mathbf{R} = (-6\mathbf{i} + 2\mathbf{j} - 2\mathbf{k})t + 2\mathbf{i}$

(d) $\mathbf{R} = (\mathbf{i} + \mathbf{j} + \mathbf{k})t$ and
$\mathbf{R} = (\mathbf{i} + \mathbf{j} - 3\mathbf{k})t - \mathbf{i} + \mathbf{j}$

1.9 SCALAR PRODUCTS

The *scalar product* of two vectors is the number

$$\mathbf{A} \cdot \mathbf{B} = |\mathbf{A}|\,|\mathbf{B}| \cos\theta \tag{1.9}$$

where θ denotes the angle between the vectors. Although $\mathbf{A}$ and $\mathbf{B}$ are *vectors*, $\mathbf{A} \cdot \mathbf{B}$ is a *number*. The scalar product is also sometimes called the *dot product* or the *inner product*. From Fig. 1.14, we identify $|\mathbf{B}| \cos\theta$ as the component of $\mathbf{B}$ parallel to $\mathbf{A}$, i.e., the length of the orthogonal projection of $\mathbf{B}$ in the direction of $\mathbf{A}$ (signed plus or minus according to whether the projection points the same as, or the opposite of, $\mathbf{A}$). Thus, we can interpret $\mathbf{A} \cdot \mathbf{B}$ as

(Length of $\mathbf{A}$) (component of $\mathbf{B}$ along $\mathbf{A}$)

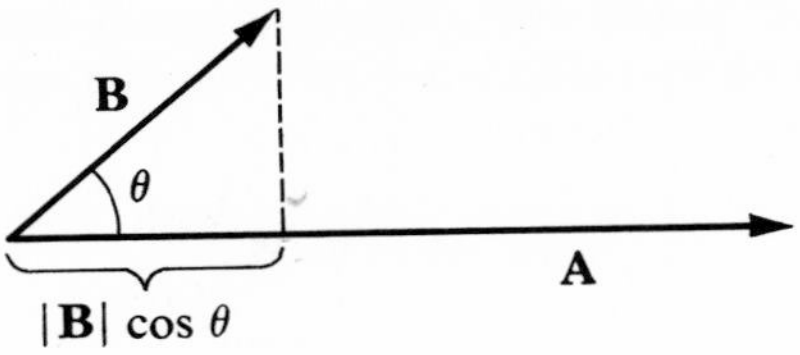

FIGURE 1.14

It can equally well be interpreted as

(Length of **B**) (component of **A** along **B**)

In a few simple cases, the scalar product of two vectors is easily computed directly from this definition. For example, the scalar product of the vectors shown in Fig. 1.15 is $9\sqrt{3}$.

If either **A** or **B** is the zero vector, we have either $|\mathbf{A}| = 0$ or $|\mathbf{B}| = 0$, so by (1.9) it follows that $\mathbf{A} \cdot \mathbf{B} = 0$. (We ignore the fact that θ is not defined in this case.)

On the other hand, it is possible to have $\mathbf{A} \cdot \mathbf{B} = 0$ even though both **A** and **B** are nonzero vectors. For example, if **A** and **B** are perpendicular, then $\cos\theta = \cos 90° = 0$ and hence $\mathbf{A} \cdot \mathbf{B} = 0$.

In Sec. 1.7, we derived a formula for $\cos\theta$ in terms of the components of the two vectors. It follows from that formula that

$$\mathbf{A} \cdot \mathbf{B} = A_1 B_1 + A_2 B_2 + A_3 B_3 \tag{1.10}$$

Memorize (1.9) and (1.10) *now*. They are important.

Example 1.10 Find the scalar product of $4\mathbf{i} - 5\mathbf{j} - \mathbf{k}$ and $\mathbf{i} + 2\mathbf{j} + 3\mathbf{k}$.

Solution $(4)(1) + (-5)(2) + (-1)(3) = -9$. (The negative sign indicates that the angle between the vectors must be greater than 90°.)

Example 1.11 Find the angle between the vectors $\mathbf{A} = 2\mathbf{i} + 2\mathbf{j} - \mathbf{k}$ and $\mathbf{B} = 3\mathbf{i} + 4\mathbf{j}$.

Solution Since (1.9) and (1.10) have already been memorized, there is no need to look up the formula derived in Sec. 1.7. We have $|\mathbf{A}| = 3$ and $|\mathbf{B}| = 5$. Using (1.10), we see that $\mathbf{A} \cdot \mathbf{B} = 14$. Substituting these values in (1.9) we solve to get $\theta = \cos^{-1} \frac{14}{15}$.

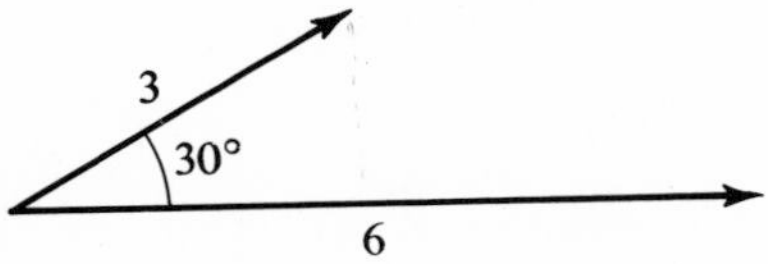

FIGURE 1.15

Example 1.12 If $\mathbf{F}$ is a constant force acting through a displacement $\mathbf{D}$, the work done by $\mathbf{F}$ is defined to be the product of the magnitude of the displacement with the component of the force in the direction of the displacement. In vector notation this is written

$$\text{Work} = \mathbf{F} \cdot \mathbf{D}$$

The following properties of the scalar product are easily verified from (1.10):

$$\mathbf{A} \cdot \mathbf{B} = \mathbf{B} \cdot \mathbf{A} \qquad \text{(symmetry)} \tag{1.11}$$

$$(s\mathbf{A}) \cdot \mathbf{B} = s(\mathbf{A} \cdot \mathbf{B}) \qquad (\mathbf{A} + \mathbf{B}) \cdot \mathbf{C} = \mathbf{A} \cdot \mathbf{C} + \mathbf{B} \cdot \mathbf{C}$$

$$\text{(linearity in the first factor)} \tag{1.12}$$

$$\mathbf{A} \cdot (t\mathbf{B}) = t(\mathbf{A} \cdot \mathbf{B}) \qquad \mathbf{A} \cdot (\mathbf{B} + \mathbf{C}) = \mathbf{A} \cdot \mathbf{B} + \mathbf{A} \cdot \mathbf{C}$$

$$\text{(linearity in the second factor)} \tag{1.13}$$

$$|\mathbf{A}|^2 = \mathbf{A} \cdot \mathbf{A} \tag{1.14}$$

(1.12) and (1.13) are known as the *distributive laws.*

Example 1.13 It is interesting to see how the cosine law of trigonometry can be derived by vector methods. By (1.14), replacing $\mathbf{A}$ by $\mathbf{A} - \mathbf{B}$, we have $|\mathbf{A} - \mathbf{B}|^2 = (\mathbf{A} - \mathbf{B}) \cdot (\mathbf{A} - \mathbf{B})$. By (1.12) and (1.13), the right side of this equation is $\mathbf{A} \cdot \mathbf{A} - \mathbf{B} \cdot \mathbf{A} - \mathbf{A} \cdot \mathbf{B} + \mathbf{B} \cdot \mathbf{B}$, which by (1.11) equals $\mathbf{A} \cdot \mathbf{A} + \mathbf{B} \cdot \mathbf{B} - 2\mathbf{A} \cdot \mathbf{B}$. Using (1.9) this becomes $|\mathbf{A}|^2 + |\mathbf{B}|^2 - 2\,|\mathbf{A}|\,|\mathbf{B}| \cos\theta$. If we interpret, $\mathbf{A}$, $\mathbf{B}$, and $\mathbf{A} - \mathbf{B}$ as the sides of a triangle, we obtain the cosine law:

$$|\mathbf{A} - \mathbf{B}|^2 = |\mathbf{A}|^2 + |\mathbf{B}|^2 - 2\,|\mathbf{A}|\,|\mathbf{B}| \cos\theta$$

Example 1.14 (A Maximum Principle) Let there be given a nonzero vector $\mathbf{D}$, and let $\mathbf{n}$ denote a variable *unit* vector. Then $|\mathbf{n}| = 1$ and $\mathbf{D} \cdot \mathbf{n} = |\mathbf{D}|\,|\mathbf{n}| \cos\theta = |\mathbf{D}| \cos\theta$. This will be a maximum when $\cos\theta = 1$, i.e., when $\theta = 0$. Thus we have derived the following maximum principle, which will be useful to us in later sections:

The unit vector making $\mathbf{D} \cdot \mathbf{n}$ *a maximum is the unit vector* $\mathbf{n}$ *pointing in the same direction as* $\mathbf{D}$.

Observe that the direction cosine of the vector $\mathbf{D}$, in the direction $\mathbf{n}$, is given by

$$\frac{\mathbf{D} \cdot \mathbf{n}}{|\mathbf{D}|}$$

In fact, we can write

$$\mathbf{D} = (\mathbf{D} \cdot \mathbf{i})\mathbf{i} + (\mathbf{D} \cdot \mathbf{j})\mathbf{j} + (\mathbf{D} \cdot \mathbf{k})\mathbf{k}$$

EXERCISES

1. Find the scalar product of $3\mathbf{i} + 8\mathbf{j} - 2\mathbf{k}$ with $5\mathbf{i} + \mathbf{j} + 2\mathbf{k}$.
2. Find the scalar product of $2\mathbf{i} + 3\mathbf{j} + 4\mathbf{k}$ with $4\mathbf{i} - 3\mathbf{k} + 9\mathbf{j}$.
3. Find the scalar product of $3\mathbf{i} + 4\mathbf{j}$ with $5\mathbf{j} - 10\mathbf{k}$.
4. Determine the angle between $2\mathbf{i} + \mathbf{j} - 2\mathbf{k}$ and $3\mathbf{i} - 4\mathbf{j}$.

5. Find the angle between $2\mathbf{i}$ and $3\mathbf{i} + 4\mathbf{j}$.
6. A force $\mathbf{F} = 2\mathbf{i} + 3\mathbf{j} + \mathbf{k}$ acts through a displacement $\mathbf{D} = -2\mathbf{i} + \mathbf{j} - \mathbf{k}$. Find the work done.
7. Find the component of $8\mathbf{i} + \mathbf{j}$ in the direction of $\mathbf{i} + 2\mathbf{j} - 2\mathbf{k}$.
8. Find the component of $\mathbf{i} + \mathbf{j} + \mathbf{k}$ in the direction of $\mathbf{i} + \mathbf{j}$.
9. Find the component of the force $5\mathbf{i} + 7\mathbf{j} - \mathbf{k}$ in the direction of the displacement PQ, where $P(3,0,1)$ and $Q(4,4,4)$ are points in space.
10. Find the vector in the same direction as $\mathbf{i} + \mathbf{j}$ whose component in the direction of $2\mathbf{i} - 4\mathbf{k}$ is unity.
11. If $\mathbf{A} \cdot \mathbf{A} = 0$ and $\mathbf{A} \cdot \mathbf{B} = 0$ what can you conclude about the vector $\mathbf{B}$?
12. By interpreting $2x + 3y + 4z$ as a scalar product, show that $2\mathbf{i} + 3\mathbf{j} + 4\mathbf{k}$ is perpendicular to the plane $2x + 3y + 4z = 0$.
13. If $\mathbf{A}$ is a fixed nonzero vector, interpret geometrically $(\mathbf{R} - \mathbf{A}) \cdot \mathbf{R} = 0$,
    (a) in the plane, $\mathbf{R} = x\mathbf{i} + y\mathbf{j}$,
    (b) in space, $\mathbf{R} = x\mathbf{i} + y\mathbf{j} + z\mathbf{k}$.
14. If $\mathbf{u}$ and $\mathbf{v}$ are unit vectors, and θ is the angle between them, find $\frac{1}{2}|\mathbf{u} - \mathbf{v}|$ in terms of θ.
15. Let $\mathbf{A} = (\cos\phi)\mathbf{i} + (\sin\phi)\mathbf{j}$ and $\mathbf{B} = (\cos\theta)\mathbf{i} + (\sin\theta)\mathbf{j}$. Draw these vectors in the xy plane. By interpreting the scalar product $\mathbf{A} \cdot \mathbf{B}$ geometrically, prove that $\cos(\phi - \theta) = \cos\phi\cos\theta + \sin\phi\sin\theta$.
16. Prove, by vector methods, that the median from the vertex angle of an isosceles triangle is perpendicular to the base.
17. Prove the parallelogram equality, i.e., the sum of the squares of the diagonals of a parallelogram equals the sum of the squares of its sides.
18. Prove the triangle inequality of Sec. 1.3,
$$|\mathbf{A} + \mathbf{B}| \leq |\mathbf{A}| + |\mathbf{B}|$$
    (*Hint*: Square both sides, and use the scalar product.)
19. The vector $\mathbf{n} = (3\mathbf{i} + 2\mathbf{j} + 6\mathbf{k})/7$ is perpendicular to a plane. A line segment representing the vector $\mathbf{A} = 2\mathbf{i} + 5\mathbf{j} + 6\mathbf{k}$ lies on one side of this plane. Regarding the plane as a mirror, write down the vector represented by the mirror image of $\mathbf{A}$.

1.10 EQUATION OF A PLANE

We shall now derive the equation of a plane by vector methods. The problem: to find an equation representing the plane passing through a given point (x_0,y_0,z_0) and perpendicular to a given nonzero vector $\mathbf{N} = a\mathbf{i} + b\mathbf{j} + c\mathbf{k}$. Let $\mathbf{R}_0 = x_0\mathbf{i} + y_0\mathbf{j} + z_0\mathbf{k}$ be the position vector of the given point, and let $\mathbf{R} = x\mathbf{i} + y\mathbf{j} + z\mathbf{k}$ be the position vector of some other point (x,y,z). Then (x,y,z) will lie in the plane only if $\mathbf{R} - \mathbf{R}_0$ is perpendicular to $\mathbf{N}$. In terms of scalar products, this condition can be written

$$(\mathbf{R} - \mathbf{R}_0) \cdot \mathbf{N} = 0 \qquad (1.15)$$

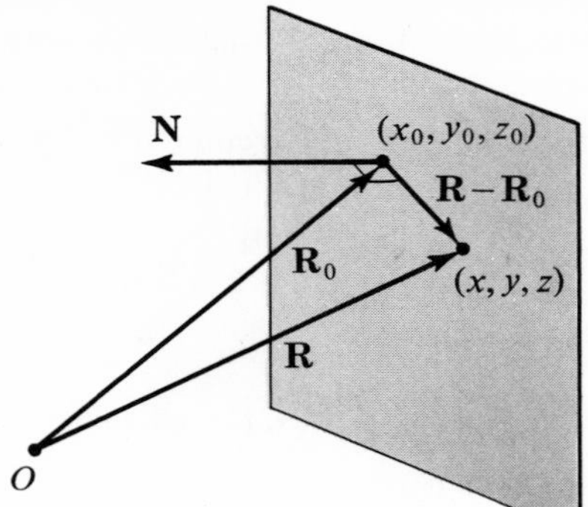

FIGURE 1.16

[This derivation assumes that (x,y,z) is not the same as (x_0,y_0,z_0). However, in that case $\mathbf{R} = \mathbf{R}_0$, so $\mathbf{R} - \mathbf{R}_0$ is the zero vector and (1.15) is still valid.]

Conversely, if (1.15) is satisfied, then (since $\mathbf{N}$ is nonzero) either $\mathbf{R} - \mathbf{R}_0$ is perpendicular to $\mathbf{N}$ or it is the zero vector. In either case this implies that $\mathbf{R}$ is the position vector of a point in the plane.

Hence (1.15) is a vector equation of the plane. In terms of components, this becomes

$$a(x - x_0) + b(y - y_0) + c(z - z_0) = 0 \tag{1.16}$$

Lumping the constant terms, this can be written

$$ax + by + cz = d \tag{1.17}$$

where $d = ax_0 + by_0 + cz_0$.

Example 1.15 Find an equation of the plane passing through $(1,3,-6)$ perpendicular to the vector $3\mathbf{i} - 2\mathbf{j} + 7\mathbf{k}$.

Solution By (1.16) we can write the equation down at once: $3(x - 1) - 2(y - 3) + 7(z + 6) = 0$. This can be simplified to $3x - 2y + 7z = -45$.

Example 1.16 Find an equation of the plane passing through $(1,2,3)$ perpendicular to the line

$$\frac{x-1}{4} = \frac{y}{5} = \frac{z+5}{6}$$

Solution We recall from an earlier section that we can find a vector parallel to the given line by reading off the coefficients in the denominators: $4\mathbf{i} + 5\mathbf{j} + 6\mathbf{k}$. This vector is perpendicular to the desired plane, and so the equation of the plane is $4(x - 1) + 5(y - 2) + 6(z - 3) = 0$.

We leave it to the reader to prove that any equation $ax + by + cz = d$, where a, b, and c are not all zero, represents a plane, and that the vector $\mathbf{N} = a\mathbf{i} + b\mathbf{j} + c\mathbf{k}$ is perpendicular to the plane. [*Hint*: If $\mathbf{R}_0$ is the position vector of a point whose coordinates satisfy the equation, then $\mathbf{R}_0 \cdot \mathbf{N} = d$. Substituting for d in the equation we get $\mathbf{R} \cdot \mathbf{N} = \mathbf{R}_0 \cdot \mathbf{N}$, so $(\mathbf{R} - \mathbf{R}_0) \cdot \mathbf{N} = 0$. Interpret geometrically.]

Example 1.17 Find a unit vector perpendicular to the plane $2x + y - 2z = 7$.

Solution Reading off the coefficients, we see that $2\mathbf{i} + \mathbf{j} - 2\mathbf{k}$ is perpendicular to the plane. Its magnitude is 3, so the desired unit vector is $\frac{2}{3}\mathbf{i} + \frac{1}{3}\mathbf{j} - \frac{2}{3}\mathbf{k}$. The negative of this vector is also a correct answer.

A vector perpendicular to a plane is sometimes called a *normal*.

Example 1.18 Find the angle between the two planes $3x + 4y = 0$ and $2x + y - 2z = 5$.

Solution. The desired angle equals the angle between the normals $\mathbf{N}_1 = 3\mathbf{i} + 4\mathbf{j}$ and $\mathbf{N}_2 = 2\mathbf{i} + \mathbf{j} - 2\mathbf{k}$. By the methods of a preceding section,

$$\cos\theta = \frac{\mathbf{N}_1 \cdot \mathbf{N}_2}{|\mathbf{N}_1|\,|\mathbf{N}_2|} = \frac{6+4}{(5)(3)} = \frac{2}{3}$$

The desired angle is approximately 48°.

Example 1.19 In books on analytic geometry, it is shown that the distance between an arbitrary point (x_1,y_1,z_1) and the plane $ax + by + cz = d$ is given by the expression

$$\frac{|ax_1 + by_1 + cz_1 - d|}{(a^2 + b^2 + c^2)^{1/2}}$$

Derive this expression by vector methods.

Solution Let $\mathbf{R}_0$ be the position vector of a point in the plane, and let $\mathbf{R}_1 = x_1\mathbf{i} + y_1\mathbf{j} + z_1\mathbf{k}$ and $\mathbf{N} = a\mathbf{i} + b\mathbf{j} + c\mathbf{k}$. The desired distance is the absolute value (distance is never negative!) of the component of $\mathbf{R}_1 - \mathbf{R}_0$ in the direction of $\mathbf{N}$. Hence this distance is

$$\frac{|(\mathbf{R}_1 - \mathbf{R}_0) \cdot \mathbf{N}|}{|\mathbf{N}|} = \frac{|\mathbf{R}_1 \cdot \mathbf{N} - d|}{|\mathbf{N}|}$$

which, written out in terms of components, is the expression given above.

Example 1.20 Find the distance between the pairs of planes $x + y + z = 5$ and $x + y + z = 10$.

Solution Take an arbitrary point in the first plane, say (1,1,3), and find its distance to the second plane by using the expression derived in Example 1.19. We obtain

$$\frac{|5 - 10|}{\sqrt{3}} = \frac{5\sqrt{3}}{3}$$

EXERCISES

1. Find unit vectors normal to the planes
(a) $2x + y + 2z = 8$
(b) $4x - 4z = 0$
(c) $-y + 6z = 0$
(d) $x = 5$
(e) $y = z + 2$
(f) $x = y$

2. Find an equation of the plane through the origin perpendicular to $2\mathbf{i} - 8\mathbf{j} + 2\mathbf{k}$.

3. Find an equation of the plane perpendicular to $\mathbf{D}$ and through P, where

$$\mathbf{D} = 10\mathbf{i} - 10\mathbf{j} + 5\mathbf{k}$$

and P is $(1,1,-3)$.

4. Find a plane passing through $(1,3,3)$, parallel to the plane $3x + y - z = 8$.

5. Is it possible to find a plane perpendicular to both $\mathbf{i}$ and $\mathbf{j}$?

6. By vector methods find the distance from the point $(3,4,7)$ to the plane $2x - y - 2z = 4$.

7. Find the distances between the pairs of planes
(a) $x + 2y + 3z = 5$ and $x + 2y + 3z = 19$
(b) $x + y = 4$ and $x + y = 10$
(c) $x = 5$ and $x = 7$ (no calculations needed here!)

8. Determine $\cos\theta$, where θ is the angle between the planes $x + y + z = 0$ and $x = 0$.

9. By vector methods, show that the line $x = y = \frac{1}{3}(z + 2)$ is parallel to the plane $2x - 8y + 2z = 5$.

10. By vector methods find the angle between the line $x = y = 2z$ and the plane $x + y + z = 0$.

11. Find the angle between the plane $x + y + z = 21$ and the line $x - 1 = y + 2 = 2z + 3$.

12. Find the equation of a line in the xy plane perpendicular to the vector $3\mathbf{i} - \mathbf{j}$.

13. Find the distance between the lines $x + y = 0$ and $x + y = 5$ in the xy plane.

14. Find a line in the xy plane parallel to $3x + 2y = 4$ passing through the point $(3,1)$.

15. Write the equation of the plane containing the lines

$$x = y = \frac{4 - z}{4}$$

and

$$2x = 2 - y = z$$

16. We are given two distinct parallel planes, and we are told the distance between the planes is d. A vector $\mathbf{v}$ is perpendicular to the planes and its magnitude is $1/d$. The planes intersect the y axis in the points $(0,1,0)$ and $(0,4,0)$ respectively. What is the y component of $\mathbf{v}$? (There are two possible answers, depending on the two possible directions of $\mathbf{v}$.)

17. Find the intersection of the following geometric objects:
(a) the plane $3x + 2y - z = -9$ and the line $\frac{1}{2}x = y - 2 = -\frac{1}{4}(z - 1)$
(b) the plane $x + y + 2z = 6$ and the line $-x = 2y = 4z + 1$
(c) the plane $3x - y + z = 3$ and the plane $2x + z = 0$
(d) the plane $x - y + 2z = 4$ and the plane $-2x + 2y - 4z = 1$.

18. (*Review*) In each case, find a vector with the stated property:
(a) extending from the point (2,0,3) to the point (4,−1,8)
(b) perpendicular to the plane $2x + 3y - 4z = 18$
(c) parallel to the line

$$\frac{x-2}{3} = y + 4 = \frac{z+1}{7}$$

(d) of unit length perpendicular to the plane $2x - 2y + z = 15$
(e) of unit length parallel to the vector $2\mathbf{i} - 12\mathbf{k}$
(f) of unit length parallel to the line

$$\frac{x-4}{3} = \frac{y+1}{4} \qquad z = 7$$

1.11 ORIENTATION

In working in the xy plane, it is conventional to take the positive x direction to the right and the positive y direction upward. Angles are then taken to be *positive* in the *counterclockwise* direction.

When working with planes in space, there is no generally accepted convention for determining the positive sense for angles. The choice is quite arbitrary. Given any plane in space, we may arbitrarily decree in which direction we shall consider angles to be positive. The plane is then said to be oriented.

One way of orienting a plane is as follows. Let **A** and **B** be nonzero vectors, not parallel, represented by arrows in the given plane. Let these arrows extend from the same point. Let **A** be rotated through the smallest angle possible to coincide in direction with **B**. The sense of this rotation is then said to be "positive" and the plane is thereby oriented. *The plane is oriented by giving the vectors* **A**, **B** *in that order.*

For example, the usual orientation of the xy plane is obtained by giving the vectors **i**, **j** in that order. By a 90° rotation the direction of **i** can be made to coincide with that of **j**, and this rotation has the conventional "positive" sense. We obtain the same orientation by giving the vectors $\mathbf{i} + \mathbf{j}$ and **j** in that order (Fig. 1.17). On the other hand, if we specified the orientation by giving **j**, **i** in that order, we would obtain the opposite orientation, whereby angles would be measured positive in the clockwise sense (which is not conventional, but is perfectly satisfactory).

Another way of orienting a plane is as follows. Let there be given a single vector that is not parallel to the plane. Let this vector be represented by an arrow that has its initial point in the plane. Then the terminal point of the arrow will be on one side of the plane, which we call (arbitrarily) the *positive* side. We now take the positive sense for angles in the plane to be such that a right-handed screw with head parallel to the plane and shank perpendicular to the plane would advance in the direction of the positive side

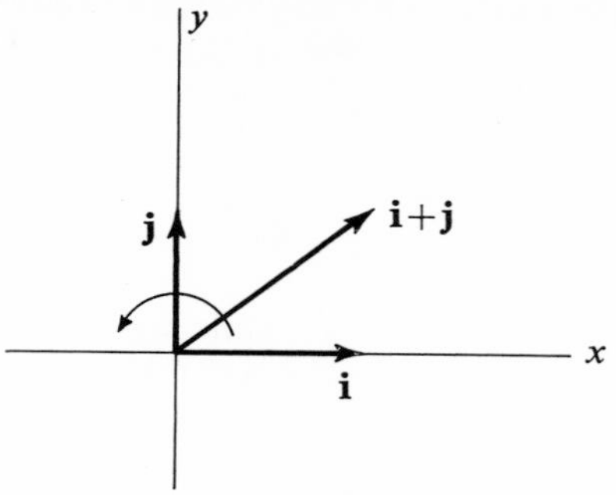

FIGURE 1.17

of the plane if rotated in the positive sense. (This is independent of the way in which the screw points.) Alternatively, if we imagine the right hand grasping the given vector, with thumb pointing in the direction of the arrowhead, the fingers will curl around the shank of the arrow in the positive sense of rotation in the plane.

In Fig. 1.18 both methods of orienting a plane are illustrated for planes perpendicular to the y axis. At the left, the plane is oriented by prescribing two vectors in the plane, **A** and **B**, in that order. On the right, the same orientation is achieved by prescribing a vector **C** extending from a point in the plane.

Now let **A**, **B**, and **C** be nonzero vectors, not all parallel to the same plane, represented by arrows with initial points at the origin (Fig. 1.19). The vectors **A** and **B** determine a plane passing through the origin. If the orientation of this plane, as determined by **A**, **B** in that order, is identical with its orientation as determined by **C**, we say that **A**, **B**, and **C** in that order form a *right-handed system*. One reason for this terminology is that if the thumb and first two fingers of the right hand are held so they are mutually perpendicular, the thumb, forefinger, and second finger form such a system. Another reason is

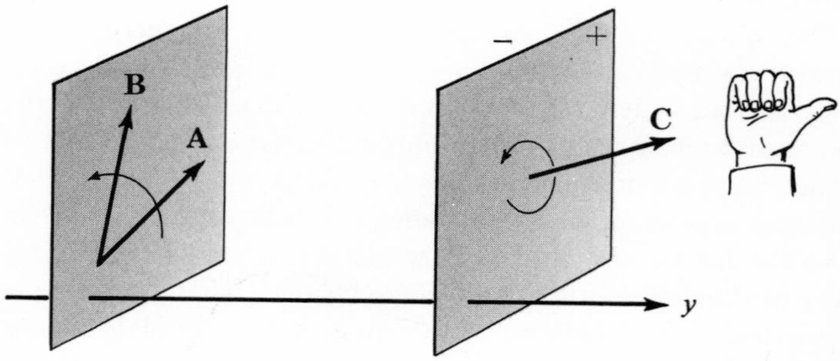

FIGURE 1.18

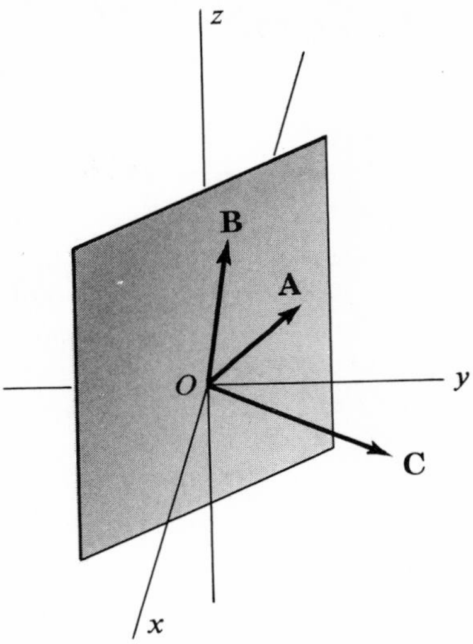

FIGURE 1.19

that if **A**, **B**, and **C**, in that order, form a *right-handed* system, the rotation of **A** into **B** (through an angle less than 180°) will advance a right-handed screw in the general direction of **C**. The vectors **A**, **B**, and **C** of Fig. 1.19 form a right-handed system, as do also the vectors **i**, **j**, and **k**.

EXERCISES

1. If an oriented plane area is represented by a vector perpendicular to the area, with magnitude numerically equal to the area, what is the geometrical significance of the components of the vector?

1.12 VECTOR PRODUCTS

We have seen that the scalar product of two vectors **A** and **B** can be interpreted as the length of **A** times the component of **B** parallel to **A**; in mechanics, it expresses the work done by a force **B** exerted through a displacement **A**, and it is also a very useful tool in analytic geometry. So we are naturally led to explore the possible advantages of defining another kind of product, given by the length of **A** times the component of **B** *perpendicular* to **A** (i.e., $|\mathbf{B}| \sin \theta$ in Fig. 1.14). Mechanics again lends a provocative interpretation to this operation.

Let us suppose we have a rigid body and, for purposes of reference, we define a right-handed coordinate system fixed in this body. We interpret **B** as a force applied to the body at the point located by the vector **A** (relative to the origin). Observe that the component of this force *perpendicular* to **A** tends to *rotate* the body about the axis normal to the plane of **A** and **B**. The rotational effect of this force is enhanced if the point of application is moved further from the origin, increasing the "leverage" of the force. In fact, this effect is measured by the vector product we just proposed. Consequently, in physics the *torque* due to the force **B** applied at the point **A** is defined to be a vector whose magnitude is this product ("lever arm times perpendicular force"), and whose direction is perpendicular to the plane of **A** and **B**, so that **A**, **B**, and the torque vector form a right-handed system (i.e., if the fingers of the right hand rotate **A** into **B** as in Fig. 1.18, the extended thumb gives the direction of the torque).

Motivated by these considerations, we now define the *vector product* of **A** and **B** to be the vector

$$\mathbf{A} \times \mathbf{B} = |\mathbf{A}|\,|\mathbf{B}| \sin\theta\,\mathbf{n}$$

where θ is the angle between the vectors, and the unit vector **n** is perpendicular to both **A** and **B**, with **A**, **B**, and **n** forming a right-handed system (see Fig. 1.20). Sometimes **A** × **B** is called the *cross product*.

Notice that |**A** × **B**| is the area of the parallelogram determined by **A** and **B** (computed as base times height). Observe further that because of the rule determining the direction of **n**, we have

$$\mathbf{A} \times \mathbf{B} = -\mathbf{B} \times \mathbf{A}$$

From these geometric considerations we see that *if two vectors are parallel, their vector product is zero.* Of course, **A** × **B** is also zero if either **A** or **B** is zero.

In order to calculate the vector product, it is convenient to have a representation of **A** × **B** in terms of the components of **A** and **B**. As a preliminary

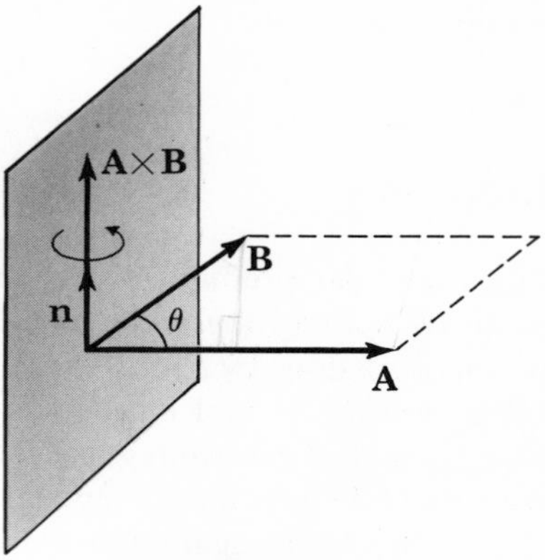

FIGURE 1.20

to this computation, we shall first show that the vector product is *distributive* over vector addition, that is,

$$\mathbf{A} \times (\mathbf{B} + \mathbf{C}) = \mathbf{A} \times \mathbf{B} + \mathbf{A} \times \mathbf{C} \tag{1.18}$$

and

$$(\mathbf{A} + \mathbf{B}) \times \mathbf{C} = \mathbf{A} \times \mathbf{C} + \mathbf{B} \times \mathbf{C} \tag{1.19}$$

Observe that we only have to prove (1.18); (1.19) will then follow since

$$\begin{aligned}(\mathbf{A} + \mathbf{B}) \times \mathbf{C} &= -\mathbf{C} \times (\mathbf{A} + \mathbf{B}) \\ &= -(\mathbf{C} \times \mathbf{A} + \mathbf{C} \times \mathbf{B}) \\ &= \mathbf{A} \times \mathbf{C} + \mathbf{B} \times \mathbf{C}\end{aligned}$$

We begin by proving (1.18) in the special case where **B** and **C** are both perpendicular to **A**; then, of course, so is (**B** + **C**). This is depicted in Fig. 1.21, where we have assumed that **A** is perpendicular to the page, pointing towards the reader. In this case it follows from the definition that **A** × **B** is a vector which can be formed from the vector **B** by multiplying its length by the factor $|\mathbf{A}|$, and rotating it through 90° about **A** as an axis. Similarly we can form **A** × **C** and **A** × (**B** + **C**). Equation (1.18) now claims that **A** × (**B** + **C**) is the diagonal of the parallelogram determined by **A** × **B** and **A** × **C**. This is easy to establish by considering the similar triangles resulting from the equal angles and proportional sides in Fig. 1.21. Details are left as an exercise for the reader.

Now we return to Eq. (1.18) in the general case, dropping our assumption about **B** and **C**. Consider the vector **B**′ formed by subtracting from **B** its component parallel to **A**; that is, **B**′ is the projection of **B** onto the plane perpendicular to **A** (see Fig. 1.22). It follows from the definition of vector product that

$$\mathbf{A} \times \mathbf{B} = \mathbf{A} \times \mathbf{B}'$$

Similarly, if **C**′ is the projection of **C** onto the plane perpendicular to **A**,

$$\mathbf{A} \times \mathbf{C} = \mathbf{A} \times \mathbf{C}'$$

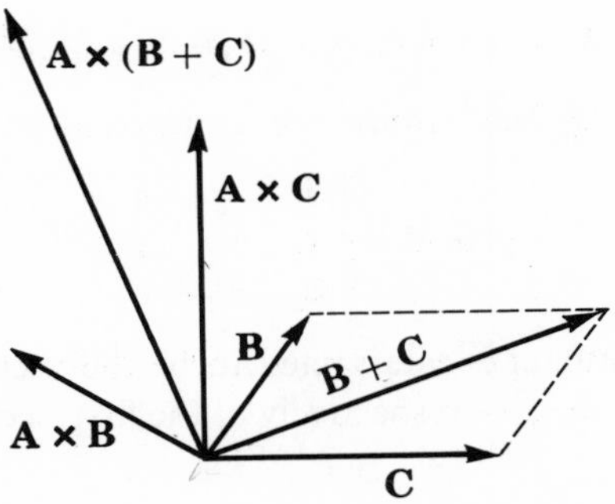

FIGURE 1.21

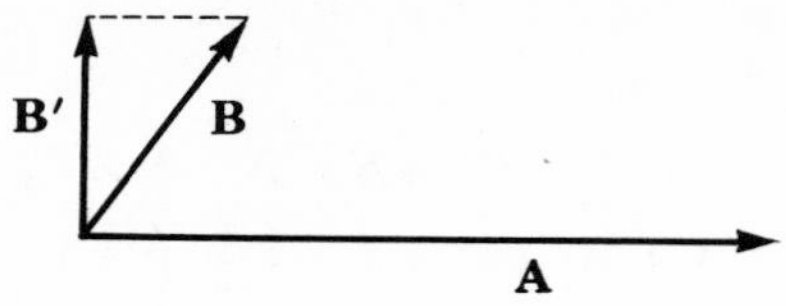

FIGURE 1.22

Now observe the following two facts:

(*i*) $\mathbf{B}' + \mathbf{C}'$ is *perpendicular* to $\mathbf{A}$, since both $\mathbf{B}'$ and $\mathbf{C}'$ are perpendicular to $\mathbf{A}$, separately,

(*ii*) $(\mathbf{B} + \mathbf{C}) - (\mathbf{B}' + \mathbf{C}')$ is *parallel* to $\mathbf{A}$, since it is the sum of $\mathbf{B} - \mathbf{B}'$ and $\mathbf{C} - \mathbf{C}'$.

It follows that $(\mathbf{B}' + \mathbf{C}')$ must be the projection of $(\mathbf{B} + \mathbf{C})$ perpendicular to $\mathbf{A}$; so, once again,

$$\mathbf{A} \times (\mathbf{B} + \mathbf{C}) = \mathbf{A} \times (\mathbf{B}' + \mathbf{C}')$$

Our earlier argument works for the vectors $\mathbf{B}'$ and $\mathbf{C}'$; therefore

$$\mathbf{A} \times (\mathbf{B}' + \mathbf{C}') = \mathbf{A} \times \mathbf{B}' + \mathbf{A} \times \mathbf{C}'$$

Combining the last four equations, we have a proof of Eq. (1.18).

Having established the distributive law for vector products, we can compute the componentwise expression for $\mathbf{A} \times \mathbf{B}$ easily:

$$\begin{aligned}\mathbf{A} \times \mathbf{B} &= (A_1\mathbf{i} + A_2\mathbf{j} + A_3\mathbf{k}) \times (B_1\mathbf{i} + B_2\mathbf{j} + B_3\mathbf{k}) \\ &= A_1B_1\mathbf{i} \times \mathbf{i} + A_1B_2\mathbf{i} \times \mathbf{j} + A_1B_3\mathbf{i} \times \mathbf{k} \\ &\quad + A_2B_1\mathbf{j} \times \mathbf{i} + A_2B_2\mathbf{j} \times \mathbf{j} + A_2B_3\mathbf{j} \times \mathbf{k} \\ &\quad + A_3B_1\mathbf{k} \times \mathbf{i} + A_3B_2\mathbf{k} \times \mathbf{j} + A_3B_3\mathbf{k} \times \mathbf{k}\end{aligned}$$

The vector products in this expression are easy to evaluate from the definition; $\mathbf{i} \times \mathbf{i} = 0$, $\mathbf{i} \times \mathbf{j} = \mathbf{k} = -\mathbf{j} \times \mathbf{i}$, etc. Thus we finally arrive at the equation

$$\mathbf{A} \times \mathbf{B} = (A_2B_3 - A_3B_2)\mathbf{i} + (A_3B_1 - A_1B_3)\mathbf{j} + (A_1B_2 - A_2B_1)\mathbf{k} \tag{1.20}$$

This definition may be conveniently memorized in determinant form:

$$\mathbf{A} \times \mathbf{B} = \begin{vmatrix} \mathbf{i} & \mathbf{j} & \mathbf{k} \\ A_1 & A_2 & A_3 \\ B_1 & B_2 & B_3 \end{vmatrix} \tag{1.20′}$$

This symbolic determinant is interpreted to be the vector whose x, y, and z components are the cofactors respectively of the first, second, and third entries in the first row.

Example 1.21 Find the vector product $\mathbf{A} \times \mathbf{B}$ if $\mathbf{A} = 3\mathbf{i} + 4\mathbf{j}$ and $\mathbf{B} = \mathbf{i} + 5\mathbf{k} - 2\mathbf{j}$.

Solution

$$\mathbf{A} \times \mathbf{B} = \begin{vmatrix} \mathbf{i} & \mathbf{j} & \mathbf{k} \\ 3 & 4 & 0 \\ 1 & -2 & 5 \end{vmatrix} = 20\mathbf{i} - 15\mathbf{j} - 10\mathbf{k}$$

For convenience, we list the algebraic properties of the vector product [which follow immediately from the expression (1.20)].

$$\begin{aligned} \mathbf{A} \times \mathbf{B} &= -(\mathbf{B} \times \mathbf{A}) \\ (\mathbf{A} + \mathbf{B}) \times \mathbf{C} &= (\mathbf{A} \times \mathbf{C}) + (\mathbf{B} \times \mathbf{C}) \\ \mathbf{A} \times (\mathbf{B} + \mathbf{C}) &= (\mathbf{A} \times \mathbf{B}) + (\mathbf{A} \times \mathbf{C}) \\ \mathbf{A} \times (s\mathbf{B}) &= s(\mathbf{A} \times \mathbf{B}) \\ (s\mathbf{A}) \times \mathbf{B} &= s(\mathbf{A} \times \mathbf{B}) \end{aligned}$$

Example 1.22 Find two unit vectors perpendicular to both $\mathbf{A} = 2\mathbf{i} + 2\mathbf{j} - 3\mathbf{k}$ and $\mathbf{B} = \mathbf{i} + 3\mathbf{j} + \mathbf{k}$.

Solution We have seen that $\mathbf{A} \times \mathbf{B}$ is perpendicular to both $\mathbf{A}$ and $\mathbf{B}$. We have

$$\mathbf{A} \times \mathbf{B} = \begin{vmatrix} \mathbf{i} & \mathbf{j} & \mathbf{k} \\ 2 & 2 & -3 \\ 1 & 3 & 1 \end{vmatrix} = 11\mathbf{i} - 5\mathbf{j} + 4\mathbf{k}$$

The length of this vector is $9\sqrt{2}$. The desired *unit* vector is therefore

$$\mathbf{n} = \frac{11}{9\sqrt{2}}\mathbf{i} - \frac{5}{9\sqrt{2}}\mathbf{j} + \frac{4}{9\sqrt{2}}\mathbf{k}$$

If we had taken $\mathbf{B} \times \mathbf{A}$ instead we would have obtained the negative of this vector. The two answers are

$$\pm\left(\frac{11\sqrt{2}}{18}\mathbf{i} - \frac{5\sqrt{2}}{18}\mathbf{j} + \frac{2\sqrt{2}}{9}\mathbf{k}\right)$$

Example 1.23 Find the area of the parallelogram determined by $\mathbf{A} = \mathbf{i} + \mathbf{j} - 3\mathbf{k}$ and $\mathbf{B} = 5\mathbf{k} - 6\mathbf{j}$.

Solution

$$\mathbf{A} \times \mathbf{B} = \begin{vmatrix} \mathbf{i} & \mathbf{j} & \mathbf{k} \\ 1 & 1 & -3 \\ 0 & -6 & 5 \end{vmatrix} = -13\mathbf{i} - 5\mathbf{j} - 6\mathbf{k}$$

$$|\mathbf{A} \times \mathbf{B}| = \sqrt{13^2 + 5^2 + 6^2} = \sqrt{230}$$

which is the desired area.

Example 1.24 Find the equations of the line passing through (3,2,−4) parallel to the line of intersection of the two planes $x + 3y - 2z = 8$, $x - 3y + z = 0$.

Solution Let $\mathbf{A} = \mathbf{i} + 3\mathbf{j} - 2\mathbf{k}$ and $\mathbf{B} = \mathbf{i} - 3\mathbf{j} + \mathbf{k}$. Since $\mathbf{A}$ is perpendicular to the first plane and $\mathbf{B}$ is perpendicular to the second, and $\mathbf{A} \times \mathbf{B}$ is perpendicular to both

A and **B**, it follows that $\mathbf{A} \times \mathbf{B}$ is parallel to both planes. Hence $\mathbf{A} \times \mathbf{B}$ is parallel to the line of intersection. We have

$$\mathbf{A} \times \mathbf{B} = \begin{vmatrix} \mathbf{i} & \mathbf{j} & \mathbf{k} \\ 1 & 3 & -2 \\ 1 & -3 & 1 \end{vmatrix} = -3\mathbf{i} - 3\mathbf{j} - 6\mathbf{k}$$

Equations of the desired line are

$$\frac{x-3}{-3} = \frac{y-2}{-3} = \frac{z+4}{-6}$$

or, equivalently,

$$x - 3 = y - 2 = \frac{z+4}{2}$$

Consider a rigid body rotating about an axis with angular velocity ω. The angular velocity is represented by a vector $\boldsymbol{\omega}$ of magnitude ω extending along the axis of rotation with sense determined by the right-hand rule: if the fingers of the right hand are wrapped about the axis in the direction of rotation, the thumb points in the direction of $\boldsymbol{\omega}$ (Fig. 1.23).

Let us assume that the origin O is on the axis of rotation, and let **R** denote the position vector of a particle in the body. Then the velocity **v** of the particle is given by

$$\mathbf{v} = \boldsymbol{\omega} \times \mathbf{R}$$

To see this, we first note that $|\mathbf{R}| \sin \theta$ is the distance of the particle from the axis of rotation, so **v** has magnitude $\omega|\mathbf{R}| \sin \theta$. Moreover, the velocity **v** is necessarily perpendicular to both **R** and $\boldsymbol{\omega}$, and the sense of $\boldsymbol{\omega}$ is such that **v** equals $\boldsymbol{\omega} \times \mathbf{R}$ rather than $\mathbf{R} \times \boldsymbol{\omega}$, as we see from Fig. 1.23.

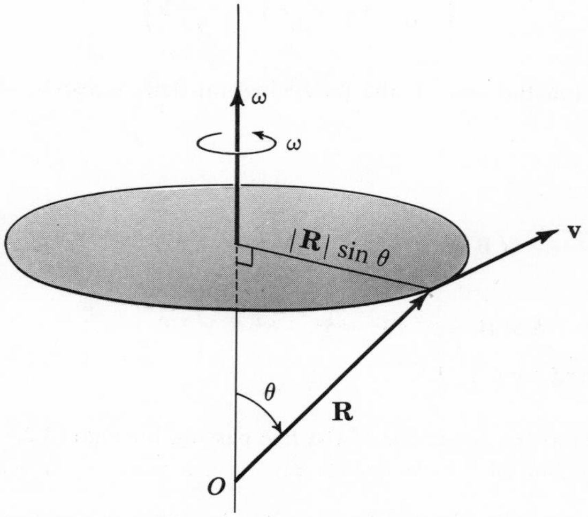

FIGURE 1.23

Example 1.25 A rigid body rotates with constant angular velocity ω about the line $x = y/2 = z/2$. Find the speed of a particle at the instant it passes through the point (2,3,5).

Solution The vector $\mathbf{i} + 2\mathbf{j} + 2\mathbf{k}$ is parallel to the axis. A unit vector parallel to the axis is $\frac{1}{3}\mathbf{i} + \frac{2}{3}\mathbf{j} + \frac{2}{3}\mathbf{k}$. Therefore

$$\boldsymbol{\omega} = \pm\omega(\tfrac{1}{3}\mathbf{i} + \tfrac{2}{3}\mathbf{j} + \tfrac{2}{3}\mathbf{k})$$

(The statement of the problem leaves the sign ambiguous.) The velocity is

$$\mathbf{v} = \boldsymbol{\omega} \times \mathbf{R} = \pm\omega \begin{vmatrix} \mathbf{i} & \mathbf{j} & \mathbf{k} \\ \frac{1}{3} & \frac{2}{3} & \frac{2}{3} \\ 2 & 3 & 5 \end{vmatrix} = \pm\omega(\tfrac{4}{3}\mathbf{i} - \tfrac{1}{3}\mathbf{j} - \tfrac{1}{3}\mathbf{k})$$

The speed is

$$|\mathbf{v}| = \omega(\tfrac{16}{9} + \tfrac{1}{9} + \tfrac{1}{9})^{1/2} = \tfrac{1}{3}\sqrt{18}\,\omega$$

EXERCISES

1. Find $\mathbf{A} \times \mathbf{B}$ where
   (a) $\mathbf{A} = 3\mathbf{i} - \mathbf{j} + 2\mathbf{k}$, $\mathbf{B} = \mathbf{i} + \mathbf{j} - 4\mathbf{k}$
   (b) $\mathbf{A} = 2\mathbf{i} + \mathbf{j} + 7\mathbf{k}$, $\mathbf{B} = 3\mathbf{i} + \mathbf{j} - \mathbf{k}$
   (c) $\mathbf{A} = \mathbf{j} + 6\mathbf{k}$, $\mathbf{B} = \mathbf{k} + 2\mathbf{j} - \mathbf{i}$
   (d) $\mathbf{A} = \mathbf{i}$, $\mathbf{B} = \mathbf{j}$
   (e) $\mathbf{B} \times \mathbf{A}$ is known to be $\mathbf{i} - \mathbf{j}$
2. Find the area of the parallelogram determined by $3\mathbf{i} + 4\mathbf{j}$ and $\mathbf{i} + \mathbf{j} + \mathbf{k}$.
3. Find the area of the triangle with vertices (1,1,2), (2,3,5), and (1,5,5).
4. Find $\mathbf{A} \times \mathbf{B}$ if $\mathbf{A} = \mathbf{i} - \mathbf{j} + \mathbf{k}$ and $\mathbf{B} = 3\mathbf{i} - 3\mathbf{j} + 3\mathbf{k}$. What is the geometrical significance of this answer?
5. Find a unit vector perpendicular to both $3\mathbf{i} + \mathbf{j}$ and $2\mathbf{i} - \mathbf{j} - 5\mathbf{k}$.
6. By vector methods, find the equations of the line through (2,3,7) parallel to the line of intersection of the planes $2x + y + z = 0$, $x - y + 7z = 0$.
7. Find equations of a line perpendicular to the lines $x = y = z$, $x = 2y = 3z$, passing through the origin.
8. Compute $(\mathbf{A} \times \mathbf{B}) \times \mathbf{C}$ and also $\mathbf{A} \times (\mathbf{B} \times \mathbf{C})$, given that $\mathbf{A} = 2\mathbf{i} + 2\mathbf{j}$, $\mathbf{B} = 3\mathbf{i} - \mathbf{j} + \mathbf{k}$, and $\mathbf{C} = 8\mathbf{i}$. Does the associative law hold for vector products?
9. By vector methods, determine the equation of the plane determined by points (2,0,1), (1,1,3), and (4,7,−2).
10. Find a unit vector in the plane of the vectors $\mathbf{A} = \mathbf{i} + 2\mathbf{j}$ and $\mathbf{B} = \mathbf{j} + 2\mathbf{k}$, perpendicular to the vector $\mathbf{C} = 2\mathbf{i} + \mathbf{j} + 2\mathbf{k}$.
11. By taking the vector cross product of $(\cos\theta)\mathbf{i} + (\sin\theta)\mathbf{j}$ and $(\cos\psi)\mathbf{i} + (\sin\psi)\mathbf{j}$ and interpreting geometrically, derive a well-known trigonometric identity.
12. If $\mathbf{A}$, $\mathbf{B}$, and $\mathbf{C}$ are vectors from the origin to points A, B, and C respectively, show that $(\mathbf{A} \times \mathbf{B}) + (\mathbf{B} \times \mathbf{C}) + (\mathbf{C} \times \mathbf{A})$ is perpendicular to the plane ABC. [*Hint*: Consider $(\mathbf{B} - \mathbf{A}) \times (\mathbf{C} - \mathbf{A})$.]

13. Find the distance from the point (5,7,14) to the line passing through (2,3,8) and (3,6,12). (*Hint*: Use a vector cross product.)

14. Find r and s if $(2\mathbf{i} + 6\mathbf{j} - 27\mathbf{k}) \times (\mathbf{i} + r\mathbf{j} + s\mathbf{k}) = 0$.

15. Given that $\mathbf{A} \cdot \mathbf{B} = 0$ and $\mathbf{A} \times \mathbf{B} = \mathbf{0}$, what can you conclude about the vectors $\mathbf{A}$ and $\mathbf{B}$?

16. Given that $\mathbf{A}$ and $\mathbf{B}$ are parallel to the yz plane, that $|\mathbf{A}| = 2$, $|\mathbf{B}| = 4$, and $\mathbf{A} \cdot \mathbf{B} = 0$, what can you say about $\mathbf{A} \times \mathbf{B}$?

17. (a) Do the lines $x/3 = y/2 = z/2$ and $x/5 = y/3 = (z - 4)/2$ intersect?
    (b) Find equations for a line perpendicular to both of these lines.
    (c) What is the distance between these lines?

18. If $\boldsymbol{\omega}$ points in the direction of $\mathbf{i} + \mathbf{j} + \mathbf{k}$ and the body rotates about an axis through the origin with angular velocity $10\sqrt{3}$ rad/sec, find the locus of points having speed 20 ft/sec. What does this locus represent?

19. Supply the missing details of the proof of the distributive law for vector products on pages 33 and 34.

20. If $\mathbf{u}$, $\mathbf{v}$, and $\mathbf{w}$ are mutually perpendicular unit vectors and $\mathbf{u} \times \mathbf{v} = \mathbf{w}$, show that $\mathbf{v} = \mathbf{w} \times \mathbf{u}$ and $\mathbf{u} = \mathbf{v} \times \mathbf{w}$.

1.13 TRIPLE SCALAR PRODUCT

The *triple scalar product* of three vectors, **A**, **B**, and **C**, is defined to be

$$[\mathbf{A},\mathbf{B},\mathbf{C}] = (\mathbf{A} \times \mathbf{B}) \cdot \mathbf{C}$$

Notice that the parentheses can be omitted because there is no other sensible way of interpreting $\mathbf{A} \times \mathbf{B} \cdot \mathbf{C}$. Using the componentwise expression derived in the previous section for the cross product, we have

$$\begin{aligned}[\mathbf{A},\mathbf{B},\mathbf{C}] = {} & A_1 B_2 C_3 + A_2 B_3 C_1 + A_3 B_1 C_2 \\ & - A_3 B_2 C_1 - A_2 B_1 C_3 - A_1 B_3 C_2 \end{aligned} \tag{1.21}$$

Alternatively, from the determinant expression for the cross product we can express $[\mathbf{A},\mathbf{B},\mathbf{C}]$ in the form

$$[\mathbf{A},\mathbf{B},\mathbf{C}] = \begin{vmatrix} C_1 & C_2 & C_3 \\ A_1 & A_2 & A_3 \\ B_1 & B_2 & B_3 \end{vmatrix}$$

which can be rewritten

$$[\mathbf{A},\mathbf{B},\mathbf{C}] = \begin{vmatrix} A_1 & A_2 & A_3 \\ B_1 & B_2 & B_3 \\ C_1 & C_2 & C_3 \end{vmatrix} \tag{1.22}$$

by two interchanges of rows in the determinant.

The triple scalar product has a geometric interpretation. Consider the parallelepiped with **A**, **B**, and **C** as coterminal edges, as in Fig. 1.24. The

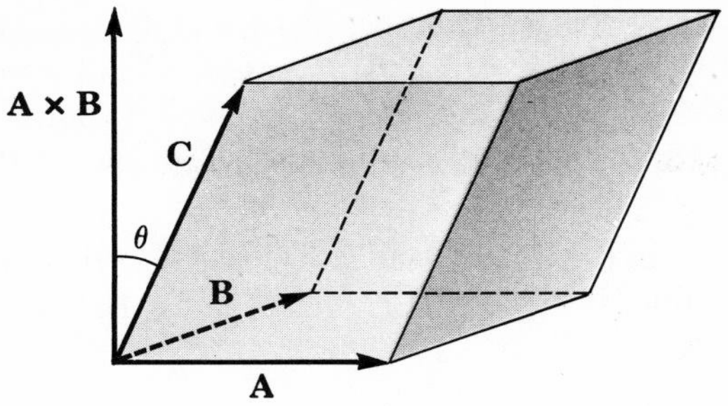

FIGURE 1.24

base of this solid is a parallelogram whose area is given, as we saw previously, by $|\mathbf{A} \times \mathbf{B}|$. Its height is the length of the component of **C** perpendicular to the base, which can be regarded as the component of **C** *parallel* to $\mathbf{A} \times \mathbf{B}$, or $|\mathbf{C}| \cos \theta$, as shown in Fig. 1.24. To be precise we should say this height is the *magnitude* of $|\mathbf{C}| \cos \theta$, because $\cos \theta$ would be negative if **C** pointed to the opposite side of the plane of **A** and **B**, i.e., if **A**, **B**, and **C** formed a left-handed system. Thus we see that the volume of the parallelepiped, computed as base area times height, equals the magnitude of $|\mathbf{A} \times \mathbf{B}| \cos \theta\, |\mathbf{C}|$. But this is precisely $\mathbf{A} \times \mathbf{B} \cdot \mathbf{C}$, the triple scalar product! Summarizing, we can say that *the volume of the parallelepiped with coterminal edges* **A**, **B**, **C** *is given, up to sign, by* $[\mathbf{A},\mathbf{B},\mathbf{C}]$. Furthermore, $[\mathbf{A},\mathbf{B},\mathbf{C}]$ *is positive if and only if* **A**, **B**, *and* **C** *form a right-handed system.*

Example 1.26 Compute $[\mathbf{A},\mathbf{B},\mathbf{C}]$ if $\mathbf{A} = 2\mathbf{i} + \mathbf{k}$, $\mathbf{B} = 3\mathbf{i} + \mathbf{j} + \mathbf{k}$, and $\mathbf{C} = \mathbf{i} + \mathbf{j} + 4\mathbf{k}$.

Solution

$$[\mathbf{A},\mathbf{B},\mathbf{C}] = [2\mathbf{i} + \mathbf{k},\ 3\mathbf{i} + \mathbf{j} + \mathbf{k},\ \mathbf{i} + \mathbf{j} + 4\mathbf{k}]$$

$$= \begin{vmatrix} 2 & 0 & 1 \\ 3 & 1 & 1 \\ 1 & 1 & 4 \end{vmatrix} = 8 + 3 - 1 - 2 = 8$$

Example 1.27 Compute $[\mathbf{i}, \mathbf{j}, \mathbf{i} + 2\mathbf{j}]$.

Solution

$$[\mathbf{i}, \mathbf{j}, \mathbf{i} + 2\mathbf{j}] = \begin{vmatrix} 1 & 0 & 0 \\ 0 & 1 & 0 \\ 1 & 2 & 0 \end{vmatrix} = 0$$

(The vectors are coplanar, so the parallelepiped has zero volume.)

We list the following properties of the triple scalar product. These properties are easily verified from the expression (1.21) or (1.22), and will be familiar to the student who has studied determinants.

$$[\mathbf{i},\mathbf{j},\mathbf{k}] = 1 \qquad (1.23)$$

For any three vectors **A**, **B**, and **C**, we have [**A**,**B**,**C**] = [**B**,**C**,**A**] = [**C**,**A**,**B**] = −[**B**,**A**,**C**] = −[**A**,**C**,**B**] = −[**C**,**B**,**A**]. In other words, the *absolute value* of the triple scalar product does not depend on the order, but whenever two of the vectors are interchanged the *sign* changes. (1.24)

If two or more of the vectors **A**, **B**, and **C** are equal, then [**A**,**B**,**C**] = 0. (For example, [**i** + **j**, 3**i** − **k**, **i** + **j**] = 0, since the first and third factors are equal.) (1.25)

The triple scalar product is *homogeneous* in each of its three factors. This means that, for any number s, we have [s**A**,**B**,**C**] = s[**A**,**B**,**C**], [**A**,s**B**,**C**] = s[**A**,**B**,**C**], and [**A**,**B**,s**C**] = s[**A**,**B**,**C**]. (For example, [3**i**, **j**,**k**] = 3[**i**, **j**,**k**] = 3.) (1.26)

The triple scalar product is *additive* in each of its three factors. This means that

$$\begin{aligned} [\mathbf{A}+\mathbf{D},\mathbf{B},\mathbf{C}] &= [\mathbf{A},\mathbf{B},\mathbf{C}]+[\mathbf{D},\mathbf{B},\mathbf{C}] \\ [\mathbf{A},\mathbf{B}+\mathbf{E},\mathbf{C}] &= [\mathbf{A},\mathbf{B},\mathbf{C}]+[\mathbf{A},\mathbf{E},\mathbf{C}] \\ \text{and}\quad [\mathbf{A},\mathbf{B},\mathbf{C}+\mathbf{F}] &= [\mathbf{A},\mathbf{B},\mathbf{C}]+[\mathbf{A},\mathbf{B},\mathbf{F}] \end{aligned} \tag{1.27}$$

It is interesting to notice that by using properties (1.23) through (1.27) it is possible to evaluate any scalar triple product without using (1.21) or (1.22). For example, let **A** = **i** + 3**j**, **B** = **i** + **k**, and **C** = −**k**. Then

$$\begin{aligned} [\mathbf{A},\mathbf{B},\mathbf{C}] &= [\mathbf{i}+3\mathbf{j},\ \mathbf{i}+\mathbf{k},\ -\mathbf{k}] \\ &= [\mathbf{i},\ \mathbf{i}+\mathbf{k},\ -\mathbf{k}] + [3\mathbf{j},\ \mathbf{i}+\mathbf{k},\ -\mathbf{k}] \\ &= [\mathbf{i},\mathbf{i},-\mathbf{k}] + [\mathbf{i},\mathbf{k},-\mathbf{k}] + [3\mathbf{j},\mathbf{i},-\mathbf{k}] + [3\mathbf{j},\mathbf{k},-\mathbf{k}] \\ &= -[\mathbf{i},\mathbf{i},\mathbf{k}] - [\mathbf{i},\mathbf{k},\mathbf{k}] - 3[\mathbf{j},\mathbf{i},\mathbf{k}] - 3[\mathbf{j},\mathbf{k},\mathbf{k}] \\ &= -3[\mathbf{j},\mathbf{i},\mathbf{k}] = 3[\mathbf{i},\mathbf{j},\mathbf{k}] = 3 \end{aligned}$$

Notice that the first, second, and fourth terms vanish because they have repeated factors.

If any one of the three vectors is replaced by the sum of that one vector with a linear combination of the other two, the triple scalar product is unchanged. For example, if we replace **A** by **A** + s**B** + t**C**, where s and t are any numbers whatsoever, then [**A** + s**B** + t**C**, **B**, **C**] = [**A**,**B**,**C**]. The proof is easy:

$$[\mathbf{A}+s\mathbf{B}+t\mathbf{C},\ \mathbf{B},\ \mathbf{C}] = [\mathbf{A},\mathbf{B},\mathbf{C}] + s[\mathbf{B},\mathbf{B},\mathbf{C}] + t[\mathbf{C},\mathbf{B},\mathbf{C}]$$

and the last two terms vanish by (1.25).

Finally, we note that the position of the dot and cross in the triple scalar product can be changed at will; i.e.,

$$\mathbf{A}\times\mathbf{B}\cdot\mathbf{C} = \mathbf{A}\cdot\mathbf{B}\times\mathbf{C}$$

since

$$\mathbf{A}\times\mathbf{B}\cdot\mathbf{C} = [\mathbf{A},\mathbf{B},\mathbf{C}] = [\mathbf{B},\mathbf{C},\mathbf{A}] = \mathbf{B}\times\mathbf{C}\cdot\mathbf{A} = \mathbf{A}\cdot\mathbf{B}\times\mathbf{C}$$

EXERCISES

1. Find the triple scalar product [**A**,**B**,**C**] given that
   (a) $\mathbf{A} = 2\mathbf{i}$, $\mathbf{B} = 3\mathbf{j}$, $\mathbf{C} = 5\mathbf{k}$
   (b) $\mathbf{A} = \mathbf{i} + \mathbf{j} + \mathbf{k}$, $\mathbf{B} = 3\mathbf{i} + \mathbf{j}$, $\mathbf{C} = 5\mathbf{k} - \mathbf{j}$
   (c) $\mathbf{A} = 2\mathbf{i} - \mathbf{j} + \mathbf{k}$, $\mathbf{B} = \mathbf{i} + \mathbf{j} + \mathbf{k}$, $\mathbf{C} = 2\mathbf{i} + 3\mathbf{k}$
   (d) $\mathbf{A} = \mathbf{k}$, $\mathbf{B} = \mathbf{i}$, $\mathbf{C} = \mathbf{j}$
2. Find the volume of the parallelepiped whose coterminal edges are arrows representing the vectors $3\mathbf{i} + 4\mathbf{j}$, $2\mathbf{i} + 3\mathbf{j} + 4\mathbf{k}$, $5\mathbf{k}$.
3. Find the volume of the parallelepiped with coterminal edges AB, AC, and AD, where $A = (3,2,1)$, $B = (4,2,1)$, $C = (0,1,4)$, and $D = (0,0,7)$.
4. Find the volume of the tetrahedron with coterminal edges representing the vectors $\mathbf{i} + \mathbf{j}$, $\mathbf{i} - \mathbf{j}$, $2\mathbf{k}$. Illustrate with a sketch. (*Note*: The volume of the tetrahedron is one sixth the volume of the parallelepiped having the same coterminal edges.)
5. Find the area of the parallelogram in the plane with vertices at (0,0), (1,1), (3,4), (4,5). (*Hint*: Convert this to a three-dimensional problem, finding the volume of the parallelepiped with this parallelogram as base, taking the third edge to be of unit length along the z axis.)
6. Find the equation of the plane passing through the origin parallel to the vectors $\mathbf{A} = 3\mathbf{i} + \mathbf{j} - 2\mathbf{k}$ and $\mathbf{B} = \mathbf{i} - \mathbf{j} + 5\mathbf{k}$. [*Hint*: The point (x,y,z) is in this plane if and only if $[\mathbf{R},\mathbf{A},\mathbf{B}] = 0$, where $\mathbf{R} = x\mathbf{i} + y\mathbf{j} + z\mathbf{k}$.]
7. Find the equation of the plane passing through $(3,4,-1)$ parallel to the vectors $\mathbf{A} = 2\mathbf{i} + \mathbf{j} + \mathbf{k}$ and $\mathbf{B} = \mathbf{i} - 3\mathbf{k}$. (*Hint*: Let $\mathbf{R}_0 = 3\mathbf{i} + 4\mathbf{j} - \mathbf{k}$. Consider $[\mathbf{R} - \mathbf{R}_0, \mathbf{A}, \mathbf{B}]$.)
8. (a) Show that the vectors $\mathbf{i} - \mathbf{j}$, $\mathbf{j} - \mathbf{k}$, $\mathbf{k} - \mathbf{i}$ are parallel to a plane.
   (b) Find an equation of the plane passing through the origin that is parallel to these three vectors.
9. Consider

$$\mathbf{A} = \mathbf{i} + \mathbf{j} + \mathbf{k} \qquad \mathbf{B} = \mathbf{i}$$
$$\mathbf{C} = C_1\mathbf{i} + C_2\mathbf{j} + C_3\mathbf{k}$$

   (a) If $C_1 = 1$, $C_2 = 2$, find C_3 to make the three vectors coplanar.
   (b) If $C_2 = -1$ and $C_3 = 1$, show that no value of C_1 can be found to make the three vectors coplanar.
   (c) Discuss the geometrical reason for the result in part (b).
10. Find the altitude of a parallelepiped determined by **A**, **B**, and **C**, if the base is taken to be the parallelogram determined by **A** and **B**, and if

$$\mathbf{A} = \mathbf{i} + \mathbf{j} + \mathbf{k}$$
$$\mathbf{B} = 2\mathbf{i} + 4\mathbf{j} - \mathbf{k}$$
$$\mathbf{C} = \mathbf{i} + \mathbf{j} + 3\mathbf{k}$$

   (*Hint*: Think of the geometrical interpretation of $[\mathbf{A},\mathbf{B},\mathbf{C}]/|\mathbf{A} \times \mathbf{B}|$.)
11. Sketch the vectors $\mathbf{A} = \mathbf{i} + \mathbf{j}$, $\mathbf{B} = \mathbf{i} + 2\mathbf{j} + 2\mathbf{k}$, and $\mathbf{C} = \mathbf{i} + 3\mathbf{k}$. Determine whether or not **A**, **B**, and **C** in that order form a right-handed system. Check by determining the sign of [**A**,**B**,**C**].

12. What can you conclude about nonzero vectors **A**, **B**, **C**, and **D**, given that $|(\mathbf{A} \times \mathbf{B}) \cdot \mathbf{C}| + |(\mathbf{B} \times \mathbf{C}) \cdot \mathbf{D}| = 0$?

13. (a) Let **u**, **v**, and **w** be mutually perpendicular unit vectors, forming a right-handed system. Show that the vector $\mathbf{A} = \mathbf{i} \times \mathbf{u} + \mathbf{j} \times \mathbf{v} + \mathbf{k} \times \mathbf{w}$ makes the same angle with **i** that it does with **u**.

(b) Find a vector extending along the axis of that rotation which carries **i**, **j**, and **k** into **u**, **v**, and **w** respectively.

14. Show that an arbitrary vector **V** can be expressed in terms of any three non-coplanar vectors **A**, **B**, and **C**, according to

$$\mathbf{V} = \frac{[\mathbf{V},\mathbf{B},\mathbf{C}]}{[\mathbf{A},\mathbf{B},\mathbf{C}]}\mathbf{A} + \frac{[\mathbf{V},\mathbf{C},\mathbf{A}]}{[\mathbf{A},\mathbf{B},\mathbf{C}]}\mathbf{B} + \frac{[\mathbf{V},\mathbf{A},\mathbf{B}]}{[\mathbf{A},\mathbf{B},\mathbf{C}]}\mathbf{C} \tag{1.28}$$

(*Hint*: We know that **V** can be expressed as $a\mathbf{A} + b\mathbf{B} + c\mathbf{C}$; to find a, take the scalar product of **V** with $\mathbf{B} \times \mathbf{C}$.)

15. (*Connection with Linear Algebra*) The concepts in this section are closely akin to the linear algebra of three-dimensional vector spaces. For example, algebraists would say that the three vectors **A**, **B**, and **C** are *linearly dependent* if one of them could be expressed as a linear combination of the other two, and a well-known test for linear dependence is the vanishing of the determinant of the matrix whose rows are the components of **A**, **B**, and **C**. The geometer will interpret the linear dependence of these vectors as a declaration that they are coplanar; the determinant in question is precisely [**A**,**B**,**C**] and its vanishing implies that the associated parallelepiped is, indeed, flat. In this regard, show that Eq. (1.28) can be interpreted as the statement of *Kramer's rule* for three equations in three unknowns.

16. (*Review*) State which of the following have meaning. Do not evaluate. Assume $\mathbf{B} \neq \mathbf{0}$.

(a) $\mathbf{A} \times 5\mathbf{B}$

(b) $[\mathbf{A}, 3\mathbf{B}, \mathbf{C} - \mathbf{D}]$

(c) $(\mathbf{A} \times \mathbf{B}) \cdot \mathbf{C}$

(d) $(\mathbf{A} \times \mathbf{B}) \cdot (\mathbf{C} \cdot \mathbf{D})$

(e) $(\mathbf{A} \cdot \mathbf{B}) \times (\mathbf{C} \times \mathbf{D})$

(f) $(\mathbf{A} \cdot \mathbf{B}) \times (\mathbf{C} \cdot \mathbf{D})$

(g) $\mathbf{A} \times [(\mathbf{B} \cdot \mathbf{C})\mathbf{D}]$

(h) $\mathbf{A}/|\mathbf{B}|$

(i) $\mathbf{A}/\mathbf{B}$

1.14 VECTOR IDENTITIES

Of the following identities, the first is the most important because the other three can be derived from it fairly easily.

$$\mathbf{A} \times (\mathbf{B} \times \mathbf{C}) = (\mathbf{A} \cdot \mathbf{C})\mathbf{B} - (\mathbf{A} \cdot \mathbf{B})\mathbf{C} \tag{1.29}$$

$$(\mathbf{A} \times \mathbf{B}) \times \mathbf{C} = (\mathbf{A} \cdot \mathbf{C})\mathbf{B} - (\mathbf{B} \cdot \mathbf{C})\mathbf{A} \tag{1.30}$$

$$(\mathbf{A} \times \mathbf{B}) \times (\mathbf{C} \times \mathbf{D}) = [\mathbf{A},\mathbf{C},\mathbf{D}]\mathbf{B} - [\mathbf{B},\mathbf{C},\mathbf{D}]\mathbf{A} \tag{1.31}$$

$$(\mathbf{A} \times \mathbf{B}) \cdot (\mathbf{C} \times \mathbf{D}) = (\mathbf{A} \cdot \mathbf{C})(\mathbf{B} \cdot \mathbf{D}) - (\mathbf{A} \cdot \mathbf{D})(\mathbf{B} \cdot \mathbf{C}) \tag{1.32}$$

In formula (1.29), if $\mathbf{V} = \mathbf{A} \times (\mathbf{B} \times \mathbf{C})$ is not the zero vector, then it must be perpendicular to $\mathbf{B} \times \mathbf{C}$. Since $\mathbf{B} \times \mathbf{C}$ is itself perpendicular to both **B** and **C**, it follows that **V** must be in the plane of **B** and **C**, and since they are nonzero vectors that are not parallel (otherwise **V** would be the zero vector), **V** must be a linear combination of **B** and **C**. Thus $\mathbf{V} = m\mathbf{B} + n\mathbf{C}$ for suitable scalars m and n. The fact that $m = \mathbf{A} \cdot \mathbf{C}$ and $n = -\mathbf{A} \cdot \mathbf{B}$ is not obvious, of course. The actual verification of (1.29) can be accomplished by working out the componentwise expression for each side of the equality. We leave this laborious computation to the energetic reader. (Or he can read Sec. 1.15.)

We suggest the following device for memorizing (1.29). As we observed, $\mathbf{A} \times (\mathbf{B} \times \mathbf{C})$ must be expressible as a linear combination of **B** and **C**. If the student can only remember that the coefficients in this expression are scalar products of the other two vectors, and that the terms have opposite signs, he will be able to write

$$\mathbf{A} \times (\mathbf{B} \times \mathbf{C}) = \pm[(\mathbf{A} \cdot \mathbf{C})\mathbf{B} - (\mathbf{A} \cdot \mathbf{B})\mathbf{C}]$$

To get the proper sign, use the familiar vectors **i**, **j**, and **k**; thus

$$\mathbf{i} \times (\mathbf{i} \times \mathbf{j}) = \mathbf{i} \times \mathbf{k} = -\mathbf{j} = \pm[(\mathbf{i} \cdot \mathbf{j})\mathbf{i} - (\mathbf{i} \cdot \mathbf{i})\mathbf{j}]$$

so the plus sign is correct. [This also works for formula (1.30), of course.]

Formula (1.30) is easily proved by observing

$$(\mathbf{A} \times \mathbf{B}) \times \mathbf{C} = -\mathbf{C} \times (\mathbf{A} \times \mathbf{B})$$

and using (1.29) for the right-hand side.

To derive (1.31), let $\mathbf{U} = \mathbf{C} \times \mathbf{D}$, whence

$$(\mathbf{A} \times \mathbf{B}) \times \mathbf{U} = (\mathbf{A} \cdot \mathbf{U})\mathbf{B} - (\mathbf{B} \cdot \mathbf{U})\mathbf{A} = [\mathbf{A},\mathbf{C},\mathbf{D}]\mathbf{B} - [\mathbf{B},\mathbf{C},\mathbf{D}]\mathbf{A}$$

To derive (1.32),

$$\begin{aligned}(\mathbf{A} \times \mathbf{B}) \cdot \mathbf{U} &= [\mathbf{A},\mathbf{B},\mathbf{U}] = \mathbf{A} \cdot (\mathbf{B} \times \mathbf{U}) = \mathbf{A} \cdot [\mathbf{B} \times (\mathbf{C} \times \mathbf{D})] \\ &= \mathbf{A} \cdot [(\mathbf{B} \cdot \mathbf{D})\mathbf{C} - (\mathbf{B} \cdot \mathbf{C})\mathbf{D}] \\ &= (\mathbf{B} \cdot \mathbf{D})(\mathbf{A} \cdot \mathbf{C}) - (\mathbf{B} \cdot \mathbf{C})(\mathbf{A} \cdot \mathbf{D})\end{aligned}$$

EXERCISES

1. Derive the identity

$$(\mathbf{A} \times \mathbf{B}) \times (\mathbf{C} \times \mathbf{D}) = [\mathbf{A},\mathbf{B},\mathbf{D}]\mathbf{C} - [\mathbf{A},\mathbf{B},\mathbf{C}]\mathbf{D}$$

2. Derive the identity

$$(\mathbf{A} \times \mathbf{B}) \cdot (\mathbf{B} \times \mathbf{C}) \times (\mathbf{C} \times \mathbf{A}) = [\mathbf{A},\mathbf{B},\mathbf{C}]^2$$

3. Derive the identity

$$\mathbf{A} \times (\mathbf{B} \times \mathbf{C}) + \mathbf{B} \times (\mathbf{C} \times \mathbf{A}) + \mathbf{C} \times (\mathbf{A} \times \mathbf{B}) = \mathbf{0}$$

4. Verify formula (1.29) by working out the componentwise expression.

5. If the vector $\boldsymbol{\omega}$ in Fig. 1.23 is constant, then the acceleration of a particle with position vector **R** is $\mathbf{a} = \boldsymbol{\omega} \times (\boldsymbol{\omega} \times \mathbf{R})$. Simplify this expression.

6. Are any of the following identities generally valid for vectors?
   (a) $\mathbf{A} \times \mathbf{B} = \mathbf{B} \times \mathbf{A}$
   (b) $(\mathbf{A} \times \mathbf{B}) \times \mathbf{C} = \mathbf{A} \times (\mathbf{B} \times \mathbf{C})$
   (c) $\mathbf{A} \times \mathbf{B} = \mathbf{A} \times \mathbf{C}$ if and only if $\mathbf{B} = \mathbf{C}$
   (d) $\mathbf{A} \times \mathbf{B} = \mathbf{0}$ if and only if $\mathbf{A} = \mathbf{0}$ or $\mathbf{B} = \mathbf{0}$
7. Simplify: $|\mathbf{A} \times \mathbf{B}|^2 + (\mathbf{A} \cdot \mathbf{B})^2 - |\mathbf{A}|^2 |\mathbf{B}|^2$

*1.15 TENSOR NOTATION

The material in this section is used only in later sections which are starred; all starred sections may be omitted without loss of continuity.

The use of distinguished symbols such as $\mathbf{A}$, $\mathbf{A} \times \mathbf{B}$, etc., to denote vectors and vector operations provides an excellent and often suggestive shorthand for expressing laws in geometry and physics. However, when we ultimately come down to the actual computations of a concrete problem, these expressions must be dealt with componentwise. Furthermore, the verification (and discovery!) of some of the more complicated vector identities such as those appearing in the previous section is often accomplished most efficiently by dealing with the components. In this section we shall introduce some notation which often facilitates this process; it is widely known as *tensor notation*. Although we do not intend to discuss tensors themselves until Chap. 5, we see no reason to designate the notational system by anything other than its proper name.

The boldface vector symbol $\mathbf{A}$ suggests, as we have said, a quantity with magnitude and direction; this quantity is equally well represented by three numbers, A_1, A_2, and A_3, the components of the vector. Every statement about the vector is actually a statement about its components. Thus $\mathbf{A} = \mathbf{B}$ means $A_1 = B_1$, $A_2 = B_2$, and $A_3 = B_3$; briefly,

$$A_i = B_i \qquad (i = 1,2,3) \tag{1.33}$$

Expressed simply, the basic idea in tensor notation is to try to write all vector equations in component form, but using dummy subscripts such as i in Eq. (1.33), rather than explicitly writing out the equation for the first component, then the second, then the third. (Whether or not this is always possible will be discussed in Chap. 5. For now, we will be satisfied with using tensor notation *when we can*.) We will indicate the components of a vector $\mathbf{A}$ by A_i, or $(\mathbf{A})_i$ if it is more convenient; we shall regard the parenthetical phrase "$(i = 1,2,3)$" as understood, and delete it. Let's try some examples.

The expression of the fact that vectors add componentwise becomes

$$(\mathbf{A} + \mathbf{B})_i = A_i + B_i$$

That is, the ith component of $\mathbf{A} + \mathbf{B}$ is the sum of the ith components of $\mathbf{A}$ and of $\mathbf{B}$. Scalar multiplication is expressed

$$(s\mathbf{A})_i = sA_i$$

The associative law for vectors, expressed componentwise, merely reduces to the associative law for *numbers*:

$$\begin{aligned}[(\mathbf{A}+\mathbf{B})+\mathbf{C}]_i &= (\mathbf{A}+\mathbf{B})_i + C_i \\ &= (A_i + B_i) + C_i \\ &= A_i + (B_i + C_i) \\ &= [\mathbf{A}+(\mathbf{B}+\mathbf{C})]_i\end{aligned}$$

The condition that **R** lie on the line through the tip of **V** and parallel to **W** is expressed

$$R_i = V_i + tW_i$$

For the scalar product, we have

$$\mathbf{A}\cdot\mathbf{B} = A_1B_1 + A_2B_2 + A_3B_3$$

This can be compacted by using the Greek letter Σ to denote summation. For any set of n numbers $\{a_l\}$ ($l = 1,2, \ldots, n$), we abbreviate

$$a_1 + a_2 + \cdots + a_n$$

by the expression

$$\sum_{l=1}^{n} a_l$$

Thus our scalar product becomes

$$\mathbf{A}\cdot\mathbf{B} = \sum_{i=1}^{3} A_i B_i \tag{1.34}$$

The componentwise expression of the cross product is a bit complicated. Observe that each component of $\mathbf{A}\times\mathbf{B}$ is a sum of products of components of **A** times components of **B**. If we (conceptually) form all the products $\{A_j B_k\}$, we can say that the ith component of $\mathbf{A}\times\mathbf{B}$ is a linear combination of these with coefficients $+1$, -1, or 0 (if the term doesn't actually appear). So by defining ε_{ijk} appropriately, we can write

$$(\mathbf{A}\times\mathbf{B})_i = \sum_{j=1}^{3}\sum_{k=1}^{3} \varepsilon_{ijk} A_j B_k \tag{1.35}$$

ε_{ijk} is the coefficient of $A_j B_k$ in the ith component of $\mathbf{A}\times\mathbf{B}$. Comparison of this with expression (1.35) in Sec. 1.12 shows

$$\varepsilon_{ijk} = \begin{cases} +1 & \text{if } (ijk) \text{ is either } (123), (231), \text{ or } (312) \\ -1 & \text{if } (ijk) \text{ is either } (321), (213), \text{ or } (132) \\ 0 & \text{otherwise} \end{cases} \tag{1.36}$$

In fact, ε_{ijk} is the coefficient of $\lambda_i \mu_j \eta_k$ in the determinant

$$\begin{vmatrix} \lambda_1 & \lambda_2 & \lambda_3 \\ \mu_1 & \mu_2 & \mu_3 \\ \eta_1 & \eta_2 & \eta_3 \end{vmatrix}$$

a fact which we could have anticipated by comparing the expression (1.35) with the determinant formula for the cross product in Sec. 1.12.

A few observations about the symbol ε_{ijk} are in order.

(*i*) $\varepsilon_{ijk} = 0$ if any of the subscripts are equal.
(*ii*) $\varepsilon_{ijk} = \varepsilon_{jki} = \varepsilon_{kij}$, i.e., the subscripts can be permuted cyclically.
(*iii*) $\varepsilon_{ijk} = -\varepsilon_{jik}$, i.e., the sign changes if two subscripts are switched.

Of course, the scalar product $\mathbf{A} \cdot \mathbf{B}$ is also composed of products of **A**'s components with **B**'s components, and if the expression (1.34) weren't so simple already, we would write it

$$\mathbf{A} \cdot \mathbf{B} = \sum_{i=1}^{3} \sum_{j=1}^{3} \delta_{ij} A_i B_j$$

where

$$\delta_{ij} = \begin{cases} 1 & \text{if } i = j \\ 0 & \text{otherwise} \end{cases} \tag{1.37}$$

The effect of δ_{ij} in an expression is simple if the subscripts are summed; since $\delta_{ij} = 0$ unless $i = j$, one can merely drop the δ and substitute i for j. Thus,

$$\sum_{i=1}^{3} \sum_{j=1}^{3} \delta_{ij} A_i B_j = \sum_{j=1}^{3} A_j B_j \qquad (= \mathbf{A} \cdot \mathbf{B})$$

For this reason, δ_{ij} is sometimes called the *substitution tensor*. It's also known as the "Kronecker delta".

Example 1.28 Show that the triple scalar product can be computed as a determinant.

Solution In the expression $\mathbf{A} \cdot \mathbf{B} \times \mathbf{C}$, we first use tensor notation for the scalar product:

$$\mathbf{A} \cdot \mathbf{B} \times \mathbf{C} = \sum_{i=1}^{3} A_i (\mathbf{B} \times \mathbf{C})_i$$

Now using (1.35) for the vector product,

$$\begin{aligned} \mathbf{A} \cdot \mathbf{B} \times \mathbf{C} &= \sum_{i=1}^{3} A_i \sum_{j=1}^{3} \sum_{k=1}^{3} \varepsilon_{ijk} B_j C_k \\ &= \sum_{i=1}^{3} \sum_{j=1}^{3} \sum_{k=1}^{3} \varepsilon_{ijk} A_i B_j C_k \end{aligned} \tag{1.38}$$

As we observed earlier, this is the expansion of the determinant

$$\begin{vmatrix} A_1 & A_2 & A_3 \\ B_1 & B_2 & B_3 \\ C_1 & C_2 & C_3 \end{vmatrix}$$

Notice that every time we have used the summation symbol Σ, the subscript over which we were summing occurred *twice* in the term expressing the addend; i is repeated in (1.34), j and k are repeated in (1.35), etc. This happens so often that the following convention is used in tensor notation: *whenever a subscript appears more than once in a single term, it is understood that this particular term is to be summed over all values* (1,2, and 3) *of the repeated subscript*. Scalar products are thus written $A_i B_i$, and the ith component of $\mathbf{A} \times \mathbf{B}$ is $\varepsilon_{ijk} A_j B_k$. In fact, we have $\delta_{ii} = 3$. *Exceptions to this rule must be explicitly indicated.*

The manipulation of expressions involving more than one cross product is aided by the following identity:

$$\varepsilon_{ikm}\varepsilon_{psm} = \delta_{ip}\delta_{ks} - \delta_{is}\delta_{kp} \tag{1.39}$$

(Observe that m is summed over.) To prove this, we notice that the right hand side is zero unless it has the form $1 - 0$ or $0 - 1$. Thus

$$\delta_{ip}\delta_{ks} - \delta_{is}\delta_{kp} = \begin{cases} 1 & \text{if } i = p \text{ and } k = s \text{ but } i \neq s \text{ (or } k \neq p) \\ -1 & \text{if } i = s \text{ and } k = p \text{ but } i \neq p \text{ (or } k \neq s) \\ 0 & \text{otherwise} \end{cases}$$

On the left of (1.39), ε is zero unless all subscripts are different; in which case, $i \neq k$ and $p \neq s$ and m must be different from i, p, k, or s. So, there is actually only one nonzero term in the sum over values of m! The product is $+1$ if (ikm) is a cyclic permutation of (psm), which can only happen if $i = p$ and $k = s$; and -1 results if (ikm) is in the opposite order as (psm), which requires $i = s$ and $k = p$. Comparing these conditions, we see that the left and right-hand sides of (1.39) are equal.

Example 1.29 Simplify $\mathbf{A} \times (\mathbf{B} \times \mathbf{C})$.

Solution The ith component is

$$\begin{aligned} \varepsilon_{ijk} A_j(\mathbf{B} \times \mathbf{C})_k &= \varepsilon_{ijk} A_j \varepsilon_{klm} B_l C_m \\ &= \varepsilon_{ijk}\varepsilon_{klm} A_j B_l C_m \end{aligned}$$

Remember that we are summing over repeated subscripts. First we sum over k. Since the other terms do not depend on k, we can compute $\varepsilon_{ijk}\varepsilon_{klm}$; this the same as $\varepsilon_{ijk}\varepsilon_{lmk}$ which, by Eq. (1.39), is $\delta_{il}\delta_{jm} - \delta_{im}\delta_{jl}$. So the above expression equals

$$(\delta_{il}\delta_{jm} - \delta_{im}\delta_{jl}) A_j B_l C_m$$

Now sum out the substitution tensors one at a time. Summing over m we get

$$\delta_{il} A_j B_l C_j - \delta_{jl} A_j B_l C_i$$

and, summing over l,

$$A_j C_j B_i - A_j B_j C_i$$

Identifying the scalar products, we recognize that this is the ith component of $(\mathbf{A} \cdot \mathbf{C})\mathbf{B} - (\mathbf{A} \cdot \mathbf{B})\mathbf{C}$. We have proved formula (1.29)!

Example 1.30 Simplify $(\mathbf{A} \times \mathbf{B}) \times (\mathbf{C} \times \mathbf{D})$.

Solution The ith component is

$$\varepsilon_{ijk}(\mathbf{A} \times \mathbf{B})_j(\mathbf{C} \times \mathbf{D})_k = \varepsilon_{ijk}\,\varepsilon_{jmn}\,A_m\,B_n\,\varepsilon_{kpq}\,C_p\,D_q$$

If we sum over j first, only the first two factors are involved. Rewriting them as $\varepsilon_{kij}\,\varepsilon_{mnj}$, we use (1.39) to transform the expression to

$$(\delta_{km}\,\delta_{in} - \delta_{kn}\,\delta_{im})\,A_m\,B_n\,\varepsilon_{kpq}\,C_p\,D_q$$

Summing over the subscripts of the substitution tensors is easy, yielding

$$A_k\,B_i\,\varepsilon_{kpq}\,C_p\,D_q - A_i\,B_k\,\varepsilon_{kpq}\,C_p\,D_q$$

Now we identify $\varepsilon_{kpq}\,A_k\,C_p\,D_q$ as the triple scalar product, recalling Eq. (1.38); similarly for $\varepsilon_{kpq}\,B_k\,C_p\,D_q$. So we are left with

$$[\mathbf{A},\mathbf{C},\mathbf{D}]B_i - [\mathbf{B},\mathbf{C},\mathbf{D}]A_i$$

which is the ith component of $[\mathbf{A},\mathbf{C},\mathbf{D}]\mathbf{B} - [\mathbf{B},\mathbf{C},\mathbf{D}]\mathbf{A}$. We have "discovered" formula (1.31).

EXERCISES

1. Simplify $(\mathbf{A} \times \mathbf{B}) \cdot \mathbf{C}$.

2. Simplify $(\mathbf{A} \times \mathbf{B}) \cdot (\mathbf{C} \times \mathbf{D})$.

3. Simplify $(\mathbf{A} \times \mathbf{B}) \cdot (\mathbf{B} \times \mathbf{C}) \times (\mathbf{C} \times \mathbf{A})$.

CHAPTER 2

Vector Functions of a Single Variable

2.1 DIFFERENTIATION

The theory of vector functions parallels that of real-valued functions. A vector-valued function $\mathbf{F}(t)$ is a rule that associates a vector $\mathbf{F}$ with each real number t in some set, usually an interval $(t_1 \le t \le t_2)$ or a collection of intervals. For example, $\mathbf{F}(t) = (1/t)\mathbf{i}$ is defined for $-\infty < t < 0$ and $0 < t < \infty$.

The concept of a limit can be applied to vector functions. The expression

$$\lim_{t \to t_0} \mathbf{F}(t) = \mathbf{A} \tag{2.1}$$

means that, given any positive number ε, no matter how small, one can find a positive number δ such that $|\mathbf{F}(t) - \mathbf{A}| < \varepsilon$ whenever $|t - t_0| < \delta$.

This has a simple intuitive meaning. It means that the magnitude of $\mathbf{F}(t)$ is approaching the magnitude of $\mathbf{A}$, and that (if $\mathbf{A}$ is nonzero) the angle between them is approaching zero (see Fig. 2.1). Equivalently, the *components* of $\mathbf{F}(t)$ are approaching the *components* of $\mathbf{A}$.

The definition just given is identical to that given in calculus books for real-valued functions, except that the expression $|\mathbf{F}(t) - \mathbf{A}|$ now refers to the magnitude of a vector rather than to the absolute value of a number.

A vector function $\mathbf{F}$ is said to be *continuous* at t_0 if

$$\lim_{t \to t_0} \mathbf{F}(t) = \mathbf{F}(t_0) \tag{2.2}$$

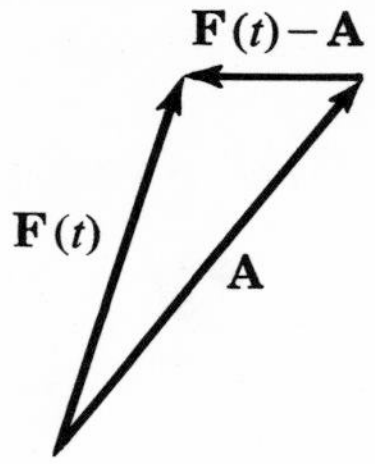

FIGURE 2.1

It is said to be *differentiable* at t_0 if the limit

$$\lim_{\Delta t \to 0} \frac{\mathbf{F}(t_0 + \Delta t) - \mathbf{F}(t_0)}{\Delta t} \tag{2.3}$$

exists; this limit is then called the *derivative of* $\mathbf{F}(t)$ *at* t_0 and is written $\mathbf{F}'(t_0)$ or $\frac{d\mathbf{F}}{dt}(t_0)$. It is also a vector function.

If $\mathbf{F}(t)$ is continuous (or differentiable) at *every* point t for which it is defined, we shall simply say $\mathbf{F}(t)$ *is continuous* (or *differentiable*).

The fundamental theorems concerning differentiation of vector-valued functions are similar to those for real-valued functions, except that when differentiating the vector product of two vector functions, one must be careful to preserve the order of factors, since the vector product is not a commutative operation.

THEOREM 2.1 *If* $\mathbf{F}$ *and* $\mathbf{G}$ *are differentiable vector functions, then so also is their sum* $\mathbf{F} + \mathbf{G}$, *and the derivative of the function* $\mathbf{F} + \mathbf{G}$ *is the sum of the derivatives of* $\mathbf{F}$ *and* $\mathbf{G}$ *respectively,*

$$\frac{d}{dt}(\mathbf{F} + \mathbf{G}) = \frac{d\mathbf{F}}{dt} + \frac{d\mathbf{G}}{dt} \tag{2.4}$$

THEOREM 2.2 *If* $\mathbf{F}$ *is a differentiable vector function, and* s *is a differentiable scalar function, then the product* $s\mathbf{F}$ *is a differentiable vector function, and*

$$\frac{d}{dt}(s\mathbf{F}) = \frac{ds}{dt}\mathbf{F} + s\frac{d\mathbf{F}}{dt} \tag{2.5}$$

THEOREM 2.3 *If* $\mathbf{F}$ *and* $\mathbf{G}$ *are differentiable vector functions, then* $\mathbf{F} \cdot \mathbf{G}$ *is a differentiable scalar function, and*

$$\frac{d}{dt}(\mathbf{F} \cdot \mathbf{G}) = \frac{d\mathbf{F}}{dt} \cdot \mathbf{G} + \mathbf{F} \cdot \frac{d\mathbf{G}}{dt} \tag{2.6}$$

THEOREM 2.4 *If* **F** *and* **G** *are differentiable vector functions, then* **F** × **G** *is also a differentiable vector function, and*

$$\frac{d}{dt}(\mathbf{F} \times \mathbf{G}) = \frac{d\mathbf{F}}{dt} \times \mathbf{G} + \mathbf{F} \times \frac{d\mathbf{G}}{dt} \tag{2.7}$$

The reader who is familiar with the proofs of the sum and product formulas of elementary calculus will have no difficulty filling in the proofs of these theorems.

Example 2.1 Prove Theorem 2.4.

Solution With the definition of the derivative in mind, we write

$$\frac{\mathbf{F}(t+\Delta t) \times \mathbf{G}(t+\Delta t) - \mathbf{F}(t) \times \mathbf{G}(t)}{\Delta t}$$
$$= \frac{[\mathbf{F}(t+\Delta t) - \mathbf{F}(t)] \times \mathbf{G}(t+\Delta t)}{\Delta t} + \frac{\mathbf{F}(t) \times [\mathbf{G}(t+\Delta t) - \mathbf{G}(t)]}{\Delta t}$$

As $\Delta t \to 0$, the right-hand side approaches a limiting value given by

$$\frac{d\mathbf{F}}{dt} \times \mathbf{G} + \mathbf{F} \times \frac{d\mathbf{G}}{dt}$$

Since the limit of the left-hand side is $\frac{d}{dt}(\mathbf{F} \times \mathbf{G})$, we have proved the theorem.

It follows from (2.4) and (2.5) that if

$$\mathbf{F}(t) = P(t)\mathbf{i} + Q(t)\mathbf{j} + R(t)\mathbf{k}$$

then

$$\mathbf{F}'(t) = P'(t)\mathbf{i} + Q'(t)\mathbf{j} + R'(t)\mathbf{k} \tag{2.8}$$

Example 2.2 If $\mathbf{F}(t) = \sin t\,\mathbf{i} + \cos t\,\mathbf{j} + t\mathbf{k}$, then $\mathbf{F}'(t) = \cos t\,\mathbf{i} - \sin t\,\mathbf{j} + \mathbf{k}$

Example 2.3 If $\mathbf{F}(t) = t^3\mathbf{j} - \mathbf{k}$, then $\mathbf{F}'(t) = 3t^2\mathbf{j}$.

Example 2.4 Let $\mathbf{F}(t) = \mathbf{i} + 2\mathbf{j} - \mathbf{k}$. Then **F** is a constant vector-valued function, and its derivative with respect to t is identically equal to the zero vector for all t.

Example 2.5 If $\mathbf{F}'(t) = \mathbf{0}$, then $\mathbf{F}(t) = \mathbf{C}$, where the constant **C** is a *vector*.

Example 2.6 Prove that, if $\mathbf{F}(t)$ has constant nonzero magnitude (varies only in direction), then $\mathbf{F}'(t)$ is either the z erovector or it is a nonzero vector perpendicular to $\mathbf{F}(t)$.

Solution If $|\mathbf{F}(t)| =$ constant, then we must have

$$\mathbf{F} \cdot \mathbf{F} = \text{constant}$$

and differentiating with respect to t, using (2.6), we have

$$\frac{d\mathbf{F}}{dt} \cdot \mathbf{F} + \mathbf{F} \cdot \frac{d\mathbf{F}}{dt} = 0$$

$$2\mathbf{F} \cdot \frac{d\mathbf{F}}{dt} = 0$$

Hence the scalar product of $\mathbf{F}$ with $d\mathbf{F}/dt$ is identically zero. This can happen only if the vectors $\mathbf{F}$ and $d\mathbf{F}/dt$ are perpendicular, or if one of them is the zero vector. This fact is well worth remembering: *the derivative of a vector of constant length is perpendicular to the vector, or zero.*

EXERCISES

1. Let $\mathbf{F}(t) = \sin t\,\mathbf{i} + \cos t\,\mathbf{j} + \mathbf{k}$.
   (a) Find $\mathbf{F}'(t)$.
   (b) Show that $\mathbf{F}'(t)$ is always parallel to the xy plane.
   (c) For what values of t is $\mathbf{F}'(t)$ parallel to the xz plane?
   (d) Does $\mathbf{F}(t)$ have constant magnitude?
   (e) Does $\mathbf{F}'(t)$ have constant magnitude?
   (f) Compute $\mathbf{F}''(t)$.

2. Find $\mathbf{F}'(t)$ in each of the following cases.
   (a) $\mathbf{F}(t) = 3t\mathbf{i} + t^3\mathbf{j}$
   (b) $\mathbf{F}(t) = \sin t\,\mathbf{i} + e^{-t}\mathbf{j} + 3\mathbf{k}$
   (c) $\mathbf{F}(t) = (e^t\mathbf{i} + \mathbf{j} + t^2\mathbf{k}) \times (t^3\mathbf{i} + \mathbf{j} - \mathbf{k})$
   (d) $\mathbf{F}(t) = (\sin t + t^3)(\mathbf{i} + \mathbf{j} + 2\mathbf{k})$
   (e) $\mathbf{F}(t) = 3\mathbf{i} + \mathbf{k}$

3. Find $f'(t)$ in each of the following cases.
   (a) $f(t) = (3t\mathbf{i} + 5t^2\mathbf{j}) \cdot (t\mathbf{i} - \sin t\,\mathbf{j})$
   (b) $f(t) = |2t\mathbf{i} + 2t\mathbf{j} - \mathbf{k}|$
   (c) $f(t) = [(\mathbf{i} + \mathbf{j} - 2\mathbf{k}) \times (3t^4\mathbf{i} + t\mathbf{j})] \cdot \mathbf{k}$

4. Show that $\dfrac{d}{dt}\left(\mathbf{R} \times \dfrac{d\mathbf{R}}{dt}\right) = \mathbf{R} \times \dfrac{d^2\mathbf{R}}{dt^2}$.

5. Given the three vectors $\mathbf{A} = 3\mathbf{i} + 2\mathbf{j} + 6\mathbf{k}$, $\mathbf{B} = 3\mathbf{i} + 4\mathbf{k}$, and $\mathbf{C} = 2\mathbf{i} - 2\mathbf{j} + \mathbf{k}$, evaluate
   (a) $|\mathbf{A}|$
   (b) $\mathbf{A} \cdot \mathbf{B}$
   (c) $\mathbf{B} \times \mathbf{C}$
   (d) $\mathbf{B} \cdot \mathbf{B} \times \mathbf{C}$
   (e) $[\mathbf{A},\mathbf{B},\mathbf{C}]$
   (f) $\mathbf{A}/|\mathbf{B}|$
   (g) $\mathbf{A} \times (\mathbf{B} \times \mathbf{C})$
   (h) $\dfrac{d}{dt}(\mathbf{A} + \mathbf{B}t)$
   (i) $\dfrac{d}{dt}(\mathbf{B} \times t\mathbf{C})$

   (*Note*: No distinction is intended between $\mathbf{B}t$ and $t\mathbf{B}$.)

2.2 SPACE CURVES

In the first chapter, we showed that the parametric equations of a line can be written in vector form

$$\mathbf{R} = \mathbf{R}_0 + t\mathbf{V} \tag{2.9}$$

Here $\mathbf{R}_0$ is the position vector of a fixed point on the line, $\mathbf{V}$ is parallel to the line, and as t assumes values from $-\infty$ to $+\infty$, the tip of the vector $\mathbf{R}$ traces out the line in (x,y,z) space. We can also regard (2.9) as defining $\mathbf{R}$ as a vector function of t (whose derivative is, of course, $\mathbf{V}$).

In this section we consider more general functions $\mathbf{R}(t)$, of which (2.9) is a special case.

The vector equation $\mathbf{R} = \mathbf{R}(t)$ can be written out in terms of its components, giving the system of equations

$$\begin{aligned} x &= x(t) \\ y &= y(t) \\ z &= z(t) \end{aligned} \tag{2.10}$$

where x, y, and z are simply real-valued functions of t.

As t increases from its initial value t_1 to the value t_2, the point (x,y,z) [i.e., the tip of the vector $\mathbf{R}(t)$] traces out some geometric object in space. In the case of Eq. (2.9), the object is a segment of a straight line. For more complicated (continuous) vector functions, this locus of points will be some more general kind of one-dimensional object which we can call a *space curve* or an *arc*. [We say it's *one*-dimensional because any point on it can be located, via the continuous function $\mathbf{R}(t)$, by specifying the *single* number t.] We use the term "curve" even if the trace of $\mathbf{R}(t)$ is a straight line.

Thus we have associated with every continuous vector function $\mathbf{R}(t)$ a curve in space, which is the set of values assumed by $\mathbf{R}(t)$ as t varies over an interval. Notice that this is quite different from *graphing* x, y, and/or z as functions of t; the *curve* traced by $\mathbf{R}(t)$ is a threadlike collection of points in (x,y,z) space. One cannot read, from the curve alone, the value of t corresponding to a given point. So the curve contains much less information than the *function* $\mathbf{R}(t)$. As far as the curve is concerned, t is some sort of invisible dummy variable, which we have glamorized by awarding it the officious title "parameter."

As a matter of fact, there are any number of different *parametrizations* for a given curve. For example, if $\mathbf{W} = \frac{1}{2}\mathbf{V}$, the function

$$\mathbf{R}_1(t) = \mathbf{R}_0 + t\mathbf{W}$$

traces out exactly the same straight line as (2.9) for $-\infty < t < \infty$, as does the function

$$\mathbf{R}_2(t) = \mathbf{R}_0 + \tan t\,\mathbf{W}$$

for $-\pi/2 < t < \pi/2$. Thus we must keep in mind that many different *functions* may parametrize the same *curve*.

Now let us suppose we have an arc parametrized by the function $\mathbf{R}(t)$ for $t_1 \le t \le t_2$ in such a way that the following conditions are satisfied:

(*i*) $d\mathbf{R}/dt$ exists and is a continuous function of t, for all values of t in the interval $t_1 \le t \le t_2$, (*ii*) to distinct values of t in the interval $t_1 < t < t_2$ there correspond distinct points,

(*iii*) there is no value of t in the interval $t_1 \le t \le t_2$ for which $d\mathbf{R}/dt$ is the zero vector.

Then the arc is said to be *smooth*.

A smooth arc is said to be *closed* if $\mathbf{R}(t_1) = \mathbf{R}(t_2)$.

It is especially useful to think of (x,y,z) as the location of a particle moving through space, with the parameter t representing time. During a time interval of duration Δt, the position vector of the particle changes from the value $\mathbf{R}(t)$ to a new value $\mathbf{R}(t + \Delta t)$. The *displacement* of the particle during this interval of time is

$$\Delta\mathbf{R} = \mathbf{R}(t + \Delta t) - \mathbf{R}(t) = \Delta x\,\mathbf{i} + \Delta y\,\mathbf{j} + \Delta z\,\mathbf{k} \tag{2.11}$$

If the displacement is divided by the scalar Δt, we obtain the average velocity of the particle during the time interval,

$$\frac{\Delta\mathbf{R}}{\Delta t} = \frac{\Delta x}{\Delta t}\mathbf{i} + \frac{\Delta y}{\Delta t}\mathbf{j} + \frac{\Delta z}{\Delta t}\mathbf{k} \tag{2.12}$$

(In Fig. 2.2, we take Δt less than unity; hence the vector $\Delta\mathbf{R}/\Delta t$ is greater in magnitude than $\Delta\mathbf{R}$.)

Since $\mathbf{R}$ is differentiable, the average velocity $\Delta\mathbf{R}/\Delta t$ tends to a limit as Δt tends to zero. This limit is, by definition, the (instantaneous) velocity,

$$\mathbf{v}(t) = \mathbf{R}'(t) = \frac{d\mathbf{R}}{dt} = \frac{dx}{dt}\mathbf{i} + \frac{dy}{dt}\mathbf{j} + \frac{dz}{dt}\mathbf{k}$$

It seems clear from the diagram (and it will be proved below) that the velocity vector $d\mathbf{R}/dt$ is tangential to the path.

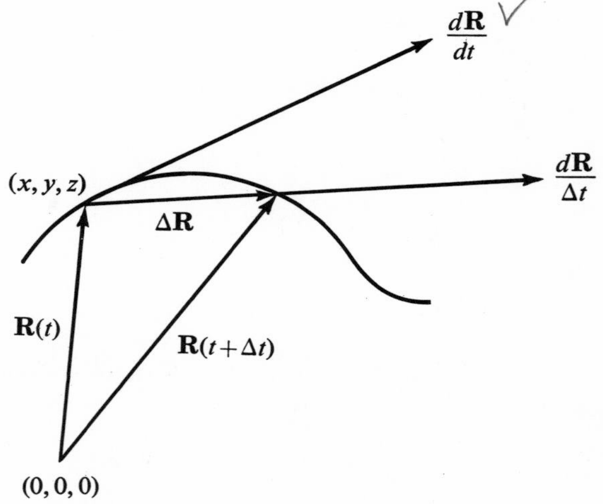

FIGURE 2.2

With this interpretation in mind, condition (i) requires that the x, y, and z components of the velocity vary so there will be no sudden changes of direction. Condition (ii) ensures that the particle does not occupy the same position twice during the same time interval. In other words, the arc does not cross itself. Condition (iii) requires that the particle is always moving (never at rest).

In Fig. 2.3 we give an example of a smooth arc. The arc in Fig. 2.4 is also a smooth arc, and is an example of one that is closed. The arc in Fig. 2.5 is not smooth because at points Q and R the derivatives are not continuous (in a physical case, this might be due to the particle colliding with other particles). The curve in Fig. 2.6 is not smooth, but it consists of three smooth arcs: PS, a closed arc SS, and another smooth arc SQ.

A *regular curve* is a parametrized curve $\mathbf{R} = \mathbf{R}(t)$ that (i) consists of a finite number of smooth arcs joined together, and (ii) does not cross itself. The curve in Fig. 2.5 is regular; that in Fig. 2.6 is not regular since it crosses itself at S. *Note*: The term "regular" is used with different meanings by different authors.

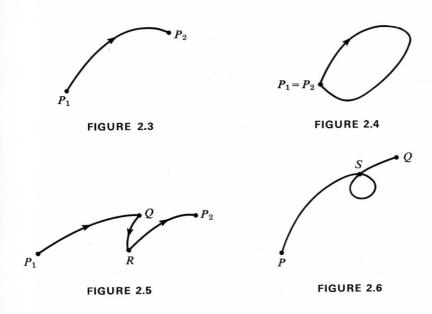

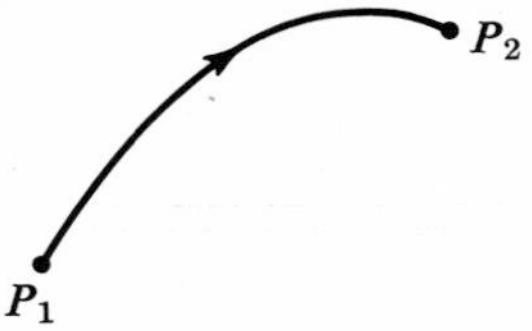

FIGURE 2.3

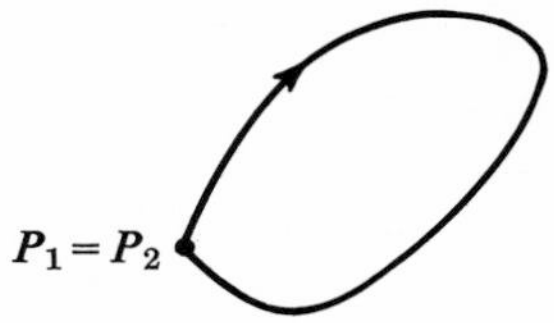

FIGURE 2.4

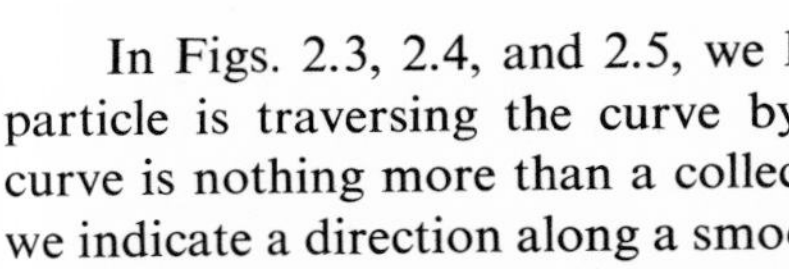

FIGURE 2.5

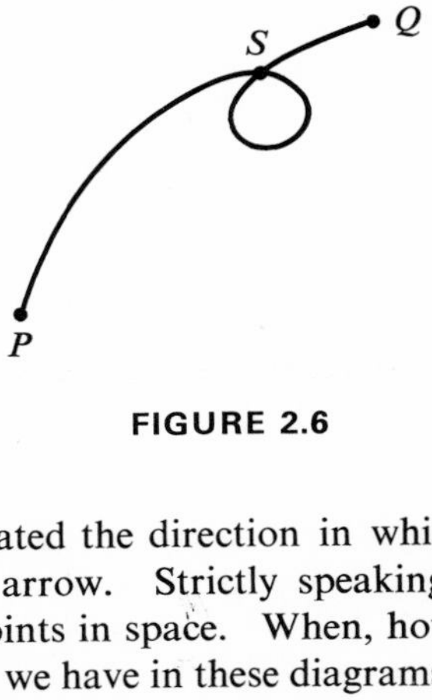

FIGURE 2.6

In Figs. 2.3, 2.4, and 2.5, we have indicated the direction in which the particle is traversing the curve by a small arrow. Strictly speaking, any curve is nothing more than a collection of points in space. When, however, we indicate a direction along a smooth arc, as we have in these diagrams, then we say that the arc has been oriented. Obviously, there are only two ways in which a smooth arc can be oriented. The arc in Fig. 2.7 is a replica of that in Fig. 2.3, but is oriented in the opposite way.

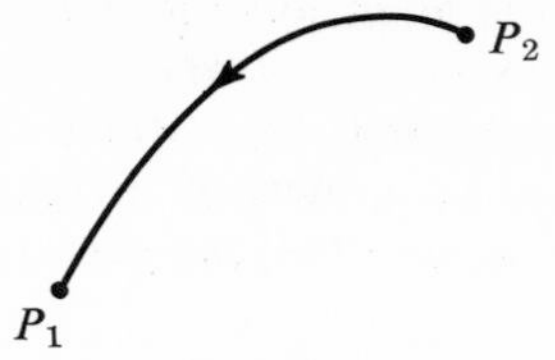

FIGURE 2.7

When an arc is described by equations such as (2.10), in terms of a parameter t, the orientation is usually understood to be determined by that parameter: the direction is the direction of increasing t. For example, the closed arc

$$\begin{aligned} x &= \cos t \\ y &= \sin t \\ z &= 0 \end{aligned} \tag{2.14}$$

is simply a circle of unit radius in the xy plane. As t increases from 0 to 2π, the point moves from its initial position (1,0,0) back to the same position, as shown in Fig. 2.8. The same arc with opposite orientation can be given parametrically by

$$\begin{aligned} x &= \cos t \\ y &= -\sin t \\ z &= 0 \end{aligned} \tag{2.15}$$

The Eqs. (2.14) specify the same arc as (2.15), but with opposite orientation, since as t increases from 0 to 2π, the point (x,y,z) traverses the circle in the opposite direction.

The same circle can be represented *nonparametrically* (i.e., without a "dummy variable") by the equations

$$\left.\begin{aligned} x^2 + y^2 &= 1 \\ z &= 0 \end{aligned}\right\} \tag{2.16}$$

There is no way of knowing from (2.16) which orientation is intended. Note that (2.16) represents the arc as the intersection of two surfaces, a cylinder and

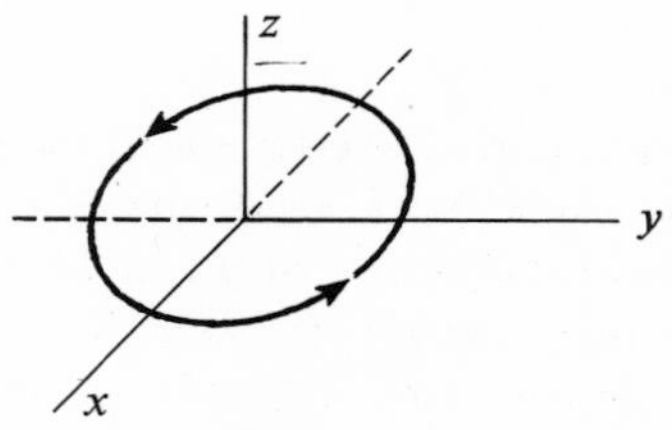

FIGURE 2.8

a plane. When one specifies an oriented arc as the intersection of two surfaces, by giving two equations, it is necessary to specify the orientation separately, either verbally or by drawing a diagram.

Let us now fulfill our earlier promise to investigate the tangents to these curves. Let $P(x,y,z)$ denote a *fixed* point on a smooth arc corresponding to some value t, and let $Q(x + \Delta x,\, y + \Delta y,\, z + \Delta z)$ denote another point on the arc corresponding to another value $t + \Delta t$. The points P and Q determine a straight line. A line passing through P is tangent to the arc at point P if the angle θ between this line and the line joining P and Q tends to zero as Δt tends to zero (Fig. 2.9).

Under the assumption that the arc is smooth, we shall prove that there must exist a tangent to the arc at any point P (except perhaps at the end-points of a closed arc), and that this tangent is parallel to the vector

$$\frac{d\mathbf{R}}{dt} = \frac{dx}{dt}\mathbf{i} + \frac{dy}{dt}\mathbf{j} + \frac{dz}{dt}\mathbf{k}$$

Proof Let l_1 denote the line passing through P parallel to $d\mathbf{R}/dt$, and let l_2 denote the line passing through P and Q. Let the vector extending from P to Q be denoted $\Delta\mathbf{R}$. If θ is the angle between these two lines, then by the methods of Sec. 1.7 we have

$$\cos\theta = \frac{(d\mathbf{R}/dt)\cdot\Delta\mathbf{R}}{|d\mathbf{R}/dt|\,|\Delta\mathbf{R}|} \tag{2.17}$$

We wish to show that, as $\Delta\mathbf{R}$ approaches the zero vector, $\cos\theta$ converges to 1. Conditions (*i*), (*ii*), and (*iii*) ensure that $\Delta\mathbf{R}$ approaches zero for t in the range $t_1 < t < t_2$ if, and only if, Δt approaches zero. Dividing numerator and denominator of (2.17) by Δt and letting $\Delta t \to 0$, then $\Delta\mathbf{R}/\Delta t \to d\mathbf{R}/dt$ by definition of the derivative, and since the operations of multiplication and division are continuous, the right side of (2.17) approaches 1. This shows that l_1 is, indeed, tangent to the curve at P.

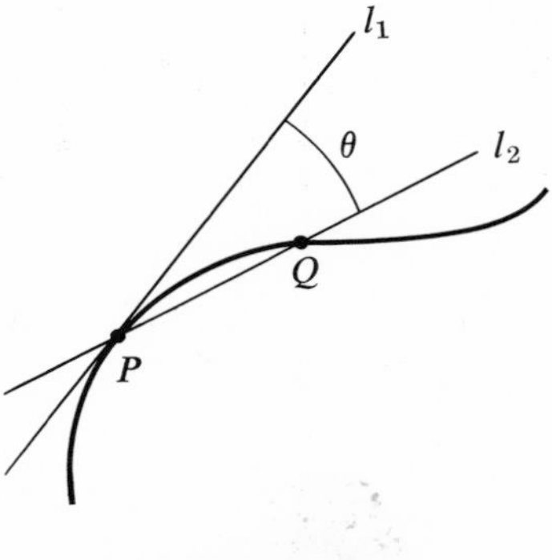

FIGURE 2.9

A vector is said to be tangent to a smooth arc at a point P if it is parallel to the line tangent to the arc at P. Thus the vector

$$\left(\frac{dx}{dt}\right)\mathbf{i} + \left(\frac{dy}{dt}\right)\mathbf{j} + \left(\frac{dz}{dt}\right)\mathbf{k}$$

evaluated at the value of t corresponding to the point P, is tangent to the arc at P.

It is conventional to denote by the letter $\mathbf{T}$ the *unit vector* tangent to an oriented smooth arc, pointing in the direction determined by the orientation. In other words, $\mathbf{T}$ is defined by the expression

$$\mathbf{T} = \frac{(dx/dt)\mathbf{i} + (dy/dt)\mathbf{j} + (dz/dt)\mathbf{k}}{\sqrt{(dx/dt)^2 + (dy/dt)^2 + (dz/dt)^2}} \tag{2.18}$$

obtained by dividing the above vector by its own magnitude.

Example 2.7 Determine the unit vector tangent to the oriented closed arc $x = \cos t$, $y = \sin t$, $z = 0$, at (a) $t = 0$; (*b*) $t = \pi/2$.

Solution The answers are obviously (a) $\mathbf{j}$, (b) $-\mathbf{i}$, as can be seen from Fig. 2.10. These answers can be obtained also by use of (2.18), which gives

$$\mathbf{T} = \frac{-\sin t\,\mathbf{i} + \cos t\,\mathbf{j}}{\sqrt{\sin^2 t + \cos^2 t}} = -\sin t\,\mathbf{i} + \cos t\,\mathbf{j}$$

At $t = 0$, we have $\mathbf{T} = -\sin 0\,\mathbf{i} + \cos 0\,\mathbf{j} = \mathbf{j}$, and at $t = \pi/2$, $\mathbf{T} = -\sin(\pi/2)\mathbf{i} + \cos(\pi/2)\mathbf{j} = -\mathbf{i}$.

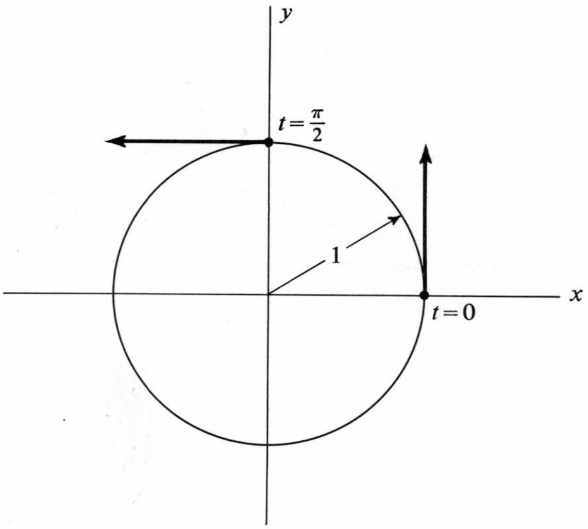

FIGURE 2.10

Example 2.8 Find the unit vector tangent to the curve $x = t$, $y = t^2$, $z = t^3$, at the point (2,4,8).

Solution By (2.18) we have

$$\mathbf{T} = \frac{\mathbf{i} + 2t\mathbf{j} + 3t^2\mathbf{k}}{\sqrt{1 + 4t^2 + 9t^4}}$$

When $t = 2$ we have $(x,y,z) = (2,4,8)$ and $\mathbf{T} = (1/\sqrt{161})(\mathbf{i} + 4\mathbf{j} + 12\mathbf{k})$.

An arc that is not smooth may not have a tangent at some points. For instance, there is no tangent at Q in Fig. 2.5.

Undoubtedly the reader is familiar with the notion of arc length, which is discussed in calculus books (at least for plane curves). This notion generalizes easily to space curves.

Suppose C is a smooth space curve. Let us subdivide C into smaller arcs, and "approximate" it by a polygonal path consisting of n straight-line segments joining the endpoints of the arcs (Fig. 2.11). That is, we select points $Q_0, Q_1, \ldots, Q_n$ along C, in that order, with Q_0 and Q_n the endpoints of C. For each $k = 0, 1, \ldots, n$, let $\mathbf{R}_k$ be the position vector to the point Q_k, and let $\Delta\mathbf{R}_k = \mathbf{R}_k - \mathbf{R}_{k-1}$, for $k = 1, 2, \ldots, n$. The total length of the polygonal path is then $\sum_{k=1}^{n} |\Delta\mathbf{R}_k|$. The length of the space curve C is then defined to be the limit of sums of this form, where the approximating polygonal paths are obtained by taking increasingly small subdivisions while n increases without bound.

We can compute this limit when the curve is parametrized by $\mathbf{R}(t)$ for, say, $a \le t \le b$ as follows. The length of $\Delta\mathbf{R}_k$ is

$$|\Delta\mathbf{R}_k| = \sqrt{(\Delta x_k)^2 + (\Delta y_k)^2 + (\Delta z_k)^2}$$

Let t_k be the values of t which correspond to the points $\mathbf{R}_k$; i.e., $\mathbf{R}_k = \mathbf{R}(t_k)$.

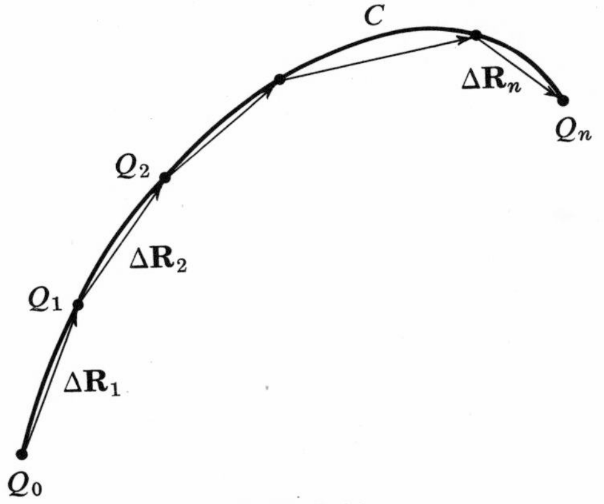

FIGURE 2.11

Then, because $d\mathbf{R}/dt$ is continuous, the mean value theorem of calculus ensures us that for some number τ_k between t_{k-1} and t_k,

$$\Delta x_k = x_k - x_{k-1} = (t_k - t_{k-1}) \frac{dx}{dt}(\tau_k)$$

Similarly, there are numbers τ_k' and τ_k'' in the same interval such that

$$\Delta y_k = (t_k - t_{k-1}) \frac{dy}{dt}(\tau_k')$$

$$\Delta z_k = (t_k - t_{k-1}) \frac{dz}{dt}(\tau_k'')$$

So for the length of the polygonal path we have

$$\sum_{k=1}^{n} |\Delta \mathbf{R}_k| = \sum_{k=1}^{n} \left[\left(\frac{dx}{dt}(\tau_k)\right)^2 + \left(\frac{dy}{dt}(\tau_k')\right)^2 + \left(\frac{dz}{dt}(\tau_k'')\right)^2\right]^{1/2} (t_k - t_{k-1})$$

Now if the polygonal subdivision is made finer, the differences $t_k - t_{k-1}$ become smaller and this sum approaches the integral

$$\int_a^b \left[\left(\frac{dx}{dt}\right)^2 + \left(\frac{dy}{dt}\right)^2 + \left(\frac{dz}{dt}\right)^2\right]^{1/2} dt \tag{2.19}$$

as a limit. Recognizing the integrand as $|d\mathbf{R}/dt|$, we see that *the length of the curve C is given by*

$$\int_a^b \left|\frac{d\mathbf{R}}{dt}\right| dt \tag{2.20}$$

The arc length of a regular curve is defined to be the sum of the lengths of the various smooth curves that constitute it.

If the arc P_1P_2 lies entirely in the xy plane, which is the simplest case treated in calculus books, then z is identically equal to zero and so $dz/dt = 0$ and, by eliminating the parameter t, (2.19) may be written in the familiar alternative form

$$\int_{x_1}^{x_2} \left[1 + \left(\frac{dy}{dx}\right)^2\right]^{1/2} dx \tag{2.21}$$

provided the integral exists, or

$$\int_{y_1}^{y_2} \left[\left(\frac{dx}{dy}\right)^2 + 1\right]^{1/2} dy \tag{2.22}$$

provided this integral exists. It is possible that these integrals may not exist. For example, if the arc P_1P_2 contains a segment that is parallel to the y axis, then dy/dx will not exist along this segment (that is, dy/dx is "infinite") and (2.21) will not make sense.

Equation (2.19) may be written in coordinate form

$$\int_{t_1}^{t_2} [(dx)^2 + (dy)^2 + (dz)^2]^{1/2} \qquad (2.23)$$

where it is understood that dx, dy, and dz are expressed in terms of the parameter t and the differential dt (so that t is the variable over which the integration is performed). Sometimes it is possible to write two of the variables, say y and z, in terms of one of the others, say x. In that case dy and dz may be expressed in terms of x and dx, and the integral is taken with respect to x, the limits of integration being the values of x corresponding to t_1 and t_2.

Example 2.9 Find the arc length between (0,0,1) and (1,0,1) of the curve

$$y = \sin 2\pi x \qquad z = \cos 2\pi x$$

(This is a helix winding about the x axis.)

Solution

$$\begin{aligned} dx^2 + dy^2 + dz^2 &= dx^2 + 4\pi^2 \cos^2 2\pi x \, dx^2 + 4\pi^2 \sin^2 2\pi x \, dx^2 \\ &= (1 + 4\pi^2)\, dx^2 \end{aligned}$$

Hence the integral is

$$\int_0^1 (1 + 4\pi^2)^{1/2}\, dx = (1 + 4\pi^2)^{1/2}$$

Returning to (2.20) we see that the arc length measured along the curve from some arbitrary initial position $\mathbf{R}(t_1)$ to a *variable* position $\mathbf{R}(t)$ is given by

$$s(t) = \int_{t_1}^{t} \left| \frac{d\mathbf{R}}{dt} \right| dt \qquad (t \geq t_1)$$

By the fundamental theorem of calculus, we then have

$$\frac{ds}{dt} = \left| \frac{d\mathbf{R}}{dt} \right|$$

In coordinate form, this becomes

$$\frac{ds}{dt} = \left[\left(\frac{dx}{dt}\right)^2 + \left(\frac{dy}{dt}\right)^2 + \left(\frac{dz}{dt}\right)^2 \right]^{1/2}$$

Since our assumptions guarantee that $ds/dt \neq 0$, it follows that dt/ds exists and by the chain rule

$$\frac{d\mathbf{R}}{ds} = \frac{d\mathbf{R}}{dt}\frac{dt}{ds}$$

Since $d\mathbf{R}/dt$ is tangent to the curve, this shows $d\mathbf{R}/ds$ is also. (This reflects the obvious fact that the tangent *direction* is independent of the parametrization used to describe the curve.) Moreover, by (2.18), we see that

$$\mathbf{T} = \frac{d\mathbf{R}}{ds}$$

The geometrical and physical interpretation of these formulas will be given in the next section.

EXERCISES

1. Suppose that P_1P_2 is a smooth arc in the xy plane. Is it necessarily true that dy/dx exists at every point on this arc?

2. Give at least one reason for imposing condition (*iii*) in the definition of smooth arc.

3. By using identities concerning hyperbolic functions, eliminate the parameter t from the equations

$$x = \cosh t \qquad y = \sinh t \qquad z = 0$$

4. As t varies from -1 to 1, the point (x,y,z) where

$$x = t \qquad y = |t| \qquad z = 0$$

traces a regular curve. At what point on this curve is there no tangent?

5. Observe that

$$x = t \qquad y = \sin 2\pi t \qquad z = \cos 2\pi t$$

is a parametrization of the helix in Example 2.9. Compute the arc length between the same two endpoints using formula (2.16). What is the unit tangent vector at (0,1,1)?

6. If $\mathbf{T}$ denotes the unit tangent to the curve

$$x = t \qquad y = 2t + 5 \qquad z = 3t$$

show that $d\mathbf{T}/dt = 0$. Interpret this.

7. Find the arc length of the curve described in Exercise 6, between (0,5,0) and (1,7,3), (a) by using (2.16), and (b) by using a little common sense.

8. Determine the arc length of the curve

$$x = e^t \cos t \qquad y = e^t \sin t \qquad z = 0$$

between $t = 0$ and $t = 1$.

9. For the curve

$$x = \sin t - t \cos t$$
$$y = \cos t + t \sin t$$
$$z = t^2$$

find (a) the arc length between (0,1,0) and $(-2\pi,1,4\pi^2)$, (b) $\mathbf{T}(t)$, (c) $\mathbf{T}(\pi)$.

10. Find the unit vector tangent to the oriented closed curve

$$x = a \cos t \qquad y = b \sin t \qquad z = 0$$

at $t = \frac{3}{2}\pi$.

f=ma
a=f/m
f/m = v²/R
f= mv²/R

2.3 VELOCITY AND ACCELERATION

In elementary physics books, it is shown that the acceleration of a particle moving in a *circular path* with *constant speed* v has magnitude v^2/ρ, where ρ is the radius of the circle. If m is the mass of the particle, the force producing this acceleration has magnitude mv^2/ρ. This force is directed towards the center of the circle and is called the *centripetal force*. (The reaction to this force is called the *centrifugal force*.)

If the speed of the particle is also changing, then the acceleration is the sum of two components, the centripetal acceleration a_n, which is normal to the path, and a component a_t that is tangential to the path. The magnitude of the centripetal acceleration is still v^2/ρ. The magnitude of the tangential acceleration is shown to be $a_t = \rho\alpha$, where α is the angular acceleration $d^2\theta/dt^2$ (θ is the angle at the center of the circle, measured in *radians*). Since arc length measured along a circle of radius ρ is $s = \rho\theta$, and since ρ is constant, we have $d^2s/dt^2 = \rho d^2\theta/dt^2 = \rho\alpha$, so we can also write $a_t = d^2s/dt^2$.

It is important to keep in mind that the acceleration of a particle is defined to be the time rate of change of its velocity. Since velocity is a vector quantity, this acceleration may arise from a change in either the magnitude or the direction of the velocity, or both. In the example just cited, the centripetal acceleration a_n arises entirely from the change in direction of velocity, whereas the tangential acceleration a_t is related entirely to the change in speed. (Recall that the speed is the magnitude of the velocity or ds/dt.)

In this section we shall prove these formulas and show that they generalize to motion along any curve. We begin by presenting a heuristic analysis which will, hopefully, motivate the subsequent rigorous discussion.

If motion along a curve is to be related to motion on a circle, we clearly need to select the circle which "best" approximates the curve at a given point; in Fig. 2.12 we indicate the circle approximating the curve at P. Two properties that the circle must have are clear: it should pass through the point P, and its tangent must coincide with the tangent to the curve at P. It remains for us to decide what radius ρ the circle should have in order that it fit the curve as well as possible.

Observe that circles with small radii are more sharply curved than circles with large radii. Thus, by choosing ρ appropriately, we ought to be able to select a circle with the same *curvature* as the given curve, at P. But how do we measure this curvature? Intuitively, curvature arises as a result of the tangent direction changing as we move along the curve; a straight line has no curvature and an arc is more sharply curved if the tangent turns faster along the length of the curve. Let us therefore *define* the curvature k as the rate at which the *unit* tangent vector turns, with respect to arc length along the curve:

$$k = \left|\frac{d\mathbf{T}}{ds}\right| \tag{2.24}$$

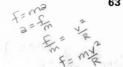

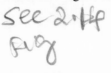

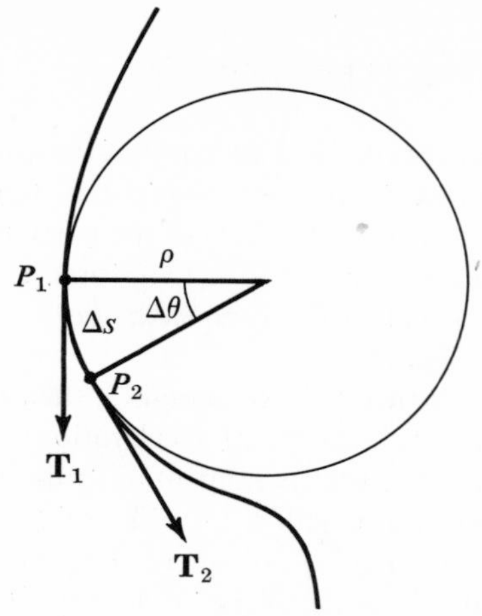

FIGURE 2.12

What does this give for the curvature of a circle of radius ρ? In Fig. 2.12 the arc length between P_1 and P_2 on the circle is $\Delta s = \rho \, \Delta\theta$. The unit tangent vectors $\mathbf{T}_1$ and $\mathbf{T}_2$ also make an angle $\Delta\theta$, and the change in the unit tangent as we proceed from P_1 and P_2 is

$$\Delta\mathbf{T} = \mathbf{T}_2 - \mathbf{T}_1$$

For small $\Delta\theta$, the magnitude of $\Delta\mathbf{T}$ is approximately $\Delta\theta$, as we see from Fig. 2.13 (keep in mind that the magnitudes of $\mathbf{T}_1$ and $\mathbf{T}_2$ are unity). Thus

$$S = \rho \theta, \quad \frac{ds}{d\theta} = \rho \frac{d\theta}{d\theta}$$

$$\therefore \frac{d\theta}{ds} = \frac{1}{\rho}$$

$$\left| \frac{\Delta\mathbf{T}}{\Delta s} \right| \approx \frac{\Delta\theta}{\Delta s} = \frac{1}{\rho}$$

This approximation improves continuously as Δs approaches zero, so we can write

$$\left| \frac{d\mathbf{T}}{ds} \right| = \frac{1}{\rho}$$

Thus the curvature of a circle, as we have defined it, is the reciprocal of its radius. This is in harmony with our intuition, and so we shall feel confident in adopting the definition (2.24).

Consequently, the radius ρ of our approximating circle (called the "osculating circle" for obvious reasons), is given by

$$\rho = \frac{1}{k} = 1 \left/ \left| \frac{d\mathbf{T}}{ds} \right| \right.$$

We let $\mathbf{N}$ denote a *unit* vector pointing towards the center of the approximating circle, and as usual let $\mathbf{T}$ denote the unit tangent vector. The directions

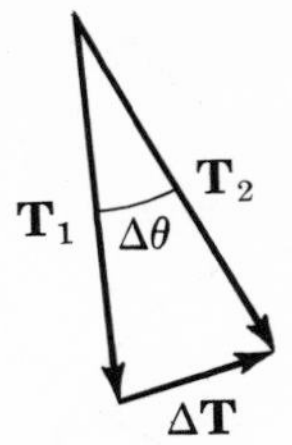

FIGURE 2.13

of both **T** and **N** may vary at different points along the curve, but they are always at right angles with each other, as shown in Fig. 2.14.

Now if our earlier considerations about circular motion can be generalized to motion along a curve, then we are led to anticipate that the acceleration **a** can be expressed as a sum of two components,

$$\mathbf{a} = a_t\mathbf{T} + a_n\mathbf{N}$$

where $a_t = d^2s/dt^2$ is the rate of change of speed, and $a_n = v^2/\rho = (1/\rho)(ds/dt)^2$ results from the change in the direction of the velocity.

With this discussion as motivation, we proceed to give a rigorous treatment of velocity and acceleration.

Since we will need to compute second derivatives, we assume that the coordinates x, y, and z are functions of t possessing second derivatives. We assume also that these functions define a smooth arc (Sec. 2.2).

The *position* vector of the particle is defined to be

$$\mathbf{R} = x\mathbf{i} + y\mathbf{j} + z\mathbf{k} \tag{2.25}$$

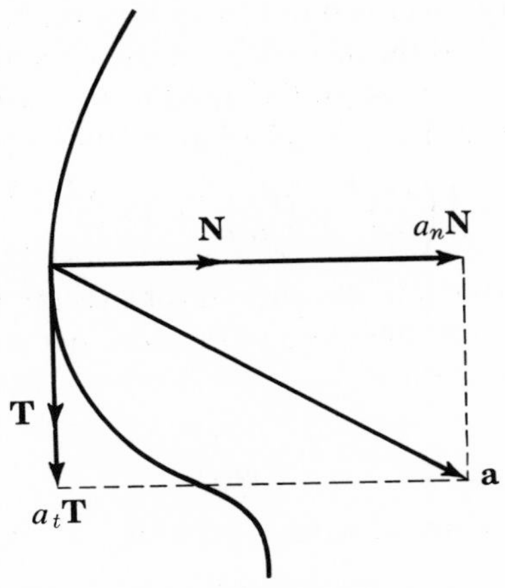

FIGURE 2.14

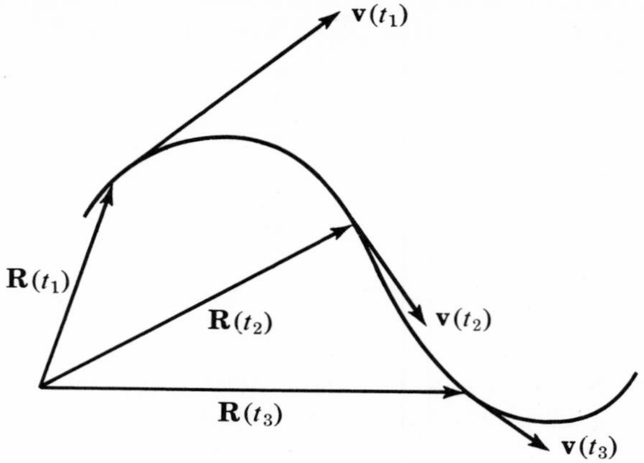

FIGURE 2.15

which we visualize as the directed line segment extending from the origin to the point at which the particle is located. Clearly, **R** is a vector-valued function of the variable t, and the above assumptions ensure that the derivatives $d\mathbf{R}/dt$ and $d^2\mathbf{R}/dt^2$ exist. These derivatives, which are the velocity **v** and the acceleration **a**, respectively, are computed as shown in Sec. 2.1,

$$\frac{d\mathbf{R}}{dt} = \frac{dx}{dt}\mathbf{i} + \frac{dy}{dt}\mathbf{j} + \frac{dz}{dt}\mathbf{k} \tag{2.26}$$

$$\frac{d^2\mathbf{R}}{dt^2} = \frac{d^2x}{dt^2}\mathbf{i} + \frac{d^2y}{dt^2}\mathbf{j} + \frac{d^2z}{dt^2}\mathbf{k} \tag{2.27}$$

It is convenient always to picture $\mathbf{v}(t)$ as a directed line segment with its tail at the point where the particle is located. As t varies, the corresponding vector $\mathbf{v}(t)$ may vary either in direction or magnitude or in both (Fig. 2.15). The speed of the particle is the magnitude of the velocity. From the definition of arc length (Sec. 2.2) we saw that the speed is ds/dt, where the arc length s is measured along the curve from some arbitrary initial point:

$$|\mathbf{v}(t)| = \left[\left(\frac{dx}{dt}\right)^2 + \left(\frac{dy}{dt}\right)^2 + \left(\frac{dz}{dt}\right)^2\right]^{1/2} = \frac{ds}{dt} \tag{2.28}$$

As noted in that section, the unit tangent vector **T** may be obtained by dividing the velocity $\mathbf{v}(t)$ by the speed $|\mathbf{v}(t)|$, since our assumptions guarantee that $|\mathbf{v}(t)|$ is never zero.

$$\mathbf{T} = \frac{\mathbf{v}(t)}{|\mathbf{v}(t)|} \tag{2.29}$$

We recall that **T** is also given by the expression

$$\mathbf{T} = \frac{d\mathbf{R}}{ds} \tag{2.30}$$

This may be seen geometrically by noting that $|\Delta\mathbf{R}|$ is approximately equal to Δs, when Δs is small, so that $d\mathbf{R}/ds$ is a unit vector; the *rigorous* proof that $d\mathbf{R}/ds$ is tangent to the curve and of unit magnitude has already been given.

The *curvature* k of the curve at any point is defined to be the *magnitude* of the vector $d\mathbf{T}/ds$ at that point:

$$k = \left|\frac{d\mathbf{T}}{ds}\right| \tag{2.31}$$

If $k \neq 0$, the *radius of curvature* ρ is defined to be the reciprocal of the curvature,

$$\rho = \frac{1}{k} \tag{2.32}$$

The motivation for this definition of ρ was given above. By introducing k we will be able to avoid using the term "infinite radius of curvature." Thus, the curvature of a straight line is $k = 0$.

Since $\mathbf{T}$ has constant *magnitude*, the derivative of $\mathbf{T}$ with respect to t is either the zero vector or it is a nonzero vector perpendicular to $\mathbf{T}$. This was proved in Example 2.6; moreover, it is clear geometrically from Fig. 2.13, where we see that $\Delta\mathbf{T}$ is approximately perpendicular to $\mathbf{T}$ if $\Delta\mathbf{T}$ is small.

If $d\mathbf{T}/dt$ is not the zero vector, we define the unit vector $\mathbf{N}$ to be $d\mathbf{T}/dt$ divided by its own magnitude,

$$\mathbf{N} = \frac{d\mathbf{T}/dt}{|d\mathbf{T}/dt|} \tag{2.33}$$

This vector is called the *principal normal.* If we apply the chain rule $d\mathbf{T}/dt = (d\mathbf{T}/ds)(ds/dt)$ to both numerator and denominator of this fraction, we can cancel ds/dt and obtain the alternative expression

$$\mathbf{N} = \frac{d\mathbf{T}/ds}{|d\mathbf{T}/ds|}$$

and since $k = |d\mathbf{T}/ds|$ we can write

$$\frac{d\mathbf{T}}{ds} = k\mathbf{N}$$

In words, we may say that $\mathbf{T}$ turns in the direction $\mathbf{N}$, at a rate k (with respect to arc length).

Now we are ready to discuss the acceleration of the particle. This has been defined as the time rate of change of the velocity,

$$\mathbf{a}(t) = \mathbf{v}'(t) = \frac{d\mathbf{v}}{dt} = \frac{d^2x}{dt^2}\mathbf{i} + \frac{d^2y}{dt^2}\mathbf{j} + \frac{d^2z}{dt^2}\mathbf{k} \tag{2.34}$$

Since $|\mathbf{v}(t)| = ds/dt$, we can write

$$\mathbf{v}(t) = \frac{ds}{dt}\mathbf{T} \tag{2.35}$$

By the product rule for derivatives (Sec. 2.1),

$$\mathbf{a}(t) = \mathbf{v}'(t) = \frac{d^2s}{dt^2}\mathbf{T} + \frac{ds}{dt}\frac{d\mathbf{T}}{dt} = \frac{d^2s}{dt^2}\mathbf{T} + \frac{ds}{dt}\frac{d\mathbf{T}}{ds}\frac{ds}{dt}$$

$$= \frac{d^2s}{dt^2}\mathbf{T} + \left(\frac{ds}{dt}\right)^2 k\mathbf{N}$$

In other words, we have

$$\mathbf{a} = a_t\mathbf{T} + a_n\mathbf{N} \tag{2.36}$$

where $a_t = d^2s/dt^2$ and $a_n = kv^2$. This is exactly what we anticipated in Eq. (2.25).

We note that at any point on the curve where $k = 0$, the normal vector $\mathbf{N}$ is not defined. This does not matter, since we have $a_n = 0$ in that case and hence have no need for $\mathbf{N}$ in (2.36). In case $k \neq 0$, we can write $a_n = v^2/\rho$, the way we did in the previous heuristic discussion.

Since $\mathbf{T}$ and $\mathbf{N}$ are mutually perpendicular vectors at any point where they are defined, we have, by the pythagorean theorem,

$$a^2 = a_t^{\,2} + a_n^{\,2} \tag{2.37}$$

To compute a, we need only find $d^2\mathbf{R}/dt^2$ by differentiation, and calculate the magnitude of this vector. To compute a_t we need only find $\mathbf{v} = d\mathbf{R}/dt$, calculate its magnitude $|d\mathbf{R}/dt| = ds/dt$, and differentiate this with respect to t. Having computed a and a_t, it is then easy to obtain a_n by using (2.37). In some problems, this is more convenient than using the expression kv^2.

In books on elementary calculus which consider only curves in a *plane*, a fairly simple expression for the curvature k is developed. Such a formula also exists for space curves. It is derived by taking the vector cross product of

$$\mathbf{R}'(t) = v\mathbf{T} \qquad \text{and} \qquad \mathbf{R}''(t) = \frac{dv}{dt}\mathbf{T} + kv^2\mathbf{N}$$

which, since $\mathbf{T} \times \mathbf{T} = \mathbf{0}$, gives

$$\mathbf{R}' \times \mathbf{R}'' = kv^3(\mathbf{T} \times \mathbf{N})$$

Since $\mathbf{T}$ and $\mathbf{N}$ are mutually perpendicular unit vectors, their cross product $\mathbf{B} = \mathbf{T} \times \mathbf{N}$ is a unit vector: this vector is called the *binormal*. We have $\mathbf{R}' \times \mathbf{R}'' = kv^3\mathbf{B}$ and

$$|\mathbf{R}' \times \mathbf{R}''| = kv^3$$

and hence

$$k = \frac{|\mathbf{R}' \times \mathbf{R}''|}{(\mathbf{R}' \cdot \mathbf{R}')^{3/2}} = \frac{|\mathbf{R}' \times \mathbf{R}''|}{|\mathbf{R}'|^3} \tag{2.38}$$

Because of its importance in geometry, it may be well to say more about the vector $\mathbf{B}$, which is a unit vector mutually perpendicular to both $\mathbf{T}$ and $\mathbf{N}$. The vectors $\mathbf{T}$, $\mathbf{N}$, $\mathbf{B}$, in that order, form a right-handed system. It is useful to

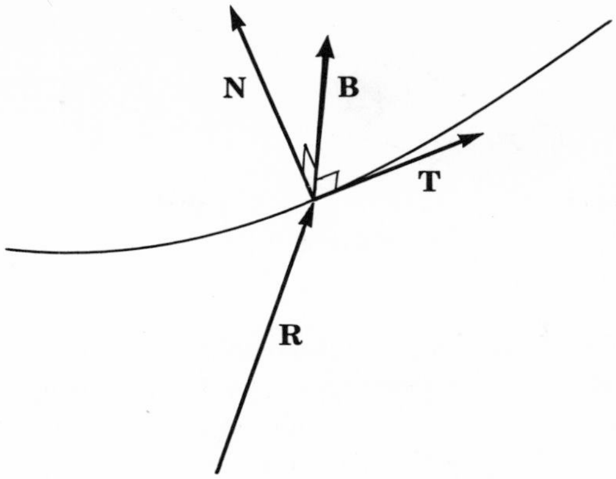

FIGURE 2.16

think of these three vectors as attached to a particle moving along the curve: as the particle moves, its associated triad of mutually perpendicular unit vectors moves and rotates (see Fig. 2.16). For a *plane curve*, **T** and **N** lie in the plane of the curve, so that **B** is a constant unit vector always perpendicular to the plane.

Let us try to describe how the triad rotates as a particle proceeds along a space curve. As we have seen, the vector **T** turns towards the vector **N** at a rate k, measured with respect to arc length.

$$\frac{d\mathbf{T}}{ds} = k\mathbf{N} \tag{2.39}$$

But since **N** is always perpendicular to **T**, these vectors will turn *together* like a rigid body. **N** must therefore turn towards the direction $-\mathbf{T}$ at the same rate, k. In addition, it is also possible for **N** to *rotate about* **T** *as an axis*; this would happen if the instantaneous plane of the curve were to "tilt". In such a case, $d\mathbf{N}/ds$ would have a component perpendicular to both **T** and **N**, i.e., along **B**. Thus we would have

$$\frac{d\mathbf{N}}{ds} = -k\mathbf{T} + \tau\mathbf{B} \tag{2.40}$$

where τ measures the rate at which the curve *twists*; accordingly, it is known as the *torsion*.

The torsion can be visualized by observing the cross section of a piece of solder wire bent into the shape of the curve, as in Fig. 2.17. The torsion, or twisting, of the wire will effect a *rotation* of the cross-sectional pattern. One can shape the wire into any plane curve without introducing torsion, but if the curve is nonplanar, the wire must twist.

Once again, the fact that **N** turns towards **B** at a rate τ, and the fact that **N** and **B** are rigidly fixed at right angles, imply that **B** turns towards $-\mathbf{N}$ at the

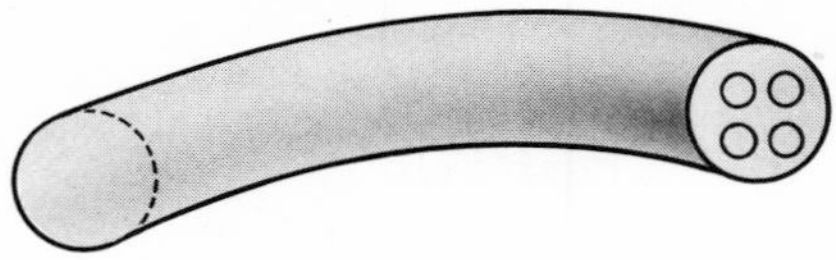

FIGURE 2.17

same rate. At first glance it seems conceivable that **B** might also rotate about **N** as an axis, thus turning in the direction of **T**. However, if this happened, **T** would be forced by rigidity into turning in the direction $-\mathbf{B}$; but **T** turns only in the direction **N**, *by definition*! Thus we have

$$\frac{d\mathbf{B}}{ds} = -\tau\mathbf{N} \tag{2.41}$$

Equations (2.39), (2.40), and (2.41) are called the *Frenet formulas*. They are of fundamental importance in differential geometry, where it is shown that any two curves with identical corresponding values of curvature and torsion are congruent (as usual, subject to certain restrictions).

Example 2.10 The position of a particle moving around the circle $x^2 + y^2 = r^2$ in the xy plane, with angular velocity ω, is

$$x = r\cos\omega t \qquad y = r\sin\omega t \qquad z = 0$$

Find the normal and tangential components of acceleration of the particle, and determine the curvature of the circle.

Solution We have

$$\mathbf{R} = r\cos\omega t\,\mathbf{i} + r\sin\omega t\,\mathbf{j}$$

$$\frac{d\mathbf{R}}{dt} = -r\omega\sin\omega t\,\mathbf{i} + r\omega\cos\omega t\,\mathbf{j}$$

$$\frac{d^2\mathbf{R}}{dt^2} = -r\omega^2\cos\omega t\,\mathbf{i} - r\omega^2\sin\omega t\,\mathbf{j}$$

The magnitudes of these vectors are

$$v = \frac{ds}{dt} = \left|\frac{d\mathbf{R}}{dt}\right| = (r^2\omega^2\sin^2\omega t + r^2\omega^2\cos^2\omega t)^{1/2} = \omega r$$

$$a = \left|\frac{d^2\mathbf{R}}{dt^2}\right| = \omega^2 r$$

Since ds/dt is a constant, $a_t = d^2s/dt^2 = 0$, and $a = a_n$. Therefore $kv^2 = \omega^2 r$; and since $v = \omega r$, we have $k = \omega^2 r/\omega^2 r^2 = 1/r$. This verifies that the curvature of a circle is the reciprocal of its radius. The answers are: $a_n = \omega^2 r$, $a_t = 0$, $k = 1/r$.

Example 2.11 The coordinates of a particle at time t are

$$x = \sin t - t\cos t$$
$$y = \cos t + t\sin t$$
$$z = t^2$$

Find the speed, the normal and tangential components of acceleration, and the curvature of the path, in terms of t.

Solution

$$\mathbf{R} = (\sin t - t\cos t)\mathbf{i} + (\cos t + t\sin t)\mathbf{j} + t^2\mathbf{k}$$

$$\frac{d\mathbf{R}}{dt} = (t\sin t)\mathbf{i} + (t\cos t)\mathbf{j} + 2t\mathbf{k}$$

$$\frac{d^2\mathbf{R}}{dt^2} = (t\cos t + \sin t)\mathbf{i} + (-t\sin t + \cos t)\mathbf{j} + 2\mathbf{k}$$

The speed is $ds/dt = |d\mathbf{R}/dt| = (t^2\sin^2 t + t^2\cos^2 t + 4t^2)^{1/2} = \sqrt{5}t$. The tangential component of acceleration is $a_t = d^2s/dt^2 = \sqrt{5}$.

From (2.37),

$$a_n = [a^2 - a_t{}^2]^{1/2}$$
$$= [(t\cos t + \sin t)^2 + (-t\sin t + \cos t)^2 + 2^2 - 5]^{1/2} = t$$

since $a_n = kv^2$ we have $k = a_n/v^2 = t/5t^2 = 1/5t$.

EXERCISES

In the first four problems below, the coordinates of a moving particle are given as a function of the time t. Find (a) the speed, (b) the tangential and normal components of acceleration, (c) the unit tangent vector $\mathbf{T}$, and (d) the curvature of the curve, as functions of time.

1. $x = e^t\cos t,\quad y = e^t\sin t,\quad z = 0$
2. $x = 3t\cos t,\quad y = 3t\sin t,\quad z = 4t$
3. $x = e^t\cos t,\quad y = e^t\sin t,\quad z = e^t$
4. $x = 5\sin 4t,\quad y = 5\cos 4t,\quad z = 10t$
5. The position vector of a moving particle is

$$\mathbf{R} = \cos t(\mathbf{i} - \mathbf{j}) + \sin t(\mathbf{i} + \mathbf{j}) + \tfrac{1}{2}t\mathbf{k}$$

   (a) Determine the velocity and the speed of the particle.
   (b) Determine the acceleration of the particle.
   (c) Find a unit tangent to the path of the particle, in the direction of motion.
   (d) Show that the curve traversed by the particle has constant curvature k, and find its value.

6. Find the curvature of the space curve

$$x = 3t^2 - t^3 \qquad y = 3t^2 \qquad z = 3t + t^3$$

7. Find the curvature and torsion for the helix

$$x = t \qquad y = \sin t \qquad z = \cos t$$

8. The position vector of a particle is given by

$$\mathbf{R}(t) = \sqrt{2}\cos 3t\,\mathbf{i} + \sqrt{2}\cos 3t\,\mathbf{j} + 2\sin 3t\,\mathbf{k}$$

Find its speed, the curvature and torsion of its path, and describe the path geometrically.

9. If $\mathbf{F}$ is a function of t possessing derivatives of all orders, find the derivative of

$$\mathbf{F} \times \frac{d\mathbf{F}}{dt} \cdot \frac{d^2\mathbf{F}}{dt^2}$$

10. By inspection, write down the values of each of the following:

(a) $\dfrac{d\mathbf{R}}{ds} \cdot \mathbf{T}$ (d) $\mathbf{T} \cdot \mathbf{N}$ (g) $[\mathbf{T},\mathbf{N},\mathbf{B}]$

(b) $\dfrac{d}{ds}(\mathbf{T} \cdot \mathbf{T})$ (e) $\dfrac{d\mathbf{R}}{dt} \cdot \mathbf{T}$ (h) $\left|\dfrac{d^2\mathbf{R}}{ds^2}\right|$

(c) $\dfrac{d^2\mathbf{R}}{dt^2} \cdot \mathbf{T}$ (f) $\dfrac{d\mathbf{N}}{ds} \cdot \mathbf{B}$ (i) $\dfrac{d\mathbf{B}}{ds}$

11. Let $\boldsymbol{\omega} = \tau\mathbf{T} + k\mathbf{B}$. Show that the equation

$$\frac{d\mathbf{R}}{ds} = \boldsymbol{\omega} \times \mathbf{R}$$

is satisfied for $\mathbf{R} = \mathbf{T}$, $\mathbf{N}$, and $\mathbf{B}$. Notice the resemblance of this equation and the equation in Sec. 1.12 describing angular velocity.

12. A rigorous derivation of the Frenet formulas proceeds as follows:
(a) Regard (2.39) as the defining equation for k and $\mathbf{N}$.
(b) Show that $\dfrac{d\mathbf{N}}{ds} + k\mathbf{T}$ is perpendicular to both $\mathbf{T}$ and $\mathbf{N}$. [Here it is helpful to differentiate the relation $\mathbf{T} \cdot \mathbf{N} = 0$. Thus (2.40) can be regarded as the defining equation for τ.]
(c) Prove (2.41) from (2.42) and (2.43) by differentiating the relation $\mathbf{B} = \mathbf{T} \times \mathbf{N}$.
Carry out the details of this program.

13. True or false:
(a) If $\mathbf{R}$ is the position vector of a particle, t denotes time, and s denotes arc length, $d^2\mathbf{R}/dt^2$ is a scalar multiple of $d^2\mathbf{R}/ds^2$.
(b) A moving particle achieves its maximum speed at the instant $t = 3$. (Before and after that instant, its speed is less than its speed at $t = 3$.) It follows from this that its acceleration is zero at the instant $t = 3$.
(c) The acceleration of a particle moving along a curve with binormal $\mathbf{B}$ is always perpendicular to $\mathbf{B}$. [More precisely, $\mathbf{a}(t)$ and $\mathbf{B}(t)$ are orthogonal for each fixed value of t.]

2.4 PLANAR MOTION IN POLAR COORDINATES

In this section we consider the motion of a particle in the xy plane in which the position of the particle is given in polar coordinates. We assume the polar coordinates (r,θ) are given as functions of the time t, and that these functions possess second derivatives.

Although it is possible to change from polar coordinates to cartesian coordinates, this may be inconvenient, which is one reason for treating this case separately. The main purpose in considering polar coordinates separately will become clear as we proceed.

In order to work directly with polar coordinates, it is convenient to introduce unit vectors $\mathbf{u}_r$ and $\mathbf{u}_\theta$ which point respectively along the position vector and at right angles to it (in the direction of increasing θ), as shown in Fig. 2.18.

It is easy to see that $\mathbf{u}_r$ and $\mathbf{u}_\theta$ can be written in terms of $\mathbf{i}$ and $\mathbf{j}$ as follows:

$$\begin{aligned} \mathbf{u}_r &= \cos\theta\,\mathbf{i} + \sin\theta\,\mathbf{j} \\ \mathbf{u}_\theta &= -\sin\theta\,\mathbf{i} + \cos\theta\,\mathbf{j} \end{aligned} \tag{2.42}$$

Note that $\mathbf{u}_r$ and $\mathbf{u}_\theta$ are functions of θ and are defined at every point in space except the origin. Unlike $\mathbf{i}$ and $\mathbf{j}$, $\mathbf{u}_r$ and $\mathbf{u}_\theta$ are not constants. For example, along the positive x axis, $\mathbf{u}_r = \mathbf{i}$, but along the positive y axis, $\mathbf{u}_r = \mathbf{j}$. It follows that we must be careful in differentiating vector fields written in terms of $\mathbf{u}_r$ and $\mathbf{u}_\theta$.

Directly from (2.42) we see that

$$\begin{aligned} \frac{d\mathbf{u}_r}{d\theta} &= \mathbf{u}_\theta \\ \frac{d\mathbf{u}_\theta}{d\theta} &= -\mathbf{u}_r \end{aligned} \tag{2.43}$$

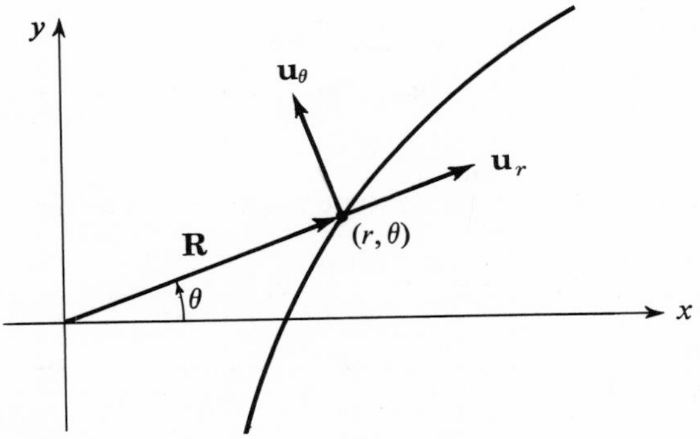

FIGURE 2.18

(Notice that these important formulas reinforce the observations we made in the previous section about the derivatives of unit vectors rigidly attached to each other.)

The position vector of a particle located at a point (r,θ) is

$$\mathbf{R} = r\mathbf{u}_r \tag{2.44}$$

We obtain the velocity by differentiating (2.44) and using the chain rule,

$$\begin{aligned}\frac{d\mathbf{R}}{dt} &= \frac{dr}{dt}\mathbf{u}_r + r\frac{d\mathbf{u}_r}{dt}\\ &= \frac{dr}{dt}\mathbf{u}_r + r\frac{d\mathbf{u}_r}{d\theta}\frac{d\theta}{dt}\end{aligned}$$

Hence, by (2.43), the velocity is given by

$$\mathbf{v} = \frac{d\mathbf{R}}{dt} = \frac{dr}{dt}\mathbf{u}_r + r\frac{d\theta}{dt}\mathbf{u}_\theta \tag{2.45}$$

This expresses the velocity as the sum of a radial component, directed away from or towards the origin with magnitude $|dr/dt|$, and a transverse component with magnitude $|r\,d\theta/dt|$.

Example 2.12 A particle moves around the circle $r = 2$ with angular velocity $d\theta/dt = 5$ rad/second. Find its speed.

Solution Since r is a constant, $dr/dt = 0$. Hence

$$\mathbf{v} = r\left(\frac{d\theta}{dt}\right)\mathbf{u}_\theta = 10\mathbf{u}_\theta$$

Therefore $|\mathbf{v}| = 10$.

Example 2.13 A circular disk rotates with constant angular velocity 3 rad/sec. A fly walks from the center of the disk outward to the rim at a rate of 2 cm/sec (relative to the disk). Find the speed of the fly 4 seconds after he starts at the center.

Solution Since $dr/dt = 2$, we have $r = r_0 + 2t$. Since the fly starts at the center, $r_0 = 0$. Hence by (2.45)

$$\mathbf{v} = 2\mathbf{u}_r + 3r\mathbf{u}_\theta$$

At time $t = 4$, $r = 2t = 8$, so $\mathbf{v} = 2\mathbf{u}_r + 24\mathbf{u}_\theta$. The speed is then $(2^2 + 24^2)^{1/2} = (580)^{1/2}$ cm/sec.

Returning to (2.45), we differentiate again to obtain the acceleration:

$$\begin{aligned}\mathbf{a} = \frac{d\mathbf{v}}{dt} &= \frac{d^2r}{dt^2}\mathbf{u}_r + \frac{dr}{dt}\frac{d\mathbf{u}_r}{dt} + \frac{dr}{dt}\frac{d\theta}{dt}\mathbf{u}_\theta + r\frac{d^2\theta}{dt^2}\mathbf{u}_\theta + r\frac{d\theta}{dt}\frac{d\mathbf{u}_\theta}{dt}\\ &= \frac{d^2r}{dt^2}\mathbf{u}_r + \frac{dr}{dt}\frac{d\mathbf{u}_r}{d\theta}\frac{d\theta}{dt} + \frac{dr}{dt}\frac{d\theta}{dt}\mathbf{u}_\theta + r\frac{d^2\theta}{dt^2}\mathbf{u}_\theta + r\frac{d\theta}{dt}\frac{d\theta}{dt}\frac{d\mathbf{u}_\theta}{d\theta}\\ &= \frac{d^2r}{dt^2}\mathbf{u}_r + 2\frac{dr}{dt}\frac{d\theta}{dt}\mathbf{u}_\theta + r\frac{d^2\theta}{dt^2}\mathbf{u}_\theta - r\left(\frac{d\theta}{dt}\right)^2\mathbf{u}_r\end{aligned}$$

Combining terms,

$$\mathbf{a} = \left[\frac{d^2r}{dt^2} - r\left(\frac{d\theta}{dt}\right)^2\right]\mathbf{u}_r + \left[r\frac{d^2\theta}{dt^2} + 2\frac{dr}{dt}\frac{d\theta}{dt}\right]\mathbf{u}_\theta \tag{2.46}$$

The first term in (2.46), $(d^2r/dt^2)\mathbf{u}_r$, is just what we would expect to have, and the third term, $r(d^2\theta/dt^2)\mathbf{u}_\theta$, is also familiar from elementary physics (it is the term a_t mentioned in the previous section.) In the special case that r is a constant, we have motion in a circle with center at the origin, a special case in which $\mathbf{u}_\theta$ and $\mathbf{u}_r$ are, respectively, the vectors $\mathbf{T}$ and $-\mathbf{N}$ of the preceding section. In this special case, the second term is the centripetal acceleration term.

The fourth term,

$$2\frac{dr}{dt}\frac{d\theta}{dt}\mathbf{u}_\theta$$

is more complicated and is usually not discussed in elementary physics textbooks. Under certain circumstances it is known as the *Coriolis acceleration*. As a careful examination of the above derivation will show, this term is due partly to the change in *direction* of the radial component of velocity, and partly to the fact that, as r changes, the transverse component of velocity changes, even if the angular velocity $d\theta/dt$ is constant.

According to Newton's second law, $\mathbf{F} = m\mathbf{a}$, where $\mathbf{F}$ is the total force acting on the particle. This force $\mathbf{F}$ may be written as the sum of two components,

$$\mathbf{F} = F_r\mathbf{u}_r + F_\theta\mathbf{u}_\theta$$

The motion of the particle is then governed by the two differential equations

$$F_r = m\frac{d^2r}{dt^2} - mr\left(\frac{d\theta}{dt}\right)^2 \tag{2.47}$$

$$F_\theta = mr\frac{d^2\theta}{dt^2} + 2m\frac{dr}{dt}\frac{d\theta}{dt} \tag{2.48}$$

If both sides of (2.48) are multiplied by r, (2.48) can be written in the form

$$rF_\theta = \frac{d}{dt}\left(mr^2\frac{d\theta}{dt}\right) \tag{2.49}$$

which in some cases may be interpreted as stating that the torque applied to the particle equals the time rate of change of its angular momentum.

If $F_\theta = 0$, (2.49) may be integrated to yield $mr^2\,d\theta/dt = C$. In other words, if the force is always directed radially toward or away from the origin (a "central force field"), then the angular momentum of the particle will be constant. This immediately implies Kepler's second law of planetary motion, that the radius vector in a central force field sweeps over area at a constant rate, since the rate at which the vector $\mathbf{R}$ sweeps out area is

$$\frac{dA}{dt} = \tfrac{1}{2}r^2\frac{d\theta}{dt}$$

EXERCISES

1. Find $d^3\mathbf{R}/dt^3$ in terms of $\mathbf{u}_r$ and $\mathbf{u}_\theta$.
2. A particle moves in a plane with constant angular velocity ω about the origin. The rate of increase of its acceleration is parallel to the position vector $\mathbf{R}$.
   (a) What is the transverse component of $d^3\mathbf{R}/dt^3$?
   (b) Show that $d^2r/dt^2 = r\omega^2/3$.
3. Find $\mathbf{v}$ and $\mathbf{a}$ if a particle moves so that

$$r = b(1 - \cos\theta)$$

and

$$\frac{d\theta}{dt} = 4$$

4. Find $\mathbf{v}$ and $\mathbf{a}$ if

$$r = b(1 + \sin t)$$
$$\theta = e^{-t} - 1$$

5. The force $\mathbf{F}$ exerted by a magnetic field $\mathbf{B}$ on a particle carrying a charge q is given by $\mathbf{F} = q(\mathbf{v} \times \mathbf{B})$, where $\mathbf{v}$ is the velocity of the particle. Draw a diagram showing the relative directions of $\mathbf{v}$, $\mathbf{B}$, and $\mathbf{F}$, in some special case. Under what circumstances will the field exert no force on the particle?
6. A particle of mass m moves in a circle of radius r in the xy plane. Assume the magnetic field $\mathbf{B}$ is constant and directed parallel to the z axis, and that the only force exerted on the particle is that force $\mathbf{F}$ given in the preceding problem. Find q/m.
7. Which terms in (2.46) will be nonzero, in each of the following cases?
   (a) A particle moves around a circle with center at the origin with constant nonzero angular velocity.
   (b) A particle moves around a circle with center at the origin with constant nonzero angular acceleration.
   (c) A particle moves along a straight line not passing through the origin, with constant speed.
   (d) A person is walking from the center of a merry-go-round towards its outer edge (discuss various possibilities).
8. A particle moves along a straight line, not passing through the origin.
   (a) Is $r(d\theta/dt)^2$ nonzero?
   (b) Can $r(d\theta/dt)^2$ be called the centripetal acceleration in this case?
9. A particle moves with constant radial speed 2 cm/sec away from the center of a platform rotating with uniform angular velocity of 30 rev/min.
   (a) What is its radial acceleration?
   (b) What is its Coriolis acceleration?
10. Find the magnitude of the Coriolis acceleration of a particle moving in the xy plane with position given by

$$x = 3t\cos 4\pi t$$
$$y = 3t\sin 4\pi t$$

11. A particle of mass m moves in a force field $\mathbf{F}$. Assume that the sum of its kinetic and potential energy is $E = \frac{1}{2}m\mathbf{v}\cdot\mathbf{v} - \int_0^t \mathbf{F}\cdot\mathbf{v}\,dt$. Using (2.45), (2.47), and (2.48), express E in polar coordinates and show that $dE/dt = 0$, and hence that E is constant.

*2.5 TENSOR NOTATION

As shown in Sec. 2.1, differentiation of a vector function proceeds componentwise. That is, the ith component of $d\mathbf{F}/dt$ is the derivative of the ith component of $\mathbf{F}$:

$$\left(\frac{d\mathbf{F}}{dt}\right)_i = \frac{dF_i}{dt}$$

This happy circumstance makes the tensor notation for the rules in Theorems 2.1 through 2.4, and their proofs, quite apparent. Thus for the cross product we have

$$\frac{d}{dt}\varepsilon_{ijk}F_jG_k = \varepsilon_{ijk}\frac{dF_j}{dt}G_k + \varepsilon_{ijk}F_j\frac{dG_k}{dt}$$

by the rules of ordinary calculus. Interpreted in vector notation, this says

$$\frac{d}{dt}(\mathbf{F}\times\mathbf{G}) = \frac{d\mathbf{F}}{dt}\times\mathbf{G} + \mathbf{F}\times\frac{d\mathbf{G}}{dt}$$

which is Eq. (2.7).

The other theorems are equally trivial.

EXERCISE

Derive the rule for the derivative of the dot product.

CHAPTER

3

Scalar and Vector Fields

3.1 SCALAR FIELDS; ISOTIMIC SURFACES; GRADIENT

If to each point (x,y,z) of a region in space there is made to correspond a number $f(x,y,z)$, we say that f is a *scalar field.* In other words, a scalar field is simply a scalar-valued function of three variables.

For the sake of fixing ideas, the following scalar fields are given as examples that will be referred to repeatedly:

1. $f(x,y,z) = x + 2y - 3z$

2. $f(x,y,z) = x^2 + y^2 + z^2$

3. $f(x,y,z) = x^2 + y^2$

4. $f(x,y,z) = \dfrac{x^2}{4} + \dfrac{y^2}{9} + z^2$

5. $f(x,y,z) = \sqrt{x^2 + y^2} - z$

6. $f(x,y,z) = \dfrac{1}{x^2 + y^2}$

The fields in examples 1 through 5 are defined at every point in space. The field in example 6 is defined at every point (x,y,z) except where $x^2 + y^2 = 0$, that is, everywhere except on the z axis.

If f is a scalar field, any surface defined by $f(x,y,z) = C$, where C is a constant, is called an *isotimic surface* (from the Greek *isotimos*, meaning *of equal value*). Sometimes, in physics, more specialized terms are used. For instance, if f denotes either electric or gravitational field potential, such surfaces are called *equipotential surfaces*. If f denotes temperature, they are called *isothermal surfaces*. If f denotes pressure, they are called *isobaric surfaces*.

In the above examples, the isotimic surfaces are:

1. All planes perpendicular to the vector $\mathbf{i} + 2\mathbf{j} - 3\mathbf{k}$.
2. All spheres with center at the origin.
3. All right circular cylinders with the z axis as axis of symmetry.
4. A family of ellipsoids.
5. A family of cones.
6. The same as in example 3.

It is impossible for distinct isotimic surfaces of the same scalar field to intersect, since only one number $f(x,y,z)$ is associated with any one point (x,y,z).

Here are some physical examples of scalar fields: the mass density of the atmosphere, the temperature at each point in an insulated wall, the water pressure at each point in the ocean, the gravitational potential of points in astronomical space, the electrostatic potential of the region between two condenser plates. Such scalar fields as density and pressure are only approximate idealizations of a complicated physical situation, since they take no account of the atomic properties of matter.

Let us consider the behavior of a scalar field in the neighborhood of a point (x_0,y_0,z_0) within its region of definition. Let us imagine a line segment passing through (x_0,y_0,z_0) parallel to a given vector $\mathbf{u}$. Let s denote the displacement measured along the line segment in the direction of $\mathbf{u}$ (Fig. 3.1) with $s = 0$ corresponding to (x_0,y_0,z_0). To each value of the parameter s there corresponds a point (x,y,z) on the line segment, and hence a corresponding scalar $f(x,y,z)$. The derivative df/ds at $s = 0$, if this derivative exists, is called the *directional derivative* of f at (x_0,y_0,z_0), in the direction of the vector $\mathbf{u}$.

In other words, the directional derivative of f is simply the rate of change of f, per unit distance, in some prescribed direction. The directional derivative

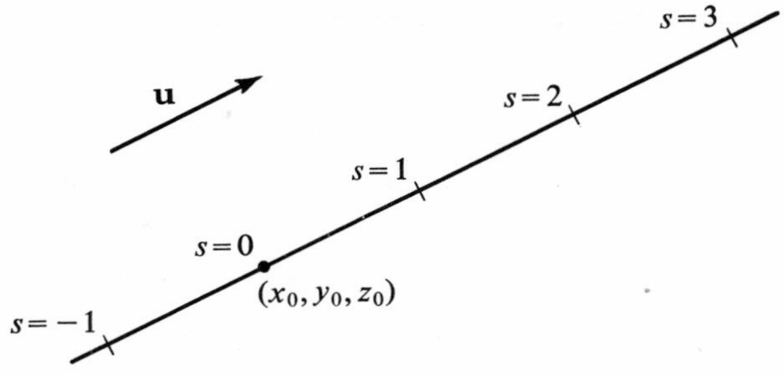

FIGURE 3.1

df/ds will generally depend on the location of the point (x_0,y_0,z_0) and also on the direction prescribed.

The directional derivative of a scalar field f in a direction parallel to the x axis, with s measured as increasing in the positive x direction, is conventionally denoted $\partial f/\partial x$, and is called the partial derivative of f with respect to x. Similarly, the directional derivative of f in the positive y direction is called $\partial f/\partial y$, and that in the positive z direction, $\partial f/\partial z$. We assume that the reader has had some experience with partial derivatives.

The directional derivative of a scalar field f in a direction that is not parallel to any of the coordinate axes is conventionally denoted df/ds, but of course this symbol is ambiguous; it would not make sense to ask "what is df/ds" without specifying the direction in which s is to be measured.

A convenient way of specifying the desired direction is by prescribing a vector **u** pointing in that direction. Although the magnitude of **u** is immaterial, it is conventional to take **u** to be a unit vector. We have already seen (Sec. 2.3) that a unit vector in a desired direction can be obtained by computing $d\mathbf{R}/ds$ in that direction, where $\mathbf{R} = x\mathbf{i} + y\mathbf{j} + z\mathbf{k}$. That is,

$$\mathbf{u} = \frac{dx}{ds}\mathbf{i} + \frac{dy}{ds}\mathbf{j} + \frac{dz}{ds}\mathbf{k} \tag{3.1}$$

is a unit vector pointing in the direction in which s is measured. Here we are thinking of x, y, and z as functions of the parameter s, for points (x,y,z) on the line segment; s is of course, arc length along the segment.

If the partial derivatives $\partial f/\partial x$, $\partial f/\partial y$, and $\partial f/\partial z$ exist and are continuous throughout a region, then it is well known (see the Appendix for a proof) that the following chain rule is valid:

$$\frac{df}{ds} = \frac{\partial f}{\partial x}\frac{dx}{ds} + \frac{\partial f}{\partial y}\frac{dy}{ds} + \frac{\partial f}{\partial z}\frac{dz}{ds} \tag{3.2}$$

If we define the *gradient* of f to be the vector

$$\mathbf{grad}\, f = \frac{\partial f}{\partial x}\mathbf{i} + \frac{\partial f}{\partial y}\mathbf{j} + \frac{\partial f}{\partial z}\mathbf{k} \tag{3.3}$$

we see that the right side of (3.2) is the dot product of **u** with **grad** f,

$$\frac{df}{ds} = \mathbf{u}\cdot\mathbf{grad}\, f \tag{3.2$'$}$$

Since **u** is a unit vector, $\mathbf{u}\cdot\mathbf{grad}\, f = |\mathbf{u}|\,|\mathbf{grad}\, f| \cos\theta = |\mathbf{grad}\, f| \cos\theta$, where θ is the angle between **grad** f and **u**. This gives us the first fundamental property of the gradient:

PROPERTY 3.1 *The component of* **grad** f *in any given direction gives the rate of change* df/ds *in that direction.*

By the maximum principle (Sec. 1.9), the largest possible value of $\mathbf{u} \cdot \mathbf{grad}\, f$, for unit vectors $\mathbf{u}$, is obtained when $\mathbf{u}$ is in the same direction as $\mathbf{grad}\, f$ (assuming $\mathbf{grad}\, f \neq \mathbf{0}$). Since $\mathbf{u} \cdot \mathbf{grad}\, f = df/ds$, it follows that the maximum value of df/ds is obtained in the direction of $\mathbf{grad}\, f$. This is the second fundamental property of the gradient:

PROPERTY 3.2 **grad** *f points in the direction of the maximum rate of increase of the function f.*

If $\mathbf{u}$ points in the direction of $\mathbf{grad}\, f$, then

$$\mathbf{u} \cdot \mathbf{grad}\, f = |\mathbf{u}|\, |\mathbf{grad}\, f| \cos\theta = |\mathbf{grad}\, f|$$

which gives the third fundamental property of the gradient:

PROPERTY 3.3 *The magnitude of* **grad** *f equals the maximum rate of increase of f per unit distance.*

Experience has shown that the wording of these fundamental properties makes them rather easy to memorize [and they *should* be memorized, together with the definition (3.3)].

The fourth fundamental property of the gradient of a function makes it possible to use the gradient concept in solving geometrical problems:

PROPERTY 3.4 *Through any point* (x_0,y_0,z_0) *where* $\mathbf{grad}\, f \neq \mathbf{0}$, *there passes an isotimic surface* $f(x,y,z) = C$; $\mathbf{grad}\, f$ *is normal (i.e., perpendicular) to this surface at the point* (x_0,y_0,z_0).

This property holds only when $\partial f/\partial x$, $\partial f/\partial y$, and $\partial f/\partial z$ exist and are continuous in a neighborhood of the point in question. The constant C is, of course, equal to $f(x_0,y_0,z_0)$. If $\mathbf{grad}\, f = \mathbf{0}$ the locus of points satisfying $f(x,y,z) = C$ might not form a surface. (Consider, for example, this locus if f is the *constant* function 5.)

We omit a detailed proof of this fourth property, but the following discussion may make it seem reasonable. Let C denote the value of f at (x_0,y_0,z_0). Since $\mathbf{grad}\, f \neq \mathbf{0}$, it follows from the preceding fundamental properties that df/ds will be positive in some direction. If, then, we proceed away from (x_0,y_0,z_0) in that direction, the value of $f(x,y,z)$ will increase, and if we proceed in the opposite direction, its value will decrease. Since f and its partial derivatives are continuous, it seems reasonable that there will be a surface passing through (x_0,y_0,z_0) on one side of which the values of f will be greater than (and on the other, less than) C. Now suppose we consider any smooth arc passing through (x_0,y_0,z_0) and entirely contained in this surface. Then $f(x,y,z) = C$ for all points on this arc and so $df/ds = 0$, where s is measured along this arc. Since $df/ds = \mathbf{u} \cdot \mathbf{grad}\, f$, and in this case $\mathbf{u}$ is a unit vector tangent to this arc, we see that $\mathbf{u} \cdot \mathbf{grad}\, f = df/ds = 0$, implying

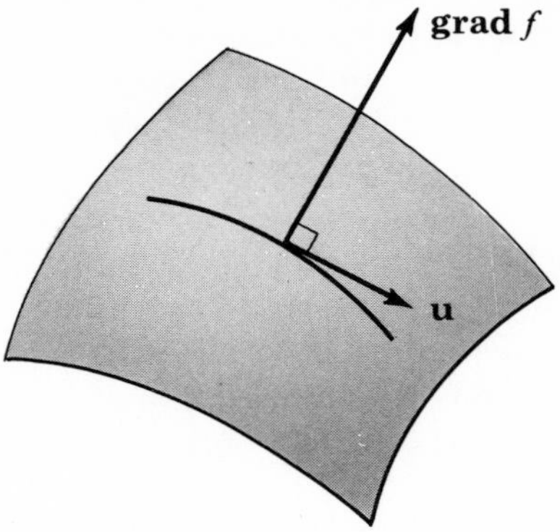

FIGURE 3.2

that **grad** f is perpendicular to **u**. This reasoning applies to any smooth arc in the surface passing through (x_0,y_0,z_0). Hence **grad** f is perpendicular to every such arc, at that point, which can be the case only if **grad** f is perpendicular to the surface (Fig. 3.2).

We now return to the six examples given previously. In each case the gradient is easily computed using the definition (3.3):

1. $\mathbf{grad}\ f = \mathbf{i} + 2\mathbf{j} - 3\mathbf{k}$
2. $\mathbf{grad}\ f = 2x\mathbf{i} + 2y\mathbf{j} + 2z\mathbf{k}$
3. $\mathbf{grad}\ f = 2x\mathbf{i} + 2y\mathbf{j}$
4. $\mathbf{grad}\ f = \dfrac{x}{2}\mathbf{i} + \dfrac{2y}{9}\mathbf{j} + 2z\mathbf{k}$
5. $\mathbf{grad}\ f = \dfrac{x\mathbf{i} + y\mathbf{j}}{\sqrt{x^2 + y^2}} - \mathbf{k}$
6. $\mathbf{grad}\ f = -\dfrac{2x}{(x^2 + y^2)^2}\mathbf{i} - \dfrac{2y}{(x^2 + y^2)^2}\mathbf{j}$

1. (This is the only one of the six examples for which **grad** f is a constant.) We already know from Sec. 1.10 that $\mathbf{i} + 2\mathbf{j} - 3\mathbf{k}$ is perpendicular to any plane of the form $x + 2y - 3z = C$. We see that $\mathbf{grad}\ f = \mathbf{i} + 2\mathbf{j} - 3\mathbf{k}$. Thus we have verified the fourth fundamental property, in this special case.
2. In this case the isotimic surfaces are spheres centered at the origin, so the normals to these surfaces must be vectors pointing directly away from the origin. Sure enough, we have $\mathbf{grad}\ f = 2x\mathbf{i} + 2y\mathbf{j} + 2z\mathbf{k} = 2\mathbf{R}$, and we know that the vector $2\mathbf{R}$ always points directly away from the origin. To see the significance of the number 2 here, let r denote the distance from the origin to the point (x,y,z). Then we can, in this example, write the function in terms of r: it is simply r^2. Moreover, if we move away from any

point in the direction of maximum increase of r^2, which obviously means moving directly away from the origin, then the element of arc length is simply dr. In this direction, the derivative df/ds is df/dr, and $(d/dr)(r^2) = 2r$. Also, $|2\mathbf{R}| = 2r$, so we have verified the third fundamental property in this special case.

3. The reader familiar with cylindrical coordinates can do the same thing here as we just did with example 2. Let $\rho = (x^2 + y^2)^{1/2}$, the distance from the point (x,y,z) to the z axis. The function f in this example is simply ρ^2, and obviously increases most rapidly in a direction perpendicular to the z axis. Its derivative in this direction is 2ρ, which is also the magnitude $|\mathbf{grad}\ f| = (4x^2 + 4y^2)^{1/2}$. This direction is clearly normal to the isotimic surfaces, since the latter are right circular cylinders centered on the z axis. The second, third, and fourth fundamental properties are extremely transparent in this case, as they were in example 2.
5. (We skip example 4.) All we care to note here is the elementary geometrical significance of the $-\mathbf{k}$ term in $\mathbf{grad}\ f$. The isotimic surfaces of this function are conical; each has an apex on the z axis and spreads outward with increasing z. Thus, we see easily that the normal to one such surface will not point directly away from the z axis, as it does in example 3, but will have an additional, constant component in the negative z direction.

The following are some sample problems that illustrate the use of the fundamental properties of the gradient of a scalar field.

Example 3.1 Find df/ds in the direction of the vector $4\mathbf{i} + 4\mathbf{j} - 2\mathbf{k}$, at the point (1,1,2), if $f(x,y,z) = x^2 + y^2 - z$.

Solution $\mathbf{grad}\, f = 2x\mathbf{i} + 2y\mathbf{j} - \mathbf{k} = 2\mathbf{i} + 2\mathbf{j} - \mathbf{k}$ at (1,1,2). A unit vector in the desired direction is $\mathbf{u} = \frac{2}{3}\mathbf{i} + \frac{2}{3}\mathbf{j} - \frac{1}{3}\mathbf{k}$ (obtained by dividing $4\mathbf{i} + 4\mathbf{j} - 2\mathbf{k}$ by its own length). Property 3.1 then gives $df/ds = \mathbf{u} \cdot \mathbf{grad}\, f = \frac{4}{3} + \frac{4}{3} + \frac{1}{3} = 3$. This means that the value of the function f is increasing 3 units per unit distance, if we proceed from (1,1,2) in the direction stated.

Example 3.2 The temperature of points in space is given by $f(x,y,z) = x^2 + y^2 - z$. A mosquito located at (1,1,2) desires to fly in such a direction that he will get cool as soon as possible. In what direction should he move?

Solution As we saw in Example 3.1, $\mathbf{grad}\, f = 2\mathbf{i} + 2\mathbf{j} - \mathbf{k}$ at (1,1,2). The mosquito should move in the direction $-\mathbf{grad}\, f$, since $\mathbf{grad}\, f$ is in the direction of increasing temperature.

Example 3.3 A mosquito is flying at a speed of 5 units of distance per second, in the direction of the vector $4\mathbf{i} + 4\mathbf{j} - 2\mathbf{k}$. The temperature is given by $f(x,y,z) = x^2 + y^2 - z$. What is his rate of increase of temperature, per unit time, at the instant he passes through the point (1,1,2)?

Solution As shown in Example 3.1 above, df/ds in this direction is 3 units per unit distance. The rate of increase of temperature per unit time is thus $df/dt = (df/ds)(ds/dt) = (3)(5) = 15$ degrees per second.

Example 3.4 What is the maximum possible df/ds, if $f(x,y,z) = x^2 + y^2 - z$, at the point (1,4,2)?

Solution $|\mathbf{grad}\, f| = |2\mathbf{i} + 8\mathbf{j} - \mathbf{k}| = \sqrt{69}$. The answer is approximately 8.31 units per unit distance.

Example 3.5 Find a unit vector normal to the surface $x^2 + y^2 - z = 6$ at the point (2,3,7).

Solution This is an isotimic surface for the function $f(x,y,z) = x^2 + y^2 - z$. At (2,3,7), we have $\mathbf{grad}\, f = 2x\mathbf{i} + 2y\mathbf{j} - \mathbf{k} = 4\mathbf{i} + 6\mathbf{j} - \mathbf{k}$. The length of this vector is $\sqrt{53}$. Thus, an answer is $(\sqrt{53}/53)(4\mathbf{i} + 6\mathbf{j} - \mathbf{k})$. (The negative of this vector is also a correct answer.)

An error commonly made in Example 3.5, for some reason the authors cannot fathom, is writing $\mathbf{grad}\, f = 4\mathbf{i} + 6\mathbf{j} - 7\mathbf{k}$, at (2,3,7), as though $\mathbf{grad}\, f$ were $2x\mathbf{i} + 2y\mathbf{j} - z\mathbf{k}$ instead of $2x\mathbf{i} + 2y\mathbf{j} - \mathbf{k}$.

EXERCISES

1. Compute **grad** f if
   (a) $f = \sin x + e^{xy} + z$
   (b) $f = \dfrac{1}{|\mathbf{R}|}$
   (c) $f = \mathbf{R} \cdot \mathbf{i} \times \mathbf{j}$
2. If $f(x,y,z) = x^2 + y^2$, what is the locus of points in space for which **grad** f is parallel to the y axis?
3. What can you say about a function whose gradient is everywhere parallel to the y axis?
4. Find all functions $f(x,y,z)$ such that $\mathbf{grad}\, f = 2x\mathbf{i} + z\mathbf{j} + y\mathbf{k}$.
5. Describe **grad** f in words, without actually doing any calculating, given that $f(x,y,z)$ is the distance between (x,y,z) and the z axis.
6. Find the derivative of $f(x,y,z) = x + xyz$ at the point $(1,-2,2)$ in the direction of (a) $2\mathbf{i} + 2\mathbf{j} - \mathbf{k}$, (b) $2\mathbf{i} + 2\mathbf{j} + \mathbf{k}$.
7. Find the directional derivative df/ds at $(1,3,-2)$ in the direction of $-\mathbf{i} + 2\mathbf{j} + 2\mathbf{k}$ if
   (a) $f(x,y,z) = yz + xy + xz$
   (b) $f(x,y,z) = x^2 + 2y^2 + 3z^2$
   (c) $f(x,y,z) = xy + x^3y^3$
   (d) $f(x,y,z) = \sqrt{x^2 + y^2 + z^2}$
8. Given $f(x,y,z) = x^2 + y^2 + z^2$, find the maximum value of df/ds at the point (3,0,4),
   (a) by using the gradient of f;
   (b) by interpreting f geometrically.

9. Find the magnitude of the greatest rate of change of $f(x,y,z) = (x^2 + z^2)^3$ at $(1,3,-2)$. Interpret geometrically.

10. Find a vector normal to the surface $x^2 + yz = 5$ at $(2,1,1)$.

11. Find an equation of the plane tangent to the sphere $x^2 + y^2 + z^2 = 21$ at $(2,4,-1)$.

12. Find a vector normal to the cylinder $x^2 + z^2 = 8$ at $(2,0,2)$,
(a) by inspection (draw a diagram);
(b) by finding the gradient of the function $f(x,y,z) = x^2 + z^2$ at $(2,0,2)$.

13. Find an equation of the plane tangent to the surface $z^2 - xy = 14$ at $(2,1,4)$.

14. Find equations of the line normal to the sphere $x^2 + y^2 + z^2 = 2$ at $(1,1,0)$,
(a) by inspection (draw a diagram);
(b) by computing the gradient of $f(x,y,z) = x^2 + y^2 + z^2$ at $(1,1,0)$, and using this to find the normal.

15. Find a unit vector normal to the plane $3x - y + 2z = 3$,
(a) by the methods of Sec. 1.10;
(b) by the methods of the preceding section.

16. Find an equation of the plane tangent to the surface $z = x^2 + y^2$ at $(2,3,13)$. [*Hint*: Consider the function $f(x,y,z) = x^2 + y^2 - z$.]

17. Find a unit vector tangent to the curve of intersection of the cylinder $x^2 + y^2 = 4$ and the sphere $x^2 + y^2 + z^2 = 9$ at the point $(\sqrt{2},\sqrt{2},\sqrt{5})$,
(a) by drawing a diagram, obtaining the answer by inspection;
(b) by finding the vector product of the normals to the two surfaces at that point;
(c) by writing the equations of the curve in parametric form, letting $x = 2 \sin t$ and $y = 2 \cos t$.

18. Determine the angle between the normals to the intersecting spheres $x^2 + y^2 + z^2 = 16$ and $(x-1)^2 + y^2 + z^2 = 16$, at the point $(1/2,3/2,3\sqrt{6}/2)$.

19. At what angle does the line $2x = y = 2z$ intersect the ellipsoid $2x^2 + y^2 + 2z^2 = 8$?

3.2 VECTOR FIELDS AND FLOW LINES

A vector field **F** is a rule associating with each point (x,y,z) in a region a vector $\mathbf{F}(x,y,z)$. In other words, a vector field is a vector-valued function of three variables.

Some vector fields are not defined for all points in space. For example, the vector field

$$\mathbf{F}(x,y,z) = \frac{x\mathbf{i} + y\mathbf{j}}{x^2 + y^2}$$

is not defined along the z axis, since $x^2 + y^2 = 0$ for points on the z axis.

In visualizing a vector field, we imagine that from each point in the region there extends a vector. Both direction and magnitude may vary with position (Fig. 3.3).

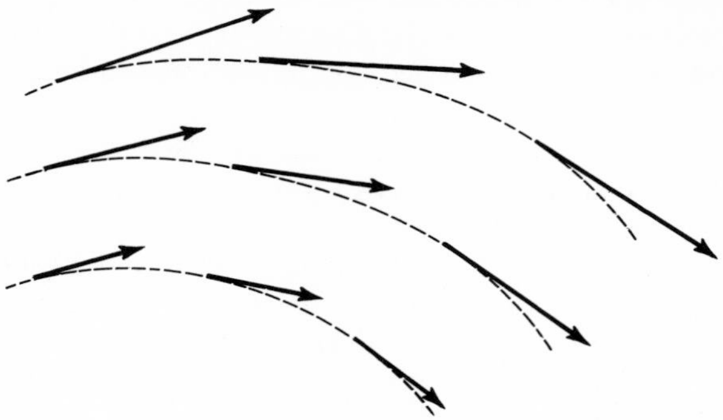

FIGURE 3.3

Any vector field may be written in terms of its components:

$$\mathbf{F}(x,y,z) = F_1(x,y,z)\mathbf{i} + F_2(x,y,z)\mathbf{j} + F_3(x,y,z)\mathbf{k}$$

Example 3.6 If $f(x, y,z)$ is a *scalar* field, **grad** f is a *vector* field.

Example 3.7 Each of the "vectors" $\mathbf{u}_r$ and $\mathbf{u}_\theta$ (Sec. 2.4) is a vector field defined in the plane.

Example 3.8 In hydrodynamics, one associates with each point of a region the velocity of the fluid passing that point. In that manner one obtains, at any instant of time, a vector field describing the instantaneous velocity of the fluid at every point.

Example 3.9 In theoretical physics, there is associated with each point in space an electric intensity vector, representing the force that would be exerted, per unit charge, on a charged particle, if it were located at that point. This electric field, at any instant of time, constitutes a vector field. (Magnetic fields and gravitational fields also provide examples of vector fields defined in space.)

Let us consider a vector field **F** that is defined and nonzero at every point of a region in space. Any curve passing through this region is called a *flow line* of **F** provided that, at every point on the curve, **F** is tangent to the curve. (Some authors call them *stream lines* or *characteristic curves* of **F**. If **F** is a force field, the flow lines are commonly called *lines of force*.) In Fig. 3.3, three flow lines are indicated as dotted curves.

This may be looked at another way. The vector field **F** determines, at each point in the region, a direction. If a particle moves in such a manner that its direction at any point coincides with the direction of the vector field **F** at that point, the space curve traced out is a flow line.

If the vector field $\mathbf{F}(x,y,z)$ describes the velocity at each point in a hydrodynamic system, the flow lines are the paths which are traversed by the component particles of the fluid. We are assuming here that **F** is not a function of the time t.

Note that, if $g(x,y,z)$ is a scalar field that is not zero at any point, the flow lines of the vector field $g(x,y,z)\mathbf{F}(x,y,z)$ will be the same as those of $\mathbf{F}(x,y,z)$, since only the *direction* of **F** at any point is relevant in determining the flow lines.

Since the direction of a flow line is uniquely determined by the field **F**, it is impossible to have two different directions at the same point, and therefore it is impossible for two flow lines to intersect. If the magnitude of **F** is zero at some point in space, then no direction is defined at that point and no flow line passes through that point.

If **R** is the position vector to an arbitrary point of a flow line, and if s represents arc length measured along the flow line, then the unit vector tangent to the curve at that point is given by

$$\mathbf{T} = \frac{d\mathbf{R}}{ds} = \frac{dx}{ds}\mathbf{i} + \frac{dy}{ds}\mathbf{j} + \frac{dz}{ds}\mathbf{k} \tag{3.4}$$

The requirement that **T** have the same direction as **F** can be written

$$\mathbf{T} = \beta\mathbf{F} \tag{3.5}$$

where β is a scalar-valued function of x, y, and z. This can be written in terms of components,

$$\beta F_1 = \frac{dx}{ds} \qquad \beta F_2 = \frac{dy}{ds} \qquad \beta F_3 = \frac{dz}{ds} \tag{3.6}$$

If F_1, F_2, and F_3 are all nonzero, we may eliminate β and write (3.6) in differential form,

$$\frac{dx}{F_1} = \frac{dy}{F_2} = \frac{dz}{F_3} \tag{3.7}$$

If exactly one of these functions (say F_3) is identically zero in a region, then we obtain directly from (3.6) that the curve lies in a plane (say, $z =$ constant) parallel to one of the coordinate planes.

Example 3.10 If $\mathbf{F} = x\mathbf{i} + y\mathbf{j} + \mathbf{k}$, then $F_1 = x$, $F_2 = y$, and $F_3 = 1$, giving $dx/x = dy/y = dz$. Solving the differential equations $dx/x = dz$ and $dy/y = dz$, we obtain $x = C_1e^z$, $y = C_2e^z$. Thus the equations of the flow line passing through the point (3,4,7) are $x = 3e^{z-7}$, $y = 4e^{z-7}$. The equations of the flow line passing through the origin are $x = 0$, $y = 0$—i.e., the z axis.

Example 3.11 If $\mathbf{F} = x\mathbf{i} + y\mathbf{j}$, then $F_1 = x$, $F_2 = y$, and $F_3 = 0$. In this case (3.6) becomes $\beta x = dx/ds$, $\beta y = dy/ds$, and $0 = dz/ds$. Eliminating β from the first two equations we obtain $dx/x = dy/y$, and, solving, we obtain $y = Cx$. From the third equation we obtain $z =$ constant. The field is zero when both x and y equal zero, and so the flow lines are not defined along the z axis. The flow lines are straight half-lines parallel to the xy plane, extending outward from the z axis.

Example 3.12 If $\mathbf{F} = -y\mathbf{i} + x\mathbf{j}$, then $-\beta y = dx/ds$, $\beta x = dy/ds$, and $0 = dz/ds$. Thus $dx/-y = dy/x$, and hence $x^2 + y^2 = \text{constant}$. Also, we have $z = \text{constant}$. The flow lines are circles surrounding the z axis and are parallel to the xy plane. As in Example 3.11, no flow lines pass through points on the z axis.

Flow lines may be infinite in extent, as in Examples 3.10 and 3.11, or they may close upon themselves, as in Example 3.12.

EXERCISES

1. A vector field $\mathbf{F}$ is defined in the xy plane by $\mathbf{F} = -y\mathbf{i} + x\mathbf{j}$. Draw a diagram similar to Fig. 3.3, showing the values of $\mathbf{F}$ at the points (1,0), (0,1), (−1,0), (0,−1), (1,1), (−1,1), (−1,−1), (1,−1), and a scattering of other points. Indicate flow lines.
2. Let $\mathbf{F} = x^2\mathbf{i} + y^2\mathbf{j} + \mathbf{k}$.
   (a) Find the general equation of a flow line.
   (b) Find the flow line through the point (1,1,2).
3. Without doing any calculating at all, describe the flow lines of the vector field $\mathbf{R} = x\mathbf{i} + y\mathbf{j} + z\mathbf{k}$. [*Hint*: If a particle located at (x, y, z) has velocity $\mathbf{R}$, in what direction is it moving relative to the origin?]
4. The flow lines of the gradient of a scalar field cross the isotimic surfaces orthogonally. Explain.

3.3 DIVERGENCE

The concept of *gradient*, as we have presented it, applies only to scalar fields. We now consider the more complicated problem of describing the rate of change of a *vector* field. There are two fundamental measures of the rate of change of a vector field: the *divergence* and the *curl*.

Roughly speaking, the divergence of a vector field is a scalar field that tells us, at each point, the extent to which the field diverges from that point. The curl of a vector field is a vector field that gives us, at each point, an indication of how the field swirls in the vicinity of that point. However, to describe divergence and curl in such a brief manner is not only useless but a bit dangerous, since (if taken literally) both of these preceding sentences are not only vague but technically incorrect. As we shall see, it is possible for a field to have a positive divergence without appearing to "diverge" at all, and it is possible for a field to have a nontrivial curl and yet have flow lines that do not bend at all.

In this section we consider only the divergence. We begin by presenting a heuristic discussion which will serve to motivate the subsequent definition.

As usual, the vector field will be denoted by

$$\mathbf{F} = F_1\mathbf{i} + F_2\mathbf{j} + F_3\mathbf{k}$$

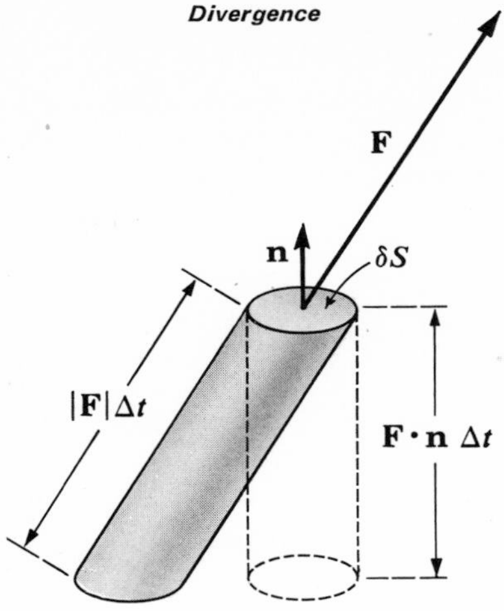

FIGURE 3.4

Let us, for the moment, interpret $\mathbf{F}(x,y,z)$ as the velocity of a fluid particle located at (x,y,z), as in Example 3.8 of the previous section; $\mathbf{F}$ is thus the velocity field of the fluid. Now consider a small planar patch of surface inside the fluid. Let δS be the area of the patch, and let $\mathbf{n}$ be a unit vector normal to the patch. We would like to find an expression for the amount of the fluid that flows through this area per unit time.

As shown in Fig. 3.4, if $\mathbf{F}$ is the velocity of the fluid at some point on the patch, then the body of fluid that will pass through the patch in the time Δt is, to a good approximation, the fluid in the tube with base δS and central axis $\mathbf{F}\,\Delta t$. The approximation is better for small δS and Δt. If we assume the density of the fluid is unity (i.e., the fluid is incompressible), then the amount of fluid in this tube is given by its volume. Its base area is δS, and its height is $\mathbf{F}\,\Delta t \cdot \mathbf{n}$. Multiplying these and dividing by Δt, we see that *the amount of fluid crossing the area* δS (in the direction $\mathbf{n}$) *per unit time is approximately* $\mathbf{F} \cdot \mathbf{n}\,\delta S$. This is called the *flux of the vector field* $\mathbf{F}$ *through the area* δS.

To define the divergence of the field $\mathbf{F}$, we consider a small rectangular parallelepiped having corners at (x,y,z), $(x + \Delta x, y, z)$, $(x, y + \Delta y, x)$, and $(x, y, z + \Delta z)$ (see Fig. 3.5). We shall compute the total flux of the field $\mathbf{F}$ through the six sides of this box in the outwards direction (i.e., on each side we choose $\mathbf{n}$ to be the outward normal). We then divide this flux by the volume of the box and take the limit as the dimensions of the box go to zero. *This limit is called the divergence of* $\mathbf{F}$ *at the point* (x,y,z).

The computation of this limit proceeds as follows. On face number I in Fig. 3.5 the outward normal is $-\mathbf{i}$. Thus, according to the above analysis, the flux out this face is approximately $-F_1(x,y,z)\,\Delta y\,\Delta z$. Since we will ultimately take limits as Δx, Δy, and Δz go to zero, this approximation is a good one. The flux out of face number II, whose outward normal is $\mathbf{i}$, is $F_1(x + \Delta x, y, z)\,\Delta y\,\Delta z$. The total flux out of faces I and II is thus

$$[F_1(x + \Delta x, y, z) - F_1(x,y,z)]\,\Delta y\,\Delta z$$

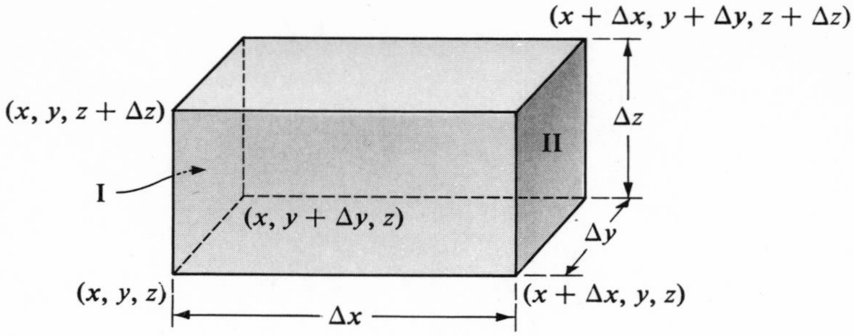

FIGURE 3.5

The difference in these values of F_1 is given, to the same order of accuracy, by

$$\frac{\partial F_1}{\partial x}\,\Delta x$$

Thus the contribution to the net outward flux from faces I and II is

$$\frac{\partial F_1}{\partial x}\,\Delta x\,\Delta y\,\Delta z$$

Similarly, the two faces in the y direction contribute

$$\frac{\partial F_2}{\partial y}\,\Delta y\,\Delta x\,\Delta z$$

and, adding the contribution of the remaining faces we see that the net outward flux is approximately

$$\left(\frac{\partial F_1}{\partial x} + \frac{\partial F_2}{\partial y} + \frac{\partial F_3}{\partial z}\right)\Delta x\,\Delta y\,\Delta z$$

After we divide by the volume $\Delta x\,\Delta y\,\Delta z$, our approximations become accurate as we take the limit and we are led to the following statement which we take as our rigorous definition of divergence:

The *divergence* of a *vector* field

$$\mathbf{F} = \mathbf{F}_1\mathbf{i} + F_2\,\mathbf{j} + F_3\,\mathbf{k} \tag{3.8}$$

is a *scalar* field, denoted div $\mathbf{F}$, defined by

$$\operatorname{div}\mathbf{F} = \frac{\partial F_1}{\partial x} + \frac{\partial F_2}{\partial y} + \frac{\partial F_3}{\partial z} \tag{3.9}$$

From definition (3.9), it is easy to compute the divergence of a vector field, as we now demonstrate with examples. *Warning*: It makes no sense to speak of the divergence of a scalar field.

Example 3.13 Find div **F**, if $\mathbf{F} = x\mathbf{i} + y^2z\mathbf{j} + xz^3\mathbf{k}$.

Solution

$$\operatorname{div} \mathbf{F} = \frac{\partial}{\partial x}(x) + \frac{\partial}{\partial y}(y^2z) + \frac{\partial}{\partial z}(xz^3)$$

$$= 1 + 2yz + 3xz^2$$

Example 3.14 Find div **F**, if $\mathbf{F} = xe^y\mathbf{i} + e^{xy}\mathbf{j} + \sin yz\,\mathbf{k}$.

Solution

$$\operatorname{div} \mathbf{F} = \frac{\partial}{\partial x}(xe^y) + \frac{\partial}{\partial y}(e^{xy}) + \frac{\partial}{\partial z}(\sin yz)$$

$$= e^y + xe^{xy} + y\cos yz$$

Example 3.15 Give an example of a vector field **F** that has divergence equal to 3 at every point in space.

Solution Many solutions can be given, for instance $\mathbf{F} = 3x\mathbf{i}$ or $\mathbf{F} = x\mathbf{i} + y\mathbf{j} + z\mathbf{k}$.

Example 3.16 In Fig. 3.6, is the divergence of **F** at point P positive or negative? Assume no variation of **F** in the z direction and that F_3 is identically zero.

Solution We see from the diagram that F_1 is approximately constant, so $\partial F_1/\partial x = 0$. Below P, F_2 is negative, and about P, F_2 is positive, so $\partial F_2/\partial y$ is positive. Since $F_3 = 0$, we have $\partial F_3/\partial z = 0$. It follows that div **F** is positive at point P.

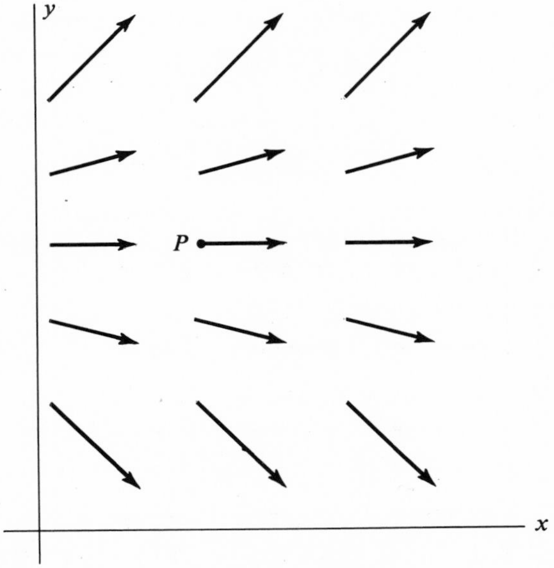

FIGURE 3.6

Heuristically, we can see that the flux through the x faces of a parallelepiped at P will cancel, while there is definitely flux *out* of both y faces. Since there is no flux in the z direction, the divergence is positive.

Example 3.17 In Fig. 3.6, is the divergence of $\mathbf{F}$ at point P positive or negative? Assume no variation of $\mathbf{F}$ in the z direction and that F_3 is identically zero.

Solution We see from the diagram that F_1 is decreasing with increasing x, hence $\partial F_1/\partial x$ is negative. F_2 and F_3 are zero at every point. It follows that the divergence of $\mathbf{F}$ is negative at every point.

Again heuristically, there is no flux in the y or z direction, and the flux in the x direction *decreases* as we move to the right. So the net flux through the sides of a box at P is inward, and the divergence must be negative.

In Fig. 3.6, where the divergence is positive, the lines of flux do, in a sense, diverge in a neighborhood of P. This is the picture that motivates the common (incorrect) statement that "positive divergence means the field is diverging, negative divergence means the field is converging." Note that in Fig. 3.7, the divergence is negative, but the flow lines are *not* converging. The divergence is negative because more fluid enters a given region from the left than leaves it to the right.

Let us mention a hydrodynamic application at this point. Again, interpret $\mathbf{F}$ as the velocity field of a fluid *whose density* ρ *may be a function of position and time*. Then a simple modification of our analysis of flux shows that the amount of fluid crossing an area δS in the direction of its unit normal $\mathbf{n}$, per unit time, is $\rho\mathbf{F}\cdot\mathbf{n}\,\delta S$. Accordingly, the amount of fluid flowing out of a small box with dimensions Δx, Δy, and Δz is approximately

$$\operatorname{div}(\rho\mathbf{F})\,\Delta x\,\Delta y\,\Delta z$$

per unit time. This must result in a *decrease* of the amount of fluid,

$$\rho\,\Delta x\,\Delta y\,\Delta z$$

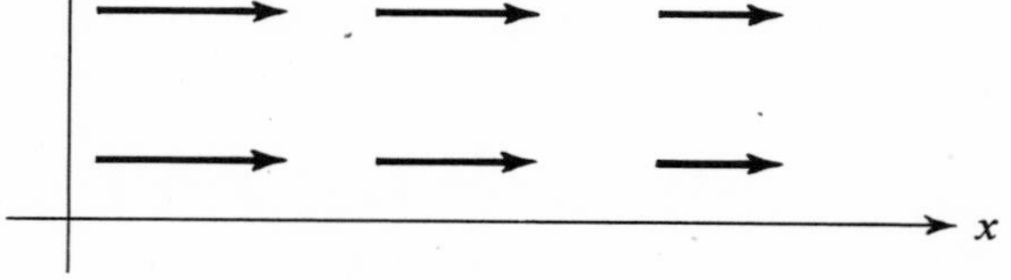

FIGURE 3.7

and hence a decrease in the density. Therefore we can write

$$\operatorname{div}(\rho\mathbf{F}) = -\frac{\partial\rho}{\partial t}$$

This is called the *equation of continuity* in fluid mechanics; it expresses the law of conservation of mass.

The heuristic reasoning employed in this section is, of course, subject to criticism, as are most arguments involving "infinitesimals." Its rigorous justification rests on a result known, appropriately enough, as the *divergence theorem*, and we will study it in the next chapter. For the present we are satisfied with having a formal, precise definition of div **F** in Eq. (3.9), and an intuitive picture of what it represents.

EXERCISES

1. Find div **F**, given that $\mathbf{F} = e^{xy}\mathbf{i} + \sin xy\,\mathbf{j} + \cos^2 zx\,\mathbf{k}$.
2. Find div **F**, given that $\mathbf{F} = x\mathbf{i} + y\mathbf{j} + z\mathbf{k}$.
3. Find div **F**, given that $\mathbf{F} = \mathbf{grad}\,\phi$ where $\phi = 3x^2y^3z$.
4. Find the divergence of the field

$$\frac{x\mathbf{i} + y\mathbf{j} + z\mathbf{k}}{(x^2 + y^2 + z^2)^{3/2}}$$

   Is the divergence of this field defined at every point in space?
5. Show in detail that $\operatorname{div}(\phi\mathbf{F}) = \phi\operatorname{div}\mathbf{F} + \mathbf{F}\cdot\mathbf{grad}\,\phi$.
6. Construct an example of a scalar field ϕ and a vector field **F**, neither of which is constant, for which $\operatorname{div}(\phi\mathbf{F})$ is identically equal to $\phi\operatorname{div}\mathbf{F}$.
7. Give an example of a nonconstant field with zero divergence.
8. Give an example of a field with a constant negative divergence.
9. Give an example of a field whose divergence depends only on x, is always positive, and increases with increasing x. (*Hint*: The function e^x is positive for every x.)
10. True or false: If **F** is everywhere nonzero and if div **F** is identically zero, the flow lines of **F** must be closed curves.
11. What can you say about the divergence of the vector field in Fig. 3.8 at points P, Q, and R?
12. What can you say about the divergence of the vector field in Fig. 3.9 at points P, Q, and R? Assume no variation of **F** in the z direction and that F_3 is identically zero.

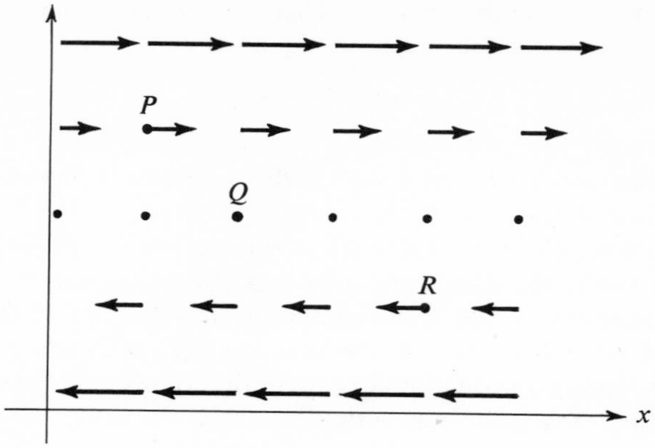

FIGURE 3.8

13. Another hydrodynamic interpretation of divergence is as follows: Let **F** be the velocity field of a fluid. Consider a small rectangular parallelepiped of fluid located at (x, y, z). Then the divergence of **F** is the time rate of change of the volume of this body of fluid, per unit volume, as the size of the box goes to zero. Show this. [*Hint*: With $\mathbf{R} = x\mathbf{i} + y\mathbf{j} + z\mathbf{k}$, the box initially has corners at $\mathbf{R}$, $\mathbf{R} + \Delta x\mathbf{i}$, $\mathbf{R} + \Delta y\mathbf{j}$, $\mathbf{R} + \Delta z\mathbf{k}$, etc. After time Δt these corners have moved to the new positions $\mathbf{R} + \mathbf{F}(x, y, z)\,\Delta t$, $\mathbf{R} + \Delta x\,\mathbf{i} + \mathbf{F}(x + \Delta x, y, z)\,\Delta t$, $\mathbf{R} + \Delta y\mathbf{j} + \mathbf{F}(x, y + \Delta y, z)\,\Delta t$, $\mathbf{R} + \Delta z\,\mathbf{k} + \mathbf{F}(x, y, z + \Delta z)\,\Delta t$, etc. Calculate the new volume using the triple scalar product, and compute the limit described above.]

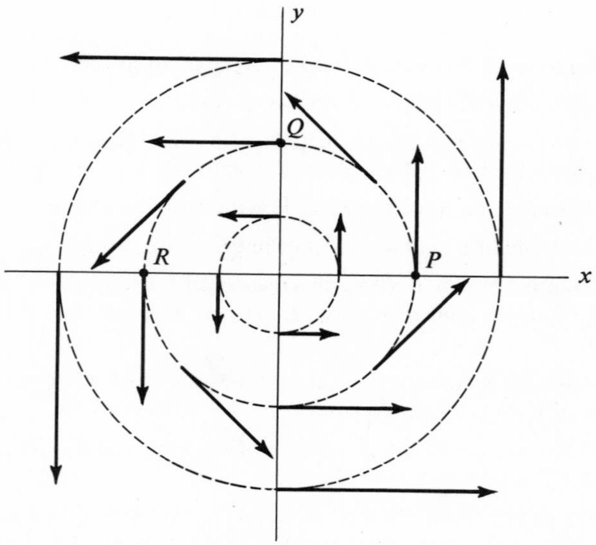

FIGURE 3.9

3.4 CURL

As in the previous section, we shall preface our formal definition of the curl of a vector field with some heuristic considerations. Once again, it is convenient to imagine that **F** represents the velocity field of a fluid. For convenience let us think of the fluid as an incompressible liquid having a fairly high mass density. Now let us imagine we have a little paddle wheel, something like that shown in Fig. 3.10, that is free to rotate about its axis AA'.

Imagine that we immerse this paddle wheel in the liquid. Because of the flow of the liquid, it will tend to rotate with some angular velocity. This angular velocity will vary, depending on where we locate the paddle wheel and on the positioning of its axis. For definiteness we shall try to compute the angular velocity with the paddle wheel lined up along the z axis.

The mechanism which rotates the wheel is provided by the tendency of the fluid to *swirl* around the z axis; this motion is due to the counterclockwise components of the velocity near the axis. If we impose a polar coordinate system centered around the paddle wheel axis, as in Fig. 3.11, then the counterclockwise component of **F** at the point (r,θ) is given by $\mathbf{F} \cdot \mathbf{u}_\theta$. This component of the velocity would turn a blade of the paddle wheel at an *angular* rate of $\mathbf{F} \cdot \mathbf{u}_\theta / r$, in radians per second. Of course, this rate will differ from point to point near the axis, so that the different blades of the wheel are "pushed" at different speeds. But it seems plausible to expect that if we took the *average* counterclockwise velocity component over a small circle around the

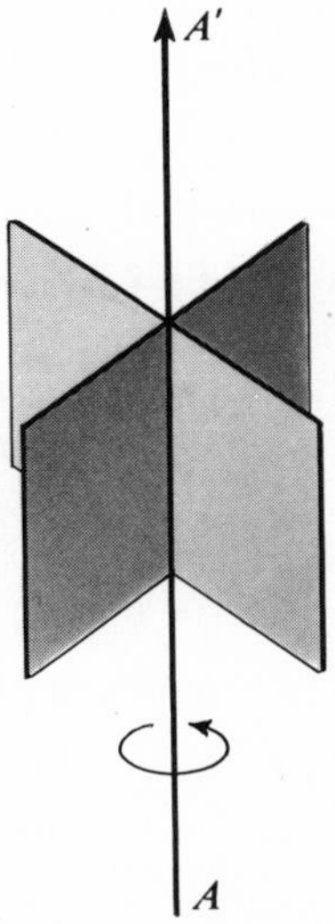

FIGURE 3.10

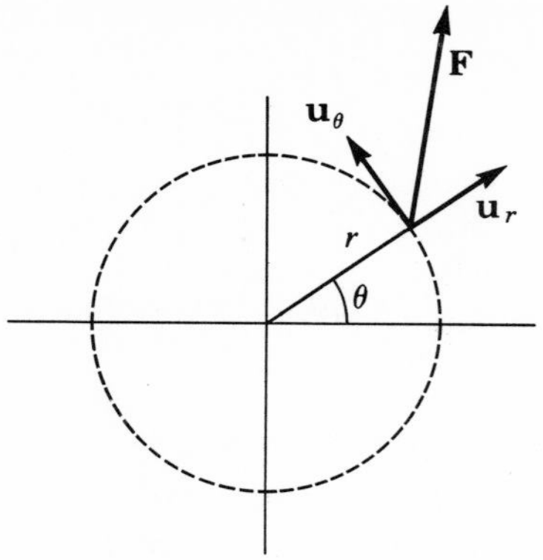

FIGURE 3.11

axis, and then divide by the radius of the circle, the quotient would give the angular velocity of the paddle wheel as a whole, whose blades we regard as rigidly fixed to each other.

Let us perform this computation. In Fig. 3.11 (x,y,z) are the coordinates of the center of the circle; the z axis comes out of the page towards the reader. At the point on the circle with coordinates $(x + \Delta x, y + \Delta y, z)$, the unit vector $\mathbf{u}_\theta$ is given in terms of the angle θ by

$$\mathbf{u}_\theta = -\sin\theta\,\mathbf{i} + \cos\theta\,\mathbf{j}$$

The components of the velocity $\mathbf{F}(x + \Delta x,\ y + \Delta y,\ z)$ at this point can be expressed, to an order of accuracy which improves as the circle becomes smaller, by

$$F_1(x + \Delta x,\ y + \Delta y,\ z) = F_1(x,y,z) + \frac{\partial F_1}{\partial x}\Delta x + \frac{\partial F_1}{\partial y}\Delta y$$

$$F_2(x + \Delta x,\ y + \Delta y,\ z) = F_2(x,y,z) + \frac{\partial F_2}{\partial x}\Delta x + \frac{\partial F_2}{\partial y}\Delta y$$

F_3 does not concern us, since we are only interested in the counterclockwise component $\mathbf{F} \cdot \mathbf{u}_\theta$. Expressing Δx and Δy in terms of r and θ,

$$\Delta x = r\cos\theta$$

$$\Delta y = r\sin\theta$$

we have, for the counterclockwise component of velocity at (r,θ) on the circle,

$$\mathbf{F} \cdot \mathbf{u}_\theta = -\left(F_1 + \frac{\partial F_1}{\partial x} r\cos\theta + \frac{\partial F_1}{\partial y} r\sin\theta\right)\sin\theta$$

$$+ \left(F_2 + \frac{\partial F_2}{\partial x} r\cos\theta + \frac{\partial F_2}{\partial y} r\sin\theta\right)\cos\theta$$

The average clockwise component around the circle will be

$$\frac{1}{2\pi}\int_0^{2\pi} \mathbf{F}\cdot\mathbf{u}_\theta \, d\theta$$

Since the integrals, over one period, of $\cos\theta$, $\sin\theta$, and $\sin\theta\cos\theta$ are zero, and since $\int_0^{2\pi}\cos^2\theta\,d\theta = \int_0^{2\pi}\sin^2\theta\,d\theta = \pi$, this average evaluated to be

$$\tfrac{1}{2}r\left(\frac{\partial F_2}{\partial x} - \frac{\partial F_1}{\partial y}\right)$$

and dividing by r, we conclude that *the angular velocity of the fluid about the z axis is*

$$\frac{1}{2}\left(\frac{\partial F_2}{\partial x} - \frac{\partial F_1}{\partial y}\right)$$

The computation of the angular velocity about the x axis yields

$$\frac{1}{2}\left(\frac{\partial F_3}{\partial y} - \frac{\partial F_2}{\partial z}\right)$$

and, for the y axis,

$$\frac{1}{2}\left(\frac{\partial F_1}{\partial z} - \frac{\partial F_3}{\partial x}\right)$$

We want the curl of a vector field to express its tendency to swirl; so, dropping the factor $\frac{1}{2}$ for convenience we formulate the following definition:

The *curl* of a vector field $\mathbf{F} = F_1\mathbf{i} + F_2\mathbf{j} + F_3\mathbf{k}$ is the vector field

$$\left(\frac{\partial F_3}{\partial y} - \frac{\partial F_2}{\partial z}\right)\mathbf{i} + \left(\frac{\partial F_1}{\partial z} - \frac{\partial F_3}{\partial x}\right)\mathbf{j} + \left(\frac{\partial F_2}{\partial x} - \frac{\partial F_1}{\partial y}\right)\mathbf{k} \tag{3.10}$$

Rather than memorize (3.10), the student is advised to write the curl in the form of a symbolic determinant:

$$\mathbf{curl\ F} = \begin{vmatrix} \mathbf{i} & \mathbf{j} & \mathbf{k} \\ \dfrac{\partial}{\partial x} & \dfrac{\partial}{\partial y} & \dfrac{\partial}{\partial z} \\ F_1 & F_2 & F_3 \end{vmatrix} \tag{3.11}$$

Example 3.18 Find **curl F**, if $\mathbf{F} = xyz\mathbf{i} + x^2y^2z^2\mathbf{j} + y^2z^3\mathbf{k}$.

Solution

$$\mathbf{curl\ F} = \begin{vmatrix} \mathbf{i} & \mathbf{j} & \mathbf{k} \\ \dfrac{\partial}{\partial x} & \dfrac{\partial}{\partial y} & \dfrac{\partial}{\partial z} \\ xyz & x^2y^2z^2 & y^2z^3 \end{vmatrix} = (2yz^3 - 2x^2y^2z)\mathbf{i} + (xy)\mathbf{j} + (2xy^2z^2 - xz)\mathbf{k}$$

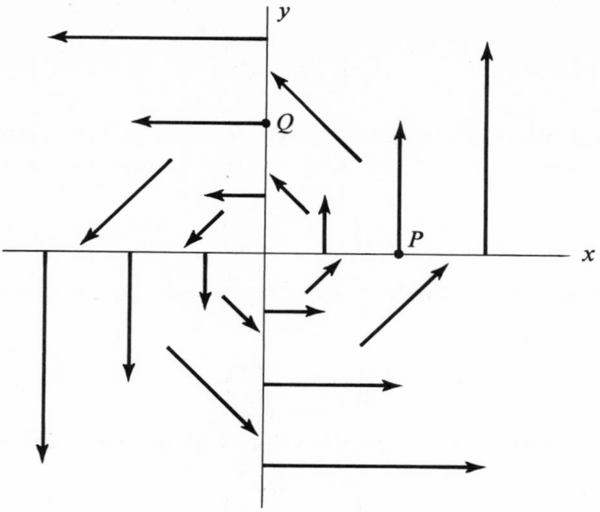

FIGURE 3.12

Example 3.19 Find **curl F** if $\mathbf{F} = x\mathbf{i} + y\mathbf{j} + z\mathbf{k}$.

Solution

$$\mathbf{curl\ F} = \begin{vmatrix} \mathbf{i} & \mathbf{j} & \mathbf{k} \\ \dfrac{\partial}{\partial x} & \dfrac{\partial}{\partial y} & \dfrac{\partial}{\partial z} \\ x & y & z \end{vmatrix} = \mathbf{0}$$

Example 3.20 In what direction is **curl F** at points P and Q in Fig. 3.12? Assume that F_3 is identically zero and that there is no variation in **F** in the z direction. (This is the velocity field for a rigid rotation, and is the same as that shown in Fig. 3.9.)

Solution It should be clear from our discussion that **curl F** points in the $+z$ direction. Using the formal definition, observe that at the point P, F_2 is increasing in the x direction, so $\partial F_2/\partial x$ is positive. Although F_1 is zero at P, it is positive below P and negative above, so F_1 is decreasing as we move through P in the y direction, that is, $\partial F_1/\partial y$ is negative. Since we assume F_3 identically zero, the derivatives $\partial F_3/\partial y$ and $\partial F_3/\partial x$ are also zero, and since we assume no variation in the z direction, $\partial F_2/\partial z$ and $\partial F_1/\partial z$ are zero. It follows that the only term in (3.10) that does not vanish is the last term, and that the last term is positive.

At point Q, F_2 is zero, but it is negative to the left of Q and positive to the right, hence $\partial F_2/\partial x$ is positive. F_1 is negative at Q and is becoming even more negative with increasing y, and so $\partial F_1/\partial y$ is negative. The term $(\partial F_2/\partial x - \partial F_1/\partial y)$ is therefore positive. The other derivatives in (3.10) equal zero. It follows that **curl F** at point Q is also perpendicular to the xy plane, directed toward the reader. (In fact, a little reflection will convince the reader that **curl F** at point P is equal to **curl F** at point Q.)

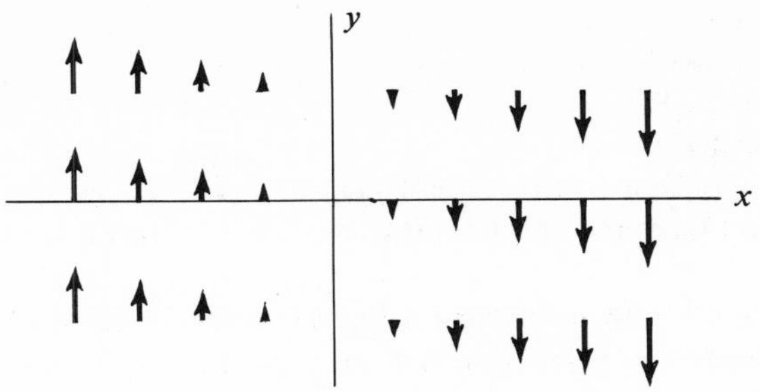

FIGURE 3.13

Example 3.21 In what direction is **curl F**, if **F** is as shown in Fig. 3.13?

Solution Since **F** is directed parallel to the y axis and appears to have magnitude proportional to x, we can guess $\mathbf{F} = Cx\mathbf{j}$, where C is a negative constant. Hence

$$\mathbf{curl\ F} = \begin{vmatrix} \mathbf{i} & \mathbf{j} & \mathbf{k} \\ \dfrac{\partial}{\partial x} & \dfrac{\partial}{\partial y} & \dfrac{\partial}{\partial z} \\ 0 & Cx & 0 \end{vmatrix} = C\mathbf{k}$$

Since C is negative, the curl is directed into the page (negative z direction).

In Fig. 3.13, the paddle wheel would tend to rotate most rapidly with its axis perpendicular to the page; it will rotate because the velocity of the fluid is greater on one side than on the other. The direction of the curl is into the page, because the paddle wheel will tend to rotate clockwise. This example shows that it is possible for a vector field to have nonzero curl even when the flow lines are straight lines; hence, to describe **curl F** as "a measure of the rate of swirling of **F**" is not completely accurate.

Example 3.22 Let us imagine that **F** represents the velocity field of a fluid of constant mass density rotating with uniform angular velocity ω about the z axis. Find **curl F**. (Assume the angular velocity vector $\boldsymbol{\omega}$ to point in the positive z direction.)

Solution Since $\boldsymbol{\omega} = \omega\mathbf{k}$, we have (Sec. 1.12) $\mathbf{F} = \omega\mathbf{k} \times \mathbf{R}$, where $\mathbf{R} = x\mathbf{i} + y\mathbf{j} + z\mathbf{k}$. Hence $\mathbf{F} = -\omega y\mathbf{i} + \omega x\mathbf{j}$. Using (3.11) we find that $\mathbf{curl\ F} = 2\omega\mathbf{k}$. As we expected, the curl of **F** is just twice the angular velocity vector; in this situation, it is the same at every point in space.

EXERCISES

In Exercises 1 through 3, find **curl F**:

1. $\mathbf{F} = xy^2\mathbf{i} + xy\mathbf{j} + xy\mathbf{k}$

2. $\mathbf{F} = e^{xy}\mathbf{i} + \sin xy\,\mathbf{j} + \cos yz^2\,\mathbf{k}$

3. $\mathbf{F} = z^2x\mathbf{i} + y^2z\mathbf{j} - z^2y\mathbf{k}$
4. Given the vector field $\mathbf{F} = (x + xz^2)\mathbf{i} + xy\mathbf{j} + yz\mathbf{k}$,
   (a) evaluate div **F**,
   (b) evaluate **curl F**.
5. Draw a rough picture of the vector field $\mathbf{F} = x\mathbf{i} + y\mathbf{j} + z\mathbf{k}$ and, thinking of the paddle wheel interpretation of **curl F**, explain why **curl F** is identically zero in this case.
6. Give an example of a vector field with curl identically equal to $2\mathbf{i}$.
7. The flow lines of a velocity field **F** are straight lines. Does this imply that **curl F** $= \mathbf{0}$?
8. Is it possible to tell anything about **curl F**, given only a description of the flow lines of **F**?
9. (*Review*) Write down, in your own words, the geometrical or physical significance of **grad** f, div **F**, and **curl F**. Avoid vague nonsense such as "divergence is represented by water spraying out of a nozzle" or "curl is what you get when you stir coffee in a cup".

3.5 DEL NOTATION

To understand properly the notion of an "operator" it is necessary to take a broader look at the concept of a "function". For this reason we digress momentarily to consider what is meant by a function.

In elementary calculus, the functions considered are usually "real-valued functions of a real variable". That is, a function f is a rule that associates with every real number x in its domain of definition a single real number $f(x)$. For example, the exponential function is defined for all x, and to each real number x associates a single real number e^x. We define this function by writing $f(x) = e^x$. Other functions are defined by writing, say, $f(x) = x^2$ or $f(x) = \sin x$. Most mathematicians nowadays distinguish rather carefully between the symbol f and the notation $f(x)$. The former denotes the function and the latter denotes the value of the function (which is a number and not a function). Thus if $f(x) = x^2$, the function f is the *rule* "square the given number", but $f(3)$ is the *number* 9.

In more advanced courses we meet functions of two or three variables. In this book "scalar fields" are simply real-valued functions of three real variables. Thus, the function f defined by $f(x,y,z) = x^2y^2z^2$ says "multiply together the squares of the given numbers". When used alone, in this context, the letter f denotes this *rule*, but if we write, say, $f(2,1,3)$, we mean the *value* of the function at the point $(2,1,3)$, which in this case is the number 36.

Most of the functions we have been considering in this chapter are described by expressions involving x, y, and z. In studying vector analysis it is useful to "visualize" such functions in geometrical or physical terms. Thus, the engineering student may think of "an arbitrary function f" as meaning "an arbitrary electric potential", or "an arbitrary temperature distribution", and the mathematics major may think of this as meaning "a rule whereby we tag each point in space with a number". The student who thinks of a function as a jumble of x's, y's, and z's doesn't have much fun, and misses much of the point.

The *vector* fields we discuss are *vector-valued* functions of three real variables. But the idea is still much the same. In this context, a function $\mathbf{F}$ is a *rule* that associates with each point (x,y,z) a single vector $\mathbf{F}(x,y,z)$.

But now we come to what is a big hurdle for some students: passing to the *general* notion of a function. Much of the mystery of modern mathematics vanishes when we realize that a mathematician uses the word "function" in a much more general way, to denote any rule that associates an object with each one of a class of objects. Thus we have not only functions that associate numbers with numbers (the functions of elementary calculus), number with points in space (scalar fields), and vectors with points in space (vector fields), but also those that associate *functions* with *functions*.

Partly for reasons of convenience, but mainly (we suspect) because so many people have old-fashioned ideas of what the word "function" means, such functions are usually called "operators". An operator is simply a rule that associates a function of some kind with each one of a particular class of functions.

To take an example from elementary calculus, the process of differentiation defines what is called the derivative operator. This is the operator that associates with every differentiable function f its derivative df/dx. This operator is sometimes denoted d/dx or sometimes, even more simply, D. It converts each differentiable function f into its derivative. We may formally write this

$$D(f) = \frac{df}{dx}$$

Some textbooks assume that the reader is incapable of understanding even so simple a concept as the derivative operator. In these textbooks it is said that D is simply an abbreviation for d/dx, and that the symbol d/dx means nothing by itself, having meaning only when it is applied to some function f. Then we may write df/dx, which of course we all understand. Other differential operators, such as $L = (d^2/dx^2) + 2(d/dx) + 4$, are similarly interpreted as symbols that are meaningless unless followed by a function. In this case we have

$$L(f) = \frac{d^2 f}{dx^2} + 2\frac{df}{dx} + 4f$$

This is to miss the whole point of the operator concept, however. It would be much better to visualize this operator as a sort of meatgrinder, into which we drop the function f, turn the handle, and out drops the function $(d^2f/dx^2) + 2(df/dx) + 4f$. There is really no insurmountable difficulty in understanding that an operator T is a *rule* that associates with a function f some other function (or possibly even the same function) $T(f)$. It is certainly idiotic to say that the symbol d/dx means nothing by itself. It means a great deal: it represents the rule whereby we associate with a differentiable function its derivative. There is no point in recounting here the basic definition of "derivative" or the innumerable techniques involved in actually computing a derivative. The point is that a differentiable function has a derivative and the derivative operator pairs the derivative with the function. (The excellent concept of "pairing" is used in many modern books in discussing the function concept. The derivative of a function is just another function, and the derivative operator is the mathematical twine that binds the two together.)

Another example of an operator is the *gradient*. We recall that the gradient of a scalar field f is a vector field **grad** f. The gradient operator may be written, symbolically,

$$\mathbf{i}\frac{\partial}{\partial x} + \mathbf{j}\frac{\partial}{\partial y} + \mathbf{k}\frac{\partial}{\partial z}$$

Divergence is also an operator. It is an operator that converts a vector field into a scalar field. Similarly, *curl* is an operator, but it is an operator that changes a vector field into another vector field.

The three operators that concern us most are gradient, divergence, and curl. Although they may be written **grad**, div, and **curl**, there is a suggestive and convenient symbolic way of writing them that is commonly used. For this purpose, we introduce the symbol ∇, called "del" (sometimes "nabla"), which is an abbreviation for $\mathbf{i}(\partial/\partial x) + \mathbf{j}(\partial/\partial y) + \mathbf{k}(\partial/\partial z)$. In terms of this symbol, we can write **grad** f as ∇f. Working with ∇ purely formally, pretending for the moment it is a vector, we see that if we form the scalar product of ∇ with a vector field $\mathbf{F}$, we obtain

$$\begin{aligned}\nabla \cdot \mathbf{F} &= \left(\mathbf{i}\frac{\partial}{\partial x} + \mathbf{j}\frac{\partial}{\partial y} + \mathbf{k}\frac{\partial}{\partial z}\right) \cdot (\mathbf{i}F_1 + \mathbf{j}F_2 + \mathbf{k}F_3) \\ &= \frac{\partial F_1}{\partial x} + \frac{\partial F_2}{\partial y} + \frac{\partial F_3}{\partial z}\end{aligned}$$

which is the divergence of $\mathbf{F}$. Similarly, if we imagine ∇ to be a vector and form the vector cross product of ∇ with $\mathbf{F}$, we obtain the curl of $\mathbf{F}$:

$$\begin{aligned}\nabla \times \mathbf{F} &= \left(\mathbf{i}\frac{\partial}{\partial x} + \mathbf{j}\frac{\partial}{\partial y} + \mathbf{k}\frac{\partial}{\partial z}\right) \times (\mathbf{i}F_1 + \mathbf{j}F_2 + \mathbf{k}F_3) \\ &= \begin{vmatrix} \mathbf{i} & \mathbf{j} & \mathbf{k} \\ \dfrac{\partial}{\partial x} & \dfrac{\partial}{\partial y} & \dfrac{\partial}{\partial z} \\ F_1 & F_2 & F_3 \end{vmatrix} = \mathbf{curl\ F}\end{aligned}$$

To recapitulate, ∇ is an abbreviation,

$$\nabla = \mathbf{i}\frac{\partial}{\partial x} + \mathbf{j}\frac{\partial}{\partial y} + \mathbf{k}\frac{\partial}{\partial z} \tag{3.12}$$

The symbols ∇f, $\nabla \cdot \mathbf{F}$, and $\nabla \times \mathbf{F}$ are defined by

$$\nabla f = \mathbf{grad}\ f \tag{3.13}$$

$$\nabla \cdot \mathbf{F} = \text{div}\ \mathbf{F} \tag{3.14}$$

$$\nabla \times \mathbf{F} = \mathbf{curl}\ \mathbf{F} \tag{3.15}$$

After (3.12) is memorized, formulas (3.13), (3.14), and (3.15) provide very convenient ways of remembering the expressions for gradient, divergence, and curl. We just operate with ∇ as though it were a vector. Henceforth we will use these abbreviations frequently.

EXERCISES

1. If $f(x,y,z) = x^2y + z$, what is $f(2,3,4)$?

2. If $f(x,y,z) = x^2y + z$, what is the value of ∇f at (2,3,4)?

3. If $g(t) = t^3$ and $f(x,y,z) = x^2 + y^2z$, what is $g[f(1,1,3)]$?

4. Given $\mathbf{F}(x,y,z) = x^2y\mathbf{i} + z\mathbf{j} - (x + y - z)\mathbf{k}$, find
  (a) $\nabla \cdot \mathbf{F}$
  (b) $\nabla \times \mathbf{F}$
  (c) $\nabla(\nabla \cdot \mathbf{F})$

5. If $\mathbf{F}$ is a vector field, is $\nabla \cdot (\nabla \times \mathbf{F})$ a scalar field or a vector field?

6. If $\mathbf{F}$ is a vector field, is $\nabla \times (\nabla \times \mathbf{F})$ a scalar field or a vector field?

7. Find $\nabla \cdot \mathbf{R}$ and $\nabla \times \mathbf{R}$ where $\mathbf{R} = x\mathbf{i} + y\mathbf{j} + z\mathbf{k}$.

8. If $f(x,y,z) = xyz + e^{xz}$, find $\nabla \cdot (\nabla f)$.

9. (a) Compute $\nabla \times (\nabla f)$ for the scalar field f defined in Exercise 8.
  (b) Now do the same thing for another scalar field f (use any of the scalar fields defined in preceding problems, or make one up yourself).
  (c) What can you conjecture from this?

10. (a) Compute $\nabla \cdot (\nabla \times \mathbf{F})$ for the vector field $\mathbf{F}$ defined in Exercise 4.
  (b) Do the same for a vector field $\mathbf{F}$ that you have made up yourself.
  (c) What can you conjecture from this?

3.6 THE LAPLACIAN

In electrostatics, the gradient of the electric potential is a scalar multiple of the electric field intensity, and the divergence of the electric intensity is related to the charge density. For this and other reasons it is convenient to introduce a single operator that is the composite of the two operators **grad** and div. This operator is called the *laplacian*.

The laplacian of a scalar field f is defined to be div (**grad** f). Note that **grad** f is a vector field and the divergence of **grad** f is a scalar field; hence the laplacian of a scalar field f is a scalar field. In del notation this is $\nabla \cdot (\nabla f)$ and for simplicity is frequently written $\nabla^2 f$. Some authors write Δf.

We have

$$\text{laplacian}\,(f) = \nabla^2 f = \nabla \cdot (\nabla f) = \frac{\partial^2 f}{\partial x^2} + \frac{\partial^2 f}{\partial y^2} + \frac{\partial^2 f}{\partial z^2} \tag{3.16}$$

since

$$\nabla \cdot (\nabla f) = \nabla \cdot \left(\frac{\partial f}{\partial x}\mathbf{i} + \frac{\partial f}{\partial y}\mathbf{j} + \frac{\partial f}{\partial z}\mathbf{k}\right) = \frac{\partial^2 f}{\partial x^2} + \frac{\partial^2 f}{\partial y^2} + \frac{\partial^2 f}{\partial z^2}$$

The symbol ∇^2 may be considered to be simply an abbreviation for

$$\frac{\partial^2}{\partial x^2} + \frac{\partial^2}{\partial y^2} + \frac{\partial^2}{\partial z^2}$$

The equation

$$\nabla^2 f = 0 \tag{3.17}$$

is called *Laplace's equation*. Any function satisfying this equation in a given region is said to be *harmonic* in that region. For example, the electric potential of a static distribution of charges is harmonic in any region where the charge density is zero. A function describing the steady-state temperature distribution of a homogeneous material is harmonic in the interior of the region occupied by the material.

The laplacian operator is by far the most important differential operator in mathematical physics. In this section we discuss its intuitive meaning without giving proofs.

If f is a scalar, then $\nabla^2 f(x,y,z)$ denotes the value of $\nabla^2 f$ at the point (x,y,z). This is a number that tells us something about the behavior of the scalar field in the vicinity of (x,y,z). Roughly speaking, it provides a measure of the *difference between the average value of the field in the immediate neighborhood of the point and the precise value of the field at the point.*

(The word "average" here refers to an average over a region of space, not to a time average. Variations with time t do not enter into the calculation of $\nabla^2 f$.)

Thus, if $\nabla^2 f$ is positive at a point, and f denotes the temperature, this means that the temperature in the vicinity of the point is, on the average, greater than the temperature at the point itself. In particular, if the temperature takes its minimum value at a certain point in space, it is reasonable to expect that the value of $\nabla^2 f$ will *not* be negative at that point. In this respect, the laplacian can be viewed as a sort of three-dimensional generalization of the ordinary operator d^2/dx^2, which is used in elementary calculus to test extreme points to see if they represent maxima or minima.

If $\nabla^2 f$ is identically zero, the average value of f throughout any sphere (or any cube) will be exactly equal to the value of f at the center of the sphere (or cube). This is an important property of harmonic functions.

Suppose that (x,y,z) is a fixed point in space, and that $\bar{f}$ denotes the mean value of f throughout the interior of a sphere (or cube) with center at (x,y,z). If this sphere (or cube) is sufficiently small, we will have (approximately)

$$\bar{f} - f(x,y,z) = K\nabla^2 f(x,y,z) \tag{3.18}$$

where K is a positive constant depending only on the dimensions of the sphere or cube. For a sphere, $K = R^2/10$, where R is the radius of the sphere. If a cube, we have $K = a^2/24$, where a is the length of the side of the cube.

Relation (3.18) is exact only in one very special instance: when $\nabla^2 f$ is a constant, independent of x, y, and z. It is approximate otherwise, but the approximation is fairly good in some sense if the sphere or cube is sufficiently small. Numerical analysts use an expression similar to (3.18), but the author knows of no practical application of (3.18) itself. However, it is very helpful in giving an intuitive meaning to expressions containing the laplacian.

The formal differential operator

$$\nabla^2 = \frac{\partial^2}{\partial x^2} + \frac{\partial^2}{\partial y^2} + \frac{\partial^2}{\partial z^2}$$

may also be applied to *vector* fields to obtain new vector fields, since if **F** is a *vector* field, $(\partial^2\mathbf{F}/\partial x^2) + (\partial^2\mathbf{F}/\partial y^2) + (\partial^2\mathbf{F}/\partial z^2)$ makes perfectly good sense. For example, if

$$\mathbf{F} = x^2y\mathbf{i} + y^2z^3\mathbf{j} + xyz^4\mathbf{k}$$

then we have

$$\frac{\partial^2\mathbf{F}}{\partial x^2} = 2y\mathbf{i}$$

$$\frac{\partial^2\mathbf{F}}{\partial y^2} = 2z^3\mathbf{j}$$

$$\frac{\partial^2\mathbf{F}}{\partial z^2} = 6y^2z\mathbf{j} + 12xyz^2\mathbf{k}$$

whence $\nabla^2\mathbf{F} = 2y\mathbf{i} + (2z^3 + 6y^2z)\mathbf{j} + 12xyz^2\mathbf{k}$. When used in this sense, to operate on vector fields to produce vector fields, we will call ∇^2 the *vector* laplacian operator. But note that ∇^2 used in this context no longer is the same as div **grad**, since if **F** is a *vector* field, **grad F** (and hence div **grad F**) does not make sense within the context of vector analysis.

EXERCISES

1. Find $\nabla^2 f$, given that $f(x,y,z) = x^5yz^3$.

2. Find $\nabla^2 f$, given that $f(x,y,z) = 1/(x^2 + y^2 + z^2)^{1/2}$.

3. Find $\nabla^2 \mathbf{F}$, given that $\mathbf{F}(x,y,z) = 3\mathbf{i} + \mathbf{j} - x^2y^3z^4\mathbf{k}$.

4. Which of the following functions satisfy Laplace's equation?
(a) $f(x,y,z) = e^z \sin y$
(b) $f(x,y,z) = \sin x \sinh y + \cos x \cosh z$
(c) $f(x,y,z) = \sin px \sinh qy$ (p and q are constants)

5. Tell whether each of the following is a vector field or a scalar field, given that f is a scalar field and $\mathbf{F}$ is a vector field. Two of the expressions are meaningless; determine which two.
(a) ∇f
(b) $\nabla \cdot \mathbf{F}$
(c) $\nabla \times \mathbf{F}$
(d) $\nabla \cdot (\nabla f)$
(e) $\nabla \times (\nabla f)$
(f) $\nabla \times f$
(g) $\nabla^2 \mathbf{F}$
(h) $\nabla \times (\nabla^2 \mathbf{F})$
(i) $\nabla \times (\nabla^2 f)$
(j) $\nabla(\nabla^2 f)$

6. (a) Show that, if f and g satisfy Laplace's equation, $f + g$ does also.
(b) Find a function satisfying Laplace's equation and also the following identities: $f(0,y,z) = 0$, $f(x,0,z) = 0$, $f(\pi,y,z) = 0$, $f(x,5,z) = \sin x + \sin 2x$. [*Hint*: Use 6(a) and 4(c) to guess an answer.]

3.7 VECTOR IDENTITIES

Although we continue to use the del notation, formally manipulating

$$\nabla = \mathbf{i}\frac{\partial}{\partial x} + \mathbf{j}\frac{\partial}{\partial y} + \mathbf{k}\frac{\partial}{\partial z}$$

as though it were a vector, this practice has certain hazards. Keep in mind that the derivative operators appearing in the del operator act only on functions appearing to the right of the del operator.

For example, supposing that

$$\mathbf{F} = x^3y\mathbf{i} + y^2\mathbf{j} + x^2z\mathbf{k} \qquad \mathbf{R} = x\mathbf{i} + y\mathbf{j} + z\mathbf{k}$$

let us compare the two expressions $(\nabla \cdot \mathbf{R})\mathbf{F}$ and $(\mathbf{R} \cdot \nabla)\mathbf{F}$. For the first of these we have

$$(\nabla \cdot \mathbf{R})\mathbf{F} = 3\mathbf{F} = 3x^3y\mathbf{i} + 3y^2\mathbf{j} + 3x^2z\mathbf{k}$$

On the other hand, in the second expression, $\mathbf{R}$ is to the left of ∇, and therefore the derivatives in the del operator do not act on $\mathbf{R}$. We have

$$\begin{aligned}(\mathbf{R} \cdot \nabla)\mathbf{F} &= \left(x\frac{\partial}{\partial x} + y\frac{\partial}{\partial y} + z\frac{\partial}{\partial z}\right)(x^3y\mathbf{i} + y^2\mathbf{j} + x^2z\mathbf{k})\\ &= x(3x^2y\mathbf{i} + 2xz\mathbf{k}) + y(x^3\mathbf{i} + 2y\mathbf{j}) + z(x^2\mathbf{k})\\ &= 4x^3y\mathbf{i} + 2y^2\mathbf{j} + 3x^2z\mathbf{k}\end{aligned}$$

To further confuse matters, parentheses are sometimes omitted; the reader must supply such parentheses as necessary to make the expression meaningful. For example, $\nabla \cdot \mathbf{RF}$ and $\mathbf{R} \cdot \nabla\mathbf{F}$ must mean $(\nabla \cdot \mathbf{R})\mathbf{F}$ and $(\mathbf{R} \cdot \nabla)\mathbf{F}$ respectively, since $\nabla \cdot (\mathbf{RF})$ and $\mathbf{R} \cdot (\nabla\mathbf{F})$ do not make sense within the framework of vector analysis. (Some books introduce the notion of a *dyadic* in order to assign a meaning to such expressions as $\nabla\mathbf{F}$. We do not discuss dyadics in this book.)

Similarly, $\nabla \cdot f\mathbf{F}$ means $\nabla \cdot (f\mathbf{F})$, simply the divergence of $f\mathbf{F}$, since $\nabla \cdot f$, and hence $(\nabla \cdot f)\mathbf{F}$, is meaningless.

In some cases where parentheses are omitted, two interpretations are possible, both of which make sense. For example, if $\mathbf{A} = A_1\mathbf{i} + A_2\mathbf{j} + A_3\mathbf{k}$ is a vector field and f is a scalar field, both $(\mathbf{A} \cdot \nabla)f$ and $\mathbf{A} \cdot (\nabla f)$ are meaningful and are sometimes written $\mathbf{A} \cdot \nabla f$. This is because both interpretations lead to exactly the same final result. We have

$$(\mathbf{A} \cdot \nabla)f = \left(A_1 \frac{\partial}{\partial x} + A_2 \frac{\partial}{\partial y} + A_3 \frac{\partial}{\partial z}\right)f = A_1 \frac{\partial f}{\partial x} + A_2 \frac{\partial f}{\partial y} + A_3 \frac{\partial f}{\partial z}$$

and also

$$\mathbf{A} \cdot (\nabla f) = \mathbf{A} \cdot \left(\frac{\partial f}{\partial x}\mathbf{i} + \frac{\partial f}{\partial y}\mathbf{j} + \frac{\partial f}{\partial z}\mathbf{k}\right) = A_1 \frac{\partial f}{\partial x} + A_2 \frac{\partial f}{\partial y} + A_3 \frac{\partial f}{\partial z}$$

both of them equal.

Because of the convention adopted above it is especially important to preserve order in working with ∇. For instance, $\nabla \cdot \mathbf{A}$ is a scalar field, simply the divergence of $\mathbf{A}$, but $\mathbf{A} \cdot \nabla$ is the differential operator

$$A_1 \frac{\partial}{\partial x} + A_2 \frac{\partial}{\partial y} + A_3 \frac{\partial}{\partial z}$$

a horse of quite a different color.

We now list a number of identities. Here $\mathbf{F}$ and $\mathbf{G}$ denote vector fields, ϕ denotes a scalar field, and $\mathbf{R} = x\mathbf{i} + y\mathbf{j} + z\mathbf{k}$. Their proofs vary in character and difficulty, and we discuss them below.

$$\nabla(\phi_1\phi_2) = \phi_1\nabla\phi_2 + \phi_2\nabla\phi_1 \tag{3.19}$$

$$\nabla \cdot \phi\mathbf{F} = \phi\nabla \cdot \mathbf{F} + \mathbf{F} \cdot \nabla\phi \tag{3.20}$$

$$\nabla \times \phi\mathbf{F} = \phi\nabla \times \mathbf{F} + \nabla\phi \times \mathbf{F} \tag{3.21}$$

$$\nabla f(u) = \frac{df}{du}\nabla u \tag{3.22}$$

$$\nabla \cdot \mathbf{R} = 3 \tag{3.23}$$

$$\nabla \times \mathbf{R} = \mathbf{0} \tag{3.24}$$

$$\nabla(|\mathbf{R}|^n) = n\,|\mathbf{R}|^{n-2}\mathbf{R} \tag{3.25}$$

$$\mathbf{F} \cdot \nabla\mathbf{R} = \mathbf{F} \tag{3.26}$$

$$\nabla(\mathbf{A} \cdot \mathbf{R}) = \mathbf{A} \qquad \text{if } \mathbf{A} \text{ is constant} \tag{3.27}$$

$$\nabla \cdot (\mathbf{F} \times \mathbf{G}) = \mathbf{G} \cdot (\nabla \times \mathbf{F}) - \mathbf{F} \cdot (\nabla \times \mathbf{G}) \tag{3.28}$$

$$\nabla \times (\mathbf{F} \times \mathbf{G}) = (\mathbf{G} \cdot \nabla)\mathbf{F} - (\mathbf{F} \cdot \nabla)\mathbf{G} + (\nabla \cdot \mathbf{G})\mathbf{F} - (\nabla \cdot \mathbf{F})\mathbf{G} \tag{3.29}$$

$$\nabla \times (\nabla \times \mathbf{F}) = \nabla(\nabla \cdot \mathbf{F}) - \nabla^2 \mathbf{F} \tag{3.30}$$

$$\nabla(\mathbf{F} \cdot \mathbf{G}) = (\mathbf{F} \cdot \nabla)\mathbf{G} + (\mathbf{G} \cdot \nabla)\mathbf{F} + \mathbf{F} \times (\nabla \times \mathbf{G}) + \mathbf{G} \times (\nabla \times \mathbf{F}) \tag{3.31}$$

$$\nabla \times \nabla(\phi) = \mathbf{0} \tag{3.32}$$

$$\nabla \cdot (\nabla \times \mathbf{F}) = 0 \tag{3.33}$$

$$\nabla \cdot (\nabla\phi_1 \times \nabla\phi_2) = 0 \tag{3.34}$$

Identities (3.19), (3.20), and (3.21) are very simple. They are based on the formula expressing the derivative of a product as the sum of two terms, each containing the derivative of one factor. Any of these is easy to verify componentwise. For instance, the z component of $\nabla \times \phi\mathbf{F}$ is

$$\frac{\partial}{\partial x}(\phi F_2) - \frac{\partial}{\partial y}(\phi F_1)$$

Breaking this up, we see that this is ϕ times the z component of $\nabla \times \mathbf{F}$, plus the z component of $(\nabla\phi) \times \mathbf{F}$.

Identity (3.22) expresses the chain rule; its x component merely says

$$\frac{\partial}{\partial x} f(u) = \frac{df}{du}\frac{\partial u}{\partial x}$$

It can be generalized to functions of more than one variable. For example, if u_1 and u_2 are functions of x, y, and z and if f is a function of u_1 and u_2, then we have

$$\nabla f(u_1,u_2) = \frac{\partial f}{\partial u_1}\nabla u_1 + \frac{\partial f}{\partial u_2}\nabla u_2$$

Identities (3.23) through (3.27), which involve the vector $\mathbf{R}$, are quite trivial but occasionally useful.

Identities (3.28) through (3.31) involve the interplay of the vector and differential properties of ∇, and they are quite complex. Any of them can be verified by laboriously working out the components, and we cheerfully invite the devoted student to do so. In the next (optional) section on tensor notation we will use some heavy notational machinery to derive these equations more efficiently. However, we would like to mention a heuristic device for guessing at the form of the identities.

Let's take identity (3.28), and go to work on

$$\nabla \cdot (\mathbf{F} \times \mathbf{G}) \tag{3.35}$$

We know that, as far as the *vector* nature of the triple scalar product is concerned, we can interchange the dot and the cross. Thus we suspect that the expression (3.35) is equal to

$$(\nabla \times \mathbf{F}) \cdot \mathbf{G} \tag{3.36}$$

However, we must interpret (3.36) in an unconventional manner, namely, the operator ∇ must continue to differentiate *both* **F** *and* **G** [and not merely **F**, as (3.36) dictates]. So to be correct we must split (3.36) into two terms, analogous to the splitting in differentiating a product. The term where **F** alone is differentiated can be expressed unambiguously as

$$\mathbf{G} \cdot (\nabla \times \mathbf{F}) \tag{3.37}$$

To get the term where **G** is differentiated, we "rewrite" (3.36) as

$$-(\nabla \times \mathbf{G}) \cdot \mathbf{F} \tag{3.38}$$

which is consistent with the *vector* nature of the triple scalar product. Clearly from (3.38) we can display the part of the formula in which **G** is differentiated as

$$-\mathbf{F} \cdot (\nabla \times \mathbf{G}) \tag{3.39}$$

Thus we are led to guess that (3.35) equals (3.37) plus (3.39), in accordance with identity (3.28)!

Let us try this out again on formula (3.29). Using our old rule for $\mathbf{A} \times (\mathbf{B} \times \mathbf{C})$, we first write, *incorrectly*,

$$\nabla \times (\mathbf{F} \times \mathbf{G}) = (\nabla \cdot \mathbf{G})\mathbf{F} - (\nabla \cdot \mathbf{F})\mathbf{G} \tag{3.40}$$

This is incorrect because we must interpret ∇ as differentiating both **F** and **G** in each expression on the right. To break up this compound derivative and get a correct expression for "$(\nabla \cdot \mathbf{G})\mathbf{F}$", we observe that $(\nabla \cdot \mathbf{G})\mathbf{F}$, interpreted conventionally, gives the term in which **G** is differentiated, while $(\mathbf{G} \cdot \nabla)\mathbf{F}$ gives the term where **G** is treated as constant and we differentiate **F**. Handling the other term in (3.40) similarly, we propose that

$$\nabla \times (\mathbf{F} \times \mathbf{G}) = (\nabla \cdot \mathbf{G})\mathbf{F} + (\mathbf{G} \cdot \nabla)\mathbf{F} - (\nabla \cdot \mathbf{F})\mathbf{G} - (\mathbf{F} \cdot \nabla)\mathbf{G}$$

This is identity (3.29).

Clearly the above reasoning is tricky, but it can be very helpful in suggesting "which way to turn" in the derivation of complicated vector equations (such as those of electromagnetic theory). Suffice it to say that one always breathes easier after verifying any such "identity" in a mathematical handbook.

Identities (3.32), (3.33), and (3.34) are based on the appearance, in each case, of differences of mixed second derivatives. For example, the z component of $\nabla \times (\nabla\phi)$ is

$$\frac{\partial}{\partial x}\frac{\partial \phi}{\partial y} - \frac{\partial}{\partial y}\frac{\partial \phi}{\partial x}$$

It is well known from advanced calculus that such mixed derivatives are the same when taken in either order; hence these terms cancel. [To be rigorous, we should stipulate that ϕ and $\mathbf{F}$ possess *continuous second derivatives* when applying (3.32), (3.33), or (3.34).] A proof of the equality of the mixed partial derivatives appears in the Appendix.

Identity (3.22) has been included because, in this book, curvilinear coordinates are not discussed in detail until very late, and many people who use this book do not proceed that far. For such readers, the labor of computing a gradient can be reduced by using (3.22) and a little common sense, and the following example should be studied carefully by anyone in this category.

Example 3.23 Find the gradient of the scalar field f given by $f(r) = 1/r$, where r is the distance from the origin, i.e. $r = \sqrt{x^2 + y^2 + z^2}$.

Solution Since r is the distance from the origin, ∇r can be computed by using Properties 3.1 through 3.4. Obviously, r increases most rapidly in the direction away from the origin, so the direction of ∇r is the same as the direction of the position vector $\mathbf{R}$, which also points away from the origin. When we move in this direction, the rate of increase of r per unit distance is simply $dr/dr = 1$. So ∇r is a unit vector directed away from the origin, and hence equals $\mathbf{R}/|\mathbf{R}|$, which is the position vector divided by its own magnitude. That is,

$$\nabla r = \frac{\mathbf{R}}{|\mathbf{R}|} = \frac{x\mathbf{i} + y\mathbf{j} + z\mathbf{k}}{(x^2 + y^2 + z^2)^{1/2}}$$

Applying (3.22) to $f(r) = 1/r$, we have $\nabla f(r) = f'(r)\nabla r = (-1/r^2)\nabla r$, and, therefore,

$$\nabla\left(\frac{1}{r}\right) = \left(-\frac{1}{r^2}\right)\nabla r = -\frac{1}{r^2}\frac{\mathbf{R}}{|\mathbf{R}|} = -\frac{x\mathbf{i} + y\mathbf{j} + z\mathbf{k}}{(x^2 + y^2 + z^2)^{3/2}}$$

This looks complicated, but in spherical coordinates it is simply $-\mathbf{R}/r^3$. Readers familiar with electric fields will recognize this expression. Except for some physical constants, it is the electric field intensity due to a point charge located at the origin.

EXERCISES

1. Verify (3.19) and (3.20).
2. Verify (3.23) through (3.27).
3. Verify (3.32), (3.33), and (3.34).
4. "Derive" (3.30) heuristically.
5. Why is the following "identity" obviously not valid?

$$\nabla \cdot (\mathbf{F} \times \mathbf{G}) = \mathbf{G} \cdot (\nabla \times \mathbf{F}) + \mathbf{F} \cdot (\nabla \times \mathbf{G})$$

*3.8 TENSOR NOTATION

The operator ∇, considered as a vector operator, has components $\partial/\partial x$, $\partial/\partial y$, and $\partial/\partial z$. In tensor notation we adopt two conventions which enable us to absorb ∇ into our system painlessly. First, we designate coordinates by the triple (x_1,x_2,x_3) instead of (x,y,z); this makes the ith component of ∇ equal $\partial/\partial x_i$. Second, we abbreviate $\partial/\partial x_i$ by ∂_i. Now let us write down the tensor expressions for the concepts introduced in this chapter.

The ith component of the gradient of ϕ is $\partial_i \phi$.

The divergence of $\mathbf{F}$ is the scalar $\partial_i F_i$ (remember summation).

The ith component of the curl, $\nabla \times \mathbf{F}$, is $\varepsilon_{ijk}\, \partial_j F_k$ (recall the determinant expression for curl).

The laplacian of ϕ is $\partial_i \partial_i \phi$. We may write this as $\partial_i^2 \phi$ if we stipulate that the summation convention applies to *squared* terms, since they would have repeated subscripts if written out.

Now the proof of the identities of the last section can be carried out easily. To check identity (3.21), observe that the ith component of $\nabla \times \phi\mathbf{F}$ is

$$\varepsilon_{ijk}\, \partial_j (\phi F_k) = \varepsilon_{ijk}(\partial_j \phi)F_k + \varepsilon_{ijk}\phi\, \partial_j F_k$$

These terms we identify as the ith components of $\nabla\phi \times \mathbf{F}$ and $\phi\nabla \times \mathbf{F}$.

To check (3.26), observe that the ith component of $\mathbf{F} \cdot \nabla\mathbf{R}$ is $F_j\, \partial_j x_i$ (summing over j). But $\partial_j x_i = \delta_{ij}$, the Kronecker delta; so this expression is $F_j\, \delta_{ij} = F_i$, the ith component of $\mathbf{F}$.

The proof of formula (3.29) proceeds as follows:

$$\begin{aligned}
\varepsilon_{ijk}\, \partial_j (\mathbf{F} \times \mathbf{G})_k &= \varepsilon_{ijk}\, \partial_j (\varepsilon_{klm} F_l G_m) \\
&= \varepsilon_{ijk}\varepsilon_{klm}\, \partial_j (F_l G_m) \\
&= (\delta_{il}\, \delta_{jm} - \delta_{im}\, \delta_{jl})\, \partial_j (F_l G_m) \\
&= \partial_j (F_i G_j) - \partial_j (F_j G_i) \\
&= G_j\, \partial_j F_i + (\partial_j G_j)F_i - (\partial_j F_j)\, G_i - F_j\, \partial_j G_i \\
&= (\mathbf{G} \cdot \nabla)\mathbf{F}_i + (\nabla \cdot \mathbf{G})\mathbf{F}_i - (\nabla \cdot \mathbf{F})\mathbf{G}_i - (\mathbf{F} \cdot \nabla)\mathbf{G}_i
\end{aligned}$$

The proof of (3.31) is rather complicated. We begin by developing the obvious expression for the ith component of $\nabla(\mathbf{F} \cdot \mathbf{G})$:

$$\partial_i (F_j G_j) = F_j\, \partial_i G_j + G_j\, \partial_i F_j \tag{3.41}$$

Now we are stumped; the terms on the right seem to have no vector analogs. How can we identify the right-hand side of identity (3.31) here? The clue lies in the tensor expression for $\mathbf{F} \times (\nabla \times \mathbf{G})$; its ith component is

$$\begin{aligned}
\varepsilon_{ijk} F_j(\varepsilon_{klm}\, \partial_l G_m) &= \varepsilon_{ijk}\varepsilon_{klm} F_j\, \partial_l G_m \\
&= (\delta_{il}\, \delta_{jm} - \delta_{im}\, \delta_{jl})F_j\, \partial_l G_m \\
&= F_j\, \partial_i G_j - F_j\, \partial_j G_i
\end{aligned}$$

We observe the appearance of one of these "mystery" terms, $F_j \partial_i G_j$, plus the ith component of $-(\mathbf{F} \cdot \nabla)\mathbf{G}$. Transposing, we see that $F_j \partial_i G_j$ is the ith component of $\mathbf{F} \times (\nabla \times \mathbf{G}) + \mathbf{F} \cdot \nabla\mathbf{G}$. Putting this into Eq. (3.41) above, and using a similar expression for $G_j \partial_i F_j$, we get

$$\nabla(\mathbf{F} \cdot \mathbf{G}) = \mathbf{F} \times (\nabla \times \mathbf{G}) + \mathbf{F} \cdot \nabla\mathbf{G} + \mathbf{G} \times (\nabla \times \mathbf{F}) + \mathbf{G} \cdot \nabla\mathbf{F}$$

We have derived the identity.

The equality of mixed second derivatives of any (twice continuously differentiable) function can be expressed in tensor notation by the equation

$$\partial_j \partial_i \phi = \partial_i \partial_j \phi$$

or, simply

$$\partial_j \partial_i = \partial_i \partial_j$$

That is, the components of ∇ *commute* with each other. (Of course, they do not commute with functions: $\partial_i \phi$ is very different from $\phi \partial_i$.) This makes the verification of identities (3.32), (3.33), and (3.34) simple. For (3.34), we use ψ and χ for ϕ_1 and ϕ_2, in order not to confuse subscripts. We then have

$$\partial_i [\varepsilon_{ijk}(\partial_j \psi)(\partial_k \chi)] = \varepsilon_{ijk}(\partial_i \partial_j \psi)(\partial_k \chi) + \varepsilon_{ijk}(\partial_j \psi)(\partial_i \partial_k \chi)$$

Because of the antisymmetric nature of ε_{ijk}, as we sum over i and j the terms $\partial_i \partial_j \psi$ and $\partial_j \partial_i \psi$ come in with opposite signs for $i \neq j$, and with coefficient zero if $i = j$. Thus all the addends in the first term cancel, as do those in the second, and we get zero, in accordance with the identity (3.34).

EXERCISES

Using the tensor notation, prove the following vector identities:

1. $\nabla \cdot \phi\mathbf{F} = \phi\nabla \cdot \mathbf{F} + \mathbf{F} \cdot \nabla\phi$
2. $\nabla(\mathbf{A} \cdot \mathbf{R}) = \mathbf{A}$ if $\mathbf{A}$ is constant.
3. $\nabla \times \mathbf{R} = \mathbf{0}$
4. $\nabla \cdot (\mathbf{F} \times \mathbf{G}) = \mathbf{G} \cdot (\nabla \times \mathbf{F}) - \mathbf{F} \cdot (\nabla \times \mathbf{G})$
5. $\nabla \times (\nabla \times \mathbf{F}) = \nabla(\nabla \cdot \mathbf{F}) - \nabla^2\mathbf{F}$
6. $\nabla \times (\nabla\phi) = \mathbf{0}$
7. $\nabla \cdot (\nabla \times \mathbf{F}) = 0$

CHAPTER 4

Line and Surface Integrals

4.1 LINE INTEGRALS

Let there be given a smooth space curve C in a region in which there is defined a continuous vector field $\mathbf{F}$. Let us subdivide C into smaller arcs, and "approximate" it by a polygonal path, as described in Sec. 2.2 (see Fig. 2.11). In the notation of that section, let $\mathbf{F}_k$ denote the value of $\mathbf{F}$ at the point Q_k, and form the sum $\sum_{k=1}^{n} \mathbf{F}_k \cdot \Delta\mathbf{R}_k$. We define

$$\int_C \mathbf{F} \cdot d\mathbf{R} \tag{4.1}$$

to be the limit of sums of this form, where the approximating polygonal paths are obtained by taking increasingly small subdivisions while n increases without bound. It can be shown that the limit exists, and is independent of the particular subdivisions chosen, provided that the maximum value of the magnitudes $|\Delta\mathbf{R}_k|$ tends to zero.

Expressions like (4.1) are called *line integrals.* (This is perhaps unfortunate, since C need not be a line segment; *curve integral* would be a better term.)

The definition thus given is ambiguous unless C is *oriented.* The direction of the vectors $\Delta\mathbf{R}_k$ is then taken to be consistent with the orientation of C, which in Fig. 2.11 is *from* Q_0 *to* Q_n. If C were oriented in the opposite way, from Q_n to Q_0, each of the vectors $\Delta\mathbf{R}_k$ would be chosen in the opposite direction.

Assuming that C is oriented, let $\mathbf{T}$ denote a unit vector tangent to the path, in the direction determined by the orientation. Then $\mathbf{T} = d\mathbf{R}/ds$ and we can write (4.1) in the equivalent form

$$\int_C \mathbf{F} \cdot \mathbf{T}\, ds \tag{4.2}$$

where s, the arc length measured along C, is taken to be *increasing* in the direction determined by the orientation of C.

Since $F_t = \mathbf{F} \cdot \mathbf{T}$ is the scalar component of $\mathbf{F}$ in the direction of the unit tangent, we can rewrite the line integral in the form

$$\int_C F_t\, ds \tag{4.3}$$

In books on advanced calculus that do not use vector notation, yet another form is used:

$$\int_C (F_1\, dx + F_2\, dy + F_3\, dz) \tag{4.4}$$

We obtain this from (4.1) by taking $\mathbf{F} = F_1\mathbf{i} + F_2\mathbf{j} + F_3\mathbf{k}$. Then, since $d\mathbf{R} = dx\,\mathbf{i} + dy\,\mathbf{j} + dz\,\mathbf{k}$, we have $\mathbf{F} \cdot d\mathbf{R} = F_1\, dx + F_2\, dy + F_3\, dz$.

An expression such as $F_1\, dx + F_2\, dy + F_3\, dz$, where F_1, F_2, and F_3 are functions of x, y, and z, is called a *differential form*. We call (4.4) the line integral of the differential form over the oriented curve C. If we reverse the orientation of C, the sign of the line integral changes. In vector language, we speak of the *line integral of the tangential component of* $\mathbf{F}$ *over the oriented curve* C. If we wish to be sloppier, we just say "the integral of $\mathbf{F}$ along C."

Many students feel queasy about line integrals, at first, because they don't see "what good" they are. A common question is "What do you have after you have computed a line integral?" The answer is: you have a number. Depending on the type of problem, this number may represent work done, change in potential energy, total heat flow, change in entropy, circulation of a fluid, and so on, but at this point the student is advised to concentrate simply on learning *how to compute* line integrals.

In a few special cases it is possible to compute a line integral directly from the definition (see Example 4.3 below). In general, this is not practical. We usually write $\mathbf{F}$ and $d\mathbf{R}$ in terms of a single parameter, and evaluate the line integral in the same manner as we would evaluate any definite integral.

For example, let C denote an oriented curve extending from a point P_1 to a point P_2. Let us assume that this curve is represented by parametric equations $x = x(t)$, $y = y(t)$, $z = z(t)$ in such a manner that the position vector $\mathbf{R} = x\mathbf{i} + y\mathbf{j} + z\mathbf{k}$ is a continuously differentiable function of t, with t_1 corresponding to the point P_1 and t_2 corresponding to P_2. Let us suppose further that $\mathbf{F} = F_1\mathbf{i} + F_2\mathbf{j} + F_3\mathbf{k}$ is continuous along C, that is, F_1, F_2, and F_3 are continuous in some region containing C, so that along the curve these functions are continuous functions of t. Then

$$\int_C \mathbf{F} \cdot d\mathbf{R} = \int_{t_1}^{t_2} \mathbf{F} \cdot d\mathbf{R} \tag{4.5}$$

When we write $\mathbf{F}$ as a vector function of t and $d\mathbf{R}$ is expressed in terms of t and dt, the right side of (4.5) is an ordinary definite integral:

$$\int_{t_1}^{t_2} \mathbf{F} \cdot \frac{d\mathbf{R}}{dt}\, dt$$

Observe, however, that the line integral has been defined without reference to the parametrization of the curve, so its value will depend only on the field $\mathbf{F}$ and the oriented curve C, not on the choice of the parameter t. Sometimes *arc length* is a convenient parameter, sometimes it is better to use an *angle* or the *time*, or one of the variables x, y, z. Examples are given below; study them carefully!

The integrals $\int_a^b f(x)\, dx$ that occur in elementary calculus can be regarded as very special kinds of line integrals. Indeed, let us suppose that $\mathbf{F}$ is always directed parallel to the x axis, so that $\mathbf{F} = f(x)\mathbf{i}$, and suppose C is a segment of the x axis, $a \le x \le b$, oriented in the direction of increasing x. Then $d\mathbf{R} = dx\, \mathbf{i}$, and $\int_C \mathbf{F} \cdot d\mathbf{R} = \int_a^b f(x)\, dx$. So you already have had some experience in evaluating line integrals! *Caution*: In general, line integrals are *not* interpreted to represent areas under curves and do *not* represent arc length.

Example 4.1 Compute the line integral $\int \mathbf{F} \cdot d\mathbf{R}$ from (0,0,0) to (1,2,4) if

$$\mathbf{F} = x^2\mathbf{i} + y\mathbf{j} + (xz - y)\mathbf{k}$$

(a) along the line segment joining these two points,
(b) along the curve given parametrically by $x = t^2$, $y = 2t$, $z = 4t^3$.

Solution (a) Parametric equations for the line segment joining (0,0,0) to (1,2,4) are $x = t$, $y = 2t$, $z = 4t$ (Sec. 1.8). We have

$$\int_C \mathbf{F} \cdot d\mathbf{R} = \int_C x^2\, dx + y\, dy + (xz - y)\, dz$$

$$= \int_0^1 t^2\, dt + (2t)(2\, dt) + (4t^2 - 2t)(4\, dt)$$

$$= \int_0^1 (17t^2 - 4t)\, dt = \tfrac{11}{3}$$

(b) In this case we have

$$\int_C \mathbf{F} \cdot d\mathbf{R} = \int_0^1 (t^4)(2t\, dt) + (2t)(2\, dt) + (4t^5 - 2t)(12t^2\, dt)$$

$$= \int_0^1 (2t^5 + 4t + 48t^7 - 24t^3)\, dt = \tfrac{7}{3}$$

Example 4.2 Find the line integral of the tangential component of $\mathbf{F} = x\mathbf{i} + x^2\mathbf{j}$ from $(-1,0)$ to $(1,0)$ in the xy plane (a) along the x axis, (b) along the semicircle $y = \sqrt{1 - x^2}$, (c) along the dotted polygonal path shown in Fig. 4.1.

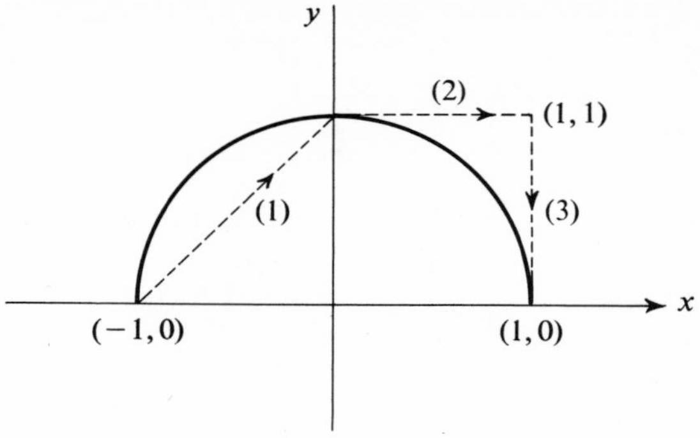

FIGURE 4.1

Solution

(a) Along the x axis, $y = 0$, hence $dy = 0 \cdot dx$ and

$$\int \mathbf{F} \cdot d\mathbf{R} = \int (x\,dx + x^2\,dy)$$

$$= \int_{-1}^{1} x\,dx = \tfrac{1}{2}x^2 \Big|_{-1}^{1} = 0$$

(b) Along the semicircle, a convenient parameter is the polar coordinate θ. Since the radius of the circle is unity, we have, for points (x,y) on this path, $x = \cos\theta$, $y = \sin\theta$, hence $dx = -\sin\theta\,d\theta$, $dy = \cos\theta\,d\theta$, and θ runs from π down to zero.

$$\int \mathbf{F} \cdot d\mathbf{R} = \int (x\,dx + x^2\,dy)$$

$$= \int_{\pi}^{0} [(\cos\theta)(-\sin\theta\,d\theta) + (\cos^2\theta)(\cos\theta\,d\theta)]$$

$$= \int_{\pi}^{0} (-\sin\theta\cos\theta + \cos^3\theta)\,d\theta$$

$$= \left[-\frac{\sin^2\theta}{2} - \sin\theta - \frac{\sin^3\theta}{2}\right]_{\pi}^{0} = 0$$

(c) Along the path labeled (1) in Fig. 4.1, $y = x + 1$, so that $dy = dx$ and

$$\int (x\,dx + x^2\,dy) = \int_{-1}^{0} [x\,dx + x^2\,dx] = -\tfrac{1}{6}$$

Along path (2), $y = 1$, so that $dy = 0 \cdot dx$ and

$$\int (x\,dx + x^2\,dy) = \int_{1}^{1} x\,dx = \tfrac{1}{2}$$

Along path (3), $x = 1$, so that $dx = 0 \cdot dy$ and

$$\int (x\,dx + x^2\,dy) = \int_1^0 dy = -1$$

[Note that we use y instead of x as the parameter along path (3).] The value of the integral is $-\frac{1}{6} + \frac{1}{2} - 1 = -\frac{2}{3}$.

Example 4.3 Let C be the curve $y = \sqrt{x}$ in the xy plane, extending from (0,0,0) to (1,1,0), and let $\mathbf{F} = xy^2\mathbf{i} + y^2\mathbf{k}$. Find $\int_C \mathbf{F} \cdot d\mathbf{R}$ directly from the definition of the integral as the limit of a sum.

Solution For convenience, let all Δx's equal $1/n$, so that

$$Q_k = (x_k, y_k, z_k) = \left(\frac{k}{n}, \sqrt{\frac{k}{n}}, 0\right)$$

$$\Delta\mathbf{R}_k = \frac{1}{n}\mathbf{i} + \left(\sqrt{\frac{k}{n}} - \sqrt{\frac{k-1}{n}}\right)\mathbf{j}$$

$$\mathbf{F}_k = x_k y_k{}^2\mathbf{i} + y_k{}^2\mathbf{k} = \frac{k^2}{n^2}\mathbf{i} + \frac{k}{n}\mathbf{k}$$

$$\sum_{k=1}^{n} \mathbf{F}_k \cdot \Delta\mathbf{R}_k = \sum_{k=1}^{n} \frac{k^2}{n^3} = \frac{1}{n^3}\sum_{k=1}^{n} k^2$$

$$= \frac{1}{n^3}\left(\frac{1}{6}\,n(n+1)(2n+1)\right) = \frac{1}{6}\left(1 + \frac{1}{n}\right)\left(2 + \frac{1}{n}\right)$$

which tends to $\frac{1}{3}$ as $n \to \infty$. Therefore

$$\int_C \mathbf{F} \cdot d\mathbf{R} = \tfrac{1}{3}$$

Example 4.4 The work W done by a force $\mathbf{F}$ in moving a particle from the initial to the final point of an oriented curve C is given by

$$W = \int_C \mathbf{F} \cdot d\mathbf{R} \tag{4.6}$$

This generalizes Example 1.12, and reduces to it in the special case where $\mathbf{F}$ is a constant.

Note: If a curve is *closed*, i.e., its initial and final points coincide, the notation $\oint \mathbf{F} \cdot d\mathbf{R}$ is frequently used. The line integral of $\mathbf{F}$ around a closed curve C is called the *circulation* of $\mathbf{F}$ about C.

In some physics courses, students are taught that the value of the integral in (4.6) depends only on the initial and the final points of C, and does not really depend on the path taken by the particle. This is true in some special cases which will be discussed further in Sec. 4.3, but this is *not* true in general, as was shown by Example 4.1 above.

EXERCISES

1. In Example 4.2 above (refer to Fig. 4.1),
(a) what is **T** along path (1), in the direction shown, in terms of **i** and **j**,
(b) what is **T** along dotted path (2), in the direction shown,
(c) along (3), in the direction shown?

2. In Example 4.2, what is ds, in terms of dx or dy,
(a) along dotted path (1),
(b) along dotted path (2),
(c) along dotted path (3)?

3. Show that $d\mathbf{R} = dx\,\mathbf{i} + dy\,\mathbf{j}$ is the same as $\mathbf{T}\,ds$ in each of the three special cases referred to in the preceding two problems. (This illustrates the general rule that, in practice, it is easier to find $d\mathbf{R}$ directly than to find **T** and ds separately and multiply.)

4. Let

$$\mathbf{F} = \frac{y}{x^2 + y^2}\,\mathbf{i} - \frac{x}{x^2 + y^2}\,\mathbf{j}$$

Find the line integral of the tangential component of **F**, from (−1,0) to (1,0),
(a) along the semicircle $y = \sqrt{1 - x^2}$;
(b) along the dotted polygonal path shown in Fig. 4.1.

5. By changing to polar coordinates, find the answers to Exercise 4 by inspection.

6. Find $\int \mathbf{F} \cdot d\mathbf{R}$ from (1,0,0) to (1,0,4), if $\mathbf{F} = x\mathbf{i} - y\mathbf{j} + z\mathbf{k}$,
(a) along the line segment joining (1,0,0) and (1,0,4);
(b) along the helix $x = \cos 2\pi t$, $y = \sin 2\pi t$, $z = 4t$.

7. Find $\int \mathbf{R} \cdot d\mathbf{R}$ from (1,2,2) to (3,6,6), along the line segment joining these points,
(a) in a straightforward manner;
(b) by observing that $\mathbf{R} \cdot d\mathbf{R} = s\,ds$, where $s = (x^2 + y^2 + z^2)^{1/2}$ is the distance from the origin, and computing $\int_3^9 s\,ds$.

8. Find the value of $\oint [(3x + 4y)\,dx + (2x + 3y^2)\,dy]$ around the circle $x^2 + y^2 = 4$.

9. Find the line integral $\int \mathbf{F} \cdot d\mathbf{R}$ along the line segment from (1,0,2) to (3,4,1) where $\mathbf{F} = 2xy\mathbf{i} + (x^2 + z)\mathbf{j} + y\mathbf{k}$.

10. Find the integral $\oint \mathbf{F} \cdot d\mathbf{R}$ around the circumference of the circle $x^2 - 2x + y^2 = 2$, $z = 1$, where $\mathbf{F} = y\mathbf{i} + x\mathbf{j} + xyz^2\mathbf{k}$.

11. Find $\int \mathbf{F} \cdot d\mathbf{R}$, where $\mathbf{F} = x^2\mathbf{i} + \mathbf{j} + yz\mathbf{k}$, along C: $x = t$, $y = 2t^2$, $z = 3t$, $0 \le t \le 1$.

12. Let $\mathbf{F} = \boldsymbol{\omega} \times \mathbf{R}$, where $\boldsymbol{\omega}$ is a constant. (Recall Example 3.22.)
(a) Compute $\int \mathbf{F} \cdot d\mathbf{R}$ along the straight line from (0,0,0) to (2,2,2). (*Hint*: Use a little thought, and you can avoid any work.)
(b) Compute the same line integral along the path $z = (x^2 + y^2)/4$ in the plane $x = y$.

4.2 DOMAINS; SIMPLY-CONNECTED DOMAINS

We recall from elementary calculus that many of the functions that arise are not defined for all values of x, but only for certain intervals. For example, the function $f(x) = 1/x$ is not defined at $x = 0$, and the function $f(x) = \csc x$ is not defined when x is an integral multiple of π.

Similarly, the vector fields that arise in practice are frequently not defined at all points (x,y,z) in space, but only in certain regions of space.

For instance, we learn in elementary physics that the magnitude of the magnetic field intensity due to a current flowing along a straight line varies inversely with the distance from that line. As we get nearer to the line the magnetic intensity increases in magnitude. The magnetic field is not defined along the line itself. The region of definition consists of all points in space except those along the line.

Similarly, the electric intensity due to a system of n point charges is defined everywhere in space except at the n points in question.

To be sure, the fields that arise in elementary physics are rather hypothetical (Is a charge really concentrated at a point?), but they are useful in theoretical discussions and their study is essential to more advanced work.

The reader with limited knowledge of electric or magnetic field theory may imagine instead that the fields we consider are the velocity fields of fluids that are in some container. Obviously, it is nonsense to speak of the velocity vector at any point outside the container. The region of definition in this case consists of all points within the container.

The vector fields that usually arise, both in theory and in practice, have two important properties. First, such a field is defined in the interior of a given region but not on the boundary of the region. Secondly, if the field is defined at two points P and Q, it is possible to find a smooth arc C joining P to Q along which the field is everywhere defined.

For instance, the velocity of a fluid in a container is not defined for points on the surface of the container, but only for points in the interior of the container. Moreover, it is unusual to consider a container with separate compartments; we usually assume that if there is fluid at two points P and Q, it is possible to move from P to Q without passing through any separating walls.

Motivated by these ideas, we now give several precise definitions.

If P is any given point and ε is any positive number (zero is excluded), we say that an ε *neighborhood of P* is the set of all points that are *less* than ε in distance away from P. Thus, if we are speaking of points in the plane, an ε neighborhood of a point P consists of all points in the interior (but not on the circumference) of a circle of radius ε and center at P. If we are speaking of points in space, an ε neighborhood of P consists of all points in the interior (but not on the surface) of a sphere of radius ε and center at P.

Given a region R, we say that P is an *interior point* of R if it is possible to find an ε neighborhood of P that lies completely within R. We say that P is a *boundary point* of R if, no matter how small we take the positive number ε, the ε neighborhood of P contains at least one point in R and one point not in R. So, by definition, an interior point cannot be a boundary point, nor can a boundary point be an interior point.

A region is said to be *open* if every point in the region is an interior point of the region. Thus, if the region of definition of a vector field is an open region, we can say: if the field is defined at a point P, it will also be defined in some ε neighborhood of P. Of course, if P is very near the boundary of the region, ε may have to be very small.

By definition, an open region does not include its boundary. (For example, the set of all points *within* a cube is an open region in space, but the set consisting of all those points either within or on the surface of a cube is not an open region.) If we say an arc C lies in an open region, then by definition C cannot intersect or even touch the boundary of the region.

Henceforth, we shall consider only open regions.

An open region R is said to be *connected* if, given any two points P and Q in R, there can be found a smooth arc in R that joins P to Q.

In Fig. 4.2, we show a region in the plane that is *not* connected. Obviously we cannot join P to Q by a smooth arc that lies completely within the region. We will have no occasion to consider such regions; henceforth we consider only connected regions.

A region that is both open and connected is called a *domain*.

The region of definition of the magnetic field due to a steady current flowing along the z axis consists of all points except those on the z axis. The region of definition of the electric field due to a system of n fixed point charges consists of all points other than the given n points. It is easy to see that in either case the region is both open and connected, so that the word "domain" applies.

In Fig. 4.3, we give an example of a region in the plane. If we let D denote the set of points within the shaded region, not including any points on either of the curves C_1 and C_2, then D is a domain. The points on the curves C_1 and C_2 constitute the boundary of the domain. In the figure we give an example of a smooth arc joining two points P and Q.

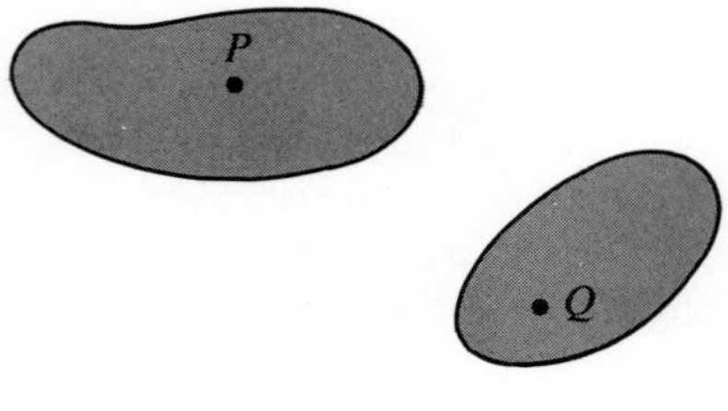

FIGURE 4.2

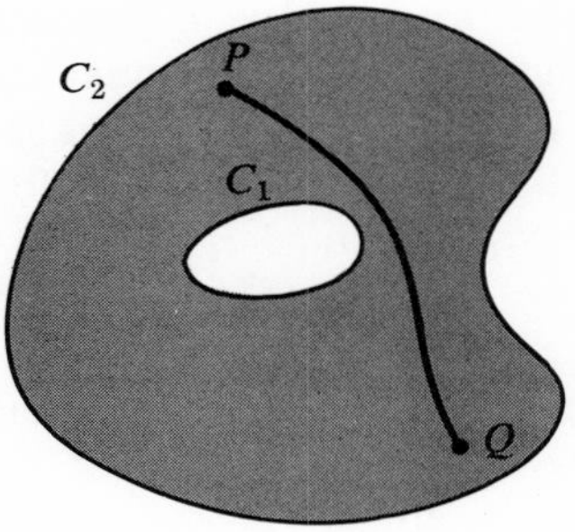

FIGURE 4.3

Of special importance are those domains that are simply-connected. In Fig. 4.4, we show a region in the plane that is simply-connected. The regions indicated in Figs. 4.3 and 4.5 are not simply-connected.

Roughly speaking, a domain is said to be simply-connected if every closed curve lying in the domain can be continuously shrunk to a point in the domain without any part of the curve passing through regions outside the domain. The plane regions indicated in Figs. 4.3 and 4.5 are not simply-connected because no closed curve surrounding one of the "holes" could be shrunk to a point while still always remaining in the domain. Thus, in the special case of a domain of points in the plane, this simply means that, given any closed curve in the domain, all points within the closed curve are also in the domain. In other words, there are no "holes" in the domain.

Simply-connected domains in space are, very roughly speaking, those domains through which no holes have been bored. Thus, the set of points in the interior of a torus (doughnut) is not simply-connected, since a closed curve within the torus surrounding the hole cannot be shrunk to a point while remaining always within the torus.

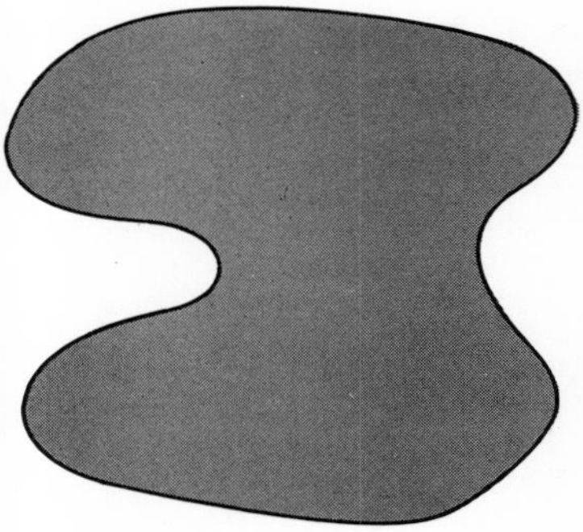

FIGURE 4.4

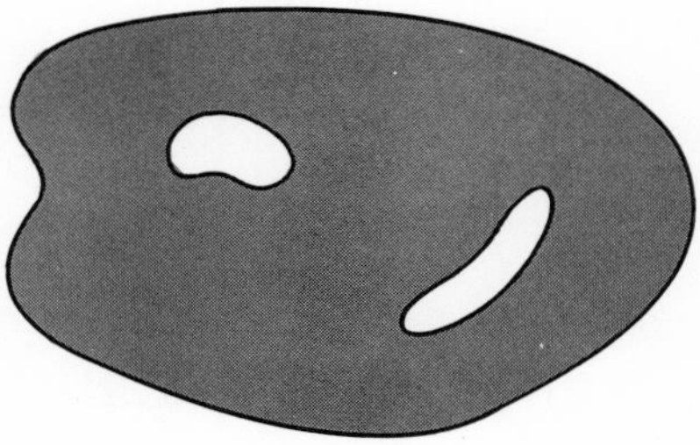

FIGURE 4.5

A closed curve C, in the process of being shrunk to a point, will generate a surface having the original curve C as its boundary. Thus, another way of wording the definition is as follows: a domain is simply-connected if, given any closed curve lying in the domain, there can be found a surface within the domain that has that curve as its boundary.

The domain consisting of all points in the interior of a sphere is simply-connected. As another example, suppose we are given two concentric spheres; then the set of points outside the inner sphere but inside the outer sphere comprises a simply-connected domain.

As a further example, consider the cylinder $x^2 + y^2 = 1$. This is a cylinder of radius 1, concentric with the z axis. Every point outside the cylinder has coordinates (x,y,z) satisfying the inequality $x^2 + y^2 > 1$ (z arbitrary), and the set of all such points is a domain that *is not* simply-connected. The set of points in the interior of the cylinder, $x^2 + y^2 < 1$, *is* simply-connected.

Vector fields defined in simply-connected regions have much simpler properties, in general, than those having domains of definition that are not simply-connected. Domains that are not simply-connected may be very complicated; the reader may wish to contemplate the region of space within an old-fashioned steam radiator, which is very far indeed from being simply-connected.

In this chapter we shall have occasion to refer to a *star-shaped domain*. A domain is called star-shaped if there is a point P in the domain such that, if Q is any other point in the domain, then the entire segment PQ lies in the domain. Sometimes we say the domain is star-shaped *with respect to P*. Fig. 4.6 illustrates some star-shaped domains.

A star-shaped domain is simply-connected; indeed, any curve can be shrunk to the point P.

EXERCISES

In each of the following cases, a region D is defined. Tell whether the region is a domain. If it is a domain, determine whether or not it is simply-connected. If it is not a domain, explain why not.

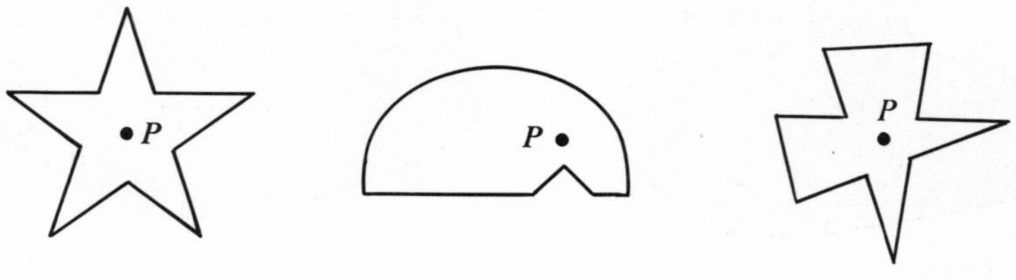

FIGURE 4.6

1. The region of definition of a magnetic field due to a steady current flowing along the z axis [in other words, the region consisting of all points (x,y,z) such that $x^2 + y^2 > 0$].
2. The region of definition of an electric field due to n point charges.
3. The region consisting of all points above the xy plane (i.e., all points (x,y,z) such that $z > 0$).
4. The region D consisting of all points $(x,y.z)$ for which $z \geq 0$.
5. The region D consisting of all points (x,y,z) such that

$$x^2 + y^2 + z^2 > 4$$

6. The region D consisting of all points (x,y,z) for which

$$1 < x^2 + y^2 < 4$$

(i.e., all points outside a cylinder of radius 1 and within a cylinder of radius 2, both cylinders concentric with the z axis).

7. The region D consisting of all points (x,y,z) for which $1 < x < 2$ (i.e., all points between the planes $x = 1$ and $x = 2$).
8. The region D consisting of all points (x,y,z) for which $z \neq 0$.

4.3 CONSERVATIVE FIELDS

In this section we let **F** denote a vector field that is defined and continuous throughout a domain D. Then

$$\mathbf{F} = F_1\mathbf{i} + F_2\mathbf{j} + F_3\mathbf{k} \tag{4.7}$$

where F_1, F_2, and F_3 are scalar-valued functions, each of which is continuous throughout D. If these three functions have partial derivatives (there will be nine such derivatives, $\partial F_1/\partial x$, $\partial F_1/\partial y$, $\ldots$, $\partial F_3/\partial z$) all of which are continuous throughout D, then **F** is said to be *continuously differentiable* in D. It follows from these definitions that, if **F** is continuously differentiable in D, then **curl F** is a vector field that is continuous in D, and div **F** is a scalar field that is continuous in D.

A vector field **F** is said to be *conservative* in a domain D if there can be found some scalar field ϕ defined in D such that $\mathbf{F} = \mathbf{grad}\,\phi$. If this is possible, then ϕ is called a *potential function* or simply a *potential* for **F**.

There is nothing unique about the potential function for a conservative field, since one can always add an arbitrary constant to ϕ to obtain a new potential whose gradient is also **F**. (Physicists conventionally choose potentials to satisfy certain natural boundary conditions; for instance, they may choose the constant so that the potential function for a gravitational field is zero along the laboratory floor, or so that the potential function for an electric field "tends to zero at infinity.")

In some textbooks a different definition of potential is used, so that one has $\mathbf{F} = -\,\mathbf{grad}\ \phi$ instead of $\mathbf{F} = \mathbf{grad}\ \phi$. The difference is one of sign, and this will give the student no difficulty when he is thoroughly familiar with the basic ideas involved.

The following theorem may indicate why conservative fields are so important:

THEOREM 4.1 *A vector field* **F** *continuous in a domain D is conservative if and only if the line integral of the tangential component of* **F** *along every regular curve in D depends only on the endpoints of the curve. In that case, the line integral is simply the difference in potential of the endpoints. That is, we have*

$$\int_C \mathbf{F} \cdot d\mathbf{R} = \int_P^Q F_1\,dx + F_2\,dy + F_3\,dz = \phi(Q) - \phi(P)$$

where P and Q are initial and terminal points of C, respectively.

Before we continue, let us be sure we understand this theorem. We are given a vector field **F** defined and continuous in a domain D. The theorem says this field is conservative if and only if the following condition holds: that if we are given any two points P and Q in D, and any regular curve C within the domain extending from P to Q, then

$$\int_P^Q \mathbf{F} \cdot d\mathbf{R}$$

depends only on the location of the endpoints P and Q and not in any way on the choice of the curve C that joins them. (We summarize this condition by saying "the line integral is independent of path.") Moreover, if this condition holds, then we can evaluate this line integral by first finding a function ϕ such that $\mathbf{F} = \mathbf{grad}\ \phi$, and then subtracting the value of ϕ at P from its value at Q.

This is the first theorem of any depth that has been stated in this book. We strongly urge the student to read carefully the following outline of the proof. We have already (in Sec. 3.7) omitted the proofs of some theorems because we felt that going through them would not be of much value to the reader. Later we shall be forced to omit some proofs because they are too technical. The proof of this theorem does not fall into either category.

Proof The proof is in four steps. First, we assume that the line integral of **F** depends only on the endpoints, and (*i*) define a function ϕ in a certain manner, (*ii*) show that ϕ is a potential for **F**, and (*iii*) show that

$$\int_P^Q \mathbf{F} \cdot d\mathbf{R} = \phi(Q) - \phi(P)$$

Then (*iv*) we prove the converse: assuming that **F** is conservative, we show that the line integral is given by $\phi(Q) - \phi(P)$ and hence is independent of path. Here we go:

(*i*) *Definition of the function*

We choose, once and for all, an arbitrary point (x_0,y_0,z_0) in D, which we call the "point of zero potential." Given any other point (x,y,z) in D, we choose arbitrarily some smooth arc C_1 in D extending from (x_0,y_0,z_0) to (x,y,z); this is possible since we assume D is a domain. We define $\phi(x,y,z)$ to be

$$\phi(x,y,z) = \int_{(x_0,y_0,z_0)}^{(x,y,z)} \mathbf{F} \cdot d\mathbf{R}$$

where we integrate along C_1. Since C_1 is smooth and **F** is continuous, there is no difficulty justifying the existence of this integral (here we omit some details, which is why this is only an "outline" of the proof). By hypothesis, this integral is independent of path, and so this definition of $\phi(x,y,z)$ does not depend on the particular arc C_1 that we choose. In other words, we have defined ϕ in an unambiguous manner. Another choice of the point of zero potential would lead to another potential function differing from this one by a constant, but that is irrelevant here.

(*ii*) *Proof that* $\mathbf{F} = \nabla\phi$

We begin by computing $\partial\phi/\partial x$ at (x,y,z). By definition this is

$$\lim_{\Delta x \to 0} \frac{\phi(x + \Delta x,\ y,\ z) - \phi(x,y,z)}{\Delta x} \tag{4.8}$$

Since D is open (every domain is) there is some ε neighborhood of (x,y,z) that is within D. Let us consider a line segment, parallel to the x axis and passing through (x,y,z), that is within this ε neighborhood. For a point $(x + \Delta x,\ y,\ z)$ along this line segment, let C_2 denote that part of the segment extending from (x,y,z) to $(x + \Delta x,\ y,\ z)$. Then C_2, being a line segment, is *a fortiori* a smooth arc, and the path from (x_0,y_0,z_0) to $(x + \Delta x,\ y,\ z)$ obtained by joining C_2 to C_1 consists of two smooth arcs and is therefore a regular curve (Fig. 4.7). We integrate along this curve to find $\phi(x + \Delta x,\ y,\ z)$ by first integrating along C_1 and then along C_2: since the first integral gives $\phi(x,y,z)$, we have

$$\phi(x + \Delta x, y, z) = \phi(x,y,z) + \int_{(x,y,z)}^{(x+\Delta x,\, y,\, z)} \mathbf{F} \cdot d\mathbf{R}$$

from which it follows that the numerator of (4.8) is simply the integral

$$\int_{(x,y,z)}^{(x+\Delta x,\, y,\, z)} \mathbf{F} \cdot d\mathbf{R}$$

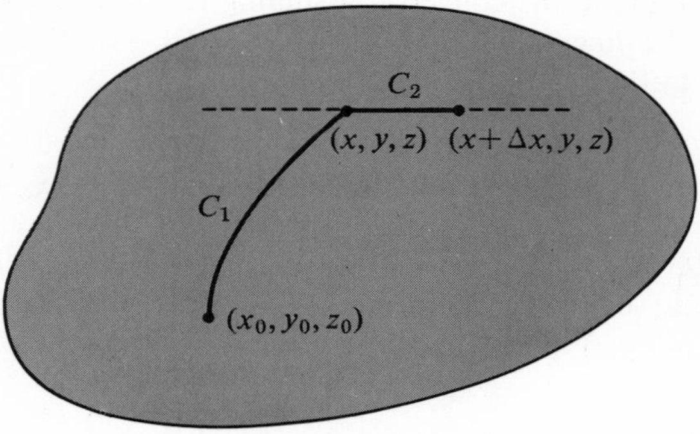

FIGURE 4.7

taken along C_2. Since y and z are constant along this line segment, we have $d\mathbf{R} = dx\,\mathbf{i}$, and hence $\mathbf{F} \cdot d\mathbf{R} = F_1\,dx$. Thus (4.8) becomes

$$\lim_{\Delta x \to 0} \frac{\displaystyle\int_{(x,y,z)}^{(x+\Delta x,\,y,\,z)} F_1\,dx}{\Delta x} \tag{4.9}$$

Only one variable is involved in (4.9) since y and z are constant along C_2; in other words, one can treat the numerator just like any integral one meets in elementary calculus. The reader will recognize this integral, divided by Δx, as simply the average value of F_1 along the line segment C_2. Since F_1 is continuous, this average value tends to $F_1(x,y,z)$ as Δx tends to zero. (This proved by a simple application of the fundamental theorem of calculus.) It follows that, at any point (x,y,z), we have $\partial\phi/\partial x = F_1$.

Similarly, we can show (taking line segments parallel to the y and z axes respectively) that $\partial\phi/\partial y = F_2$ and $\partial\phi/\partial z = F_3$. Therefore

$$\mathbf{grad}\,\phi = \frac{\partial\phi}{\partial x}\mathbf{i} + \frac{\partial\phi}{\partial y}\mathbf{j} + \frac{\partial\phi}{\partial z}\mathbf{k} = F_1\mathbf{i} + F_2\mathbf{j} + F_3\mathbf{k} = \mathbf{F}$$

proving that ϕ is a potential function for $\mathbf{F}$.

(*iii*) *Proof that* $\int_P^Q \mathbf{F} \cdot d\mathbf{R} = \phi(Q) - \phi(P)$

Let P and Q be two distinct points in D, and let C denote any regular curve extending from P to Q. Let C_1 be a smooth arc extending from (x_0,y_0,z_0) to P. Since the integral is independent of path, $\phi(Q)$ must equal the integral taken along the regular curve obtained by attaching C_1 and C together. Thus

$$\phi(Q) = \int_{C_1} \mathbf{F} \cdot d\mathbf{R} + \int_C \mathbf{F} \cdot d\mathbf{R}$$

$$= \phi(P) + \int_C \mathbf{F} \cdot d\mathbf{R}$$

from which it follows that

$$\int_C \mathbf{F} \cdot d\mathbf{R} = \phi(Q) - \phi(P)$$

(*iv*) *The converse*

To prove the converse, we *assume* **F** to be conservative, i.e. that there exists ϕ such that $\mathbf{F} = \mathbf{grad}\ \phi$. Then along any smooth arc we have **F** and $d\mathbf{R}$ expressed in terms of some parameter t and its differential dt.

$$\int_P^Q \mathbf{F} \cdot d\mathbf{R} = \int_P^Q \frac{\partial \phi}{\partial x} dx + \frac{\partial \phi}{\partial y} dy + \frac{\partial \phi}{\partial z} dz$$

$$= \int_P^Q \left(\frac{\partial \phi}{\partial x} \frac{dx}{dt} + \frac{\partial \phi}{\partial y} \frac{dy}{dt} + \frac{\partial \phi}{\partial z} \frac{dz}{dt} \right) dt$$

$$= \int_P^Q \frac{d\phi}{dt} dt = \phi(Q) - \phi(P)$$

Here we made use of the fact that, if ϕ is a function having continuous partial derivatives with respect to x, y, and z, where x, y, and z are differentiable functions of a single parameter t, then

$$\frac{d\phi}{dt} = \frac{\partial \phi}{\partial x} \frac{dx}{dt} + \frac{\partial \phi}{\partial y} \frac{dy}{dt} + \frac{\partial \phi}{\partial z} \frac{dz}{dt}$$

The above equations may be written in simplified notation:

$$\int_P^Q \mathbf{F} \cdot d\mathbf{R} = \int_P^Q d\phi = \phi(Q) - \phi(P)$$

where
$$\mathbf{F} \cdot d\mathbf{R} = d\phi = \frac{\partial \phi}{\partial x} dx + \frac{\partial \phi}{\partial y} dy + \frac{\partial \phi}{\partial z} dz$$

is the total differential of ϕ.

This completes the outline of the proof. It will be noticed that if the path C is *closed*, i.e., if P and Q coincide, then

$$\oint_C \mathbf{F} \cdot d\mathbf{R} = 0$$

since $\phi(P) - \phi(P) = 0$. Conversely, if

$$\oint_C \mathbf{F} \cdot d\mathbf{R} = 0$$

around every regular closed curve in the domain, then **F** must be conservative (see Exercise 1).

THEOREM 4.2 *A vector field* **F** *continuous in a domain D is conservative if, and only if, around every regular closed curve in D the line integral of the tangential component of* **F** *is zero.*

Example 4.5 Show that $\mathbf{F} = xy^2\mathbf{i} + x^3y\mathbf{j}$ is not conservative.

Solution A routine way of solving such problems will be given later. However, we can prove that a field is not conservative by showing that a line integral depends on the path. In this case, for instance, let us compute the integral along two paths joining (0,0) to (1,1) in the xy plane (Fig. 4.8). Along the line $y = x$ we have

$$\int_{(0,0)}^{(1,1)} (xy^2\,dx + x^3y\,dy) = \int_{x=0}^{x=1} (x^3 + x^4)\,dx = \tfrac{9}{20}$$

Now let us move along the regular path consisting of two line segments, the first joining (0,0) to (1,0) and the second joining (1,0) to (1,1). Along the first line segment $y = 0$, so that the line integral is zero. Along the second line segment $x = 1$, so that $dx = 0$ and the integral becomes

$$\int_{y=0}^{y=1} y\,dy = \tfrac{1}{2}$$

The total of the two integrals is thus $\frac{1}{2}$, differing from $\frac{9}{20}$. Hence the field is not conservative.

It is important to notice that if these two line integrals had turned out to be equal, we would not have been able to draw any conclusions from that alone. Such a result could have happened by coincidence even though the field **F** was not conservative. Since it is obviously impossible to compute $\int \mathbf{F} \cdot d\mathbf{R}$ along every conceivable regular curve, the theorem does not provide a practical way of showing that a given field *is* conservative.

Example 4.6 Show that $\mathbf{F} = xy^2\mathbf{i} + x^3y\mathbf{j}$ is not conservative, without computing any integrals.

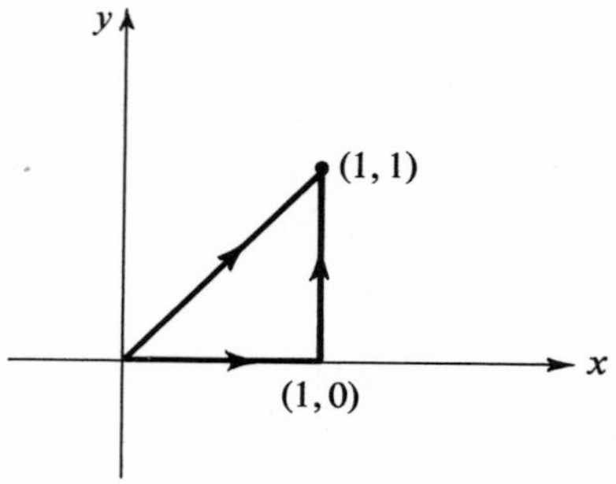

FIGURE 4.8

Solution This can be done by contradiction. Suppose **F** were conservative. Then $\mathbf{F} = \mathbf{grad}\ \phi$ for some function ϕ. Since

$$\mathbf{grad}\ \phi = \frac{\partial \phi}{\partial x}\mathbf{i} + \frac{\partial \phi}{\partial y}\mathbf{j} + \frac{\partial \phi}{\partial z}\mathbf{k}$$

we must have $\partial\phi/\partial x = xy^2$ and $\partial\phi/\partial y = x^3y$. But this is impossible, since the mixed derivatives $\partial^2\phi/\partial y\,\partial x$ and $\partial^2\phi/\partial x\,\partial y$ would be $2xy$ and $3x^2y$ respectively, whereas the theory of partial differentiation requires these derivatives (when all relevant derivatives are continuous, which they certainly are here) to be equal. This contradiction shows that such a function ϕ cannot exist, and so **F** is not conservative.

Example 4.7 Show that $\mathbf{F} = 2xy\mathbf{i} + (x^2 + 1)\mathbf{j} + 6z^2\mathbf{k}$ is conservative.

Solution Again, a routine way of solving such problems will be given later. At this point, we have no alternative but to find a function ϕ such that $\mathbf{F} = \mathbf{grad}\ \phi$. As we have remarked already, the theorems of this section are not useful in proving that a field *is* conservative since we would have to compute an infinite number of integrals. (If we were to take two points and compute line integrals along a dozen or so paths joining these points, the equality of these numbers might lead us to suspect the field to be conservative, but the experiment would not provide a rigorous proof.)

If $\mathbf{F} = \mathbf{grad}\ \phi$, then $\partial\phi/\partial x = 2xy$, $\partial\phi/\partial y = x^2 + 1$, and $\partial\phi/\partial z = 6z^2$. In computing $\partial\phi/\partial x$ one differentiates, holding y and z constant, and so evidently $\phi = x^2y +$ (either a constant term or a term involving only y and z). Let us write this as $\phi = x^2y + g(y,z)$, where g is a function not yet determined. Differentiating, we have $\partial\phi/\partial y = x^2 + (\partial g/\partial y)$. Comparing this with $\partial\phi/\partial y$ above, we see that $\partial g/\partial y = 1$. Since g is a function of y and z, evidently $g(y,z) = y +$ (either a constant term or a term involving z alone). Therefore we have $\phi = x^2y + y + h(z)$, where h depends only on z (or may possibly be a constant). Differentiating, this time with respect to z, we have $\partial\phi/\partial z = h'(z)$, and comparison with the above gives $h'(z) = 6z^2$. It follows that $h(z) = 2z^3 + C$, where C is a constant that may be chosen arbitrarily. Now we have $\phi = x^2y + y + 2z^3 + C$, and it is easy to check this to see that $\mathbf{grad}\ \phi = \mathbf{F}$. Hence **F** is conservative.

Remark: A common error is to integrate separately and add the results. Since $\partial\phi/\partial x = 2xy$, $\phi = x^2y$. Since $\partial\phi/\partial y = x^2 + 1$, $\phi = x^2y + y$. Since $\partial\phi/\partial z = 6z^2$, $\phi = 2z^3$. Adding these we obtain $\phi = 2x^2y + y + 2z^3$, which is incorrect.

EXERCISES

1. Show that, if $\oint_C \mathbf{F} \cdot d\mathbf{R} = 0$ for every regular closed curve C, then for two points P and Q,

$$\int_P^Q \mathbf{F} \cdot d\mathbf{R}$$

is independent of path. (*Hint:* Let C_1 and C_2 be two paths extending from P to Q, and let C be the closed curve obtained by joining these two paths.)

2. Using the method of Example 4.5, or some similar method, show that the following fields are not conservative:
   (a) $\mathbf{F} = -y\mathbf{i} + x\mathbf{j}$
   (b) $\mathbf{F} = y\mathbf{i} + y(x-1)\mathbf{j}$
   (c) $\mathbf{F} = y\mathbf{i} + x\mathbf{j} + x^2\mathbf{k}$ [*Suggestion*: Consider two different paths extending from (0,0,0) to (1,1,1).]
   (d) $\mathbf{F} = z\mathbf{i} + z\mathbf{j} + (y-1)\mathbf{k}$
   (e) $\mathbf{F} = \dfrac{x\mathbf{i} + x\mathbf{j}}{x^2 + x^2}$ (not defined at the origin)

3. Using methods similar to that of Example 4.6, show that the fields of Exercise 2 are not conservative.

4. Compute $\oint \mathbf{F} \cdot d\mathbf{R}$ around the closed path consisting of a circle of radius r, centered at the origin, in the xy plane, taking $\mathbf{F} = (-y\mathbf{i} + x\mathbf{j})/(x^2 + y^2)$. (*Hint:* Change to polar coordinates.)

5. If you worked correctly, you obtained a nonzero answer to Exercise 4. Yet it appears that $\mathbf{F} = \mathbf{grad}\, \phi$ where $\phi = \tan^{-1}(y/x)$, and this would contradict Theorem 4.2. Investigate this mystery.

6. Find a potential for the force field

$$\mathbf{F} = (y + z \cos xz)\mathbf{i} + x\mathbf{j} + (x \cos xz)\mathbf{k}$$

7. Show that the field $\mathbf{F} = 2xy\mathbf{i} + (x^2 + z)\mathbf{j} + y\mathbf{k}$ is conservative.

4.4 CONSERVATIVE FIELDS (CONTINUED)

In the preceding section, we saw that a continuously differentiable vector field $\mathbf{F}$ defined in a domain D is conservative if, and only if, it possesses any one (and hence all) of the following properties:

(*i*) It is the gradient of a scalar function.
(*ii*) Its integral around any regular closed curve is zero.
(*iii*) Its integral along any regular curve extending from a point P to a point Q is independent of the path.

Note that we are using slightly sloppy language here. When we say "its integral" we mean "the line integral of the tangential component," and when we say "any regular closed curve" or "any regular curve" we really do not mean *any* such curve, since we require the curve to lie completely within the domain D.

If the domain D in which $\mathbf{F}$ is defined is *simply-connected*, we can add a fourth property, equivalent to any one of the other three:

$$\mathbf{curl}\, \mathbf{F} = \mathbf{0} \tag{4.10}$$

This is of practical usefulness, since if we are given a vector field **F**, defined in a simply-connected domain D, we can test quickly to determine whether it is conservative by computing its curl. In terms of components, the test to determine whether

$$\mathbf{F} = F_1\mathbf{i} + F_2\mathbf{j} + F_3\mathbf{k}$$

is conservative consists of checking to see whether *all* the following equations are valid:

$$\frac{\partial F_1}{\partial y} = \frac{\partial F_2}{\partial x} \qquad \frac{\partial F_2}{\partial z} = \frac{\partial F_3}{\partial y} \qquad \frac{\partial F_1}{\partial z} = \frac{\partial F_3}{\partial x} \tag{4.11}$$

Equations (4.11) will be valid if and only if **curl F** = **0**, as one sees easily from the definition of **curl F**.

A vector field whose curl vanishes everywhere is said to be *irrotational.*

Some of the problems of the preceding section may be solved quite easily by using this test. For instance, consider the vector field $\mathbf{F} = y\mathbf{i} + x\mathbf{j} + x^2\mathbf{k}$. Equations (4.11) written out are

$$\frac{\partial}{\partial y}(y) = \frac{\partial}{\partial x}(x) \qquad \frac{\partial}{\partial z}(x) = \frac{\partial}{\partial y}(x^2) \qquad \frac{\partial}{\partial z}(y) = \frac{\partial}{\partial x}(x^2)$$

The first two of these equations are valid but the third is not, and so the vector field is not conservative.

In Exercise 4, Sec. 4.3, we considered the vector field

$$\mathbf{F} = \frac{-y\mathbf{i} + x\mathbf{j}}{x^2 + y^2}$$

This vector field is defined everywhere except on the z axis, where the denominator $x^2 + y^2 = 0$ and hence the expression for **F** is meaningless. Despite the fact that **curl F** = **0** in this case (as an exercise, verify this!), the field is not conservative (as shown in Exercise 4 of the preceding section) since it lacks the property (*ii*). This does not contradict the statements made above, since this domain is *not simply-connected.* The test does not apply unless the domain of definition is simply-connected.

In the succeeding problem, Exercise 5, we tried to confuse the reader a little by suggesting that $\mathbf{F} = \mathbf{grad}\ \phi$ where $\phi = \tan^{-1}(y/x)$. This suggests that (*i*) is valid but (*ii*) is not, contradicting the statements made above. This mystery vanishes when we recall that the function $\tan^{-1}(y/x)$ is ambiguous. For even when y/x makes sense, there are infinitely many angles with tangent equal to y/x. To be sure, this difficulty can be resolved by restricting the values of ϕ to the so-called "principal values" which lie in the range $-\pi/2 < \phi < \pi/2$, but in that case we obtain discontinuities on the y axis, along which x equals 0 and y/x is not defined. Alternatively, we may consider that we have $\mathbf{F} = \mathbf{grad}\ \theta$ where θ is the usual polar coordinate angle whose tangent is y/x. Along the positive x axis we have $\theta = 0$, and as we move counterclockwise around the origin, θ increases. As we return to the positive x axis through the fourth quadrant, θ tends to 2π. According to this viewpoint, θ has discontinuities of magnitude 2π along the positive x axis. (As a third alternative we can restrict θ to the range $-\pi < \theta < \pi$, but we still have discontinuities, this time along the negative x axis.) No matter how we look at it, **F** is defined except when x and y are both zero, but there is no scalar field ϕ for which $\mathbf{F} = \mathbf{grad}\ \phi$ throughout the same domain.

We shall now proceed to outline a *proof* that Eq. (4.10) is equivalent to condition (*i*) when D is simply connected.

Proof First of all, suppose that $\mathbf{F} = \mathbf{grad}\ \phi$ for some scalar field ϕ. Then by (3.32) we have $\mathbf{curl\ F} = \mathbf{0}$. In other words, condition (*i*) implies Eq. (4.10). To prove that the conditions are equivalent, it remains to show that Eq. (4.10) implies condition (*i*).

For the sake of simplicity, we shall give the proof here for star-shaped domains, which are special cases of simply-connected domains. The generalization of our result requires some topological gymnastics, and we invite the reader to refer to the first edition of this text for an indication of the procedure. Actually, the restricted form of the theorem suffices for most practical situations.

We begin by assuming **F** is a continuous differentiable vector field defined in a domain D that is star-shaped with respect to the point P, and that $\mathbf{curl\ F} = \mathbf{0}$ throughout D. Our goal is to show that there exists a scalar field ϕ such that $\mathbf{F} = \mathbf{grad}\ \phi$ throughout D.

Motivated by the considerations of the previous section, we define ϕ at the point Q to be the line integral of **F** taken along *the straight line segment from P to Q*.

We inject two comments here.

(*i*) Because the domain D is star-shaped with respect to P, this segment lies inside D and thus the integral is defined.

(*ii*) At this point we cannot assert that line integrals of **F** are independent of the path. The function $\phi(Q)$, however, is computed *in terms of a specific path*; therefore it is not ambiguous.

Now we proceed to show $\mathbf{grad}\ \phi = \mathbf{F}$. First we parametrize the path of integration. Let (x_0,y_0,z_0) be the coordinates of P, and (x,y,z) be coordinates for Q. Since we customarily use **R** to denote the vector (x,y,z), which now is an *endpoint* in our integral, we shall write

$$\phi(x,y,z) = \int_P^Q \mathbf{F} \cdot d\mathbf{r} \tag{4.12}$$

using $\mathbf{r}(t)$ to designate the path of integration. Then a parametrization for the segment is

$$\mathbf{r}(t) = x_0 + t(x - x_0),\ y_0 + t(y - y_0),\ z_0 + t(z - z_0) \qquad (0 \le t \le 1)$$

The explicit dependence of $\mathbf{F}$ on the parameter t in the integral (4.12) is given by

$$\begin{aligned}\mathbf{F} &= \mathbf{F}[x_0 + t(x - x_0),\, y_0 + t(y - y_0),\, z_0 + t(z - z_0)] \\ &= \mathbf{F}(X, Y, Z)\end{aligned}$$

where we have abbreviated the first argument, $x_0 + t(x - x_0)$, of $\mathbf{F}$ by X, the second by Y, and the third by Z.

Now we compute the gradient of ϕ. Since ∇ operates only on the variables x, y, and z

$$\nabla = \mathbf{i}\frac{\partial}{\partial x} + \mathbf{j}\frac{\partial}{\partial y} + \mathbf{k}\frac{\partial}{\partial z}$$

(and *not* on t), we can bring the differential operator inside the integral. Using identity (3.31), we find

$$\begin{aligned}\nabla\phi &= \int_0^1 \nabla\left(\mathbf{F}\cdot\frac{d\mathbf{r}}{dt}\right) dt \\ &= \int_0^1 \left[(\mathbf{F}\cdot\nabla)\frac{d\mathbf{r}}{dt} + \left(\frac{d\mathbf{r}}{dt}\cdot\nabla\right)\mathbf{F} + \mathbf{F}\times\left(\nabla\times\frac{d\mathbf{r}}{dt}\right) + \frac{d\mathbf{r}}{dt}\times(\nabla\times\mathbf{F})\right] dt\end{aligned} \tag{4.13}$$

Here we must be careful in our interpretation. ∇ operates, as we said, on x, y, and z; but the arguments of $\mathbf{F}$ are X, Y, and Z. Thus we cannot identify, for example, $\nabla \times \mathbf{F}(X, Y, Z)$ as the curl of $\mathbf{F}$, evaluated at (X, Y, Z). This latter would be

$$\nabla^* \times \mathbf{F}(X, Y, Z)$$

where ∇^* denotes the operator

$$\nabla^* = \mathbf{i}\frac{\partial}{\partial X} + \mathbf{j}\frac{\partial}{\partial Y} + \mathbf{k}\frac{\partial}{\partial Z}$$

However, we have the following relation because of the definition of X in terms of x;

$$\frac{\partial \mathbf{F}}{\partial x} = \frac{\partial X}{\partial x}\frac{\partial \mathbf{F}}{\partial X} = t\frac{\partial \mathbf{F}}{\partial X} \tag{4.14}$$

Similarly,

$$\frac{\partial \mathbf{F}}{\partial y} = t\frac{\partial \mathbf{F}}{\partial Y} \tag{4.14'}$$

$$\frac{\partial \mathbf{F}}{\partial z} = t\frac{\partial \mathbf{F}}{\partial Z}$$

It follows from these identities that

$$\nabla \times \mathbf{F}(X,Y,Z) = t\nabla^* \times \mathbf{F}(X,Y,Z)$$

By hypothesis, the curl of **F** is zero; hence, from the above,

$$\nabla \times \mathbf{F} = \mathbf{0}$$

in expression (4.13).

Furthermore, since

$$\frac{d\mathbf{r}}{dt} = (x - x_0, y - y_0, z - z_0)$$

we have

$$\nabla \times \frac{d\mathbf{r}}{dt} = \mathbf{0}$$

and

$$(\mathbf{F} \cdot \nabla)\frac{d\mathbf{r}}{dt} = \mathbf{F}$$

[Recall identities (3.24) and (3.26).]

Combining this data in (4.13), we have shown

$$\phi(x,y,z) = \int_0^1 \left[\mathbf{F} + \left(\frac{d\mathbf{r}}{dt} \cdot \nabla\right)\mathbf{F}\right] dt \tag{4.15}$$

One more simplification is possible. If we differentiate $t\mathbf{F}$ with respect to t along the curve, using the chain rule we find

$$\frac{d}{dt}(t\mathbf{F}[x_0 + t(x - x_0), y_0 + t(y - y_0), z_0 + t(z - z_0)])$$

$$= t\frac{\partial \mathbf{F}}{\partial X}(x - x_0) + t\frac{\partial \mathbf{F}}{\partial Y}(y - y_0) + t\frac{\partial \mathbf{F}}{\partial Z}(z - z_0) + \mathbf{F}$$

By Eq. (4.14), this can be written

$$\frac{d(t\mathbf{F})}{dt} = (x - x_0)\frac{\partial \mathbf{F}}{\partial x} + (y - y_0)\frac{\partial \mathbf{F}}{\partial y} + (z - z_0)\frac{\partial \mathbf{F}}{\partial z} + \mathbf{F}$$

$$= \left(\frac{d\mathbf{r}}{dt} \cdot \nabla\right)\mathbf{F} + \mathbf{F} \tag{4.16}$$

Using this in (4.15), we get

$$\phi(x,y,z) = \int_0^1 \frac{d}{dt}(t\mathbf{F})\, dt = t\mathbf{F}|_0^1 = \mathbf{F}(x,y,z)$$

We have succeeded in proving that the gradient of ϕ is **F**, i.e., **F** is conservative!

Example 4.8 Show that $\mathbf{F} = 2xy\mathbf{i} + (x^2 + 1)\mathbf{j} + 6z^2\mathbf{k}$ is conservative, and find a scalar potential ϕ.

Solution We use the test (4.11), which is acceptable since this field $\mathbf{F}$ is defined and continuously differentiable throughout space (the set of *all* points in space is obviously a star-shaped domain):

$$\frac{\partial F_1}{\partial y} = \frac{\partial F_2}{\partial x} = 2x$$

$$\frac{\partial F_2}{\partial z} = \frac{\partial F_3}{\partial y} = 0$$

and
$$\frac{\partial F_1}{\partial z} = \frac{\partial F_3}{\partial x} = 0$$

The test is positive, hence the field is conservative.

The potential may be found by the method of Example 4.7, or we may use the line integral. Because of the theorem we have just proved, we can compute ϕ by integrating along *any* curve; we are not restricted to the straight line segment.

Taking ϕ to be zero at the origin, we define $\phi(x,y,z)$ as $\int_{0,0,0}^{x,y,x} \mathbf{F} \cdot d\mathbf{R}$ along the following curve:

(*i*) from (0,0,0) to $(x,0,0)$ along the x axis,
(*ii*) from $(x,0,0)$ to $(x,y,0)$ parallel to the y axis,
(*iii*) from $(x,y,0)$ to (x,y,z) parallel to the z axis.

This is feasible since the domain is all of space. The parametrization is trivial and we have

$$\phi(x,y,z) = \int_0^x F_1(t,0,0)\,dt + \int_0^y F_2(x,t,0)\,dt + \int_0^z F_3(x,y,t)\,dt \tag{4.17}$$

Inserting the given expression for $\mathbf{F}$, we find

$$\phi(x,y,z) = 0 + (x^2t + t)\big|_0^y + 2t^3\big|_0^z = x^2y + y + 2z^3$$

The reader is advised to use the test given in this section to determine whether a given field $\mathbf{F}$ is conservative, but to use the methods of Sec. 4.3 to actually construct the potential ϕ. The reason we do not advise using (4.17) of this section is that it may be a little tricky for most students to use correctly, as will be demonstrated in the following example.

Example 4.9 Use (4.17) to find a potential for

$$\mathbf{F} = (3x^2yz + y + 5)\mathbf{i} + (x^3z + x - z)\mathbf{j} + (x^3y - y + 7)\mathbf{k}$$

which has the value 10 at the origin.

Solution By (4.17) we have

$$\begin{aligned}\phi(x,y,z) &= 10 + \int_0^x 5\,dt + \int_0^y x\,dt + \int_0^z (x^3y - y + 7)\,dt \\ &= 10 + 5t\big|_0^x + xt\big|_0^y + (x^3yt - yt + 7t)\big|_0^z \\ &= 10 + 5x + xy + x^3yz - yz + 7z\end{aligned}$$

EXERCISES

1. Test the following fields to determine whether they are conservative.

(a) $\mathbf{F} = (12xy + yz)\mathbf{i} + (6x^2 + xz)\mathbf{j} + xy\mathbf{k}$

(b) $\mathbf{F} = ze^{xz}\mathbf{i} + xe^{xz}\mathbf{k}$

(c) $\mathbf{F} = \sin x\,\mathbf{i} + y^2\mathbf{k} + e^z\mathbf{k}$

(d) $\mathbf{F} = 3x^2yz^2\mathbf{i} + x^3z^2\mathbf{j} + x^3yz\mathbf{k}$

(e) $\mathbf{F} = \dfrac{2x}{x^2 + y^2}\mathbf{i} + \dfrac{2y}{x^2 + y^2}\mathbf{j} + 2z\mathbf{k}$

2. For which one of the fields in Exercise 1 is the test given in this section not applicable? How, then, can you test this field to determine whether it is conservative in its domain of definition?

3. Let $\mathbf{F}$ and $\mathbf{G}$ be conservative vector fields with potentials ϕ and ψ respectively. Is the vector field $\mathbf{F} + \mathbf{G}$ conservative? If so, determine a potential for it.

4. Show by calculation that $\mathbf{grad}\,\phi = \mathbf{F}$ when ϕ is given by (4.17).

5. Show that the scalar field

$$\phi = -\frac{1}{|\mathbf{R}|}$$

which is defined except at the origin, is a potential function for the vector field $\mathbf{R}/|\mathbf{R}|^3$, where $\mathbf{R} = x\mathbf{i} + y\mathbf{j} + z\mathbf{k}$,

(a) by writing ϕ in terms of x, y, and z and computing its gradient;

(b) by inspection, using the second and third fundamental properties of the gradient listed in Sec. 3.1.

6. A force field is defined by

$$\mathbf{F} = \frac{x\mathbf{i} + y\mathbf{j} + z\mathbf{k}}{(x^2 + y^2 + z^2)^{3/2}}$$

at all points in space except the origin. A particle is moved along the straight line segment from the point (1,2,3) to the point (2,3,5). What is the work done by the force on the particle? (*Hint:* Avoid a lot of work by making use of the statement of Exercise 5.)

7. Would your answer to Exercise 6 be any different if the path extending from (1,2,3) to (2,3,5) were not straight?

*4.5 VECTOR POTENTIALS

In the previous section, we discussed a *partial converse* to identity (3.32), which states that the curl of a gradient is zero. It is a *converse* because it states that, if the curl of a field is zero, the field is a gradient, but it is only a *partial* converse because it is only valid, in general, for simply-connected domains.

An astute reader will wonder if there is also a converse, or at least a partial converse, to identity (3.33), which asserts that the divergence of a curl is zero. If the divergence of a vector field is zero, is that field necessarily the curl of another vector field? The answer is *yes*, provided the domain of definition is star-shaped.

A vector field whose divergence is everywhere zero is called *solenoidal.* If $\mathbf{F} = \nabla \times \mathbf{G}$, $\mathbf{G}$ is called a *vector potential* for $\mathbf{F}$. Notice that $\mathbf{G}$ is not unique; in fact, according to (3.33), we can add the gradient of any scalar to $\mathbf{G}$.

Now let us prove the statement about the existence of a vector potential.

Proof We assume $\mathbf{F}$ is solenoidal in a domain D which is star-shaped with respect to the point P. We wish to find $\mathbf{G}(x,y,z)$ so that $\mathbf{F} = \nabla \times \mathbf{G}$.

The proof is quite similar to that in the previous section. (In fact, both theorems are special cases of a result known as *Poincaré's lemma.*) We again parametrize the straight line segment from $P(x_0,y_0,z_0)$ to $Q(x,y,z)$ by

$$\begin{aligned} \mathbf{r}(t) &= (x_0 + t(x - x_0),\ y_0 + t(y - y_0),\ z_0 + t(z - z_0)) \\ &= (X, Y, Z) \end{aligned} \tag{4.18}$$

(using the same notation as in the previous section).

Now we define $\mathbf{G}(x,y,z)$:

$$\mathbf{G}(x,y,z) = \int_0^1 t\mathbf{F} \times \frac{d\mathbf{r}}{dt}\,dt \tag{4.19}$$

where the dependence of $\mathbf{F}$ and $\mathbf{r}$ on t is exactly as in the previous section. Equation (4.19) is, as it stands, simply the integral of a vector function of t; however, it lends an obvious interpretation to an expression like $\int_P^Q t\mathbf{F} \times d\mathbf{r}$.

We compute the curl of $\mathbf{G}$. Again, ∇ may be taken inside the integral and by identity (3.29), we have

$$\begin{aligned} \nabla \times \mathbf{G} &= \int_0^1 t\nabla \times \left(\mathbf{F} \times \frac{d\mathbf{r}}{dt}\right) dt \\ &= \int_0^1 \left[\left(\frac{d\mathbf{r}}{dt} \cdot \nabla\right)\mathbf{F} - (\mathbf{F} \cdot \nabla)\frac{d\mathbf{r}}{dt} + \left(\nabla \cdot \frac{d\mathbf{r}}{dt}\right)\mathbf{F} - (\nabla \cdot \mathbf{F})\frac{d\mathbf{r}}{dt}\right] t\,dt \end{aligned} \tag{4.20}$$

As in the previous section,

$$\frac{d\mathbf{r}}{dt} = (x - x_0,\ y - y_0,\ z - z_0)$$

so that

$$\nabla \cdot \frac{d\mathbf{r}}{dt} = 3$$

and

$$(\mathbf{F} \cdot \nabla)\frac{d\mathbf{r}}{dt} = \mathbf{F}$$

For the reasons stated in the previous section, $\nabla \cdot \mathbf{F}(X, Y, Z)$ is not the divergence of $\mathbf{F}$, but because

$$\nabla \cdot \mathbf{F}(X, Y, Z) = t\nabla^* \cdot \mathbf{F}(X, Y, Z)$$

with ∇^* defined as before, we see that $\nabla^* \cdot \mathbf{F} = 0$ implies $\nabla \cdot \mathbf{F} = 0$.

Incorporating all this into (4.20), we get

$$\nabla \times \mathbf{G} = \int_0^1 \left[\left(\frac{d\mathbf{r}}{dt} \cdot \nabla \right) \mathbf{F} - \mathbf{F} + 3\mathbf{F} \right] t\, dt \tag{4.21}$$

Now using Eq. (4.16), we find that

$$\frac{d(t^2\mathbf{F})}{dt} = t\,\frac{d(t\mathbf{F})}{dt} + (t\mathbf{F})\frac{dt}{dt} = 2t\mathbf{F} + t\left(\frac{d\mathbf{r}}{dt} \cdot \nabla \right)\mathbf{F}$$

This is precisely what we have in (4.21); therefore

$$\nabla \times \mathbf{G} = \int_0^1 \frac{d}{dt}(t^2\mathbf{F})\, dt = t^2\mathbf{F}|_0^1 = \mathbf{F}(x,y,z)$$

i.e., $\mathbf{F}$ is the curl of $\mathbf{G}$.

Example 4.10 Find a vector potential for

$$\mathbf{F} = \boldsymbol{\omega} \times \mathbf{R}$$

where $\boldsymbol{\omega}$ is a constant vector (recall Example 3.22).

Solution The verification that $\nabla \cdot \mathbf{F} = 0$ is immediate. Taking P to be the origin in the above equations, we have the parametrization of the segment PQ:

$$\mathbf{r}(t) = (tx, ty, tz) = t\mathbf{R}$$

Therefore, since $\mathbf{F} = \boldsymbol{\omega} \times \mathbf{r}(t)$ in Eq. (4.19),

$$\mathbf{G}(x,y,z) = \int_0^1 t(\boldsymbol{\omega} \times t\mathbf{R}) \times \mathbf{R}\, dt$$

$$= (\boldsymbol{\omega} \times \mathbf{R}) \times \mathbf{R} \int_0^1 t^2\, dt$$

So we obtain

$$\mathbf{G}(x,y,z) = \tfrac{1}{3}(\boldsymbol{\omega} \times \mathbf{R}) \times \mathbf{R}$$

The reader is invited to verify that $\nabla \times \mathbf{G} = \mathbf{F}$.

We have now proved results which state that irrotational vector fields are derivable from scalar potentials and solenoidal fields are derivable from vector potentials. The natural question arises: Can an *arbitrary* vector field be expressed as a gradient of a scalar field plus a curl of another vector field, under appropriate circumstances? This conjecture is true, and is known as the *fundamental theorem of vector analysis*. Its proof, however, involves the use of potential theory. In fact, the theorem has considerably less practical utility than the two results we have demonstrated, despite its ostentatious soubriquet.

EXERCISES

1. Verify that $\mathbf{F} = \nabla \times \mathbf{G}$ in Example 4.10.
2. Find a vector potential for $\mathbf{F} = x\mathbf{j}$.
3. Prove: If $\mathbf{F}$ and $\mathbf{G}$ are irrotational, then $\mathbf{F} \times \mathbf{G}$ is solenoidal. Can you find the vector potential for $\mathbf{F} \times \mathbf{G}$? (*Hint:* This problem is considerably easier if you have mastered tensor notation.)

4.6 ORIENTED SURFACES

A surface S is said to be *smooth* if it is possible to choose a unit normal vector $\mathbf{n}$ at every point of S in such a way that $\mathbf{n}$ varies continuously on S. It is said to be *piecewise smooth* if it consists of a finite number of smooth parts joined together. Thus, the surface of a sphere is smooth, whereas the surface of a cube is piecewise smooth (consisting of six smooth surfaces joined together).

At every point of a smooth surface there will, of course, be two choices for the unit normal $\mathbf{n}$. There will therefore be two ways in which we can define a field of unit normal vectors continuous on S. [If, for instance, the surface is given by an equation of the form $f(x,y,z) = C$, then the two fields are

$$\frac{\mathbf{grad}\, f}{|\mathbf{grad}\, f|} \quad \text{and} \quad \frac{-\mathbf{grad}\, f}{|\mathbf{grad}\, f|}$$

(Sec. 3.1).] In choosing one of these two possibilities we *orient* the surface. Thus, there are always two possible orientations of a smooth surface. We have already discussed orientation for the special case of a plane (Sec. 1 11). The situation is somewhat the same for more general surfaces. When a smooth surface has been oriented by choosing a particular unit normal field $\mathbf{n}$, then a positive direction for angles is determined at each point of the surface (Fig. 4.9). If the surface is bounded by a regular closed curve C, the orientation also determines what we mean by the *positive direction* along C. This is determined by the requirement that an observer on the positive side of the surface (i.e., the side on which $\mathbf{n}$ emerges), walking in the positive direction along the boundary, always have the surface at his left.

A piecewise-smooth surface is oriented by choosing $\mathbf{n}$ at every point (except along certain edges, perhaps) in such a manner that along every edge

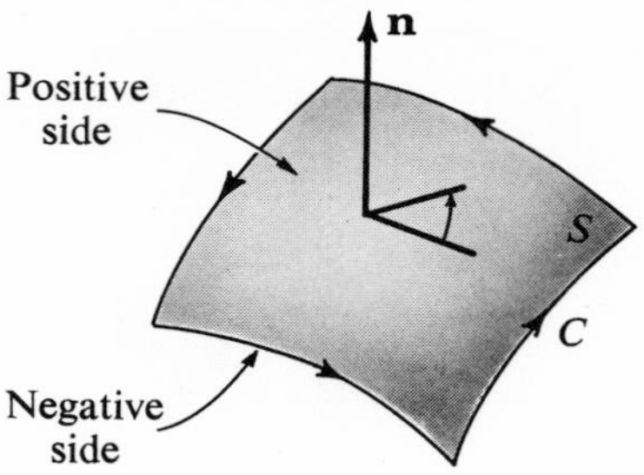

FIGURE 4.9

that is the common boundary of two smooth surfaces the positive direction relative to one of the surfaces is opposite to the positive direction relative to the other. This is shown for the surfaces of a cube and a cylinder in Figs. 4.10 and 4.11.

A *closed surface* is one that has no boundary. Thus the surfaces of Figs. 4.10 and 4.11 are closed, whereas the surface in Fig. 4.9 has a boundary and is not closed. It is conventional to take the orientation of a closed surface, which encloses a region of space, to be such that the unit normal **n** always points *away* from the enclosed region, as illustrated in Figs. 4.10 and 4.11.

A surface can be oriented only if it has two sides; the process of orientation consists essentially in choosing which side we will call "positive" and which "negative". (If the surface is closed, it is more natural to speak of the "outside" and the "inside".)

Not all surfaces can be oriented. The reader may be familiar with the *Möbius strip*, obtained by twisting and pasting together the ends of a strip of paper (Fig. 4.12). This surface is nonorientable because it has only one side.

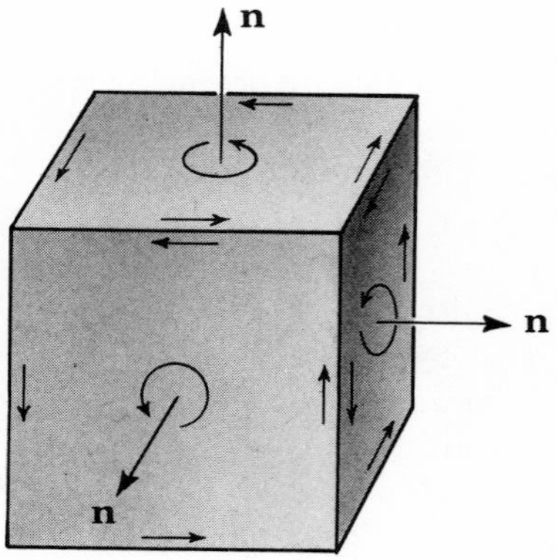

FIGURE 4.10

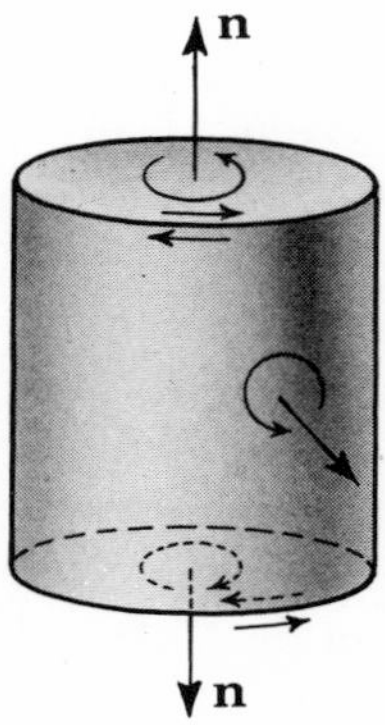

FIGURE 4.11

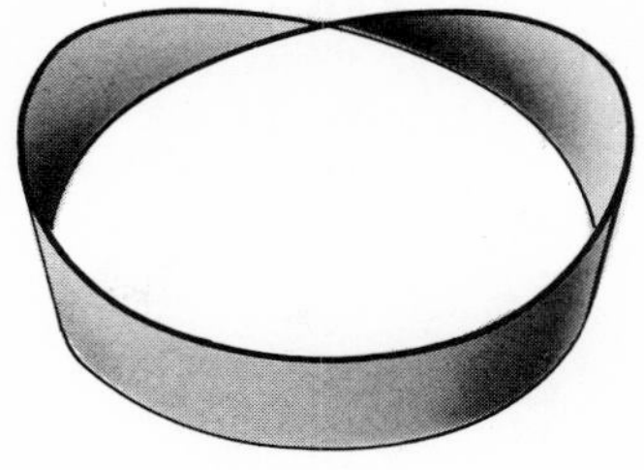

FIGURE 4.12

If **n** is a unit vector normal to the surface at a point P, then as it moves around the strip its direction is reversed by the time it reaches P again, which contradicts the requirement that **n** be unambiguous at every point and still vary continuously.

The reader may amuse himself by taking two strips of paper (adding-machine tape is especially convenient) and preparing two strips, one with a twist and one without. If the strips are long enough to dangle on the floor, no one will notice the difference between them. Have someone cut along a central line of the cylindrical band at the same time that you cut the Möbius strip. The cylindrical band will separate into two cylindrical bands, but the Möbius strip will not separate into distinct portions. This trick astonishes most children and those few adults who have never seen it before.

Nonorientable surfaces have other mathematical properties that are rather amazing, so amazing in fact that we must exclude them from further consideration. Henceforth, whenever we say "surface" we mean an orientable surface.

Just as it is possible to write the equation of a space curve in parametric form, giving x, y, and z as functions of a *single* parameter t (because the curve is a *one*-dimensional beast), it is also possible to represent these (*two*-dimensional) surfaces parametrically by giving x, y, and z as functions of two parameters u and v:

$$x = x(u,v) \qquad y = y(u,v) \qquad z = z(u,v) \tag{4.22}$$

This can also be written in vector notation:

$$\mathbf{R} = \mathbf{R}(u,v) \tag{4.22$'$}$$

If we hold one of these parameters fixed and vary the other, the point (x,y,z) will trace out a curve on the surface. Thus we obtain a family of curves along each of which u has a different constant value, and another family of curves for different constant values of v (Fig. 4.13).

Along any one of these curves, the theory developed in Sec. 2.2 is applicable. It follows that at any point the vector

$$\frac{\partial \mathbf{R}}{\partial v} = \frac{\partial x}{\partial v}\mathbf{i} + \frac{\partial y}{\partial v}\mathbf{j} + \frac{\partial z}{\partial v}\mathbf{k} \tag{4.23}$$

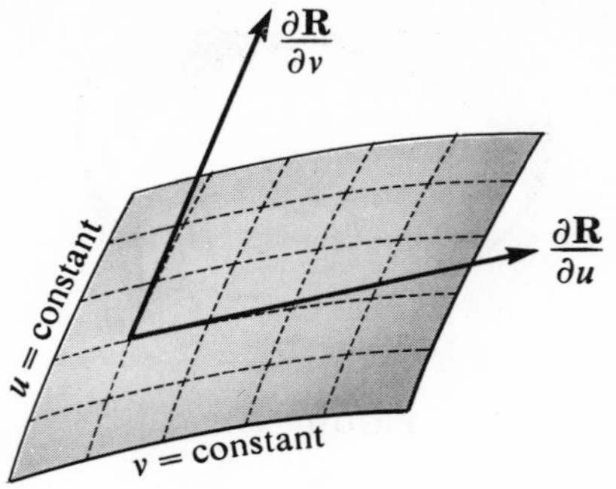

FIGURE 4.13

is tangent to a curve, $u =$ constant, passing through that point, and similarly

$$\frac{\partial \mathbf{R}}{\partial u} = \frac{\partial x}{\partial u}\mathbf{i} + \frac{\partial y}{\partial u}\mathbf{j} + \frac{\partial z}{\partial u}\mathbf{k} \tag{4.24}$$

is tangent to a curve with equation $v =$ constant. We assume here that all the relevant derivatives exist, that $\partial\mathbf{R}/\partial v$ and $\partial\mathbf{R}/\partial u$ are nonzero and not parallel at every point, and that these derivatives are continuous on the surface. It follows that at any point P the vector

$$\frac{\partial \mathbf{R}}{\partial u} \times \frac{\partial \mathbf{R}}{\partial v} \tag{4.25}$$

is normal to the surface at P. Dividing this vector by its own length we obtain at each point a unit vector $\mathbf{n}$. The opposite orientation is given by dividing $(\partial\mathbf{R}/\partial v) \times (\partial\mathbf{R}/\partial u)$ by its length.

Any portion of a surface that can be represented by equations of the form (4.22) in such a manner that to distinct ordered pairs (u,v) there correspond distinct points (x,y,z) on the surface, and satisfying the above differentiability and continuity requirements, is called a *regular surface element*. The surface area of such a surface element is defined by the double integral

$$\iint \left| \frac{\partial \mathbf{R}}{\partial u} \times \frac{\partial \mathbf{R}}{\partial v} \right| du\, dv \tag{4.26}$$

where appropriate limits of integration must be supplied. We assume here that the boundary of the surface element is such that the integral (4.26) exists.

As motivation for (4.26), we note that the patch of surface bounded by lines of constant u, $u + \Delta u$, v, and $v + \Delta v$ is approximately a parallelogram with

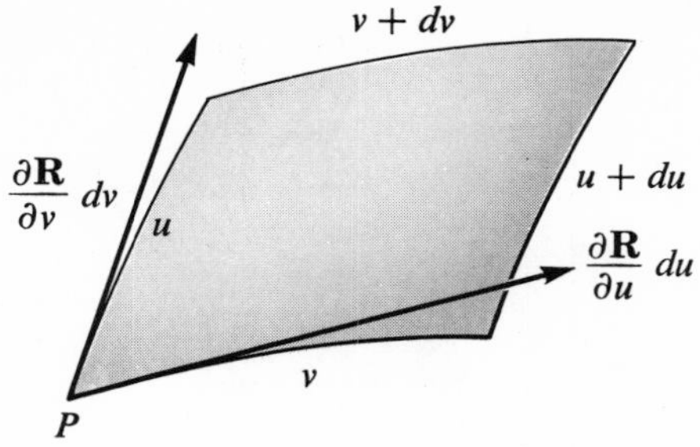

FIGURE 4.14

sides $(\partial\mathbf{R}/\partial u)\,\Delta u$ and $(\partial\mathbf{R}/\partial v)\,\Delta v$ (Fig. 4.14); its area δS is thus

$$\Delta S \approx \left| \frac{\partial \mathbf{R}}{\partial u} \times \frac{\partial \mathbf{R}}{\partial v} \right| \Delta u\, \Delta v$$

As Δu and Δv approach zero, formula (4.26) results.

If we introduce the notation

$$d\mathbf{S} = \frac{\partial \mathbf{R}}{\partial u}\, du \times \frac{\partial \mathbf{R}}{\partial v}\, dv$$

then we see that $d\mathbf{S}$ is a vector normal to the surface at P whose magnitude $dS = |d\mathbf{S}|$ is the element of area. The integral (4.26) may be written in the alternative forms

$$\iint |d\mathbf{S}|$$

or

$$\iint dS$$

or even

$$\iint \mathbf{n} \cdot d\mathbf{S}$$

where $\mathbf{n}$ is a unit normal in the same direction as $d\mathbf{S}$.

We now consider a *special case* of (4.26) that will illustrate further its geometrical significance. Let us suppose that the surface we consider is given in the form $z = f(x,y)$. In other words, we are told how far above the xy plane the surface is for each point (x,y) in the xy plane. Then it is convenient to use x and y instead of u and v as the parameters. Let us suppose that the projection of the surface element on the xy plane is bounded by the curves

$$y = y_1(x) \qquad y = y_2(x) \qquad x = a \qquad x = b$$

as shown in Fig. 4.15.

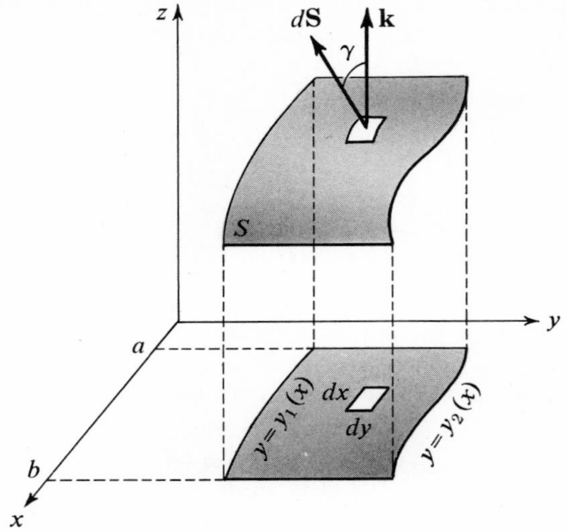

FIGURE 4.15

We can write $x = u$, $y = v$, and $z = f(u,v)$, in order to make use of the preceding formulas. From (4.23) we have

$$\frac{\partial \mathbf{R}}{\partial v} = \frac{\partial \mathbf{R}}{\partial y} = \mathbf{j} + \left(\frac{\partial f}{\partial y}\right)\mathbf{k}$$

and by (4.24)

$$\frac{\partial \mathbf{R}}{\partial u} = \frac{\partial \mathbf{R}}{\partial x} = \mathbf{i} + \left(\frac{\partial f}{\partial x}\right)\mathbf{k}$$

Taking the vector cross product,

$$\frac{\partial \mathbf{R}}{\partial u} \times \frac{\partial \mathbf{R}}{\partial v} = \begin{vmatrix} \mathbf{i} & \mathbf{j} & \mathbf{k} \\ 1 & 0 & \dfrac{\partial f}{\partial x} \\ 0 & 1 & \dfrac{\partial f}{\partial y} \end{vmatrix} = \mathbf{k} - \frac{\partial f}{\partial x}\mathbf{i} - \frac{\partial f}{\partial y}\mathbf{j}$$

The magnitude of this vector is $\sqrt{1 + (\partial f/\partial x)^2 + (\partial f/\partial y)^2}$, so that the integral (4.26) is

$$\int_a^b \int_{y_1(x)}^{y_2(x)} \sqrt{1 + \left(\frac{\partial f}{\partial x}\right)^2 + \left(\frac{\partial f}{\partial y}\right)^2}\, dy\, dx \qquad (4.27)$$

The geometrical significance of this is seen by considering the angle γ between $d\mathbf{S}$ and $\mathbf{k}$. By a simple calculation using scalar products we see that

$$|\cos \gamma| = \frac{|d\mathbf{S}\cdot\mathbf{k}|}{|d\mathbf{S}|} = \left[1 + \left(\frac{\partial f}{\partial x}\right)^2 + \left(\frac{\partial f}{\partial y}\right)^2\right]^{-1/2}$$

so that (4.27) is simply

$$\int_a^b \int_{y_1(x)}^{y_2(x)} \frac{dx\,dy}{|\cos \gamma|} \tag{4.28}$$

This integral could have been obtained heuristically by considering the *area cosine principle* which says that, if we look at a plane area A whose normal makes an acute angle θ with the line of sight, the area we appear to see is $A \cos \theta$. This is because distances in one direction will appear to be shorter by a factor of $\cos \theta$ and distances in a perpendicular direction will not change at all. Let us digress for a moment to use this law to determine the area of the ellipse shown in Fig. 4.16. Let us pretend that this ellipse is really a circle of radius a that we are viewing at an angle. In other words, we imagine that this is a circle of radius a (area πa^2) that has been tipped in such a manner that vertical distances are shortened by a factor b/a. The area we see will be $A \cos \theta = (\pi a^2)(b/a) = \pi ab$. Thus we find the area of this ellipse to be πab, by a method that is much easier than using integral calculus.

Returning to Fig. 4.15, we can consider an element of area in S whose projection on the xy plane has area $dx\,dy$. The angle between the normal to this area and the "line of sight" (imagine that you are below the xy plane looking up at the surface) is γ. By the area cosine principle, the area $dx\,dy$ that we see equals $dS\,|\cos \gamma|$. It follows that

$$dS = \frac{dx\,dy}{|\cos \gamma|}$$

The absolute value is unnecessary if γ is acute.

Frequently, a judicious use of the area cosine principle makes it unnecessary to use (4.26). The cosine of the relevant angle, in this case γ, is easily computed since we can find a normal to the surface by methods we have already learned and then use scalar products to find the desired cosine. For instance, the surface $z = f(x,y)$ can be represented by the equation $z - f(x,y) = 0$, and the gradient of the function $z - f(x,y)$ is $\mathbf{k} - (\partial f/\partial x)\mathbf{i} - (\partial f/\partial y)\mathbf{j}$. This is easier than computing the vector cross product given above. *Caution*: Using gradients to give a normal vector $\mathbf{N}$ may give a

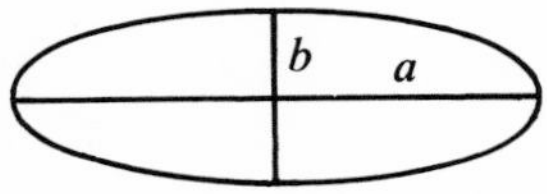

FIGURE 4.16

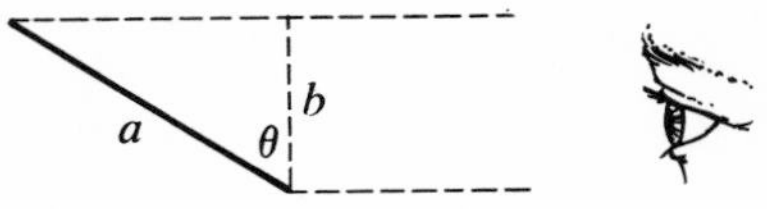

FIGURE 4.17

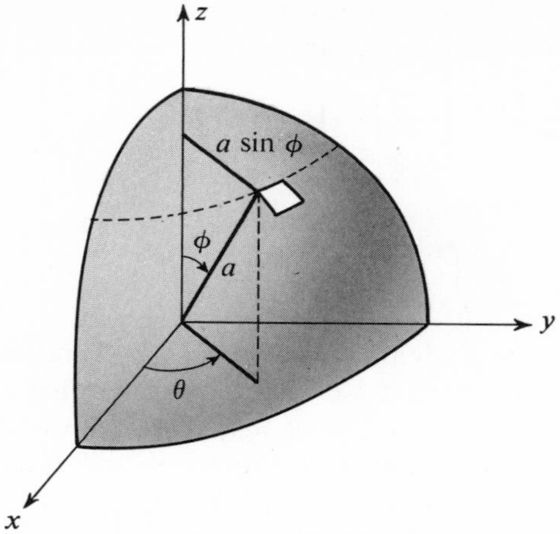

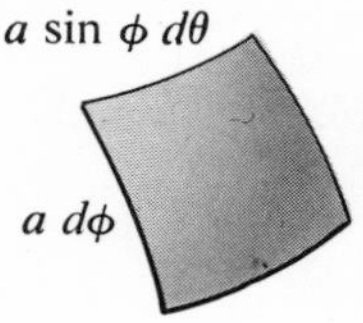

FIGURE 4.18

vector $\mathbf{N}\,du\,dv$ that does not equal $d\mathbf{S}$ but is only a scalar multiple of it. However, this makes no difference since we are only interested in computing $\cos\gamma = \mathbf{N}\cdot\mathbf{k}/|\mathbf{N}|$ when using (4.28).

In practice it is frequently unnecessary to use (4.26) at all, or even expressions derived from it, such as (4.28). For example, suppose S is part of the sphere $x^2 + y^2 + z^2 = a^2$. Using spherical coordinates (Fig. 4.18) we have

$$x = a\sin\phi\cos\theta \qquad y = a\sin\phi\sin\theta \qquad z = a\cos\phi$$

Using the two parameters ϕ and θ instead of u and v, we obtain

$$\frac{\partial\mathbf{R}}{\partial\phi} = a\cos\phi\cos\theta\,\mathbf{i} + a\cos\phi\sin\theta\,\mathbf{j} - a\sin\phi\,\mathbf{k} \tag{4.29}$$

$$\frac{\partial\mathbf{R}}{\partial\theta} = -a\sin\phi\sin\theta\,\mathbf{i} + a\sin\phi\cos\theta\,\mathbf{j} \tag{4.30}$$

whereupon we compute to show that

$$\frac{\partial\mathbf{R}}{\partial\phi}\times\frac{\partial\mathbf{R}}{\partial\theta} = a^2\sin^2\phi\cos\theta\,\mathbf{i} + a^2\sin^2\phi\sin\theta\,\mathbf{j} + a^2\sin\phi\cos\phi\,\mathbf{k} \tag{4.31}$$

The magnitude of the vector is a $a^2\sin\phi$, so it follows that

$$dS = a^2\sin\phi\,d\phi\,d\theta \tag{4.32}$$

This result can be visualized (heuristically) from Fig. 4.18. Holding θ fixed and varying ϕ by an amount $d\phi$ we trace out an arc of length $a\,d\phi$. Holding ϕ fixed and varying θ, we trace out an arc of a circle of radius $a\sin\phi$, the length of this arc being $a\sin\phi\,d\theta$. For small $d\phi$ and $d\theta$ this gives us very nearly a rectangle with area $a^2\sin\phi\,d\phi\,d\theta$.

EXERCISES

1. Draw a diagram similar to those of Figs. 4.10 and 4.11 for the surface of a tetrahedron.
2. Consider the triangle with vertices (1,0,0), (0,1,0), and (0,0,1).
   (a) Find a unit vector **n** normal to this triangle, pointing away from the origin.
   (b) Determine $\cos \gamma$ for this vector.
   (c) Supply the appropriate limits for the integral

$$\iint \frac{dx\,dy}{|\cos \gamma|}$$

   if it is to represent the area of this triangle.
   (d) Evaluate the integral.
   (e) Obtain the same answer by applying the area cosine principle to the projection of this triangle on the xy plane.
3. (a) Derive (4.31) from (4.29) and (4.30).
   (b) Show that the magnitude of this vector is $a^2 \sin \phi$.
4. Determine the element of surface area dS in the special case of the surface $z = x^2 + y^2$.
5. Find the area of the section of the surface

$$x = u^2 \qquad y = uv \qquad z = \tfrac{1}{2}v^2$$

   bounded by the curves $u = 0$, $u = 1$, $v = 0$, and $v = 3$.

4.7 SURFACE INTEGRALS

Let S denote a smooth surface and let $f(x,y,z)$ be a function defined and continuous on S. The surface integral of f over S is denoted

$$\iint_S f(x,y,z)\,dS$$

and is defined to be the limit of sums obtained in the following manner. We imagine the surface cut up into n pieces having area $\delta S_1, \delta S_2, \ldots, \delta S_n$. In each piece we choose a point (x_i,y_i,z_i), evaluate $f(x_i,y_i,z_i)$, and form $f(x_i,y_i,z_i)\,\delta S_i$. We sum these numbers:

$$\sum_{i=1}^{n} f(x_i,y_i,z_i)\,\delta S_i \tag{4.33}$$

In this way we obtain a single number. Now let n tend to infinity, at the same time letting the pieces grow smaller so that the maximum dimension of the areas $\delta S_1, \delta S_2, \ldots, \delta S_n$ tends to zero. In other words, we are dividing the surface into smaller and smaller elements of area, each time forming a sum of form (4.33). If these sums tend to a limit, independent of the way we form the repeated subdivisions, that limit is called the surface integral of f over S:

$$\iint_S f(x,y,z)\, dS = \lim_{\substack{\max \delta S_i \to 0 \\ n \to \infty}} \sum_{i=1}^{n} f(x_i,y_i,z_i)\, \delta S_i \tag{4.34}$$

We omit a theoretical discussion of surface integrals in favor of the following discussion which serves to motivate the definition and show how important surface integrals are in applications. It is important for the reader to know at the outset that only very seldom will he be called upon to actually evaluate a surface integral. It is the *concept* that is important, for surface integrals provide a convenient language for expressing certain fundamental ideas in mathematics and physics. The actual computation of a surface integral may be very difficult. They are rarely computed directly from the definition we have just given!

Suppose, for instance, that at any point (x,y,z) on a surface S, $f(x,y,z)$ gives the rate of flow of heat per unit area at that point, in units (say) of calories per second per square centimeter. Then $f(x_i,y_i,z_i)\, \delta S_i$ gives, approximately, the number of calories per second flowing across the element of area δS_i. The sum (4.33) then gives, approximately, the total number of calories per second flowing across the entire surface S. If $f(x,y,z)$ varies from point to point on the surface, this sum will generally be only an approximation, but one that can be improved by taking smaller elements of area (and hence more such elements). The limit

$$\iint_S f(x,y,z)\, dS$$

gives exactly the number of calories per second flowing across the surface.

If we assume a steady-state temperature distribution, where $T(x,y,z)$ denotes the temperature at each point in space, and if the region we consider is filled with a homogeneous material having coefficient of thermal conductivity k, then the vector

$$\mathbf{Q} = -k\nabla T \tag{4.35}$$

gives, at each point in space, the direction in which the heat is flowing. The magnitude of $\mathbf{Q}$ gives the rate of heat flow per unit area across an area perpendicular to $\mathbf{Q}$. More generally, we can say that the scalar component of $\mathbf{Q}$ in the direction of a unit vector $\mathbf{n}$ (equal to $\mathbf{Q} \cdot \mathbf{n}$) gives the number of calories per unit time and per unit area across an element of area perpendicular to $\mathbf{n}$. It follows that, to find the total number of calories per second flowing across a surface S, we form the surface integral

$$\iint_S (-k\nabla T) \cdot \mathbf{n}\, dS \tag{4.36}$$

The reason for the negative sign in (4.35) and (4.36) is that the temperature gradient ∇T points in the direction of maximum rate of increase of the temperature, whereas heat flows in the opposite direction, from hot to cold.

More generally, if we are given any vector field **F**, continuous in a region containing an oriented smooth surface S, we can form the surface integral

$$\iint_S \mathbf{F} \cdot \mathbf{n}\, dS \tag{4.37}$$

where, at any point on the oriented surface, **n** is the unit normal to S. The physical meaning of the integral depends on the nature of the physical quantity represented by **F**.

Let us consider another situation in physics in which surface integrals arise. If **F** denotes the velocity field of a fluid and ρ its density, then as we saw in Sec. 3.3, the amount of fluid crossing a patch of surface with area δS and unit normal **n**, per unit time, is approximately $\rho \mathbf{F} \cdot \mathbf{n}\, \delta S$. This formula is accurate for small areas δS. Then we can see that

$$\iint_S \rho \mathbf{F} \cdot \mathbf{n}\, dS \tag{4.38}$$

gives the rate of flow of liquid across the surface S, expressed as mass per unit time.

As yet another example, consider an electrostatic field **E** defined in a region of space. One can form

$$\iint_S \mathbf{n} \cdot \mathbf{E}\, dS$$

which is the surface integral of the normal component of **E** over the surface S. This integral arises in connection with Gauss's law of electrostatics which states that if S is a closed surface,

$$\iint_S \mathbf{n} \cdot \mathbf{E}\, dS = \frac{q}{\varepsilon_0} \tag{4.39}$$

where q is the total charge enclosed by the surface and ε_0 is a constant that depends on the system of units. The numerical value of the surface integral in (4.39) is sometimes called the *flux* across S or the *number of flow lines of the vector field* **E** *crossing the surface*. This last phrase is not to be taken literally, since there will usually be a flow line crossing every point of S and therefore there are really an infinite number of flow lines crossing S. However, in drawing diagrams, it is impossible to draw an infinite number of flow lines, so it may be convenient to visualize (4.39) as giving a measure of the number of flow lines we wish to picture crossing the surface. [This number is necessarily approximate since the value of (4.39) may not be a whole number.]

Returning to (4.37), we note that in the notation of the preceding section we can use the alternative forms

$$\iint_S \mathbf{F} \cdot d\mathbf{S} \tag{4.37$'$}$$

and

$$\iint_S \mathbf{F} \cdot \frac{\partial \mathbf{R}}{\partial u} \times \frac{\partial \mathbf{R}}{\partial v}\, du\, dv \tag{4.37$''$}$$

and when the surface is specified by giving z as a function of x and y, we can write

$$\iint \mathbf{F} \cdot \mathbf{n} \frac{dx\, dy}{|\cos \gamma|} \tag{4.37$'''$}$$

where the limits of integration are determined by the projection of S onto the xy plane [with an obvious modification for surfaces described by, say, $x = x(y,z)$].

If the surface S is only piecewise smooth, we integrate over each smooth part separately and add the numbers obtained.

Example 4.11 Compute

$$\iint_S \mathbf{F} \cdot d\mathbf{S}$$

where S is the surface of the sphere $x^2 + y^2 + z^2 = 4$ and

$$\mathbf{F} = x\mathbf{i} + y\mathbf{j} + z\mathbf{k}$$

Solution We recall that at a point (x,y,z) the vector $x\mathbf{i} + y\mathbf{j} + z\mathbf{k}$ points directly away from the origin. The outward normal $\mathbf{n}$ to this sphere also points away from the origin, since the center of the sphere is at the origin. Hence for points on the surface

$$\mathbf{F} \cdot \mathbf{n} = |\mathbf{F}|\, |\mathbf{n}| \cos \theta = |\mathbf{F}| = (x^2 + y^2 + z^2)^{1/2} = 2$$

and

$$\iint_S \mathbf{F} \cdot d\mathbf{S} = \iint_S \mathbf{F} \cdot \mathbf{n}\, dS = \iint_S 2dS = 2 \text{ (total surface area)}$$
$$= 2(4\pi r^2) = 32\pi$$

since $r = 2$ is the radius of the sphere.

Note that, in the above example, no integration was needed, since $\mathbf{F} \cdot \mathbf{n}$ was constant over the entire surface.

Example 4.12 Compute

$$\iint_S \mathbf{F} \cdot d\mathbf{S}$$

where S is the surface of the cube bounded by the planes $x = 0$, $x = 1$, $y = 0$, $y = 1$, $z = 0$, $z = 1$, and $\mathbf{F} = x\mathbf{i} + y\mathbf{j} + z\mathbf{k}$.

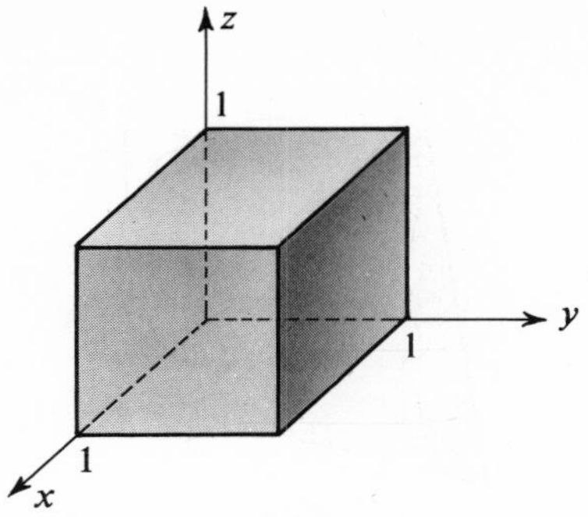

FIGURE 4.19

Solution We see from Fig. 4.19 that the unit normal to the front face of the cube is $\mathbf{n} = \mathbf{i}$, so

$$\mathbf{F} \cdot \mathbf{n} = \mathbf{i} \cdot (x\mathbf{i} + y\mathbf{j} + z\mathbf{k}) = x = 1$$

on this face. It follows that the integral over this face is

$$\iint \mathbf{F} \cdot d\mathbf{S} = \iint \mathbf{F} \cdot \mathbf{n}\, dS = \iint dS = 1$$

since the area of this face is unity. On the opposite face (in the yz plane) $\mathbf{n} = -\mathbf{i}$ so that $\mathbf{F} \cdot \mathbf{n} = -x$, but $x = 0$ for all points in this face and hence

$$\iint \mathbf{F} \cdot \mathbf{n}\, dS = 0$$

On the top of the cube we have

$$\iint \mathbf{F} \cdot \mathbf{n}\, dS = \iint \mathbf{F} \cdot \mathbf{k}\, dS = \iint z\, dS = \iint dS = 1$$

and on the bottom we have

$$\iint \mathbf{F} \cdot \mathbf{n}\, dS = \iint (-z)\, dS = 0$$

since $z = 0$ in the xy plane. Along the right side we have $\mathbf{n} = \mathbf{j}$ so that the normal component of $\mathbf{F}$ is unity and the integral over this face is unity. Along the left side $\mathbf{n} = -\mathbf{j}$ and $\mathbf{F} \cdot \mathbf{n} = -y = 0$, so that the contribution to the integral is zero. Summing, we find that

$$\iint_S \mathbf{F} \cdot \mathbf{n}\, dS = 3$$

Example 4.13 Compute the surface integral of the normal component of $\mathbf{F} = x^2\mathbf{i} + yx\mathbf{j} + zx\mathbf{k}$ over the triangle with vertices (1,0,0), (0,2,0), (0,0,3). Consider the triangle oriented so that its positive side is that away from the origin (Fig. 4.20).

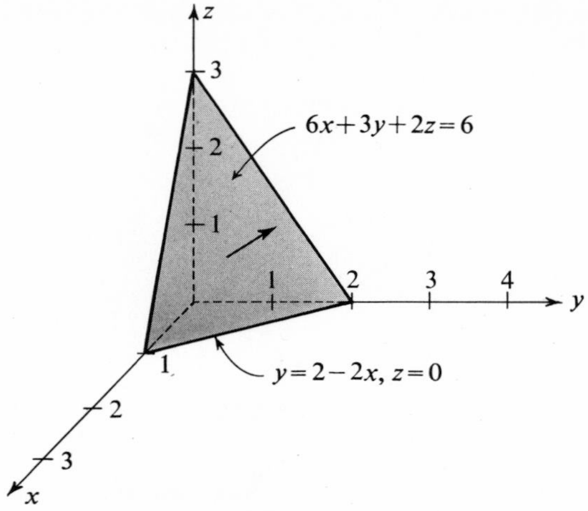

FIGURE 4.20

Solution By the methods of Chap. 1 we find easily that $\mathbf{n} = \frac{6}{7}\mathbf{i} + \frac{3}{7}\mathbf{j} + \frac{2}{7}\mathbf{k}$. Hence $\mathbf{F} \cdot \mathbf{n} = \frac{6}{7}x^2 + \frac{3}{7}yx + \frac{2}{7}zx$ and

$$\cos \gamma = \mathbf{n} \cdot \mathbf{k} = \tfrac{2}{7}$$

Using (4.37‴) we have

$$\iint_S \mathbf{F} \cdot \mathbf{n}\, dS = \int_0^1 \int_0^{2-2x} \tfrac{7}{2}(\tfrac{6}{7}x^2 + \tfrac{3}{7}yx + \tfrac{2}{7}zx)\, dy\, dx$$

$$= \int_0^1 \int_0^{2-2x} (3x^2 + \tfrac{3}{2}yx + zx)\, dy\, dx$$

On S we have $z = 3 - 3x - \frac{3}{2}y$ so that $zx = 3x - 3x^2 - \frac{3}{2}yx$, and the integral becomes

$$\int_0^1 \int_0^{2-2x} 3x\, dy\, dx = \int_0^1 3x(2 - 2x)\, dx = 3x^2 - 2x^3 \Big|_0^1 = 1$$

Example 4.14 Compute

$$\iint_S \mathbf{F} \cdot \mathbf{n}\, dS$$

over the surface of the tetrahedron with vertices (1,0,0), (0,2,0), (0,0,3), (0,0,0), where $\mathbf{F} = x^2\mathbf{i} + yx\mathbf{j} + zx\mathbf{k}$ (Fig. 4.20).

Solution We have already computed the integral over one surface. Along the bottom face we have $\mathbf{n} = -\mathbf{k}$ and, hence, $\mathbf{F} \cdot \mathbf{n} = -zx$, but since $z = 0$ the integral over the bottom face is zero. On the face at the left we have $\mathbf{n} = -\mathbf{j}$ and $\mathbf{F} \cdot \mathbf{n} = -yx$, which is also zero since $y = 0$ there. On the rear face, in the yz plane, $\mathbf{n} = -\mathbf{i}$ and $\mathbf{F} \cdot \mathbf{n} = -x^2 = 0$. It follows that

$$\iint_S \mathbf{F} \cdot d\mathbf{S} = 1$$

the only nonzero contribution being the integral already computed in Example 4.13.

Note that in Examples 4.11, 4.12, and 4.14 we took $\mathbf{n}$ to be the *outward* normal, the usual convention for closed surfaces.

Example 4.15 Use Gauss's law (4.39) to determine the magnitude of the electric field intensity at a point r units away from a point charge of magnitude q.

Solution Let S be a sphere of radius r with the charge q at its center. Symmetry considerations lead us to believe that $\mathbf{n} \cdot \mathbf{E}$ will be constant over the surface of this sphere, and that $\mathbf{E}$ will be normal to the surface. Hence, we can bring $\mathbf{n} \cdot \mathbf{E}$ outside the integral, and we obtain

$$\iint \mathbf{n} \cdot \mathbf{E}\, dS = \mathbf{n} \cdot \mathbf{E} \iint dS = 4\pi r^2(\mathbf{n} \cdot \mathbf{E})$$

It then follows from (4.39) that $\mathbf{n} \cdot \mathbf{E} = q/4\pi\varepsilon_0 r^2$. Hence, if the charge is positive, $|\mathbf{E}| = q/4\pi\varepsilon_0 r^2$ and $\mathbf{E}$ is directed away from q. If q is negative, $\mathbf{E}$ will be directed towards the charge q.

Example 4.16 Use Gauss's law (4.39) to determine the magnitude of the electric field intensity at a point r units away from an infinite plate carrying a charge of density σ (charge per unit area).

Solution Let S be the surface of a right circular cylinder of length $2r$ and base area A, bisected by the charged sheet. We take the bases parallel to the sheet, so by symmetry we expect $\mathbf{E}$ to be perpendicular to the bases (Fig. 4.21).

The charge within S is $q = \sigma A$. On each of the two bases we have (by symmetry, since we assume the charged sheet infinite in extent) $\mathbf{n} \cdot \mathbf{E} =$ constant, and there will be no contribution to the integral around the curved surface of the cylinder because $\mathbf{E}$ is parallel to this surface; therefore

$$\iint_S \mathbf{n} \cdot \mathbf{E}\, dS = \mathbf{n} \cdot \mathbf{E} \iint_S dS = (\mathbf{n} \cdot \mathbf{E})(2A)$$

By (4.39) we have $(\mathbf{n} \cdot \mathbf{E})(2A) = \sigma A/\varepsilon_0$, so $\mathbf{n} \cdot \mathbf{E} = \sigma/2\varepsilon_0$. If σ is positive, this shows that $\mathbf{E}$ is in the same direction as $\mathbf{n}$ and $|\mathbf{E}| = \sigma/2\varepsilon_0$, independent of r.

These last two examples are typical, in that they show the role played by symmetry considerations in applying Gauss's law to determine $\mathbf{E}$.

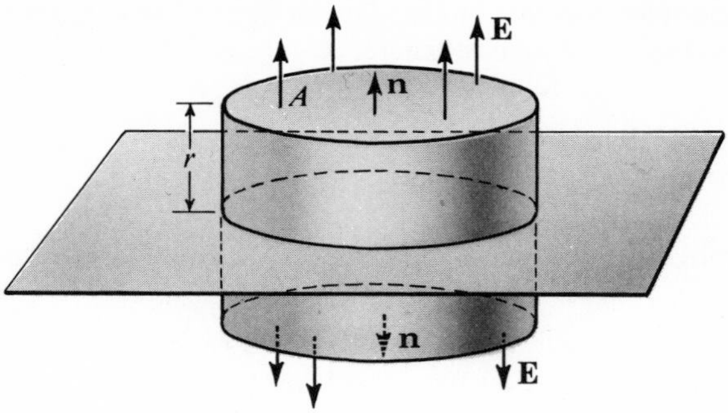

FIGURE 4.21

Example 4.17 Consider a cylindrical heat insulator surrounding a steampipe. Let the inner and outer radii of the insulator be $r = a$ and $r = b$ respectively, and let T_a and T_b be the temperatures, respectively, of the inner and outer surfaces of the insulator. Find the temperature T within the insulator as a function of r (Fig. 4.22).

Solution A section of the insulator, of length L, is shown in the figure. By symmetry, we assume that T is a function of r alone, so that $\nabla T = \mathbf{grad}\, T$ is directed radially towards the center of the pipe, with magnitude $-dT/dr$. (On the assumption that the pipe is hotter than the surroundings, dT/dr will be negative.) Let S be a cylindrical surface of radius r and length L within the insulator. By (4.35) we have

$$\mathbf{Q} \cdot \mathbf{n} = (-k\nabla T) \cdot \mathbf{n} = -\frac{k\, dT}{dr}$$

(as usual, we take $\mathbf{n}$ to be outward, so $\nabla T \cdot \mathbf{n} = |\nabla T|\,|\mathbf{n}| \cos 180^\circ = -|\nabla T| = dT/dr$).

Assuming steady-state heat flow, the number of calories of heat flowing across any such surface S will be the same as that across any other such surface, since

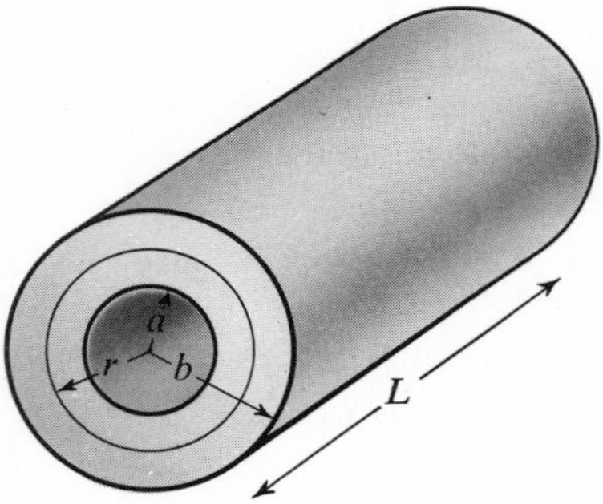

FIGURE 4.22

otherwise the temperature would change with time. The quantity of heat flow per unit time across any such surface is

$$H = \iint_S \mathbf{Q} \cdot \mathbf{n}\, dS = \iint_S -k \frac{dT}{dr}\, dS = -k \frac{dT}{dr} \iint_S dS$$

$$= -k \frac{dT}{dr}(2\pi L r)$$

Here again we are using symmetry considerations in assuming that dT/dr is constant along any one surface S (but not necessarily the same as for surfaces with different r), and so dT/dr can be brought outside the integral sign.

Since H is independent of r, we treat it as a constant in solving the differential equation

$$H = -2\pi k L r \frac{dT}{dr}$$

Separating variables,

$$H \frac{dr}{r} = -2\pi k L\, dT$$

we integrate

$$H \int_a^b \frac{dr}{r} = -2\pi k L \int_{T_a}^{T_b} dT$$

which ultimately yields

$$H = \frac{2\pi L k (T_a - T_b)}{\ln (b/a)}$$

Substituting this value of H and integrating

$$H \int_a^r \frac{dr}{r} = -2\pi k L \int_{T_a}^{T} dT$$

we finally obtain

$$T = T_a - (T_a - T_b) \frac{\ln (r/a)}{\ln (b/a)}$$

EXERCISES

1. If $\mathbf{F} = z\mathbf{k}$, find the surface integral of the normal component of $\mathbf{F}$ over the closed surface of the right circular cylinder with curved surface $x^2 + y^2 = 9$ and bases in the planes $z = 0$ and $z = 2$. (Mental arithmetic should suffice.)
2. Compute

$$\iint \mathbf{F} \cdot d\mathbf{S}$$

where S is the surface of the cube bounded by the planes $x = \pm 1$, $y = \pm 1$, $z = \pm 1$, if

(a) $\mathbf{F} = x\mathbf{i}$
(b) $\mathbf{F} = x\mathbf{i} + y\mathbf{j}$
(c) $\mathbf{F} = x\mathbf{i} + y\mathbf{j} + z\mathbf{k}$
(d) $\mathbf{F} = x^2\mathbf{i} + y^2\mathbf{j} + z^2\mathbf{k}$
(e) $\mathbf{F} = y\mathbf{i}$
(f) $\mathbf{F} = z\mathbf{i}$
(g) $\mathbf{F} = z^2\mathbf{i}$

3. Compute the surface integral of the normal component of $\mathbf{F} = x\mathbf{i}$ over the triangle with vertices (1,0,0), (0,2,0), (0,0,3), taking the normal on the side away from the origin.

4. Use Gauss's law to determine the magnitude of the electric field intensity at a point r units away from an infinitely long thin wire carrying a charge of λ units per unit length. (Consider a cylinder of length L and radius r concentric with the wire.)

5. Fill in the missing steps in Example 4.17.

6. Consider a hollow sphere of homogeneous material, with inner radius a and outer radius b, and inner temperature T_a and outer temperature T_b.
(a) Find the steady-state temperature as a function of the distance r from the center, for values of r between a and b.
(b) For a value of r halfway between a and b, is T halfway between T_a and T_b?

7. Given $\mathbf{F} = x\mathbf{i} - y\mathbf{j}$, find the value of

$$\iint \mathbf{F} \cdot \mathbf{n}\, dS$$

over the closed surface bounded by the planes $z = 0$, $z = 1$, and the cylinder $x^2 + y^2 = a^2$, where $\mathbf{n}$ is the unit outward normal,
(a) by direct calculation (*Hint*: The element of area is

$$dS = a\, d\theta\, dz$$

in cylindrical coordinates on the curved surface.);
(b) by symmetry considerations, without changing to cylindrical coordinates.

8. Given $\mathbf{F} = x\mathbf{i} + y\mathbf{j} + (z^2 - 1)\mathbf{k}$, find

$$\iint \mathbf{F} \cdot \mathbf{n}\, dS$$

over the closed surface bounded by the planes $z = 0$, $z = 1$, and the cylinder $x^2 + y^2 = a^2$, where $\mathbf{n}$ is the unit outward normal.

9. Given that $\mathbf{F} = y\mathbf{i} + \mathbf{k}$, find the surface integral of the normal component of $\mathbf{F}$ over the box shown in Fig. 4.23, taking $\mathbf{n}$ to be the unit outward normal. Assume this box to have a bottom but no top, i.e., roughly like a shoe. (*Note*: Later on you will be asked to do the same problem by mental arithmetic, as a demonstration of the power of the divergence theorem. Take a furtive peek ahead at Exercise 7, Sec. 4.9.)

10. Let D be the region $x \geq 0$, $y \geq 0$, $z \geq 0$, $x + \frac{1}{2}y + \frac{1}{3}z \leq 1$.
(a) Is this region a domain?
(b) Is this region simply-connected?
(c) If $\mathbf{F} = 2x\mathbf{i} + y\mathbf{i} + z\mathbf{k}$, find the surface integral of the normal component of $\mathbf{F}$ over the boundary of this region, oriented by selecting the outward normal.

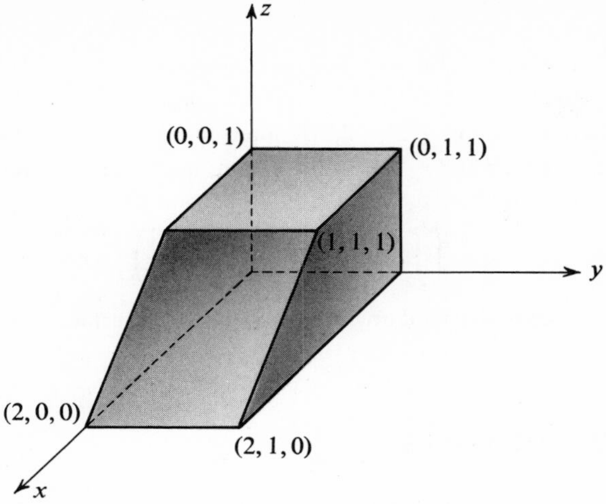

FIGURE 4.23

11. Calculate $\iint \mathbf{F} \cdot d\mathbf{S}$ over the section of surface described in Exercise 5, Sec. 4.6, for the vector field

$$\mathbf{F} = y\mathbf{i} - x\mathbf{j} + xy\mathbf{k}$$

12. Let us suppose that a field $\mathbf{F}$ due to a point "source" of "strength" q located at a point P has potential ϕ at a point Q given by $\phi(Q) = q/r$, where r is the distance from P to Q. Except when $r = 0$, ϕ is a harmonic function, that is, $\nabla^2\phi = 0$. Now suppose that the source is not concentrated at a single point but is distributed uniformly with density σ (source strength per unit area) over the surface of a sphere of radius a. If Q is the point (x_0,y_0,z_0), the potential at Q must then be found by integration,

$$\phi(x_0,y_0,z_0) = \iint \frac{\sigma\, dS}{\sqrt{(x-x_0)^2 + (y-y_0)^2 + (z-z_0)^2}}$$

where the integral is over the surface of the sphere. Give a heuristic line of reasoning to show that the potential is

(a) constant within the sphere, equal to $4\pi a\sigma$;

(b) equal to $4\pi a^2\sigma/b$ at any point outside the sphere a distance b from the center of the sphere. (*Hint*: Think of $\mathbf{F}$ as a scalar multiple of the electric field intensity due to a charge distribution and use Gauss's law.)

13. By interpreting the following integrals as potentials, find their values. Take the surface S to be the sphere $x^2 + y^2 + z^2 = 4$.

(a) $$\iint_S \frac{dS}{\sqrt{(x-1)^2 + y^2 + z^2}}$$

(b) $$\iint_S \frac{dS}{\sqrt{(x-3)^2 + y^2 + z^2}}$$

14. Evaluate

$$\iint_S \frac{dS}{\sqrt{(x-3)^2+(y-2)^2+z^2}}$$

over the surface $x^2+y^2+z^2=25$ by interpreting the integral as a potential.

15. Let $\mathbf{R} = x\mathbf{i} + y\mathbf{j} + z\mathbf{k}$ and $r = |\mathbf{R}|$. Show that, under certain circumstances, the integral

$$\omega = \iint \frac{\mathbf{R}}{r^3} \cdot \mathbf{n}\, dS = -\iint \left(\nabla \frac{1}{r}\right) \cdot \mathbf{n}\, dS$$

over a surface gives the solid angle subtended by the surface at the origin.

4.8 VOLUME INTEGRALS

We consider a function f (i.e., a scalar field) defined within and on the boundary of a domain V. We imagine that V is *bounded*, i.e., that there exists a cube R sufficiently large that every point of V is within R. We imagine the cube R subdivided into rectangular parallelepipeds by planes parallel to the coordinate planes. Ignoring those parallelepipeds that contain no points of V, we let the volumes of the parallelepipeds that do overlap V be denoted $\delta V_1, \delta V_2, \ldots, \delta V_n$, and in each parallelepiped select a point (x_i,y_i,z_i) in V. We form the sum $\sum_{i=1}^{n} f(x_i,y_i,z_i)\,\delta V_i$ and define the volume integral of f over V, if it exists, to be

$$\iiint_V f(x,y,z)\, dV = \lim \sum_{i=1}^{n} f(x_i,y_i,z_i)\,\delta V_i \tag{4.40}$$

that is, the limit as the dimensions of each volume δV_i tends to zero (which also makes n tend to infinity). For (4.40) to make sense in an unambiguous way, we require that the limit exist independently of the particular manner of subdivision. It can be shown that this is the case if f is continuous within and on the boundary of V; we omit the proof.

In general, as the reader has no doubt observed, we omit details of integration theory. The reader who is not familiar already with triple integration will want to study this subject elsewhere; perhaps it will suffice to review carefully the examples given in this section. In practice one is not often required to compute volume integrals, although they do arise somewhat more often than surface integrals, and are usually easier to compute. Since the volume of a rectangular parallelepiped with edges dx, dy, and dz is $dV = dx\,dy\,dz$, one sometimes writes

$$\iiint_V f(x,y,z)\, dx\, dy\, dz$$

instead of

$$\iiint_V f(x,y,z)\, dV$$

The volume of the domain V is defined by (4.40), taking $f(x,y,z)$ to be identically equal to unity:

$$\text{volume of } V = \iiint_V dV = \iiint_V dx\,dy\,dz \tag{4.41}$$

This notation tends to suggest the possibility of evaluating volume integrals by successively integrating with respect to x, then y, then z. This procedure is valid and we illustrate it below.

Since most students have less difficulty with volume integrals than with surface integrals, we shall not pause to give more than a few physical examples. One obvious example is that in which the function to be integrated is the mass density of a material. Let $\rho(x,y,z)$ denote the mass density of a material, say in grams per cubic centimeter, at a point (x,y,z). If ρ is a constant, the mass of any material occupying a volume δV is precisely $\rho\,\delta V$. If ρ varies from point to point, as may very well be the case for a compressible fluid, then if we take a point (x,y,z) in a small region of volume δV we can say that $\rho(x,y,z)\,\delta V$ gives approximately the mass of the material within this region. We can then interpret the sum $\sum_{i=1}^{n} f(x_i,y_i,z_i)\,\delta V_i$ as giving an approximation to the mass within the entire domain V, an approximation that improves as we take larger n and smaller δV_i. The integral (4.40) gives, in this case, precisely the mass contained in V.

Similarly, if f represents the charge density (charge per unit volume), the volume integral of f over V gives the net total charge contained in the region V.

Example 4.18 Find the volume of the region of space above the xy plane and beneath the plane $z = 2 + x + y$, bounded by the planes $y = 0$, $x = 0$, and the surface $y = 1 - x^2$.

Solution By (4.19), the volume is

$$\iiint_V dx\,dy\,dz$$

If we integrate with respect to z first, we obtain the volume of a strip with cross section $dx\,dy$; then letting y vary, we obtain the volume of a slice with thickness dx, and finally we integrate over x to obtain the total volume. Thus:

$$\begin{aligned}\int_0^1\int_0^{1-x^2}\int_0^{2+x+y} dz\,dy\,dx &= \int_0^1\int_0^{1-x^2}(2+x+y)\,dy\,dx\\ &= \int_0 (2y + xy + \tfrac{1}{2}y^2)\Big|_0^{1-x^2} dx\\ &= \int_0^1 (\tfrac{5}{2} + x - 3x^2 - x^3 + \tfrac{1}{2}x^4)\,dx\\ &= \tfrac{37}{20}\end{aligned}$$

Notice especially that in the first integral we give the limits on z as a function of x and y. This gives the integrand $(2 + x + y)\,dy\,dx$, which is the volume of a strip erected on the point (x,y) in the xy plane. Then we integrate, letting y vary, the limits of integration depending on x, to obtain the volume of a slice; the volume of this slice will depend of course on its x coordinate and on its thickness dx, as we see from Fig. 4.24. Then we "add up" the slices, beginning with that nearest the yz plane and ending with the slice at $x = 1$.

The volume could also have been computed by means of the integral

$$\int_0^1 \int_0^{(1-y)^{1/2}} \int_0^{2+x+y} dz\,dx\,dy$$

letting x vary before y. When this procedure is used, the last integration represents the summing up of slices parallel to the xz plane, beginning with the slice nearest the xz plane and ending with the slice at $y = 1$ (not shown in the figure).

Example 4.19 Find the volume integral of $f(x,y,z) = x + yz$ over the box bounded by the coordinate planes, $x = 1$, $y = 2$, and $z = 1 + x$.

Solution As in the preceding example, we can let z vary first, and then let either x or y vary. In Fig. 4.25, we let x vary before y, in contrast to the way we proceeded in Fig. 4.24. We obtain

$$\begin{aligned}\int_0^2 \int_0^1 \int_0^{1+x} (x + yz)\,dz\,dx\,dy &= \int_0^2 \int_0^1 (xz + \tfrac{1}{2}yz^2)\Big|_0^{1+x} dx\,dy \\ &= \int_0^2 \int_0^1 (x + x^2 + \tfrac{1}{2}y + yx + \tfrac{1}{2}yx^2)\,dx\,dy \\ &= \int_0^2 (\tfrac{5}{6} + \tfrac{7}{6}y)\,dy = 4\end{aligned}$$

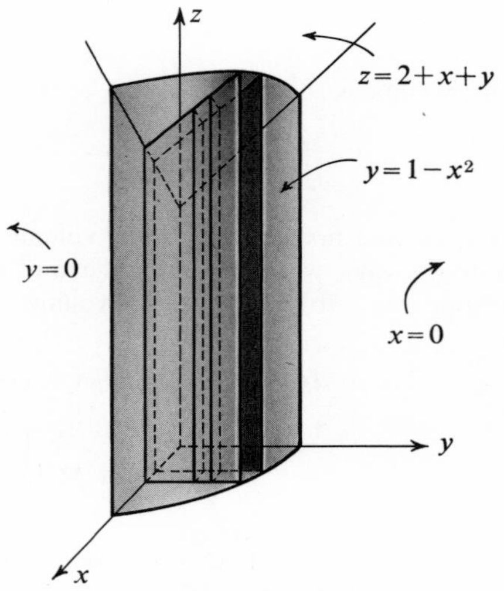

FIGURE 4.24

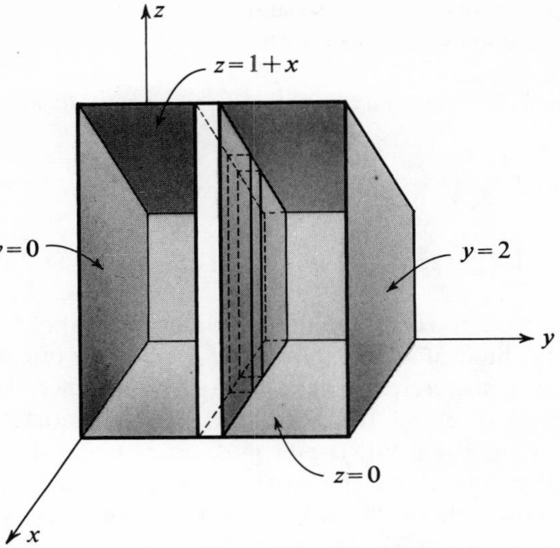

FIGURE 4.25

If we had let y vary before x, we would have had

$$\int_0^1 \int_0^2 \int_0^{1+x} (x + yz)\, dz\, dy\, dx = \int_0^1 \int_0^2 (x + x^2 + \tfrac{1}{2}y + yx + \tfrac{1}{2}yx^2)\, dy\, dx$$

$$= \int_0^1 (xy + x^2y + \tfrac{1}{4}y^2 + \tfrac{1}{2}y^2x + \tfrac{1}{4}y^2x^2)\Big|_0^2\, dx$$

$$= \int_0^1 (1 + 4x + 3x^2)\, dx = 4$$

We see from Fig. 4.25 that we could have let y vary first:

$$\int_0^1 \int_0^{1+x} \int_0^2 (x + yz)\, dy\, dz\, dx = \int_0^1 \int_0^{1+x} (xy + \tfrac{1}{2}y^2z)\Big|_0^2\, dz\, dx$$

$$= \int_0^1 \int_0^{1+x} (2x + 2z)\, dz\, dx$$

$$= \int_0^1 (2xz + z^2)\Big|_0^{1+x}\, dx$$

$$= \int_0^1 (1 + 4x + 3x^2)\, dx = 4$$

On the other hand, it is inconvenient to let x vary first, since when z is less than 1, x must range from 0 to 1, but when z is between 1 and 2, x ranges from $(z - 1)$

to 1. To let x vary first, we must separate the region into two parts by the plane $z = 1$ and write separate integrals for each part:

$$\int_0^1 \int_0^2 \int_0^1 (x + yz)\, dx\, dy\, dz + \int_1^2 \int_0^2 \int_{z-1}^1 (x + yz)\, dx\, dy\, dz$$

$$= \int_0^1 \int_0^2 (\tfrac{1}{2} + yz)\, dy\, dz + \int_1^2 \int_0^2 (2yz - \tfrac{1}{2}z^2 + z - yz^2)\, dy\, dz$$

$$= \int_0^1 (1 + 2z)\, dz + \int_1^2 (6z - 3z^2)\, dz = 2 + 2 = 4$$

As we have observed, although the volume integral of f over a domain V is defined as the limit of a sum, in practice the process of computing such an integral involves successive integrations. For instance, suppose that the domain V consists of all the points (x,y,z) that satisfy the inequalities $x_1 \le x \le x_2$, $y_1(x) \le y \le y_2(x)$, $z_1(x,y) \le z \le z_2(x,y)$. This means that V consists of all points above the surface $z = z_1(x,y)$ and below the surface $z = z_2(x,y)$, to the right of the surface $y = y_1(x)$ and to the left of the surface $y = y_2(x)$ (compare Fig. 4.24, where the latter two surfaces were $y = 0$ and $y = 1 - x^2$), and bounded behind by the plane $x = x_1$ and in front by the plane $x = x_2$ (in Fig. 4.24, the domain is bounded behind by $x = 0$, but no plane $x = x_2$ was specified since the surface $y = 1 - x^2$ bends around to provide the front boundary as well as the boundary on the right). Then the volume integral of f over V is

$$\iiint_V f(x,y,z)\, dx\, dy\, dz = \int_{x_1}^{x_2} \left[\int_{y_1(x)}^{y_2(x)} \left(\int_{z_1(x,y)}^{z_2(x,y)} f(x,y,z)\, dz \right) dy \right] dx$$

In computing the inner integral, y and x are treated as constants and only z is variable. In the next integration, x is treated as a constant and only y is variable. The last (outer) integral is an ordinary definite integral with x varying from x_1 to x_2. The variables disappear in steps: after the first integration, z vanishes; after the second, no y remains; and after the last integration x is gone and we are left with a numerical value.

EXERCISES

1. In Example 4.19, one volume integral was computed in four different ways. Repeat all of this, filling in all the missing steps in the calculations.

2. The volume of the region described in Example 4.19 obviously equals 3. Verify this four times by repeating each of the integrations given in Example 4.19, taking $f(x,y,z) = 1$ instead of $f(x,y,z) = x + yz$.

3. Sketch the region whose volume is represented by the triple integral

$$\int_0^2 \int_0^3 \int_0^{\sqrt{9-y^2}} dx\, dy\, dz$$

4. In this exercise you will be asked to make a simple conjecture on the basis of what you find on carrying out the following requests.

(a) Let $\mathbf{F}(x,y,z) = x^2\mathbf{i} + y\mathbf{j} + z\mathbf{k}$. Compute

$$\iint_S \mathbf{F} \cdot d\mathbf{S}$$

over the surface of the cube bounded by the planes $x = 0$, $x = 1$, $y = 0$, $y = 1$, $z = 0$, $z = 1$ (Fig. 4.26).

(b) Let $f(x,y,z) = \nabla \cdot \mathbf{F}$, and compute

$$\iiint_V f(x,y,z)\, dV$$

over the cube. Notice that here limits are no problem; we have simply

$$\int_0^1 \int_0^1 \int_0^1 f(x,y,z)\, dx\, dy\, dz$$

(c) If your answers to (a) and (b) are not equal, check your work until you find the mistake.

(d) Now invent another vector field $\mathbf{F}$ and repeat steps (a) and (b) above.

(e) What do you conjecture from this?

5. Let V be a domain with volume v. Let $\mathbf{F} = x\mathbf{i} + y\mathbf{j} + z\mathbf{k}$.

(a) What is

$$\iiint_V \nabla \cdot \mathbf{F}\, dV$$

(b) On the basis of your answer to Exercise 4, what do you conjecture is the value of

$$\iint_S \mathbf{F} \cdot d\mathbf{S}$$

the surface integral of the normal component of $\mathbf{F}$ over the boundary of V?

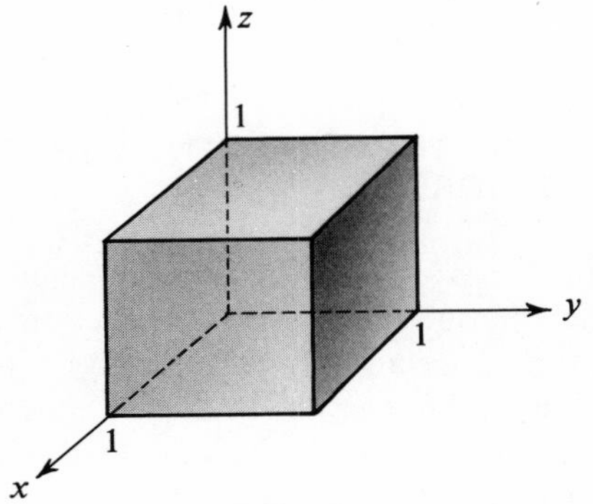

FIGURE 4.26

6. Find the volume of the region bounded by the surface $z = e^{-(x^2+y^2)}$, the cylinder $x^2 + y^2 = 1$, and the plane $z = 0$. (*Hint*: In cylindrical coordinates, $dV = r\,dr\,d\theta\,dz$.)

7. If $\rho(x,y,z)$ denotes the *charge density* (charge per unit volume) in a region of space, then the total charge in this region V is

$$q = \iiint_V \rho(x,y,z)\,dV$$

By Gauss's law we have

$$\iint_S \mathbf{E}\cdot d\mathbf{S} = \frac{1}{\varepsilon_0}q = \frac{1}{\varepsilon_0}\iiint_V \rho(x,y,z)\,dV$$

Combine this with your conjecture of Exercise 4 concerning

$$\iiint_V \nabla\cdot\mathbf{E}\,dV$$

What might this lead you to guess about the relationship between the divergence of $\mathbf{E}$ and the charge density?

8. Evaluate the following integrals over the region of space within the sphere $x^2 + y^2 + z^2 = 4$, by interpreting them as potentials and using Gauss's law. (See Exercise 11 of the previous section.)

(a)
$$\iiint \frac{dx\,dy\,dz}{\sqrt{(x-1)^2 + y^2 + z^2}}$$

(b)
$$\iiint \frac{dx\,dy\,dz}{\sqrt{(x-3)^2 + y^2 + z^2}}$$

9. Evaluate

$$\iiint \frac{dx\,dy\,dz}{\sqrt{(x-9)^2 + (y-2)^2 + z^2}}$$

where the integral extends over the interior of the sphere $x^2 + y^2 + z^2 = 4$, by interpreting the integral as a potential.

4.9 INTRODUCTION TO THE DIVERGENCE THEOREM AND STOKES' THEOREM

With these preliminaries on integration completed, we can now turn to the interesting part of our work. In this section we introduce two theorems of fundamental importance in vector analysis; most of our work so far has been intended as preliminary to these two theorems. They will be stated more precisely in later sections; here we intend to state them in crude form, without giving the precise conditions on continuity, differentiability, etc., and we will give proofs for the theorems that are instructive but quite nonrigorous. In later sections more careful proofs will be given. First we present the divergence theorem.

THEOREM 4.3. *The volume integral of the divergence* of a vector field, taken throughout a bounded domain D, *equals the surface integral of the normal component* of the vector field taken over the boundary of D. In other words, the total divergence within D equals the net flux emerging from D.

Here is a "simplified proof"; a rigorous proof will be given later.

Proof First let us consider a small rectangular parallelepiped bounded by planes of constant x, $x + dx$, y, $y + dy$, z, and $z + dz$. The surface integral of $\mathbf{F} \cdot \mathbf{n}$ over the six faces of this solid is the total flux of $\mathbf{F}$ out of the box. In Sec. 3.3 we showed that this flux is approximately given by

$$\nabla \cdot \mathbf{F}\, dx\, dy\, dz$$

Now let us divide the domain D into many small parallelepipeds. The net outward flux of $\mathbf{F}$ from D is the sum of the net outward flux over all the little parallelepipeds, since if two such parallelepipeds are adjacent, the flux outward from one over the surface they have in common is exactly equal to the flux inward to the other, so that all we have left is the flux over the exterior surfaces. It follows that the net outward flux of $\mathbf{F}$ from D equals approximately $\sum$ (div $\mathbf{F}$) δV, where we sum over all the parallelepipeds. Passing to the limit by taking repeatedly smaller subdivisions, we see that the net flux emerging from D equals

$$\iiint \operatorname{div} \mathbf{F}\, dV$$

There are some weaknesses, of course, in the above "proof". One of the biggest flaws in it is the assumption that the domain can be divided up into rectangular boxes by planes parallel to the coordinate planes. Even for a sphere this is impossible; some of the parallelepipeds would need to have inclined surfaces. Of course, there is nothing disgraceful about such "simplified proofs"; often a mathematician develops such an argument, even though obviously faulty, as a preliminary to constructing a rigorous proof.

The divergence theorem is sometimes called Gauss's theorem, because of its close relationship to Gauss's law (Sec. 4.7). To see the connection, it is necessary to know that the divergence of electric field intensity is a scalar multiple of the charge density. Hence the volume integral of the divergence over any domain gives a scalar multiple of the total charge q within the domain. It follows from the divergence theorem that the surface integral of the normal component of the electric intensity, over the boundary of a domain, is a scalar multiple of the charge inside. However, Gauss's law is not just a special case of the divergence theorem, since it can be applied to point charges where the concept of charge per unit volume, in the ordinary sense, is meaningless.

Until some years ago, the divergence theorem was called Green's theorem in three dimensions.

Now let us turn to Stokes' theorem, the other fundamental theorem in vector analysis.

THEOREM 4.4 *The surface integral of the normal component of the curl* of a vector field, taken over a bounded surface, *equals the line integral of the tangential component* of the field, taken over the closed curve bounding the surface.

As with the divergence theorem, we have italicized the colloquial expression for the theorem, which is convenient to memorize.

Here we are considering a closed curve C in space and a surface S that is bounded by the curve. The theorem states that

$$\iint_S (\textbf{curl F}) \cdot \mathbf{n}\, dS = \int_C \mathbf{F} \cdot \mathbf{T}\, ds \tag{4.42}$$

where dS refers to the element of *area* and ds refers to *arc length*. We assume that S is a surface oriented by a field of unit normals $\mathbf{n}$, and that the line integral is taken along C in the direction determined positive by the orientation.

The "proof" we give is as follows (a more rigorous proof will be given later).

Proof. We subdivide the surface S into a set of small surface elements, each approximately rectangular. We first prove the theorem for each of these separate little rectangles. This suffices to prove the theorem in general, since we can sum over the rectangles. The sum of the surface integrals over the separate rectangles equals the surface integral over the whole surface, and the sum of all the line integrals equals the line integral around C since the line integrals over interior boundaries cancel in pairs (Fig. 4.27).

To prove (4.42) for a small rectangular area, we choose the coordinate axes so that the x and y axes are along the sides of the rectangle and the z axis is in the direction of $\mathbf{n}$. We then have $\mathbf{n} = \mathbf{k}$; hence

$$(\textbf{curl F}) \cdot \mathbf{n} = (\textbf{curl F}) \cdot \mathbf{k} = \frac{\partial F_2}{\partial x} - \frac{\partial F_1}{\partial y}$$

Therefore the left side of (4.42) is

$$\iint \left(\frac{\partial F_2}{\partial x} - \frac{\partial F_1}{\partial y}\right) dx\, dy$$

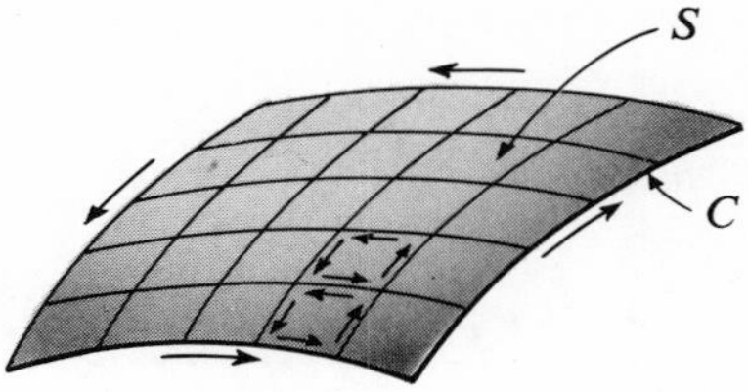

FIGURE 4.27

We split this up into two integrals, choosing the order of integration differently in the two cases:

$$\int_0^b \int_0^a \frac{\partial F_2}{\partial x}\,dx\,dy - \int_0^a \int_0^b \frac{\partial F_1}{\partial y}\,dy\,dx$$

$$= \int_0^b F_2(x,y)\Big|_{x=0}^{x=a} dy - \int_0^a F_1(x,y)\Big|_{y=0}^{y=b} dx$$

$$= \int_0^b [F_2(a,y) - F_2(0,y)]\,dy - \int_0^a [F_1(x,b) - F_1(x,0)]\,dx$$

$$= \int_0^b F_2(a,y)\,dy + \int_b^0 F_2(0,y)\,dy + \int_a^0 F_1(x,b)\,dx + \int_0^a F_1(x,0)\,dx$$

$$= \int_0^a F_1(x,0)\,dx + \int_0^b F_2(a,y)\,dy + \int_a^0 F_1(x,b)\,dx + \int_b^0 F_2(0,y)\,dy$$

This is precisely the line integral of **F** around the sides of the rectangle, $\int_C \mathbf{F} \cdot \mathbf{T}\,ds$, as we wished to prove.

What mistakes are involved in this "proof"? First, it is generally not possible to chop up a surface S into a number of rectangles, and what precisely is meant by the term "approximately rectangular" used above? Even if we could give some precise definition, we would need to pass to a limit in some sense, taking smaller subdivisions, and show that both sides of (4.42) converge to the actual surface and line integrals, respectively, over S and around C

This is not the main objection, however; there is a more fundamental one, involved in choosing the coordinate axes so that the x and y axes are along two sides of the rectangle. Let us analyze this more closely.

Suppose, for the sake of argument, that the surface S is a rectangle. Then the first objection above does not apply, we do not need to chop up S at all. If it happens that S is already in the xy plane, lying along the x and y axes as shown in Fig. 4.28, then there is no objection to the proof given above (provided we assume continuity of the relevant partial derivatives, etc., so that the integrals exist). But suppose S is not in the xy plane. The above procedure amounts to choosing a new set of coordinates x', y', z' so that S is in the plane

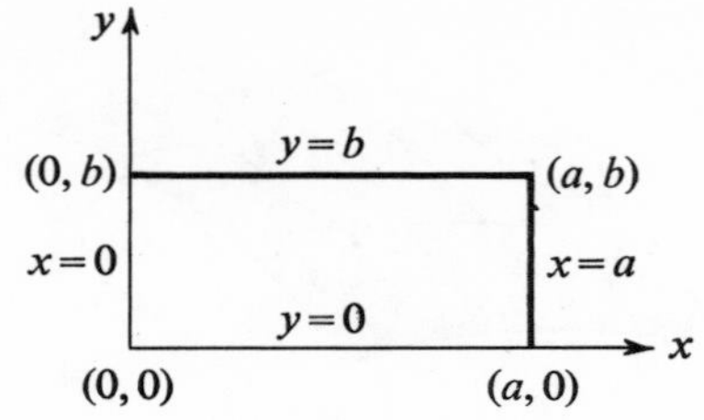

FIGURE 4.28

$z' = 0$ and has sides along the x' and y' axes, and the above argument shows that (4.42) is valid when we compute everything relative to the coordinates x', y', and z'. *But how do we know that* (4.42) *is valid relative to the original coordinates x, y, and z?* This is a serious objection, because we have defined **curl F** in terms of a fixed set of coordinates, and we have not yet studied what happens when we change to another set of coordinates.

Let us be very explicit about this, because it is conceptually very important. Let us suppose we are given a vector field **F** in terms of coordinates x, y, and z. Suppose now we are given new coordinates x', y', and z', which we can express as functions of the old coordinates x, y, and z. Substituting into $\mathbf{F}(x,y,z)$, we can now write **F** in terms of x', y', and z'. Now let us compute **curl F** in terms of x', y', and z', and afterward change back to x, y, and z, so that we have **curl F** in terms of x, y, and z. The question is, do we get the same thing as we would get computing **curl F** directly, from the very beginning, in terms of x, y, and z?

In other words, does the curl of a vector field depend only on the nature of the field, or does it also depend on our particular choice of coordinate axes?

We shall show in the next chapter that the curl does not depend on the choice of coordinate axes provided (*i*) that we always choose axes that are mutually perpendicular, (*ii*) that we are consistent in the way we mark off distances on these axes (physically, this means that we select some unit of distance, say centimeters, and mark all axes so that distances come out in centimeters), (*iii*) and that we always take a right-handed coordinate system, i.e., one for which $\mathbf{i} \times \mathbf{j} = \mathbf{k}$.

In fact, we should expect this to be true; after all, we saw in Sec. 3.4 that the curl has a "coordinate-free" interpretation, as the local angular velocity of a fluid. Similarly, the divergence measures the rate of change of density of a compressible fluid (Sec. 3.3), and the gradient gives the direction and magnitude of the maximum rate of change of a scalar. Therefore it should not be surprising that these three quantities behave in an "invariant" manner under coordinate transformations.

In this connection, it is worth mentioning that some textbooks (not written in English) consistently use left-handed coordinates, as in Fig. 4.29. Then either $\mathbf{i} \times \mathbf{j} = -\mathbf{k}$ or the definition of vector cross products must be

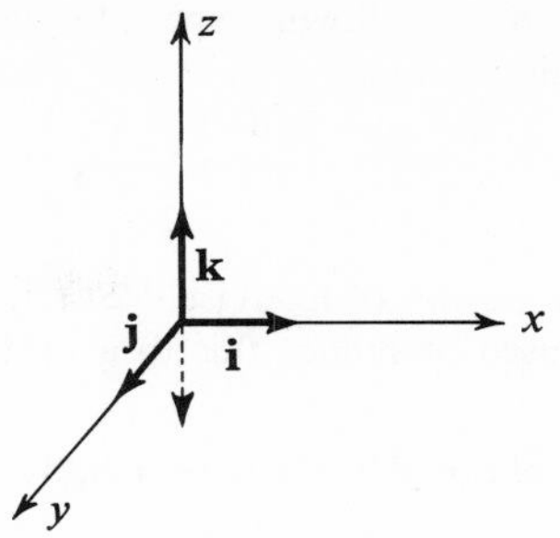

FIGURE 4.29

modified to give $\mathbf{i} \times \mathbf{j} = \mathbf{k}$, in which case our "right-hand rule" (Sec. 1.12) becomes a "left-hand rule." (This convention has an obvious advantage for a right-handed student who is pressed for time when taking an examination; he need not put his pencil down when applying the left-hand rule, since his left hand is free.)

We shall return later on to this important matter of coordinate transformations.

Summarizing, we have given rough statements of the divergence theorem and Stokes' theorem, and have given instructive but incorrect proofs of both theorems. Before proceeding to a more careful analysis the reader is strongly urged to study the following examples and work the exercises. These are the most important theorems in this book and they must ultimately be thoroughly understood.

The student who has studied attentively up to this point is "over the hump". *The rest of this book is devoted entirely to the deeper study of concepts already introduced.*

EXERCISES

1. Use the divergence theorem to solve Exercise 1, Sec. 4.7.
2. Do all seven parts of Exercise 2, Sec. 4.7, by computing

$$\int_{-1}^{1}\int_{-1}^{1}\int_{-1}^{1} \nabla \cdot \mathbf{F}\, dx\, dy\, dz$$

   in each case.
3. Use the divergence theorem to solve
   (a) Exercise 7, Sec. 4.7;
   (b) Exercise 8, Sec. 4.7.
4. Use Stokes' theorem to solve Exercise 8, Sec. 4.1.
5. Use Stokes' theorem to solve Exercise 10, Sec. 4.1.

6. Verify Stokes' theorem in the following special cases. Let C be the square in the xy plane with equation $|x| + |y| = 1$. Let $\mathbf{F}$ be as follows:
(a) $\mathbf{F} = x\mathbf{i}$
(b) $\mathbf{F} = y\mathbf{i}$
(c) $\mathbf{F} = -y\mathbf{i} + x\mathbf{j}$
(d) $\mathbf{F} = \mathbf{i} + \mathbf{j}$
(e) $\mathbf{F} = y^3\mathbf{i}$

7. Despite the fact that the surface of Exercise 9, Sec. 4.7, is not closed, the divergence theorem can be used to reduce this to a problem in mental arithmetic. Show how to do this.

8. The moment of inertia about the z axis of a body is defined as

$$\iiint_V (x^2 + y^2)\, dx\, dy\, dz$$

Express this as the flux of some vector field through the surface of the body.

9. One can compute the volume of a room by calculating the flux of the vector $\mathbf{R}$ through the walls. Show this.

10. By means of Stokes' theorem, find

$$\int \mathbf{F} \cdot d\mathbf{R}$$

around the ellipse $x^2 + y^2 = 1$, $z = y$, where

$$\mathbf{F} = x\mathbf{i} + (x + y)\mathbf{j} + (x + y + z)\mathbf{k}$$

11. The abstract concept of a gooney sphere is derived from the shape of a gooney egg. A gooney bird is born with a pointed head and a prominent stubby tail; therefore the shape of the egg is roughly ellipsoidal but with pointed ends. Surface integrals over gooney spheres are difficult to compute; tables of gooney functions are needed, but these were tabulated during the war and are still classified top secret. All that is known is that a gooney sphere of minimal diameter $d = 1$ has volume approximately 0.7. (a) Find the surface integral of the normal component of $\mathbf{F} = x\mathbf{i} + y\mathbf{j} + z\mathbf{k}$ over the surface of a gooney sphere with center at the origin and minimal diameter $d = 2$, making any assumptions you deem reasonable. (b) Would your answer be the same if the gooney sphere had center at $(2,7,-3)$?

12. If electric field intensity is $\mathbf{E} = (x + 1)^2\mathbf{i} + y\mathbf{j} + z\mathbf{k}$, relevant to suitable choices of the units involved, what is the total charge within the cube bounded by the planes $x = 0$, $x = 1$, $y = 0$, $y = 1$, $z = 0$ and $z = 1$? Evaluate the left side of (4.39), (a) directly, (b) by the divergence theorem.

13. If $\mathbf{R} + x\mathbf{i} + y\mathbf{j} + z\mathbf{k}$ and $r = |\mathbf{R}|$, find

$$\iint r\mathbf{R} \cdot \mathbf{n}\, dS$$

over the surface of a sphere of radius b and center at the origin,
(a) by interpreting the integrand geometrically;
(b) by using the divergence theorem.

14. Given

$$\mathbf{F} = \frac{x\mathbf{i} + y\mathbf{i} + z\mathbf{k}}{x^2 + y^2 + z^2}$$

find the surface integral of the normal component of **F** over the surface of the sphere $x^2 + y^2 + z^2 = 4$. Can you use the divergence theorem?

15. Given $\phi(x,y,z) = xyz + 5$, find the surface integral of the normal component of **grad** ϕ over $x^2 + y^2 + z^2 = 9$.

16. (a) Show that, if ϕ is harmonic, $\nabla \cdot (\phi \nabla \phi) = |\nabla \phi|^2$.
(b) Given $\phi = 3x + 2y + 4z$, evaluate

$$\iint \phi \frac{\partial \phi}{\partial n}\, dS$$

over the surface $x^2 + y^2 + z^2 = 4$. Here, $\partial\phi/\partial n$ represents the normal derivative of ϕ, that is, $\mathbf{n} \cdot \nabla\phi$.

17. Let $\mathbf{F} = \phi\nabla\phi$. Find the surface integral of the normal component of **F** over the surface of a sphere of radius 3 and center at the origin,
(a) if $\phi = x + y + z$;
(b) if $\phi = x^2 + y^2 + z^2$.

4.10 THE DIVERGENCE THEOREM

As previously promised, we shall now delve into a more careful, detailed analysis of the divergence theorem. To fix ideas for the moment, let us consider a vector field

$$\mathbf{F} = F_1\mathbf{i} + F_2\mathbf{j} + F_3\mathbf{k}$$

defined throughout a region, with components F_1, F_2, F_3 having continuous partial derivatives in this region. Let S denote the surface of a sphere, located within the region, and let D denote the set of points within S. Let **n** denote the field of unit vectors normal to S. At each point on S, we take **n** to be the *outward* normal, thus orienting S in the conventional way.

Consider the surface integral

$$\iint_S \mathbf{F} \cdot \mathbf{n}\, dS \tag{4.43}$$

Written out in terms of its components, this becomes

$$\iint_S (F_1\mathbf{i} + F_2\mathbf{j} + F_3\mathbf{k}) \cdot \mathbf{n}\, dS \tag{4.44}$$

which equals

$$\iint_S F_1(\mathbf{n} \cdot \mathbf{i})\, dS + \iint_S F_2(\mathbf{n} \cdot \mathbf{j})\, dS + \iint_S F_3(\mathbf{n} \cdot \mathbf{k})\, dS \tag{4.45}$$

Let us concentrate on only one of these integrals, the one in the middle. Consider the sphere to be cut up into filaments, each parallel to the y axis. A typical filament is shown in Fig. 4.30. It has cross-sectional area $dx\,dz$ and cuts out two portions from S, having areas $\delta S'$ and $\delta S''$. The contribution to the middle integral of the two portions is approximately

$$F_2'(\mathbf{n}' \cdot \mathbf{j})\,\delta S' + F_2''(\mathbf{n}'' \cdot \mathbf{j})\,\delta S''$$

where F_2' and F_2'' are, respectively, values of F_2 at points on the two portions. By the area cosine principle (Sec. 4.6), $(\mathbf{n}'' \cdot \mathbf{j})\,\delta S''$ and $(\mathbf{n}' \cdot \mathbf{j})\,\delta S'$ are approximately equal to $dx\,dz$ and $-(dx\,dz)$ respectively, since the scalar product of two unit vectors equals the cosine of the angle between them. Therefore, the contribution from these two portions is $(F_2'' - F_2')\,dx\,dz$.

Since, by the fundamental theorem of calculus, we have

$$\int_{y'}^{y''} \frac{\partial F_2}{\partial y}\,dy = F_2'' - F_2'$$

it follows from the above discussion that the middle integral in (4.45) can be written

$$\iint_S \left(\int_{y'}^{y''} \frac{\partial F_2}{\partial y}\,dy\right) dx\,dz$$

where the middle integral is taken with y varying from y' to y'' within the sphere, and the double integral is taken over the projection of S on the xz plane. This equals the volume integral over D; hence we can write

$$\iiint_D \frac{\partial F_2}{\partial y}\,dx\,dy\,dz$$

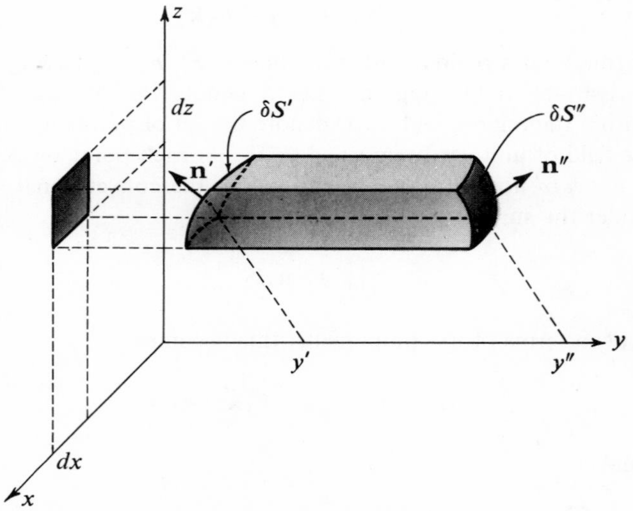

FIGURE 4.30

This shows that the surface integral of $F_2(\mathbf{n} \cdot \mathbf{j})$ over S equals the volume integral of $\partial F_2/\partial y$ throughout the domain enclosed by S.

Similarly, we can show that the surface integral of $F_1(\mathbf{n} \cdot \mathbf{i})$ over S equals the volume integral of $\partial F_1/\partial x$ throughout D; and $F_3(\mathbf{n} \cdot \mathbf{k})$ and $\partial F_3/\partial z$ are similarly related. Therefore (4.45) becomes

$$\iiint_D \left(\frac{\partial F_1}{\partial x} + \frac{\partial F_2}{\partial y} + \frac{\partial F_3}{\partial z}\right) dx\, dy\, dz$$

This is simply the volume integral, throughout D, of the divergence of the vector field $\mathbf{F}$. Since (4.43) equals (4.45) we obtain

$$\iint_S \mathbf{F} \cdot \mathbf{n}\, dS = \iiint_D \operatorname{div} \mathbf{F}\, dV \tag{4.46}$$

In this way we have proved the divergence theorem, already stated roughly in the preceding section. Notice that the same proof applies when S is the surface of an ellipsoid, a cube, a right circular cylinder, or even a potato-shaped region of a fairly arbitrary nature. Here is a more precise statement of the theorem.

THEOREM 4.3 (*The Divergence Theorem*) *Let D be any domain with the property that each straight line through any interior point of the domain cuts the boundary in exactly two points, and such that the boundary S is a piecewise-smooth, closed, oriented surface with unit normal directed outward from the domain. Let* $\mathbf{F}$ *be a vector field,* $\mathbf{F} = F_1\mathbf{i} + F_2\mathbf{j} + F_3\mathbf{k}$, *continuous throughout a region containing D and its boundary, and such that the partial derivatives of F_1, F_2, and F_3 are also continuous in this region. Then*

$$\iiint_E \operatorname{div} \mathbf{F}\, dV = \iint_S \mathbf{F} \cdot \mathbf{n}\, dS$$

In proving this theorem, we made strong use of the idea of cutting up the sphere by filaments parallel to a coordinate axis. We assumed in Fig. 4.30 that any such filament cuts out two portions from the surface. Thus the proof does not apply without modification to a domain such as the dumbbell-shaped one in Fig. 4.31. Here, such a filament can cut out four portions from the surface. However, it is easy to see that the theorem still applies to such a domain, since the dumbbell can be cut in the middle and the theorem applied separately to the two parts. The volume integral over the whole domain equals the sum of the two separate volume integrals, and the corresponding surface integrals add up to give the surface integral over the dumbell (there will be two contributions from the common boundary B, but they will cancel each other, since $\mathbf{n}$ will have opposite directions in the two integrals).

Let us now investigate one interesting consequence of the divergence theorem. Let us suppose that the domain D is a very small one surrounding a point P. If it is sufficiently small, div $\mathbf{F}$ will be approximately constant,

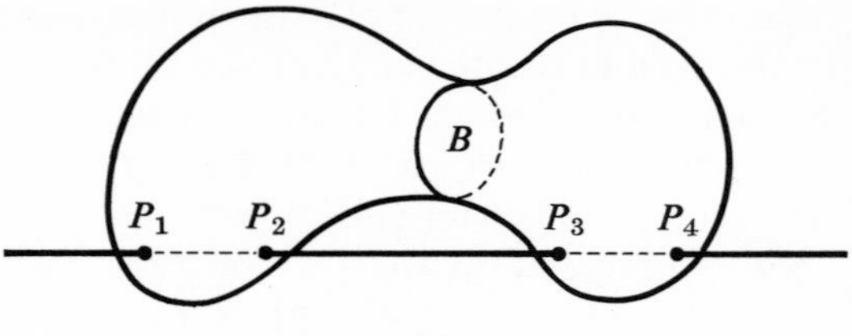

FIGURE 4.31

and the volume integral of div **F** over the volume V will be approximately equal to the product (div **F**)V. More precisely, we have

$$\lim_{V \to 0} \frac{\iiint \operatorname{div} \mathbf{F}\, dV}{V} = \operatorname{div} \mathbf{F}$$

By the divergence theorem, we can replace the volume integral of div **F** by the surface integral of **F** over the boundary enclosing the volume, from which it follows that

$$\operatorname{div} \mathbf{F} = \lim_{V \to 0} \frac{\iint_S \mathbf{F} \cdot \mathbf{n}\, dS}{V}$$

This was our original (motivating) definition of divergence; recall the discussion given in Sec. 3.3. We are now justified in saying that the divergence of a vector field **F** gives, at any point P, the flux output per unit volume at point P.

EXERCISES

Note: Computational exercises on the divergence theroem were given at the end of Sec. 4.9, and more are given at the end of this chapter. The following exercises are relatively more theoretical. Throughout these exercises, D and S have the properties stated in the divergence theorem.

1. At what point in the proof of the divergence theorem did we make use of the requirement that the partial derivative $\partial F_2/\partial y$ be a continuous function of y?

2. In the proof, we required that the three partial derivatives be continuous, i.e., that each of them be continuous in all three variables. Why, for example, should we care whether or not the partial derivative $\partial F_2/\partial y$ is a continuous function of x?

3. Show, by a diagram similar to that of Fig. 4.30, that the volume integral of a function, taken over D, can be obtained by first integrating with respect to z and then integrating over the projection of S on the xy plane.

4. Outline a proof of the divergence theorem, taking Exercise 3 as the starting point. Start with

$$\iiint_D \operatorname{div} \mathbf{F}\, dV$$

integrating first with respect to z. Your proof will differ only slightly from that given in this section, i.e., you will integrate first with respect to z rather than y. By using the definition of surface integral you can avoid completely any use of such words as "approximately"; for simplicity, assume that S is a smooth surface.

5. Where, in your "proof" (Exercise 4) did you make unconscious use of the fact that the points on S with normals parallel to the xy plane have a projection on the xy plane of zero area? [*Hint*: Look again at the definition of the area of a surface (Sec. 4.6). What is $\cos \gamma$ for such points?]

6. What is the flux output per unit volume at $(3,1,-2)$ if $\mathbf{F} = x^3\mathbf{i} + yx\mathbf{j} - x^3\mathbf{k}$?

7. What is the flux output from an ellipsoid of volume v if $\mathbf{F} = 3x\mathbf{i} + y\mathbf{j} + z\mathbf{k}$?

8. If $\mathbf{F} = 3x^2\mathbf{i} + y\mathbf{j} + z\mathbf{k}$, would the flux output from an ellipsoid depend on the location of the ellipsoid as well as on its volume?

9. (a) Describe the oriented surface enclosing the region

$$1 \leq x^2 + y^2 + z^2 \leq 4$$

assuming the usual convention concerning the orientation of a closed surface. (In Sec. 4.6 it was mentioned that if a surface encloses a region of space, the unit normal points away from the enclosed region; in this problem, the surface has two disconnected parts.)

(b) How would you compute the surface integral of the normal component of a vector field $\mathbf{F}$ over this surface?

(c) If $\operatorname{div} \mathbf{F} = 0$ except perhaps at the origin, what can you say about

$$\iint \mathbf{F} \cdot \mathbf{n}\, dS$$

over the two parts comprising this surface, taking $\mathbf{n}$ to be the unit normal outward from the origin in each case?

(d) Would your answer to (c) be any different if the region were that between the sphere $x^2 + y^2 + z^2 = 1$ and the ellipsoid

$$\frac{x^2}{4} + \frac{y^2}{9} + \frac{z^2}{16} = 1$$

(e) Compute the surface integral of the normal component of

$$\mathbf{F} = \frac{x\mathbf{i} + y\mathbf{j} + z\mathbf{k}}{(x^2 + y^2 + z^2)^{3/2}}$$

over the ellipsoid

$$\frac{x^2}{4} + \frac{y^2}{9} + \frac{z^2}{16} = 1$$

10. Using the divergence theorem, prove that

$$\iiint_D \nabla^2\phi \, dV = \iint_S \frac{\partial \phi}{\partial n} \, dS$$

where $\partial\phi/\partial n$, at any point on S, denotes the rate of change of the scalar field in the direction of the outward normal to S at that point. (*Hint*: Let $\mathbf{F} =$ **grad** ϕ).

11. Let ϕ be a scalar field, and define the *lumpiness* of ϕ at any point to be the scalar

$$-\lim_{V\to 0} \frac{\displaystyle\iint_S \frac{\partial \phi}{\partial n}\, dS}{V}$$

with notation as used in this section.

(a) Explain in your own words why the word "lumpiness" is appropriate. (*Hint*: Think of ϕ as the density of a fluid or, if you prefer, as the concentration of salt at each point in a brine solution.)

(b) How is lumpiness related to the laplacian?

(c) What can you say about the lumpiness of a harmonic function? (See Section 3.6.)

12. Let $\phi(x,y,z)$ be the temperature at (x,y,z). If ϕ represents a steady-state temperature distribution, show that ϕ is a harmonic function. [*Hint*: This can be done directly, using the fact (Sec. 4.7) that $\mathbf{Q} = -k$ **grad** ϕ gives the rate of heat flow per unit area, by drawing a small parallelepiped. However, it is intended here that you make use of Exercise 10 and the ideas of Exercise 11.]

13. Suppose that ϕ represents a temperature distribution that is not steady-state, so that ϕ is a function of both position and time. Find the relationship between the laplacian of ϕ and the time rate of change of ϕ at each point. (Let k denote the coefficient of thermal conductivity, let c denote specific heat capacity, and ρ the mass density.)

14. Let S be a sphere of radius b and center at a point P and let ϕ be a continuous function. Consider the integral

$$\iint_S \phi\nabla\left(\frac{1}{r}\right)\cdot \mathbf{n}\, dS$$

where $\mathbf{n}$ is the unit outward normal, and $r = |\mathbf{R}|$ where $\mathbf{R}$ extends from the center of the sphere to a variable point on the surface. What is the limit of this integral as b tends to zero? (You cannot use the divergence theorem since $1/r$ is not defined at $r = 0$. Observe that

$$\nabla\left(\frac{1}{r}\right) = -\frac{\mathbf{R}}{r^3} \quad \text{and} \quad \mathbf{n} = \frac{\mathbf{R}}{r}$$

whence

$$\nabla\left(\frac{1}{r}\right)\cdot\mathbf{n} = -\frac{1}{r^2} = -\frac{1}{b^2}$$

for points on the surface.)

15. Let $\mathbf{F}$ be a vector field, defined and continuously differentiable everywhere except at a point P, and having zero divergence (except at P). Let S' be a closed surface (say, an ellipsoid) enclosing P, and let S denote the surface of a small sphere with center at P completely within S'. Compare

$$\iint_S \mathbf{F} \cdot \mathbf{n}\, dS \qquad \text{and} \qquad \iint_{S'} \mathbf{F} \cdot \mathbf{n}\, dS'$$

where $\mathbf{n}$ denotes the *outward* unit normal in each case.

16. Let ϕ be a function that is continuously differentiable and harmonic in a region bounded by a (suitably smooth) surface S, and let r denote the distance from a fixed point P in the interior of the region. Show that the value of ϕ at P is given by the formula

$$\phi(P) = \frac{1}{4\pi} \iint_S \left[\frac{1}{r}\frac{\partial \phi}{\partial n} - \phi \frac{\partial}{\partial n}\left(\frac{1}{r}\right) \right] dS$$

(*Hint*: Use the results of Exercises 14 and 15.) (This formula is of considerable importance in the theory of harmonic functions.)

17. Evaluate

$$\iint_S \left[\frac{1}{r}\frac{\partial \phi}{\partial n} - \phi \frac{\partial}{\partial n}\left(\frac{1}{r}\right) \right] dS$$

over the surface of the sphere $(x - 3)^2 + y^2 + z^2 = 25$, where $r^2 = x^2 + y^2 + z^2$ and $\phi = xyz + 5$. By using the formula given in Exercise 16, you should be able to write the answer down at once.

18. Evaluate

$$\iint_S \left[\phi \frac{\partial}{\partial n}\left(\frac{1}{r}\right) - \frac{1}{r}\frac{\partial \phi}{\partial n} \right] dS$$

(a) over the surface of the ellipsoid $\dfrac{x^2}{9} + \dfrac{y^2}{16} + \dfrac{z^2}{25} = 1$ where $r^2 = x^2 + (y - 1)^2 + z^2$ and $\phi = x^2 + y^2 - 2z^2 + 4$;

(b) over the surface of the cylindrical pillbox bounded by $x^2 + y^2 = 25$ and $z = \pm 10$, where $r^2 = (x - 2)^2 + (y - 1)^2 + (z - 3)^2$ and $\phi = x^2 - z^2 + 5$.

19. What is the value of the surface integral (Exercise 16) if P is outside the closed surface S?

4.11 GREEN'S THEOREM

This section is relatively elementary and is intended to provide some preparation for the next section.

Let us work entirely in the xy plane. Let C denote a closed smooth arc in the plane (Fig. 4.32). Consider the line integral

$$\int_C y\, dx$$

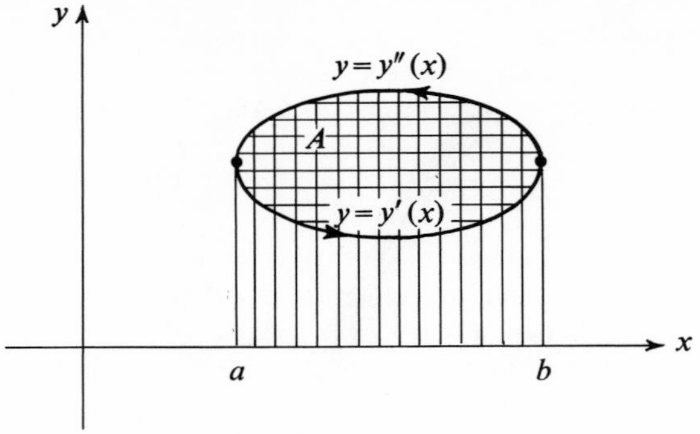

FIGURE 4.32

Since it is conventional to orient closed curves in the xy plane so that **k** is the positive normal to the plane, we traverse C in a counterclockwise direction. Therefore, the line integral can be expressed as the sum of two ordinary integrals,

$$\int_C y\,dx = \int_a^b y'(x)\,dx + \int_b^a y''(x)\,dx \tag{4.47}$$

where the first integral is along the bottom portion of the curve and the second is along the top portion; the notation should be self-evident from the figure. (Note that the primes here do *not* denote derivatives.)

The first integral gives the area beneath the lower curve and above the x axis. The second integral equals

$$-\int_a^b y''(x)\,dx$$

and gives the negative of the area beneath the upper curve and above the x axis. Therefore the sum of the two integrals is $-A$, the negative of the area within C,

$$\int_C y\,dx = -A \tag{4.48}$$

Here we assumed C to be in the upper half-plane, but the reader can easily verify that (4.48) also holds if C intersects the x axis or if C is beneath the x axis.

A similar argument shows that

$$\int_C x\,dy = A \tag{4.49}$$

Here we obtain A rather than $-A$, and is easily seen from Fig. 4.33.

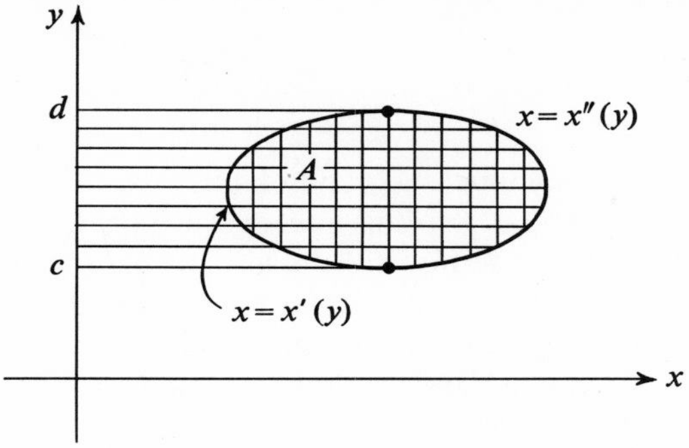

FIGURE 4.33

Now let us consider various other simple line integrals about C. For instance, it is easy to verify that

$$\int_C x\,dx = 0 \tag{4.50}$$

Indeed, $x\,dx$ is the differential of the function $x^2/2$ so that the line integral of $x\,dx$ gives the change in $x^2/2$ as we move from initial point to final point, but for any closed curve these points coincide and hence the line integral is zero. In similar fashion, since $y\,dy$ is an exact differential, we have

$$\int_C y\,dy = 0 \tag{4.51}$$

Also, we have

$$\int_C dx = 0 \tag{4.52}$$

$$\int_C dy = 0 \tag{4.53}$$

It is entertaining, though not particularly instructive, to combine these line integrals in various ways. For instance, if x_0 is a constant, we derive

$$\int_C (x - x_0)\,dy = A \tag{4.54}$$

by using (4.48) and (4.53). Similarly,

$$\int_C (x - x_0)\,dx = 0 \tag{4.55}$$

by (4.49) and (4.52).

Somewhat more interesting is

$$\int_C \tfrac{1}{2}(x\,dy - y\,dx) = A \tag{4.56}$$

which we obtain by combining (4.47) and (4.48).

In view of the fact that the line integrals in (4.47), (4.48), (4.54), and (4.56) may be interpreted in terms of the area A within C, it is natural to ask whether there are any similar interpretations for the other line integrals. More generally, suppose we are given an arbitrary differential $F_1(x,y)\,dx + F_2(x,y)\,dy$, where F_1 and F_2 are continuous functions. Is there any connection between the line integral of this differential about C and the area within?

The answer is both "yes" and "no". In general, there is no connection in the sense that we can draw a picture like that of Fig. 4.33 and interpret the integral in terms of areas. There is, however, a connection between the line integral about C and a double integral taken over the region within C. We will show that

$$\int_C F_1\,dx + F_2\,dy = \iint_D \left(\frac{\partial F_2}{\partial x} - \frac{\partial F_1}{\partial y}\right) dx\,dy \tag{4.57}$$

where D is the domain within C (having area A). In the special case that the integrand in the double integral on the right side of (4.57) is identically equal to one, the right side of (4.57) gives precisely A. If the integrand is zero, we get zero for the integral. In general, however, our result may not be related to A in any elementary manner and may be difficult to compute even with the help of (4.57).

The reader will recognize (4.57) as a special case of Stoke's theorem, discussed briefly in Sec. 4.9. To see this, let $\mathbf{F} = F_1\mathbf{i} + F_2\mathbf{j}$ and $\mathbf{n} = \mathbf{k}$. The integral on the left is the line integral of the tangential component of $\mathbf{F}$ about C, and that on the right is the surface integral of the normal component of **curl F** over the surface enclosed by C.

This special case of Stokes' theorem is sometimes called *Green's theorem*. (Several other theorems are also called Green's theorem, incidentally.) The precise statement of the theorem is as follows:

THEOREM 4.5 *Let F_1 and F_2 be continuous functions of x and y for which the partial derivatives $\partial F_2/\partial x$ and $\partial F_1/\partial y$ exist and are continuous throughout a domain D in the xy plane. We require that D be bounded by a regular closed curve C, oriented by choosing* **k** *as the unit normal to the plane. We also require that any line passing through an interior point and parallel to either coordinate axis cuts the boundary in exactly two points. Then* (4.57) *is valid. More generally,* (4.57) *is valid for regions in the plane that can be decomposed into finitely many domains having these properties.*

The proof of the theorem is similar to that of the divergence theorem and goes as follows.

Proof Let us first look at the right side of (4.57). The integral can be broken up into two integrals, of which the first is

$$\iint_D \frac{\partial F_2}{\partial x}\,dx\,dy$$

Integrating first with respect to x, we have (with notation as in Fig. 4.33)

$$\int_c^d \int_{x'(y)}^{x''(y)} \frac{\partial F_2}{\partial x}\,dx\,dy = \int_c^d [F_2(x'',y) - F_2(x',y)]\,dy = \int_C F_2\,dy$$

Similarly,

$$-\iint \frac{\partial F_1}{\partial y}\,dx\,dy = -\int_a^b \int_{y'(x)}^{y''(x)} \frac{\partial F_1}{\partial y}\,dy\,dx$$

$$= \int_a^b [F_1(y') - F_1(y'')]\,dx = \int_C F_1\,dx$$

Adding these two gives the desired result. If D is a region that can be decomposed into finitely many domains having the stated properties, we simply sum the integrals involved over all the domains. The double integral must extend over all the parts, and the line integral over the entire boundary. If the boundaries of two parts have arcs in common, these arcs may be neglected, since the integrals will cancel.

EXERCISES

1. Use Green's theorem to derive (4.48).
2. Use Green's theorem to derive (4.49).
3. Use Green's theorem to derive (4.50).
4. Use Green's theorem to derive (4.56).
5. Let $\mathbf{R} = x\mathbf{i} + y\mathbf{j}$ and $d\mathbf{R} = dx\,\mathbf{i} + dy\,\mathbf{j}$.
   (a) Compute the magnitude of the vector cross product $\mathbf{R} \times (\mathbf{R} + d\mathbf{R})$.
   (b) Thus give a direct geometrical interpretation of the integrand of (4.56). [*Hint*: Consider the triangle with vertices (0,0), (x,y), and $(x + dx, y + dy)$.]
   (c) Using Fig. 4.34, given an alternative derivation of (4.56).
6. Let $\mathbf{F} = x\mathbf{i} + y\mathbf{j}$, and let C be an oriented closed curve enclosing an area A. What is

$$\int_C \mathbf{F} \cdot \mathbf{T}\,ds$$

(As usual, $\mathbf{T}$ denotes the unit tangent to C in the positive direction.)

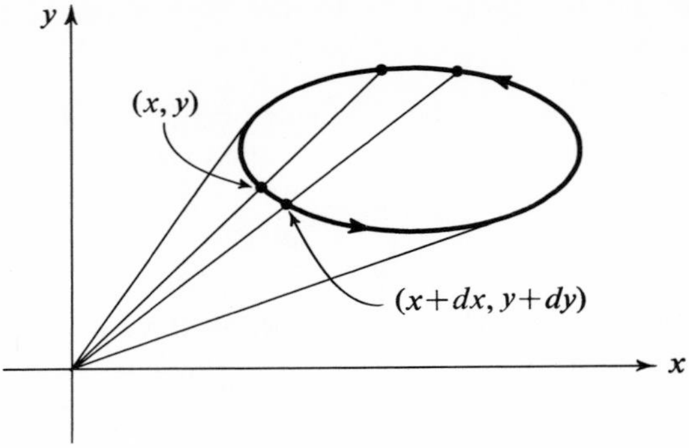

FIGURE 4.34

7. Let C denote the circle $x^2 + y^2 = 9$, and let $\mathbf{F} = y\mathbf{i} - 3x\mathbf{j}$. What is the line integral of the tangential component of $\mathbf{F}$ around C, taken in the usual counterclockwise direction?

8. Let C denote the ellipse $(x^2/4) + (y^2/9) = 1$, and let

$$\mathbf{F} = (3y^2 - y)\mathbf{i} + (x^2 + 2)\mathbf{j}$$

(a) What is the area enclosed by C? (Don't integrate, for heaven's sake; we have already derived the area of an ellipse by using the area cosine principle.)

(b) Find the line integral of the tangential component of $\mathbf{F}$ around C, in the counterclockwise direction. [*Hint*: By Green's theorem, this resolves itself to a double integral, but no computation is necessary if you observe that the symmetry enables you to ignore certain terms. Just multiply the area by the average value of $(\partial F_2/\partial x) - (\partial F_1/\partial y)$.]

9. Compute

$$\int_C 4y^3\,dx - 2x^2\,dy$$

around the square bounded by the lines $x = \pm 1$ and $y = \pm 1$,

(a) directly, by performing the line integration;

(b) by using Green's theorem.

(c) By symmetry, it is obvious that one of the terms in the integrand of the above line integral can be ignored. Which term?

10. Let $\mathbf{F} = 4z\mathbf{i} - 3x\mathbf{k}$. Compute the line integral of the tangential component of $\mathbf{F}$ about the circle $(x - 5)^2 + (z - 7)^2 = 4$ in the xz plane. Orient the plane by taking $\mathbf{j}$ to be unit normal. [*Careful*: If you just replace y by z in (4.57) you will get the wrong orientation.]

11. In (4.57), the functions F_1 and F_2 are fairly arbitrary functions of x and y (we only require that certain partial derivatives be continuous). It therefore appears that we can interchange F_1 and F_2 and also x and y to obtain the formula

$$\int_C F_2\,dy + F_1\,dx = \iint_D \left(\frac{\partial F_1}{\partial y} - \frac{\partial F_2}{\partial x}\right) dy\,dx$$

The left side of this equation is the same as the left side of (4.57), but the right side has the opposite sign. It follows that this expression is incorrect. Give a clue, *in only one word*, to explain away this paradox.

4.12 STOKES' THEOREM

Let S_{xyz} be a portion of a smooth, oriented surface in space, bounded by a piecewise-smooth, closed curve C_{xyz} whose orientation is consistent with that of S_{xyz}. We assume that parameters u and v can be introduced to provide a coordinate system on S_{xyz} and that x, y, and z are differentiable functions of u and v with continuous second partial derivatives. Let the orientation be so chosen that $(\partial\mathbf{R}/\partial u) \times (\partial\mathbf{R}/\partial v)$ points in the direction of the unit normal $\mathbf{n}$ (see Fig. 4.35).

Then there will be a region S_{uv} in the uv plane so that, to any point (u,v) in S_{uv} there corresponds a point (x,y,z) on S_{xyz}. We assume that distinct points in S_{uv} correspond to distinct points in S_{xyz}, and that S_{uv} is a simply-connected region with boundary C_{uv} (Fig. 4.36) for which Green's theorem applies:

$$\int_{C_{uv}} A_1\,du + A_2\,dv = \iint_{S_{uv}} \left(\frac{\partial A_2}{\partial u} - \frac{\partial A_1}{\partial v}\right) du\,dv \tag{4.58}$$

We will use (4.58) to derive Stokes' theorem:

THEOREM 4.4′

$$\int_{C_{xyz}} \mathbf{F}\cdot d\mathbf{R} = \iint_{S_{xyz}} \mathbf{curl\,F}\cdot d\mathbf{S} \tag{4.59}$$

assuming that $\mathbf{F}$ *is a continuously differentiable vector field.*

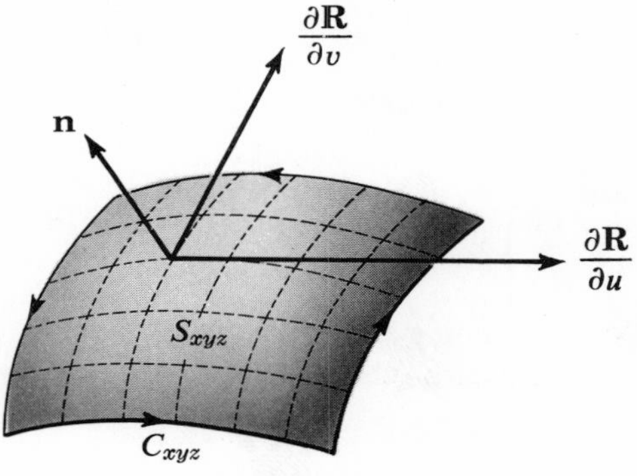

FIGURE 4.35

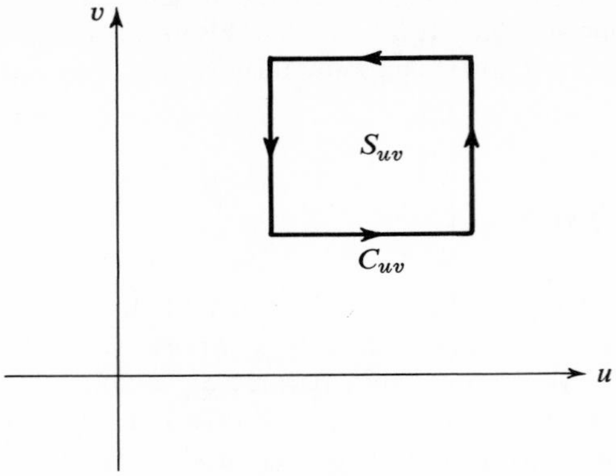

FIGURE 4.36

Observe that we are using the notation

$$d\mathbf{S} = \frac{\partial \mathbf{R}}{\partial u}\,du \times \frac{\partial \mathbf{R}}{\partial v}\,dv \tag{4.60}$$

introduced in Sec. 4.6. In the derivation we will use the identities

$$d\mathbf{R} = \frac{\partial \mathbf{R}}{\partial u}\,du + \frac{\partial \mathbf{R}}{\partial v}\,dv \tag{4.61}$$

and

$$\frac{\partial}{\partial u} = \frac{\partial \mathbf{R}}{\partial u} \cdot \nabla \tag{4.62}$$

$$\frac{\partial}{\partial v} = \frac{\partial \mathbf{R}}{\partial v} \cdot \nabla \tag{4.63}$$

Before going through the derivation, the reader may wish to review Sec. 4.6, and also the operator convention (first paragraph of Sec. 3.7). Thus, to derive (4.62), we simply use the chain rule in operator form,

$$\frac{\partial}{\partial u} = \frac{\partial x}{\partial u}\frac{\partial}{\partial x} + \frac{\partial y}{\partial u}\frac{\partial}{\partial y} + \frac{\partial z}{\partial u}\frac{\partial}{\partial z} = \frac{\partial \mathbf{R}}{\partial u} \cdot \nabla$$

and (4.63) is derived similarly. We will also use

$$\left(\frac{\partial \mathbf{R}}{\partial u} \times \frac{\partial \mathbf{R}}{\partial v}\right) \times \nabla = \frac{\partial \mathbf{R}}{\partial v}\left(\frac{\partial \mathbf{R}}{\partial u} \cdot \nabla\right) - \frac{\partial \mathbf{R}}{\partial u}\left(\frac{\partial \mathbf{R}}{\partial v} \cdot \nabla\right) \tag{4.64}$$

which is obtained by expanding the triple vector product and by using the operator convention. Similarly, the interchange of the $\cdot$ and $\times$ in

$$\mathbf{A} \cdot \nabla \times \mathbf{B} = \mathbf{A} \times \nabla \cdot \mathbf{B} \tag{4.65}$$

is easily verified.

Do not let these formalities obscure the basic idea, which is that the position vector **R**, for points on S_{xyz}, and also **F** itself at these points, can be written as functions of the parameters u and v, so the integrals in (4.59) can be written in terms of u and v. After we have done this, it appears that we are working in the uv plane.

Proof We write

$$\int_{C_{xyz}} \mathbf{F}\cdot d\mathbf{R} = \int_{C_{uv}} \left[\left(\mathbf{F}\cdot\frac{\partial \mathbf{R}}{\partial u}\right) du + \left(\mathbf{F}\cdot\frac{\partial \mathbf{R}}{\partial v}\right) dv\right] \quad \text{[by (4.61)]}$$

$$= \iint_{S_{uv}} \left[\frac{\partial}{\partial u}\left(\mathbf{F}\cdot\frac{\partial \mathbf{R}}{\partial v}\right) - \frac{\partial}{\partial v}\left(\mathbf{F}\cdot\frac{\partial \mathbf{R}}{\partial u}\right)\right] du\, dv \quad \text{[by (4.58)]}$$

$$= \iint_{S_{uv}} \left[\frac{\partial \mathbf{F}}{\partial u}\cdot\frac{\partial \mathbf{R}}{\partial v} + \mathbf{F}\cdot\frac{\partial^2 \mathbf{R}}{\partial u\,\partial v} - \mathbf{F}\cdot\frac{\partial^2 \mathbf{R}}{\partial v\,\partial u} - \frac{\partial \mathbf{F}}{\partial v}\cdot\frac{\partial \mathbf{R}}{\partial u}\right] du\, dv$$

$$= \iint_{S_{uv}} \left(\frac{\partial \mathbf{R}}{\partial v}\frac{\partial}{\partial u} - \frac{\partial \mathbf{R}}{\partial u}\frac{\partial}{\partial v}\right)\cdot \mathbf{F}\, du\, dv$$

$$= \iint_{S_{uv}} \left[\frac{\partial \mathbf{R}}{\partial v}\left(\frac{\partial \mathbf{R}}{\partial u}\cdot\nabla\right) - \frac{\partial \mathbf{R}}{\partial u}\left(\frac{\partial \mathbf{R}}{\partial v}\cdot\nabla\right)\right]\cdot \mathbf{F}\, du\, dv$$

[by (4.62) and (4.63)]

$$= \iint_{S_{uv}} \left(\frac{\partial \mathbf{R}}{\partial u}\times\frac{\partial \mathbf{R}}{\partial v}\right)\times\nabla\cdot\mathbf{F}\, du\, dv \quad \text{[by (4.64)]}$$

$$= \iint_{S_{uv}} \left(\frac{\partial \mathbf{R}}{\partial u}\times\frac{\partial \mathbf{R}}{\partial v}\right)\cdot\nabla\times\mathbf{F}\, du\, dv \quad \text{[by (4.65)]}$$

$$= \iint_{S_{uv}} (\mathbf{curl\ F})\cdot\left(\frac{\partial \mathbf{R}}{\partial u}\times\frac{\partial \mathbf{R}}{\partial v}\right) du\, dv$$

$$= \iint_{S_{xyz}} \mathbf{curl\ F}\cdot d\mathbf{S} \quad \text{[by (4.60)]} \tag{4.59}$$

which completes the derivation.

EXERCISES

1. At any point P in space, define the "swirl" of **F** at P in a direction **n** to be

$$\lim_{A\to 0}\frac{1}{A}\int_C \mathbf{F}\cdot d\mathbf{R} \tag{4.66}$$

where C is the circumference of a circle of area A centered at P with unit normal **n**. Using the word "swirl," define **curl F**. [*Hint*: Use Stokes' theorem to show that (4.66) equals (**curl F**) · **n**. Then use the maximum principle of Sec. 1.9

to define the direction of **curl F**.] Show that this justifies our "paddlewheel" definition in Sec. 3.4.

2. Be a bit fanciful, and imagine that S is the surface of a laundry bag with a draw-string forming the boundary C. Then Stokes' theorem states that the surface integral of the normal component of **curl F** over the laundry bag equals the line integral of its tangential component around the drawstring. Now suppose that we close the bag by pulling the drawstring; the effective length of the drawstring becomes zero and the line integral is therefore zero. S has become a closed surface.

(a) What is the surface integral of the normal component of **curl F** over a closed surface?

We now apply the divergence theorem, which says that the volume integral of the divergence of a vector field through the interior of a closed laundry bag equals the surface integral of the normal component of the field over its surface. Let the vector field be **curl F**.

(b) What is the volume integral of the divergence of **curl F** over a domain?

If the laundry bag is very, very small, the divergence of **curl F** will be approximately constant throughout, and the volume integral of div (**curl F**) will be approximately div (**curl F**), at a point within the laundry bag, times the volume the bag encloses.

(c) What is div (**curl F**) at any point P?

(d) To which of the identities of Sec. 3.7 is this related?

3. This is very similar to Exercise 2, but the point of view is somewhat different, Let S be the surface of a sphere, and let us imagine the sphere divided into two parts, an upper hemisphere and a lower hemisphere, by a plane parallel to the xy plane passing through its center. (Draw a diagram.) Let **F** be a vector field, and consider the surface integral of the normal component of **curl F** over the upper hemisphere. Relate this mentally to the line integral

$$\int_C \mathbf{F} \cdot d\mathbf{R}$$

where C is the equator, oriented relative to the outward normal of the upper hemisphere (i.e., the positive direction is west to east). Now do the same thing for the lower hemisphere: the surface integral of (**curl F**) $\cdot$ **n** over the lower hemisphere equals the line integral over the equator with, however, an east-to-west direction of integration. Add the two.

(a) What is the surface integral of the normal component of **curl F** over a sphere?

(b) What is the volume integral of div (**curl F**) through the interior of a sphere?

(c) Let the sphere shrink to a point; what does this say about div (**curl F**) at a point?

4. Suppose that $\mathbf{F} = \mathbf{grad}\ \phi$, so that the line integral of the tangential component of **F** along any curve is equal to the difference in the values of ϕ at the endpoints of the curve. In particular, if C is a closed curve,

$$\int_C \mathbf{F} \cdot d\mathbf{R} = 0$$

Let S be a surface with boundary C.

(a) What is the surface integral of the normal component of **curl (grad** ϕ**)** over a surface S?

If S is a very small element of surface, bounded by a closed curve C, **curl (grad** ϕ**)** will be approximately constant on S, and the surface integral of the normal component of **curl (grad** ϕ**)** will be approximately $\mathbf{n} \cdot$ **curl (grad** ϕ**)** times the area of the surface.

(b) For any unit vector **n**, and any point in space, what is $\mathbf{n} \cdot$ **curl (grad** ϕ**)** at this point?

(c) Since this result is independent of the direction of **n**, what can you say about **curl (grad** ϕ**)**?

(d) To which of the identities of Sec. 3.7 is this related?

5. Let **J** denote electric current density (a vector in the direction of the current, with magnitude in units of current/area) and **B** denote the magnetic field intensity. One of Maxwell's laws of electromagnetism states that, in the absence of a time-varying electric field,

$$\mathbf{curl}\ \mathbf{B} = \mu_0 \mathbf{J} \tag{4.67}$$

where μ_0 is a constant. Use Stokes' theorem to derive

$$\int_C \mathbf{B} \cdot d\mathbf{R} = \mu_0 i \tag{4.68}$$

In words: the line integral of the tangential component of magnetic field intensity, around a closed loop, is proportional to the current i passing across any surface bounded by the loop.

6. Given the vector field $\mathbf{F} = 3y\mathbf{i} + (5 - 2x)\mathbf{j} + (z^2 - 2)\mathbf{k}$, find (a) div **F**, (b) **curl F**, (c) the surface integral of the normal component of **curl F** over the open hemispherical surface $x^2 + y^2 + z^2 = 4$ above the xy plane. [*Hint*: By a double application of Stokes' theorem, part (c) can be reduced to a triviality.]

7. Given that $\mathbf{curl}\ \mathbf{F} = 2y\mathbf{i} - 2z\mathbf{j} + 3\mathbf{k}$, find the surface integral of the normal component of **curl F** (*not* **F**) over (a) the open hemispherical surface $x^2 + y^2 + z^2 = 9$, $z > 0$, and (b) the sphere $x^2 + y^2 + z^2 = 9$. (In both parts, you should be able to write the answer down by inspection.)

4.13 ORTHOGONAL CURVILINEAR COORDINATES

In practice, it is common to use coordinate systems other than cartesian coordinates. For example, one frequently uses spherical or cylindrical coordinates (Figs. 4.37 and 4.38). Other coordinate systems are also used, but less frequently. Since the coordinates in such systems (for example, ϕ in spherical coordinates) need not represent lengths, certain complications are introduced. Indeed, these complications are present even with cartesian coordinates, if one is rash enough to take, say, units of inches along one axis and units of feet along another.

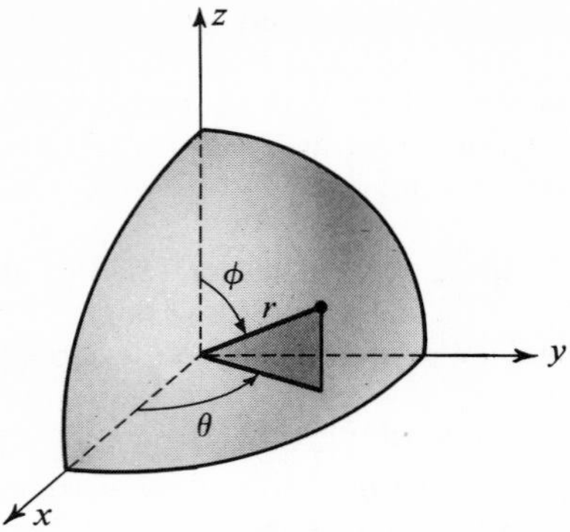

FIGURE 4.37

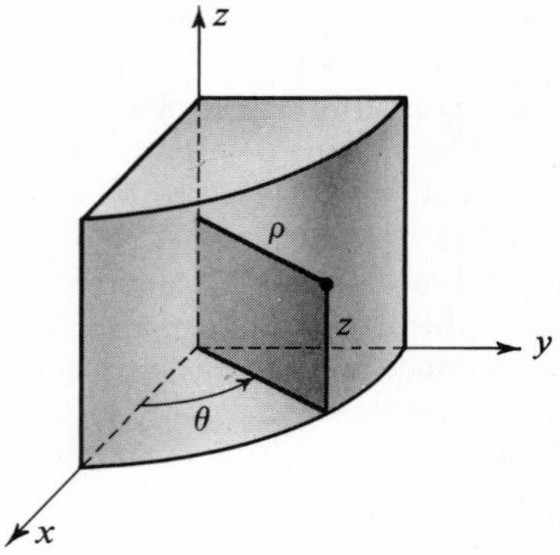

FIGURE 4.38

Let us suppose that we have one fixed set of cartesian coordinates x, y, and z, and that we agree to call

$$\sqrt{(x_1 - x_2)^2 + (y_1 - y_2)^2 + (z_1 - z_2)^2}$$

the distance between the points (x_1,y_1,z_1) and (x_2,y_2,z_2). Physically, this simply means we have agreed on some unit of length, say the centimeter, and that we mark the axes accordingly. Now suppose we let u_1, u_2, and u_3 be another set of coordinates. In other words, we have three functions

$$u_1 = f(x,y,z) \qquad u_2 = g(x,y,z) \qquad u_3 = h(x,y,z) \tag{4.69}$$

by which we associate to any point (x,y,z) an ordered triple (u_1,u_2,u_3) that we now call the curvilinear coordinates of (x,y,z).

For example, the equations

$$\begin{aligned} r &= \sqrt{x^2 + y^2 + z^2} \\ \phi &= \cos^{-1} \frac{z}{\sqrt{x^2 + y^2 + z^2}} \qquad (0 \leq \phi \leq \pi) \\ \theta &= \sin^{-1} \frac{y}{\sqrt{x^2 + y^2}} = \cos^{-1} \frac{x}{\sqrt{x^2 + y^2}} \qquad (-\pi < \theta \leq \pi) \end{aligned} \tag{4.70}$$

define what we mean by the spherical coordinates (r,ϕ,θ) of a point (x,y,z).

Polar coordinates (Fig. 4.38) are defined by the equations

$$\begin{aligned} z &= z \\ \rho &= \sqrt{x^2 + y^2} \\ \theta &= \sin^{-1} \frac{y}{\sqrt{x^2 + y^2}} = \cos^{-1} \frac{x}{\sqrt{x^2 + y^2}} \qquad (-\pi < \theta \leq \pi) \end{aligned} \tag{4.71}$$

It is not possible to define useful curvilinear coordinates by taking the functions f, g, and h entirely arbitrarily. For example, the curvilinear coordinates $u_1 = x^2$, $u_2 = y - z$, $u_3 = 2y - 2z$ would not be very useful because such pairs of points as (1,2,3) and (1,3,4) would have identical curvilinear coordinates $(1, -1, -2)$.

Therefore we shall assume that the functions f, g, and h assign different ordered triples to different points. Furthermore, we assume that they possess continuous partial derivatives of all orders, and that at every point P the gradients of these functions are nonzero and mutually perpendicular. To avoid difficulties with orientation, we assume that **grad** f, **grad** g, and **grad** h, in that order, form a right-handed system. If these conditions are satisfied, we say that (4.69) defines an *orthogonal coordinate system* in the domain.

Sometimes we do not require that the coordinates satisfy these requirements at every point in space. For example, if we pass through the z axis along a line parallel to the x axis, the spherical coordinate θ undergoes a discontinuous jump from 0 to π. We shall generally ignore this difficulty, and work only in a domain where the conditions are satisfied.

Example 4.20 Show that spherical and cylindrical coordinates each define orthogonal coordinate systems.

Solution Imagine that the sphere in Fig. 4.37 represents the surface of the earth. From our geometric interpretation of the gradient, we can see that **grad** r points in the local vertical direction, while **grad** ϕ and **grad** θ point south and east, respectively. These are mutually perpendicular and form a right-handed system.

Similarly, from Fig. 4.38 we see that **grad** z points upward, **grad** ρ points away from the z axis, and **grad** θ points counterclockwise in the xy plane; again these form a right-handed orthogonal system.

The conditions stated ensure that through each point P in the domain, having curvilinear coordinates (c_1,c_2,c_3), there will pass three isotimic surfaces $u_1 = c_1$, $u_2 = c_2$, $u_3 = c_3$. These surfaces intersect at P and intersect in pairs to give three curves passing through P (Fig. 4.39). Only one coordinate varies along each of these curves, which are called *coordinate curves.* The

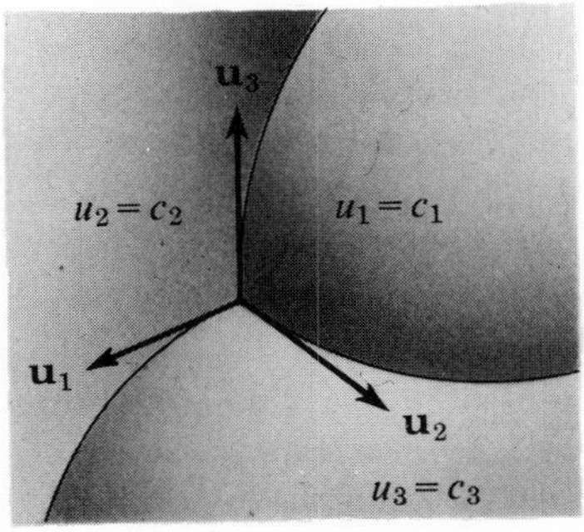

FIGURE 4.39

tangent to the curve along which, say, u_1 increases is parallel to the gradient of the function u_1, as the following argument shows.

(*i*) This curve lies in both surfaces: $u_2 = c_2$, $u_3 = c_3$; hence its tangent is perpendicular to the normals of both surfaces. These are **grad** u_2 and **grad** u_3, respectively.

(*ii*) **grad** u_1 is also perpendicular to **grad** u_2 and **grad** u_3, by definition of orthogonal coordinates.

(*iii*) This implies that the tangent to the curve is parallel or, perhaps, antiparallel to **grad** u_1. Since each points in the direction of *increasing* u_1, we conclude that they are parallel.

Thus the coordinate curves through P have mutually perpendicular tangents.

Along each coordinate curve, arc length is a function of only one curvilinear coordinate. Letting s_1, s_2, and s_3 denote the arc lengths measured along the coordinate curves in the direction of increasing u_1, u_2, and u_3 respectively, we define

$$h_1 = \frac{ds_1}{du_1} \qquad h_2 = \frac{ds_2}{du_2} \qquad h_3 = \frac{ds_3}{du_3} \tag{4.72}$$

where the derivatives are evaluated at point P. We call these the *scale factors* at P.

From the discussion in Sec. 2.2, we see that we can write

$$\frac{ds_1}{du_1} = \left|\frac{\partial \mathbf{R}}{\partial u_1}\right|$$

and similarly for u_2 and u_3; thus the scale factors can be evaluated from the formulas

$$h_i = \left|\frac{\partial \mathbf{R}}{\partial u_i}\right| \qquad (i = 1,2,3) \tag{4.73}$$

Example 4.21 Evaluate the scale factors for spherical coordinates.

Solution Inverting Eqs. (4.70), we express $\mathbf{R} = x\mathbf{i} + y\mathbf{j} + z\mathbf{k}$ in terms of r, ϕ, and θ:

$$\mathbf{R} = r \sin\phi \cos\theta\, \mathbf{i} + r \sin\phi \sin\theta\, \mathbf{j} + r\cos\phi\, \mathbf{k}$$

Thus

$$\begin{aligned} h_r &= \left|\frac{\partial \mathbf{R}}{\partial r}\right| = |\sin\phi\cos\theta\,\mathbf{i} + \sin\phi\sin\theta\,\mathbf{j} + \cos\theta\,\mathbf{k}| \\ &= 1 \\ h_\phi &= \left|\frac{\partial \mathbf{R}}{\partial \phi}\right| = |r\cos\phi\cos\theta\,\mathbf{i} + r\cos\phi\sin\theta\,\mathbf{j} - r\sin\phi\,\mathbf{k}| \\ &= r \\ h_\theta &= \left|\frac{\partial \mathbf{R}}{\partial \theta}\right| = |-r\sin\phi\sin\theta\,\mathbf{i} + r\sin\phi\cos\theta\,\mathbf{j}| \\ &= r\sin\phi \end{aligned}$$

These scale factors will allow us to write general formulas for arc length, volume, gradient, divergence, and curl in terms of curvilinear coordinates. In this section we will present heuristic derivatives for these expressions, postponing the rigorous arguments until Chap. 5, where we will generalize the theory to cover the case of nonorthogonal coordinates.

From the discussion above we can say that ds_i is the arc length along the ith coordinate curve, corresponding to a change in the ith coordinate from u_i to $u_i + du_i$. Since an arbitrary displacement $d\mathbf{R}$ is generated by changes du_1, du_2, and du_3, each in mutually perpendicular directions, we can express the element of arc length $|d\mathbf{R}|$ by the pythagorean theorem as

$$|d\mathbf{R}|^2 = {ds_1}^2 + {ds_2}^2 + {ds_3}^2$$

Using the scale factors from Eq. (4.72), we find that the *arc length along a curve C is given by the line integral*

$$\int |d\mathbf{R}| = \int ds = \int \sqrt{(h_1\, du_1)^2 + (h_2\, du_2)^2 + (h_3\, du_3)^2} \tag{4.74}$$

generalizing the formula in Sec. 2.2. In fact, since we also have

$$|d\mathbf{R}| = \sqrt{dx^2 + dy^2 + dz^2}$$

we can sometimes use (4.74) to identify the scale factors, as in the following example.

Example 4.22 Find the scale factors for cylindrical coordinates, using (4.74).

Solution Inverting Eqs. (4.71) we find

$$\begin{aligned} x &= \rho \cos\theta \\ y &= \rho \sin\theta \\ z &= z \end{aligned}$$

For the arc length we have

$$\begin{aligned} ds^2 &= dx^2 + dy^2 + dz^2 \\ &= (\cos\theta\, d\rho - \rho \sin\theta\, d\theta)^2 + (\sin\theta\, d\rho + \rho\cos\theta\, d\theta)^2 + dz^2 \\ &= d\rho^2 + \rho^2\, d\theta^2 + dz^2 \end{aligned}$$

Comparing this with (4.74), we see that

$$h_\rho = 1 \qquad h_\theta = \rho \qquad h_z = 1 \tag{4.75}$$

For the two cases we have examined, the scale factors can actually be determined directly by examining Figs. 4.37 and 4.38. In cylindrical coordinates (Fig. 4.38) the arc length ds_z generated by a displacement dz is equal to dz; the arc length for the displacement $d\rho$ is equal to $d\rho$; and the arc length for the displacement $d\theta$ is given by $\rho\, d\theta$. Thus the scale factors must be those in Eqs. (4.75). Similarly Example 4.20 could be analyzed geometrically by studying Fig. 4.37.

We can immediately generalize the discussion above to conclude that the line integral of a continuous function $f(u_1,u_2,u_3)$ along a curve C is obtained by

$$\int f(u_1,u_2,u_3)\sqrt{(h_1\,du_1)^2 + (h_2\,du_2)^2 + (h_3\,du_3)^2} \tag{4.76}$$

where, in practice, one usually has u_1, u_2, and u_3 given in terms of some parameter t; (4.76) then ultimately becomes an integral involving t and dt.

From Fig. 4.40 we observe that the solid generated by displacements du_1, du_2, and du_3 is approximately a rectangular parallelepiped with edges $h_1\,du_1$, $h_2\,du_2$, and $h_3\,du_3$. Its volume is, therefore,

$$dV = h_1 h_2 h_3\,du_1\,du_2\,du_3$$

Hence *the volume integral of a function* $f(u_1,u_2,u_3)$ *is given by*

$$\iiint f(u_1,u_2,u_3)\,dV = \iiint f(u_1,u_2,u_3) h_1 h_2 h_3\,du_1\,du_2\,du_3 \tag{4.77}$$

Again, we can integrate (4.77) iteratively, once the limits are specified. In spherical coordinates, $dV = r^2 \sin\phi\,dr\,d\theta\,d\phi$; in cylindrical coordinates, $dV = \rho\,d\rho\,d\theta\,dz$.

To express the gradient of $f(u_1,u_2,u_3)$ in curvilinear coordinates, we first define $\mathbf{u}_1$, $\mathbf{u}_2$, and $\mathbf{u}_3$ to be unit tangent vectors at the point P in the directions of increasing u_1, u_2, and u_3 respectively (Fig. 4.39). Thus

$$\mathbf{u}_i = \frac{\mathbf{grad}\,u_i}{|\mathbf{grad}\,u_i|} \qquad (i = 1,2,3)$$

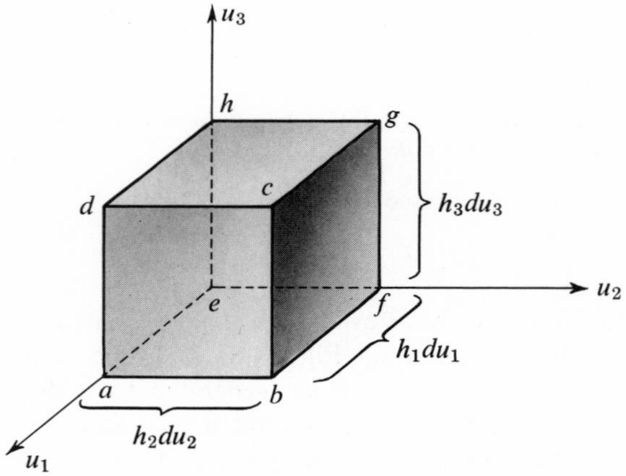

FIGURE 4.40

as we saw earlier. In Sec. 3.1 it was shown that the component of **grad** f in the $\mathbf{u}_1$ direction is given by df/ds_1, the rate of change of f with respect to distance in the $\mathbf{u}_1$ direction. Since $\mathbf{u}_1$, $\mathbf{u}_2$, and $\mathbf{u}_3$ are mutually orthogonal unit vectors, we can immediately express **grad** f in terms of these:

$$\mathbf{grad}\, f = \frac{df}{ds_1}\mathbf{u}_1 + \frac{df}{ds_2}\mathbf{u}_2 + \frac{df}{ds_3}\mathbf{u}_3$$

or, introducing the scale factors,

$$\mathbf{grad}\, f = \frac{1}{h_1}\frac{\partial f}{\partial u_1}\mathbf{u}_1 + \frac{1}{h_2}\frac{\partial f}{\partial u_2}\mathbf{u}_2 + \frac{1}{h_3}\frac{\partial f}{\partial u_3}\mathbf{u}_3 \tag{4.78}$$

The expression for divergence is more complicated. Let

$$\mathbf{F} = F_1\mathbf{u}_1 + F_2\mathbf{u}_2 + F_3\mathbf{u}_3$$

be the vector field, given in terms of the unit vectors $\mathbf{u}_1$, $\mathbf{u}_2$, and $\mathbf{u}_3$. We will calculate div **F** as the flux of **F** out of the sides of the box in Fig. 4.40, divided by the volume of the box, in accordance with the interpretation of divergence given in Secs. 3.3 and 4.9.

The flux density normal to the face *abcd* is $\mathbf{F} \cdot \mathbf{u}_1 = F_1$ and the area of this face is $h_2h_3\, du_2\, du_3$. Therefore the flux outward from that face is $F_1h_2h_3\, du_2\, du_3$. The unit outward normal to face *efgh* is $-\mathbf{u}_1$, so that the flux outward from that face is $-F_1h_2h_3\, du_2\, du_3$. Since F_1, h_2, and h_3 are functions of u_1 as we move along the u_1-coordinate curve, the sum of these two is approximately

$$\left[\frac{\partial}{\partial u_1}(F_1h_2h_3)\, du_1\right] du_2\, du_3$$

From this and similar expressions for the other two pairs of faces we see that the net flux outward from the parallelepiped is approximately

$$\left[\frac{\partial}{\partial u_1}(F_1h_2h_3) + \frac{\partial}{\partial u_2}(F_2h_1h_3) + \frac{\partial}{\partial u_3}(F_3h_1h_2)\right] du_1\, du_2\, du_3$$

and so the flux output per unit volume is this expression divided by the volume $h_1h_2h_3\, du_1\, du_2\, du_3$. Hence

$$\operatorname{div} \mathbf{F} = \frac{1}{h_1h_2h_3}\left[\frac{\partial}{\partial u_1}(F_1h_2h_3) + \frac{\partial}{\partial u_2}(F_2h_1h_3) + \frac{\partial}{\partial u_3}(F_3h_1h_2)\right] \tag{4.79}$$

Using (4.78) and (4.79), we have the expression for the laplacian:

$$\nabla^2 f = \operatorname{div}\, \mathbf{grad}\, f$$

$$= \frac{1}{h_1h_2h_3}\left[\frac{\partial}{\partial u_1}\left(\frac{h_2h_3}{h_1}\frac{\partial f}{\partial u_1}\right) + \frac{\partial}{\partial u_2}\left(\frac{h_1h_3}{h_2}\frac{\partial f}{\partial u_2}\right) + \frac{\partial}{\partial u_3}\left(\frac{h_1h_2}{h_3}\frac{\partial f}{\partial u_3}\right)\right] \tag{4.80}$$

Now let us find the expression for **curl F**. We shall use the "swirl" characterization described in Exercise 1 of Sec. 4.12. The component of **curl F** in the direction $\mathbf{u}_1$ will be the line integral of the tangential component of **F** around the curve *efghe* in Fig. 4.40, divided by the area enclosed by this curve. [Recall that, by Stokes' theorem, $\int_{efghe} \mathbf{F} \cdot d\mathbf{R}$ equals $\iint (\mathbf{curl\ F}) \cdot \mathbf{n}\, dS$, which is approximately $(\mathbf{curl\ F}) \cdot \mathbf{u}_1$ times the area.] The integral along the edge of *ef* is approximately

$$F_2(u_1,u_2,u_3)h_2(u_1,u_2,u_3)\, du_2$$

Along *gh* we are proceeding in the opposite direction; furthermore, the third coordinate is now $u_3 + du_3$, so the line integral is

$$-F_2(u_1,u_2,u_3 + du_3)h_2(u_1,u_2,u_3 + du_3)\, du_2$$

Thus the net contribution from *ef* and *gh* is given by

$$-\frac{\partial}{\partial u_3}(F_2h_2)\, du_3\, du_2$$

Similarly, the contribution from *fg* and *he* is

$$\frac{\partial}{\partial u_2}(F_3h_3)\, du_2\, du_3$$

Dividing by the area $h_2\, du_2\, h_3\, du_3$, we have

$$(\mathbf{curl\ F}) \cdot \mathbf{u}_1 = \frac{1}{h_2h_3}\left(\frac{\partial}{\partial u_2}(F_3h_3) - \frac{\partial}{\partial u_3}(F_2h_2)\right)$$

Reasoning similarly for the other components, we find that the curl is given by

$$\begin{aligned}\mathbf{curl\ F} &= \frac{1}{h_2h_3}\left(\frac{\partial}{\partial u_2}(F_3h_3) - \frac{\partial}{\partial u_3}(F_2h_2)\right)\mathbf{u}_1 \\ &\quad + \frac{1}{h_1h_3}\left(\frac{\partial}{\partial u_3}(F_1h_1) - \frac{\partial}{\partial u_1}(F_3h_3)\right)\mathbf{u}_2 \\ &\quad + \frac{1}{h_1h_2}\left(\frac{\partial}{\partial u_1}(F_2h_2) - \frac{\partial}{\partial u_2}(F_1h_1)\right)\mathbf{u}_3 \qquad (4.81) \\ &= \frac{1}{h_1h_2h_3}\begin{vmatrix} h_1\mathbf{u}_1 & h_2\mathbf{u}_2 & h_3\mathbf{u}_3 \\ \dfrac{\partial}{\partial u_1} & \dfrac{\partial}{\partial u_2} & \dfrac{\partial}{\partial u_3} \\ F_1h_1 & F_2h_2 & F_3h_3 \end{vmatrix}\end{aligned}$$

For reference purposes, we list the divergence, curl, and laplacian, in spherical coordinates:

$$\nabla \cdot \mathbf{F} = \frac{1}{r^2}\frac{\partial}{\partial r}(r^2 F_r) + \frac{1}{r \sin \phi}\frac{\partial}{\partial \phi}(F_\phi \sin \phi) + \frac{1}{r \sin \phi}\frac{\partial F_\theta}{\partial \theta}$$

$$\nabla \times \mathbf{F} = \frac{1}{r^2 \sin \phi}\begin{vmatrix} \mathbf{u}_r & r\mathbf{u}_\phi & (r \sin \phi)\mathbf{u}_\theta \\ \dfrac{\partial}{\partial r} & \dfrac{\partial}{\partial \phi} & \dfrac{\partial}{\partial \theta} \\ F_r & rF_\phi & (r \sin \phi)F_\theta \end{vmatrix}$$

$$\nabla^2 f = \frac{1}{r^2}\frac{\partial}{\partial r}\left(r^2 \frac{\partial f}{\partial r}\right) + \frac{1}{r^2 \sin \phi}\frac{\partial}{\partial \phi}\left(\sin \phi \frac{\partial f}{\partial \phi}\right) + \frac{1}{r^2 \sin^2 \phi}\frac{\partial^2 f}{\partial \theta^2}$$

Here are the corresponding expressions in cylindrical coordinates. We follow the usual practice of writing r instead of ρ, but the cylindrical coordinate r should not be confused with the spherical coordinate r.

$$\nabla f = \mathbf{u}_r \frac{\partial f}{\partial r} + \mathbf{u}_\theta \frac{1}{r}\frac{\partial f}{\partial \theta} + \mathbf{u}_z \frac{\partial f}{\partial z}$$

$$\nabla \cdot \mathbf{F} = \frac{1}{r}\frac{\partial}{\partial r}(rF_r) + \frac{1}{r}\frac{\partial F_\theta}{\partial \theta} + \frac{\partial F_z}{\partial z}$$

$$\nabla \times \mathbf{F} = \frac{1}{r}\begin{vmatrix} \mathbf{u}_r & r\mathbf{u}_\theta & \mathbf{u}_z \\ \dfrac{\partial}{\partial r} & \dfrac{\partial}{\partial \theta} & \dfrac{\partial}{\partial z} \\ F_r & rF_\theta & F_z \end{vmatrix}$$

$$\nabla^2 f = \frac{1}{r}\frac{\partial}{\partial r}\left(r \frac{\partial f}{\partial r}\right) + \frac{1}{r^2}\frac{\partial^2 f}{\partial \theta^2} + \frac{\partial^2 f}{\partial z^2}$$

EXERCISES

1. Work Example 4.21 geometrically, using Fig. 4.37.
2. By using the "lumpiness" definition of the laplacian (Exercise 11, Sec. 4.10) applied to a rectangular parallelepiped, give a direct derivation of (4.80).
3. By substituting into the formulas, obtain the expressions for divergence, curl, and the laplacian in spherical coordinates.
4. Evaluate and simplify $\nabla^2(r^n)$ by any convenient method, given that $r^2 = x^2 + y^2 + z^2$.
5. By substituting into the formulas, obtain the expressions for gradient, divergence, curl, and the laplacian in cylindrical coordinates.

6. By changing to cylindrical coordinates, find the divergence and the curl of

$$\mathbf{F} = \frac{x\mathbf{i} + y\mathbf{j}}{x^2 + y^2}$$

7. In cartesian coordinates, $dV = dx\,dy\,dz$. Beginning with (4.70), differentiate to form dx, dy, and dz in terms of dr, $d\phi$, and $d\theta$, and multiply to obtain $dx\,dy\,dz$.
   (a) Does this give dV in spherical coordinates?
   (b) Explain this phenomenon.

8. Let $u_1 = x + y$, $u_2 = x - y$, and $u_3 = 2z$.
   (a) Is this an orthogonal coordinate system?
   (b) Solve for x, y, and z in terms of u_1, u_2, and u_3.
   (c) Find ds^2 and hence determine h_1, h_2, and h_3 for this coordinate system.
   (d) What is the laplacian relative to this coordinate system?
   (e) Let $f(u_1,u_2,u_3) = u_1 + u_2 + 2u_3$. Find **grad** f.

9. Let $u_1 = x + y$, $u_2 = x - 2y$, and $u_3 = 2z$.
   (a) Solve for x, y, and z in terms of u_1, u_2, and u_3.
   (b) Attempt to determine the scale factors h_1, h_2, and h_3.
   (c) What is "wrong"?

10. What is the element of volume relative to the coordinate system $u_1 = e^x$, $u_2 = y$, $u_3 = z$? (Notice that the verification of orthogonality is easy in this case.)

11. Consider the coordinate system $u_1 = y$, $u_2 = x$, $u_3 = z$. The scale factors are all equal to unity, so that (4.81) takes an especially simple form.
   (a) Let $\mathbf{F} = -u_2\mathbf{u}_1 + u_1\mathbf{u}_2$. Show that (4.81) gives

$$\mathbf{curl}\,\mathbf{F} = 2\mathbf{u}_3$$

   (b) Obviously $\mathbf{u}_1 = \mathbf{j}$, $\mathbf{u}_2 = \mathbf{i}$, and $\mathbf{u}_3 = \mathbf{k}$, so that $\mathbf{F} = y\mathbf{i} - x\mathbf{j}$ and by part (a), $\mathbf{curl}\,\mathbf{F} = 2\mathbf{k}$. But direct calculation of $\mathbf{curl}\,\mathbf{F}$ in cartesian coordinates shows that $\mathbf{curl}\,\mathbf{F} = -2\mathbf{k}$, not $2\mathbf{k}$. What is "wrong"?

12. Letting $\mathbf{R} = x\mathbf{i} + y\mathbf{j} + z\mathbf{k}$, and $r = |\mathbf{R}|$, write the vector field $\mathbf{F} = \mathbf{R}/r^3$ in terms of r and $\mathbf{u}_r$.
   (a) Show that div $\mathbf{F}$ is identically zero throughout the domain of definition of $\mathbf{F}$.
   (b) Show that the surface integral of the normal component of $\mathbf{F}$ over the surface of the unit sphere $r = 1$ is 4π.
   (c) Explain why (a) and (b) above do not contradict the divergence theorem.
   (d) What is the surface integral of the normal component of $\mathbf{F}$ over the surface of a unit sphere with center 4 units away from the origin?

13. Evaluate $\iiint (x^2 + y^2 + z^2)^{3/2}\,dx\,dy\,dz$, integrated over the intersection of the sphere of radius 2 centered at the origin, and the first octant ($x > 0, y > 0, z > 0$). (*Hint*: Use spherical coordinates.)

14. Suppose that u, v, w are orthogonal curvilinear coordinates for which $ds^2 = v^2\,du^2 + u^2\,dv^2 + dw^2$.
   (a) Calculate the divergence of $\mathbf{u}$, where $\mathbf{u}$ is the unit vector tangent to a u curve.
   (b) Determine the laplacian of the function $\phi = uvw$.

CHAPTER

5

Advanced Topics

5.1 INTRODUCTION

The preceding chapters were devoted to vector algebra and vector analysis. Vector algebra includes the study of scalar and vector products, and vector analysis centers mostly about the various integral theorems, such as the divergence theorem and Stokes' theorem. The reader who wishes to study these topics more intensively may proceed from here in many directions. If interested in studying more of the same material, he can study many excellent books on vector analysis that carry the integral theorems further to give a more complete analysis of vector fields. If interested mainly in applications, he is already prepared to study texts on hydrodynamics or electromagnetic wave theory, or he can proceed to the study of tensor analysis, with its interesting applications to elasticity and the theory of relativity. If interested in pure mathematics, he can proceed either in an algebraic direction, to study vector spaces and normed linear spaces, or in a geometrical direction to study differential geometry.

But if he does this immediately, he will always thereafter think of vector analysis as an isolated part of his curriculum, a good preparation for certain specialized courses, but not in the main stream of his mathematical development. There is a simple reason for this, which is that vector analysis, as usually presented, tends to cover up many essential aspects of mathematics.

For one thing, vector analysis is a highly polished subject. As a beautiful mixture of algebra, geometry, and analysis, it somehow manages at times to avoid an important concept in one area by substituting a relatively simple idea in another. For example, the *area cosine principle*, discussed in Sec. 4.6, is a geometrical way to avoid discussing an important idea of advanced calculus, namely the idea of a *jacobian*. Nowhere in the first four chapters of this book is a jacobian explicitly mentioned, so don't feel ashamed if you don't know what a jacobian is; it is even possible that a student reading this book *after* taking a course in advanced calculus might not spot the jacobians that are lurking around. [If you are such a student, and if you have read Sec. 4.13, did you spot the jacobian $h_1 h_2 h_3$ in (4.77) of that section?]

On the other hand, the notation of vector analysis tends to make some things look quite different when, in fact, they are closely related. In vector analysis, the ideas of gradient, curl, and divergence seem to be quite different, but in the language of *differential forms* they turn out to be much the same. Both the divergence theorem and Stokes' theorem turn out to be different special cases of the same theorem. It would take a mighty brilliant student to recognize this from exposure to the classical treatment of vector analysis.

To turn to another matter, both scalar fields and vector fields are special cases of what is known as a *tensor* field. Vector analysis is a special case of *tensor* analysis. Sooner or later, the reader may wish to study a book on tensor analysis. The difficulty that arises here is that most books on tensor analysis do *not* carry on where vector analysis leaves off, but immediately consider much more general situations: spaces that are of higher dimension, or spaces that are noneuclidean. Many students find this transition quite difficult.

It is hoped that the student who studies this chapter, or parts of it, will understand the preceding chapters somewhat better, and will be better prepared to do more advanced work of a related nature.

If the reader wishes, he can skip Secs. 5.2 and 5.3 with no loss in continuity, returning to them later if he desires to do so. Possibly Sec. 5.4 can be quickly scanned on first reading. The remaining sections are devoted to a discussion of vector analysis in general curvilinear coordinates, in ordinary three-dimensional euclidean space, using the notation of tensor analysis. The author has deliberately avoided any attempt to achieve greater generality. The level of mathematical rigor is somewhat lower than in the preceding chapters; for example, all functions possess derivatives, and no attention is paid to the question of whether coordinate systems overlap properly: it seems silly to pay lip service to such matters when they are, at best, subordinate to the central theme.

5.2 DIFFERENTIAL FORMS

In this section, we present an elementary introduction to differential forms. Most students find this an extremely interesting subject.

We begin with some definitions which produce a rather strange-looking algebraic system. By the end of the section, however, we will have unmasked these creatures, who are in reality old friends in disguise.

We will restrict our discussion to scalar fields and vector fields defined in space. In vector analysis, a real-valued function of x, y, and z is called a *scalar field*. In the theory of differential forms it is called a *zero-form*. No new notation is involved. Thus, if $f(x,y,z)$ denotes the temperature at the point (x,y,z), we will call f a zero-form.

By a *one-form* we mean an expression of the form $F_1\,dx + F_2\,dy + F_3\,dz$, where F_1, F_2, and F_3 are functions of x, y, and z. We will say that the vector field $F_1\mathbf{i} + F_2\mathbf{j} + F_3\mathbf{k}$ is *associated* with the one-form $F_1\,dx + F_2\,dy + F_3\,dz$. Thus, to obtain the vector field associated with a one-form, simply replace dx by $\mathbf{i}$, dy by $\mathbf{j}$, and dz by $\mathbf{k}$. Conversely, to obtain the one-form associated with a vector field, replace $\mathbf{i}$ by dx, $\mathbf{j}$ by dy, and $\mathbf{k}$ by dz.

By a *two-form* in "standard order" we mean an expression of the form

$$F_1\,dy \wedge dz + F_2\,dz \wedge dx + F_3\,dx \wedge dy \tag{5.1}$$

The inverted v's are called *carets* or *wedges*, and they serve to distinguish between a two-form, such as $3x^2\,dy \wedge dz$, and objects such as $3x^2\,dy\,dz$ that occur in double integrals where the order of the differentials is not so important. We also regard the wedge as a symbol denoting a type of multiplication. The rules for this kind of multiplication will be given presently.

The two-form (5.1) and the vector field $F_1\mathbf{i} + F_2\mathbf{j} + F_3\mathbf{k}$ are said to be *associated*. Thus, to find the two-form associated with a vector field, replace $\mathbf{i}$ by $dy \wedge dz$, $\mathbf{j}$ by $dz \wedge dx$, and $\mathbf{k}$ by $dx \wedge dy$. *The order is important.*

By a *three-form* in standard order we mean an expression of the form

$$f\,dx \wedge dy \wedge dz \tag{5.2}$$

where f is a function of x, y, and z. The three-form (5.2) and the scalar field f are said to be *associated*.

We see that a scalar field can be associated with either a zero-form or a three-form, and that a vector field can be associated with either a one-form or a two-form.

In applications, a "true" scalar field (such as a temperature distribution) is usually associated with a zero-form, whereas scalar "densities" (such as charge density) are associated with three-forms. Similarly, there are certain types of vector fields (those commonly related to a scalar potential, such as electric field intensity) that are usually associated with one-forms, and others (those related to curls, such as magnetic field intensity) that are more commonly associated with two-forms. However, the choice is largely a matter of convenience, and need not concern us at the moment.

We are allowed to change the order of the differentials in a two-form or a three-form, provided we change the sign each time we interchange two differentials. Thus

$$x^2\, dy \wedge dz = -x^2\, dz \wedge dy$$

$$4xyz\, dx \wedge dy \wedge dz = -4xyz\, dy \wedge dx \wedge dz = 4xyz\, dy \wedge dz \wedge dx$$
$$= -4xyz\, dz \wedge dy \wedge dx = 4xyz\, dz \wedge dx \wedge dy = -4xyz\, dx \wedge dz \wedge dy$$

Thus, the multiplication denoted by the caret, which is sometimes called *wedge multiplication*, is *anticommutative*.

Provided we keep this in mind, we can manipulate differential forms algebraically according to the usual rules of elementary algebra. For any $p = 0, 1, 2$, or 3, we can add two p-forms to obtain their sum, which is also a p-form. We can multiply a p-form by a scalar field to obtain a new p-form. The wedge product of a p-form and a q-form is a $(p + q)$-form.

As a matter of convention, the function identically equal to zero is called a p-form for *every* p. Thus, $0\, dx \wedge dy = 0$ is both a two-form and a zero-form. Since wedge multiplication of differentials is anticommutative, these rules force us to set any wedge product of a differential with itself equal to zero. Thus, $dx \wedge dx = 0$, $dx \wedge dy \wedge dy = 0$, etc. With the exception of the trivial form that is identically equal to zero, it is impossible for any p-form to be equal to a q-form unless $p = q$.

Example 5.1 Write the two-form $(x\, dx + y\, dz) \wedge (y\, dx - y^2\, dy)$ in standard order.

Solution We multiply in the usual manner, being careful to preserve the order of the differentials (but we allow multiplication by the scalar coefficients to commute with everything else):

$$xy\, dx \wedge dx + y^2\, dz \wedge dx - xy^2\, dx \wedge dy - y^3\, dz \wedge dy$$

The first term is set equal to 0, since it contains a repeated differential. Writing the remaining terms in standard order, we obtain

$$y^3\, dy \wedge dz + y^2\, dz \wedge dx - xy^2\, dx \wedge dy$$

Example 5.2 Write the following three-form in standard order:

$$(2\, dx + dz) \wedge (3\, dx + dy + dz) \wedge (dx + dy + 4\, dz)$$

Solution Wedge multiplication is associative, so it doesn't matter how we group the factors. Multiplying the first two factors, we reduce the product to

$$(2\, dx \wedge dy + 2\, dx \wedge dz + 3\, dz \wedge dx + dz \wedge dy) \wedge (dx + dy + 4\, dz)$$

Notice that two terms disappeared because of repeated differentials. We immediately simplify this to

$$(2\, dx \wedge dy + dz \wedge dx + dz \wedge dy) \wedge (dx + dy + 4\, dz)$$

In the next multiplication, we again ignore any products that contain repeated differentials. (For example, the first term, $2\, dx \wedge dy \wedge dx$, equals zero because dx occurs twice.) We obtain

$$8\, dx \wedge dy \wedge dz + dz \wedge dx \wedge dy + dz \wedge dy \wedge dx$$

Since $dz \wedge dx \wedge dy = -dz \wedge dy \wedge dx$, the final answer is $8\, dx \wedge dy \wedge dz$.

Example 5.3 Let $\alpha = 3\,dx + 4\,dy + 2x^2\,dz$ and let $\beta = 5\,dy \wedge dz - dz \wedge dx + 3\,dx \wedge dy$. Find $\alpha \wedge \beta$ and $\beta \wedge \alpha$.

Solution Six of the nine terms are zero, since they contain repeated differentials. Ignoring them, we have

$$\begin{aligned}\alpha \wedge \beta &= 15\,dx \wedge dy \wedge dz - 4\,dy \wedge dz \wedge dx + 6x^2\,dz \wedge dx \wedge dy \\ &= (11 + 6x^2)\,dx \wedge dy \wedge dz\end{aligned}$$

We compute $\beta \wedge \alpha$ similarly, and notice that we obtain exactly the same answer. This is no accident: one-forms commute with two-forms. (Why?)

These three examples were chosen not only to illustrate calculation with differentials, but also to provide examples for the following three theorems:

THEOREM 5.1 *The product of one-forms associated with a pair of vector fields is the two-form associated with the vector cross product of the fields.*

The proof consists of a routine calculation and is omitted. Compare the result of Example 5.1 with the vector product to which it corresponds:

$$(x\mathbf{i} + y\mathbf{k}) \times (y\mathbf{i} - y^2\mathbf{j}) = y^3\mathbf{i} + y^2\mathbf{j} - xy^2\mathbf{k}$$

THEOREM 5.2 *The product of three one-forms associated with three vector fields is the three-form associated with the triple scalar product of the fields.*

Compare Example 5.2 with the triple scalar product

$$[2\mathbf{i} + \mathbf{k}, 3\mathbf{i} + \mathbf{j} + \mathbf{k}, \mathbf{i} + \mathbf{j} + 4\mathbf{k}] = \begin{vmatrix} 2 & 0 & 1 \\ 3 & 1 & 1 \\ 1 & 1 & 4 \end{vmatrix} = 8$$

THEOREM 5.3 *The product of a one-form associated with a vector field and a two-form associated with another vector field is the three-form associated with the scalar product of the two vector fields.*

Compare Example 5.3 with

$$(3\mathbf{i} + 4\mathbf{j} + 2x^2\mathbf{k}) \cdot (5\mathbf{i} - \mathbf{j} + 3\mathbf{k}) = 11 + 6x^2$$

The preceding three theorems show how differential forms are related to vector *algebra*. Now let us see how they are related to vector *analysis*.

For this purpose, we must define the *differential* of a differential form. We will make repeated use of the expression

$$df = \frac{\partial f}{\partial x}\,dx + \frac{\partial f}{\partial y}\,dy + \frac{\partial f}{\partial z}\,dz \tag{5.3}$$

for the total differential of a function f.

If f is a zero-form, df is defined directly by (5.3). *The differential of a zero-form is a one-form.*

THEOREM 5.4 *If f is the zero-form associated with a scalar field, df is the one-form associated with the gradient of the scalar field.*

We see this immediately from (5.3). To obtain **grad** f, simply replace dx by **i**, dy by **j**, and dz by **k**.

If α is a one-form

$$\alpha = M\,dx + N\,dy + P\,dz \tag{5.4}$$

we define $d\alpha$ to be the two-form obtained by the rule

$$d\alpha = dM \wedge dx + dN \wedge dy + dP \wedge dz \tag{5.5}$$

In using this rule, it is understood that we must obtain the total differentials of M, N, and P by using (5.3), substitute into (5.5), multiply and simplify.

Example 5.4 Find $d\alpha$, given that $\alpha = xy\,dx + z\,dy + y^3\,dz$.

Solution

$$\begin{aligned} d\alpha &= (x\,dy + y\,dx) \wedge dx + dz \wedge dy + 3y^2\,dy \wedge dz \\ &= x\,dy \wedge dx + (3y^2 - 1)\,dy \wedge dz \\ &= (3y^2 - 1)\,dy \wedge dz - x\,dx \wedge dy \end{aligned}$$

The only reason for the last step is to obtain $d\alpha$ in standard order. We see that it represents the vector field $(3y^2 - 1)\mathbf{i} - x\mathbf{k}$. This is the curl of the vector field $xy\mathbf{i} + z\mathbf{j} + y^3\mathbf{k}$. This illustrates the following general theorem.

THEOREM 5.5 *If α is the one-form associated with a vector field, $d\alpha$ is the two-form associated with the curl of the vector field.*

The proof is left as a simple exercise.

Finally, we define the differential of a two-form

$$\beta = Q\,dy \wedge dz + R\,dz \wedge dx + S\,dx \wedge dy \tag{5.6}$$

to be the three-form

$$d\beta = dQ \wedge dy \wedge dz + dR \wedge dz \wedge dx + dS \wedge dx \wedge dy \tag{5.7}$$

Because of the repeated differentials that arise, most of the terms will be zero, and (5.7) immediately reduces to

$$d\beta = \left(\frac{\partial Q}{\partial x} + \frac{\partial R}{\partial y} + \frac{\partial S}{\partial z}\right) dx \wedge dy \wedge dz \tag{5.8}$$

which proves the following theorem.

THEOREM 5.6 *If β is the two-form associated with a vector field, $d\beta$ is the three-form associated with the divergence of the vector field.*

Example 5.5 Let $\alpha = 3x^5\, dy \wedge dz + 5y^2x\, dz \wedge dx + 8z\, dx \wedge dy$. Find $d\alpha$.

Solution

$$\begin{aligned} d\alpha &= 15x^4\, dx \wedge dy \wedge dz + (10yx\, dy + 5y^2\, dx) \wedge dz \wedge dx + 8\, dz \wedge dx \wedge dy \\ &= 15x^4\, dx \wedge dy \wedge dz + 10yx\, dy \wedge dz \wedge dx + 8\, dz \wedge dx \wedge dy \\ &= (15x^4 + 10yx + 8)\, dx \wedge dy \wedge dz \end{aligned}$$

In this solution, we made use of (5.7). We could have obtained the answer more rapidly by using (5.8).

These procedures must be slightly modified if, instead of working in cartesian coordinates x, y, and z, we are working in orthogonal curvilinear coordinates u_1, u_2, u_3. (See Sec. 4.12 for an explanation of the notation used here.) The one-form associated with a vector field

$$F_1\mathbf{u}_1 + F_2\mathbf{u}_2 + F_3\mathbf{u}_3 \tag{5.9}$$

is taken to be

$$F_1h_1\, du_1 + F_2h_2\, du_2 + F_3h_3\, du_3 \tag{5.10}$$

and the two-form associated with (5.9) is

$$F_1h_2h_3\, du_2 \wedge du_3 + F_2h_3h_1\, du_3 \wedge du_1 + F_3h_1h_2\, du_1 \wedge du_2 \tag{5.11}$$

The three-form associated with a scalar field f is

$$fh_1h_2h_3\, du_1 \wedge du_2 \wedge du_3 \tag{5.12}$$

(It is understood that the coordinate system is right-handed, as required in Sec. 4.13.)

It is fairly easy to see why these associations must be made. At any point, the vectors $\mathbf{u}_1$, $\mathbf{u}_2$, and $\mathbf{u}_3$ play the same role as $\mathbf{i}$, $\mathbf{j}$, and $\mathbf{k}$, and the differentials $h_1\, du_1$, $h_2\, du_2$, $h_3\, du_3$ represent differentials of arc length and hence play the same role as dx, dy, and dz. This accounts for (5.10). In order that Theorem 5.1 be valid, the two-form associated with (5.9) must be (5.11). For instance, $\mathbf{u}_1 \times \mathbf{u}_2 = \mathbf{u}_3$ is written, in the notation of differential forms, $(h_1\, du_1) \wedge (h_2\, du_2) = h_1h_2\, du_1 \wedge du_2$, and the presence of two h's in the other two terms of (5.11) is similarly motivated.

One of the beauties of using differential forms is that (5.10), (5.11), and (5.12) are quite easy to remember, and in combination with the elegant Theorems 5.4, 5.5, and 5.6 (which can be shown to hold in curvilinear coordinates) it is possible to reproduce the formulas of Sec. 4.13 rather quickly and neatly.

Example 5.6 In the manner just suggested, find the expression for div $\mathbf{F}$ in orthogonal curvilinear coordinates.

Solution By (5.11), the two-form associated with **F** is given by (5.11). Because of the presence of repeated differentials, the differential of this two-form is [compare (5.8), which was obtained the same way]

$$\left(\frac{\partial}{\partial u_1}(F_1h_2h_3)+\frac{\partial}{\partial u_2}(F_2h_3h_1)+\frac{\partial}{\partial u_3}(F_3h_1h_2)\right)du_1\wedge du_2\wedge du_3$$

In passing from the three-form (5.12) to the scalar field, one removes the differentials and divides by $h_1h_2h_3$. Thus

$$\operatorname{div}\mathbf{F}=\frac{1}{h_1h_2h_3}\left(\frac{\partial}{\partial u_1}(F_1h_2h_3)+\frac{\partial}{\partial u_2}(F_2h_3h_1)+\frac{\partial}{\partial u_3}(F_3h_1h_2)\right)$$

in harmony with Sec. 4.13.

Example 5.7 In cylindrical coordinates, what is the scalar field associated with the three-form $dr\wedge d\theta\wedge dz$?

Solution In cylindrical coordinates, the differentials of arc length in the three coordinate directions are dr, $r\,d\theta$, and dz. Therefore the "standard order" (5.12) for this three-form is $(1/r)r\,dr\wedge d\theta\wedge dz$ and the corresponding scalar field is $1/r$.

At this point, it would be well for the reader to get some practice manipulating differential forms, by performing the following exercises.

EXERCISES

1. Find $\alpha\wedge\beta$ given that
 (a) $\alpha=dx-dy+dz$ and $\beta=3\,dx-3\,dy+3\,dz$ (compare Exercise 4, Sec. 1.12.);
 (b) $\alpha=2x\,dx\wedge dy+3z^3\,dy\wedge dz$ and $\beta=5\,dx+y\,dz$;
 (c) α and β are two-forms.

2. Find $d\alpha$ given that
 (a) $\alpha=xy^2z^3$;
 (b) $\alpha=x\,dx+y\,dy+z\,dz$;
 (c) $\alpha=xyz\,dz+x^2y^2z^2\,dy+y^2z^3\,dz$ (compare Example 3.18);
 (d) $\alpha=x\,dy\wedge dz+y^2z\,dz\wedge dx+xz^3\,dx\wedge dy$.

3. (a) Find dx, given that $x=r\cos\theta$, in terms of r, θ, dr, and $d\theta$.
 (b) Similarly, find dy, given that $y=r\sin\theta$.
 (c) Find $dx\wedge dy$ in terms of r, θ, and $dr\wedge d\theta$. Do you recognize this?

4. Given that $x=r\sin\phi\cos\theta$, $y=r\sin\phi\sin\theta$, and $z=r\cos\phi$, find dx, dy, and dz in terms of r, ϕ, θ, and their differentials, and compute $dx\wedge dy\wedge dz$ as a scalar multiple of $dr\wedge d\phi\wedge d\theta$.

5. In Sec. 4.13, with x, y, and z as in the preceding exercise, we found $dx^2+dy^2+dz^2$. Is this the same as $dx\wedge dx+dy\wedge dy+dz\wedge dz$?

6. (a) Show that, in cylindrical coordinates, the one-form associated with $\mathbf{F}=F_r\,\mathbf{u}_r+E_\theta\,\mathbf{u}_\theta+F_z\,\mathbf{u}_z$ is

$$F_r\,dr+F_\theta\,r\,d\theta+F_z\,dz \qquad (5.13)$$

and the two-form associated with **F** is

$$F_r\, r\, d\theta \wedge dz + F_\theta\, dz \wedge dr + F_z\, r\, dr \wedge d\theta \tag{5.14}$$

and the three-form associated with a scalar field f is

$$fr\, dr \wedge d\theta \wedge dz \tag{5.15}$$

(b) What are the forms associated with $3\mathbf{u}_r + 5\mathbf{u}_\theta + 7r\mathbf{u}_z$?
(c) Find the divergence of $\mathbf{u}_r$.
(d) What vector field corresponds to the form $dr + d\theta$?
(e) What vector field is associated with $d\theta \wedge dz + 3\, dz \wedge dr$?

7. In spherical coordinates, the one-form associated with $\mathbf{F} = F_r \mathbf{u}_r + F_\phi \mathbf{u}_\phi + F_\theta \mathbf{u}_\theta$ is

$$F_r\, dr + F_\phi\, r\, d_\phi + F_\theta\, r \sin\phi\, d\theta \tag{5.16}$$

(a) What is the two-form associated with **F**?
(b) What is the three-form associated with a scalar field f?
(c) What vector corresponds to the differential form $3\, dr + 8r\, d\phi + r^5 \sin\phi\, d\theta$?
(d) What vector corresponds to the differential form $df = (\partial f/\partial r)\, dr + (\partial f/\partial \phi)\, d\phi + (\partial f/\partial \theta)\, d\theta$? (Notice that your answer gives a formula for **grad** f in spherical coordinates.)

8. In the manner suggested in this section, find the expression for **grad** f in orthogonal curvilinear coordinates.

9. Similarly, find the expression for **curl F** in orthogonal curvilinear coordinates.

10. (a) Using your answer to Exercise 8, find the two-form corresponding to **grad** f in the same coordinates.
(b) Differentiate this to find its divergence, i.e., the three-form associated with its divergence.
(c) Hence, show that differential forms can be used to derive an expression for the laplacian of a scalar field in orthogonal curvilinear coordinates.

5.3 THE GENERALIZED STOKES THEOREM

In Sec. 4.3 we learned that

$$\int_P^Q \mathbf{grad}\, \phi \cdot d\mathbf{R} = \phi(Q) - \phi(P) \tag{5.17}$$

Let us rewrite this in the notation of differential forms. We have $\mathbf{grad}\, \phi \cdot d\mathbf{R} = (\partial\phi/\partial x)\, dx + (\partial\phi/\partial y)\, dy + (\partial\phi/\partial z)\, dz = d\phi$. Letting C denote an oriented curve extending from point P to point Q, we can write the left side of (5.17) in the simple form $\int_C d\phi$.

Now let $\beta(C)$ denote the pair of points P and Q, in that order, and call $\beta(C)$ the *oriented boundary* of the curve C. [If C had been oriented the other way, extending from Q to P, then $\beta(C)$ would be the points Q, P (the same points in the opposite order).] Define the symbol $\int_{\beta(C)} \phi$ to mean

$\phi(Q) - \phi(P)$, and call this the *integral* of the zero-form ϕ over the oriented boundary P, Q.

Then (5.17) can be written in the rather unusual form

$$\int_C d\phi = \int_{\beta(C)} \phi \tag{5.18}$$

The reader may well object to this, on the grounds that the integral on the right side of (5.18) is not an integral at all, but simply an abbreviation for the difference between the value of ϕ at the endpoint of C and its value at the initial point of C. Nevertheless, it fits in quite well with the general scheme of things, as we will soon see.

Sometimes it is convenient to write $Q - P$ instead of $\beta(C)$ to denote the oriented boundary of an oriented curve extending from P to Q. This does not mean that we have suddenly found a way to subtract points! If you like, think of $Q - P$ as a set consisting of two points P and Q, in which we are thinking of Q as a "positive" point and P as a "negative" point. Thus we are extending the idea of *orientation*, already discussed in connection with *curves* and *surfaces*, to *points* as well. Thus we can write

$$\beta(C) = Q - P \tag{5.19}$$

$$\int_{\beta(C)} \phi = \int_{Q-P} \phi = \phi(Q) - \phi(P) \tag{5.20}$$

when ϕ is a zero-form.

We can regard (5.18) as a symbolic expression of the fundamental theorem of calculus, which asserts that, under certain conditions, one can evaluate a definite integral by finding an "antiderivative" ϕ and subtracting the values of ϕ at two endpoints. This is one of the greatest labor-saving devices known to man: integral calculus would be impossibly complicated if all definite integrals had to be calculated as limits of sums in the manner of Example 4.3. Unfortunately, students become so accustomed to computing definite integrals by using antiderivatives (i.e. indefinite integrals) that they tend to forget a theorem is involved.

What is more interesting is that many engineers and scientists who use Stokes' theorem and the divergence theorem are not aware that these are simply *higher-dimensional counterparts* of the same theorem. The purpose of this section is to explain what this means. Unfortunately, our discussion must be far from rigorous: entire books can be (and have been) written on the subject of dimension alone.

Roughly speaking, we regard a set consisting of isolated points as *zero-dimensional*, a curve as *one-dimensional*, a surface in space as *two-dimensional*, and an open domain in space as *three-dimensional*.

Thus, $Q - P$ denotes an oriented *zero-dimensional region*, and (5.20) defines what we mean by the integral of a *zero-form* over this region.

Let C be an oriented curve and let

$$\alpha = F_1\, dx + F_2\, dy + F_3\, dz \tag{5.21}$$

be a one-form. Let **F** be the vector field associated with this one-form $\mathbf{F} = \mathbf{F}_1\mathbf{i} + F_2\mathbf{j} + F_3\mathbf{k}$, and define the integral of α over C by

$$\int_C \alpha = \int_C \mathbf{F} \cdot d\mathbf{R} \tag{5.22}$$

which is not very profound, since $\mathbf{F} \cdot d\mathbf{R} = F_1\, dx + F_2\, dy + F_3\, dz = \alpha$. The point is this: we now know what we mean by the integral of a *one-form* over a *one-dimensional oriented region.*

Now we must define what is meant by the integral of a *two-form* over a *two-dimensional oriented region.* Let the two-form be written in standard order,

$$\alpha = F_1\, dy \wedge dz + F_2\, dz \wedge dx + F_3\, dx \wedge dy \tag{5.23}$$

and let $\mathbf{n}$ be the unit vector field of normals to the surface S. Let **F** be the vector field associated with α and define the integral by

$$\int_S \alpha = \iint_S \mathbf{F} \cdot \mathbf{n}\, dS \tag{5.24}$$

In other words, we are defining the integral of α over S to be what is obtained by replacing α with its associated vector field, and integrating the normal component of that field over S. [It is more elegant to define the integral by other methods and then prove (5.24) as a theorem, but that would take us beyond the scope of this book.]

Next, we must define what is meant by the integral of a *three-form* over a *three-dimensional oriented region.* Here we run into a complication: we have not defined what is meant by an oriented region in space.

The process of orientation essentially amounts to creating two objects where originally there was only one. Thus for any given curve, there are two oriented curves (depending on the choice of direction along the curve). For any given surface, provided it can be oriented at all, there are two oriented surfaces. For any given point P there are two oriented points, P and $-P$. We could orient an open region in space in the same way that we orient a point, by simply calling it "positive" or "negative", but that is not the way it is usually done.

Instead, we orient an open region in space (which we assume to be connected) by giving it a "screw sense". To explain this in a somewhat dramatic (but not very mathematical) way, we decide once and for all whether screw manufacturers living in this space will thread their screws one way or the other. This amounts to giving a preference to either right-handed or left-handed systems.

Throughout this book, preference has been given to right-handed systems. If our preference had been otherwise, we would have defined the vector cross product in another manner, which would interchange the role of $\mathbf{A} \times \mathbf{B}$ and $\mathbf{B} \times \mathbf{A}$. This, in turn, would modify the definition of the curl of a vector field.

Thus, to take account of the two possible orientations for open regions in space, we would have to reexamine everything that has been discussed earlier. Therefore we shall drop further discussion of the matter. If α is a three-form, write it in standard order,

$$\alpha = f\, dx \wedge dy \wedge dz \tag{5.25}$$

and define the integral of α over a three-dimensional region D by

$$\int_D \alpha = \iiint_D f\, dx\, dy\, dz \tag{5.26}$$

The orientation of D is automatically taken into account by the requirement that the coordinate system is right-handed, a convention that has been used throughout this book.

The reader may wonder if there is a misprint on the left sides of (5.24) and (5.26). Only a single integral sign occurs, despite the fact that these are multiple integrals! This was done deliberately, in order that a single formula can suffice to describe a theorem that is independent of the dimension.

In vector notation, Stokes' theorem is written

$$\iint_S (\mathbf{curl\ F}) \cdot \mathbf{n}\, dS = \int_C \mathbf{F} \cdot d\mathbf{R} \tag{5.27}$$

To indicate that C is the oriented boundary of the oriented surface S, we write $C = \beta(S)$. By (5.22) we can replace the right side of (5.27) by $\int_C \alpha$ or, what is the same, $\int_{\beta(S)} \alpha$. If α is the one-form associated with the vector field $\mathbf{F}$, $d\alpha$ is the two-form associated with **curl F**, by Theorem 5.5. Hence we can write the left side of (5.27) in the form $\int_S d\alpha$. Therefore, in the notation, of differential forms, we write Stokes' theorem as follows:

$$\int_S d\alpha = \int_{\beta(S)} \alpha \tag{5.28}$$

Formally, this is identical with (5.18), except that the one-dimensional region C has been replaced by the two-dimensional region S, and the zero-form ϕ has been replaced by a one-form α.

In vector notation, the divergence theorem is written

$$\iiint_D \operatorname{div} \mathbf{F}\, dV = \iint_S \mathbf{F} \cdot \mathbf{n}\, dS \tag{5.29}$$

If we let α denote the two-form associated with the vector field $\mathbf{F}$ (not the one-form, as in the preceding paragraph), and write $S = \beta(D)$ to indicate that S is the oriented boundary of the domain D, the right side of (5.29) can be written $\int_{\beta(D)} \alpha$. By Theorem 5.6, $d\alpha$ will then be the three-form associated with div $\mathbf{F}$, and by (5.26) we can replace the left side of (5.29) by $\int_D d\alpha$. Therefore, in the notation of differential forms, the divergence theorem is

$$\int_D d\alpha = \int_{\beta(D)} \alpha \tag{5.30}$$

This is formally the same as (5.28) except that the two-dimensional region S has been replaced by the three-dimensional region D, and the α in (5.30) represents a two-form whereas in (5.28) it denotes a one-form.

Therefore (5.18), (5.28), and (5.30) are simply special cases of the following theorem:

THEOREM 5.7 *The integral of the differential of a p-form over an oriented $p + 1$-dimensional region equals the integral of the p-form itself over the oriented boundary of the region.*

This is called the *generalized Stokes theorem.* When $p = 0$, it reduces to the fundamental theorem of calculus. When $p = 1$, it is the usual Stokes' theorem. When $p = 2$, it is the divergence theorem.

Additional material on differential forms will be found in the exercises.

EXERCISES

1. Let α be a three-form, i.e., $\alpha = f\, dx \wedge dy \wedge dz$ where f is a function of x, y, and z Define $d\alpha$ by

$$d\alpha = df \wedge dx \wedge dy \wedge dz \tag{5.31}$$

(a) Letting $\alpha = x^2yz^3\, dx \wedge dy \wedge dz$, compute $d\alpha$.
(b) Is it purely coincidental that you obtained such a trivial answer?

2. (a) Show that, if ϕ is a zero form, $d(d\phi) = 0$.
(b) To which of the identities in Sec. 3.7 is this related?

3. (a) Show that, if α is a one-form, $d(d\alpha) = 0$.
(b) To which of the identities in Sec. 3.7 is this related?

4. A special case of (5.19) is

$$\beta(PQ) = Q - P \tag{5.32}$$

where PQ denotes (as in Sec. 1.1) the directed line segment extending from P to Q. What geometrical significance would you give to the following:

$$\beta(PQR) = QR - PR + PQ \tag{5.33}$$

[*Hint*: PQR denotes an oriented triangle. Giving the vertices P, Q, and R, in that order, is a neat way to decree the sense in which angles are to be taken as positive (see Sec. 1.11).]

5. (a) Let the four vertices of a tetrahedron be labelled P, Q, R, and S, so chosen that the sense of rotation determined by the oriented triangle PQR (see the hint following Exercise 4) would advance a right-handed screw in the general direction of vertex S (rather than away from S). Show that the following expression describes the oriented boundary of the tetrahedron.

$$\beta(PQRS) = QRS - PRS + PQS - PQR \tag{5.34}$$

(b) Use this to explain why, in Sec. 4.6, we adopted the convention of taking the orientation of such closed surfaces to be such that the unit normal points *away* from the enclosed region.

6. The following assertion is the *converse* of the assertion made in Exercise 2(a). If α is a one-form and $d\alpha = 0$, then there exists a zero-form ϕ such that $\alpha = d\phi$.
(a) Translate this assertion into vector language.
(b) Is the assertion true?

7. Use (5.26) to determine $\int_D \alpha$ where D is a region whose numerical volume is 8 cubic units and $\alpha = 3\, dy \wedge dx \wedge dz$.

8. Let $\alpha = 2\, dx \wedge dy + 3\, dx \wedge dz + 4\, dy \wedge dz$. For what vector field $\mathbf{F}$ is $\int_S \alpha = \iint_S \mathbf{F} \cdot \mathbf{n}\, dS$?

9. There is no difference between $\int_0^1 \int_0^2 x^2 y\, dx\, dy$ and $\int_0^2 \int_0^1 x^2 y\, dy\, dx$: they are both integrals over the rectangle $0 \leq x \leq 2$, $0 \leq y \leq 1$ in the xy plane. Let S be this rectangle, oriented by choosing $\mathbf{k}$ as its unit normal.
(a) Is there any difference between $\int_S x^2 y\, dx \wedge dy$ and $\int_S x^2 y\, dy \wedge dx$?
(b) If so, which of the two integrals in (a) matches these double integrals?

5.4 MATRICES

The reader will have already seen much of the material in this section in his other courses; in fact, some of it was presented in the earlier optional sections. Its inclusion here is motivated by the authors' desire to give a unified treatment of the subject matter of this chapter.

A *matrix* is an array. An $n \times m$ (n by m) matrix is a matrix with n rows and m columns. By convention, if T denotes a matrix, then T^i_j denotes the entry in the ith row and the jth column of the matrix. This convention can be remembered easily by either of the mnemonic devices

$$T^{\text{Roman}}_{\text{Catholic}} \qquad \text{or} \qquad T^{\text{Railway}}_{\text{Car}}$$

the initial letters suggesting *r*ow and *c*olumn.

Throughout this section, we will be concerned mainly with *real matrices*, i.e., matrices whose entries are real numbers. Everything that we say will apply equally well, however, to matrices with entries that are complex numbers. Later on, we will consider matrices whose entries are functions.

An $n \times 1$ matrix has but a single column and is called a *column matrix*. If v is a column matrix, the entry in the ith row is denoted v^i, there being little point in retaining the subscript $j = 1$. Similarly, a matrix having only one row is called a *row matrix* and the superscript $i = 1$ is deleted, so the jth entry in a row matrix w is denoted w_j. For example, if we have

$$w = \begin{pmatrix} 1 & 3 & 2 & -4 \end{pmatrix} \qquad T = \begin{pmatrix} 3 & 4 & 0 \\ 2 & -1 & 8 \\ 0 & 6 & 3 \\ 3 & 3 & 4 \end{pmatrix} \qquad v = \begin{pmatrix} 9 \\ 8 \\ 2 \end{pmatrix}$$

w is a 1×4 matrix, T is a 4×3 matrix, and v is a 3×1 matrix. We see that w is a row matrix and v is a column matrix. We have $w_2 = 3$, $T_3^2 = 8$, $T_3^4 = 4$, $v^1 = 9$, etc.

Sometimes the notation T_{ij} or T^{ij} is used instead. These symbols also refer to the entry in the ith row and jth column.

The notation $T = (T_j^i)$ is an abbreviation for the sentence "T is a matrix, and T_j^i denotes the entry in the ith row and jth column of T." In a later section, after introducing some symbols g_{ij}, we will write $G = (g_{ij})$. All this means is that we have decided to let G denote the matrix whose entries are the g_{ij}'s.

There is nothing special about the choice of letters. For example, S_p^q denotes the entry in the qth row and pth column of the matrix S.

Do not confuse *matrices* with *determinants*. More will be said about determinants later on.

Two $n \times m$ matrices are said to be *equal* if and only if their corresponding entries are equal. Thus the matrices

$$T = \begin{pmatrix} 0 & 2 \\ 8 & 0 \end{pmatrix} \qquad S = \begin{pmatrix} 0 & 2 \\ 8 & 1 \end{pmatrix}$$

are *not equal*, $T \neq S$, because $T_2^2 \neq S_2^2$. (They happen to have the same determinant, but that is irrelevant.) If even a single entry of matrix T differs from the corresponding entry of S, then $T \neq S$. Matrices of different "sizes" can never be equal; for example, a 3×4 matrix can never be equal to a 4×3 matrix.

The *sum* of two $n \times m$ matrices, $R = S + T$, is defined by adding corresponding entries. The entry in the ith row and jth column may be denoted either R_j^i or $(S + T)_j^i$. We have

$$R_j^i = (S + T)_j^i = S_j^i + T_j^i$$

by definition. For example

$$\begin{pmatrix} 0 & 2 & 3 \\ 1 & -1 & 5 \end{pmatrix} + \begin{pmatrix} 8 & 7 & -3 \\ 2 & 2 & 2 \end{pmatrix} = \begin{pmatrix} 8 & 9 & 0 \\ 3 & 1 & 7 \end{pmatrix}$$

The operation of addition is defined only for matrices of the same size. Thus, we cannot add a 3×4 matrix to a 4×3 matrix.

Scalar multiples of matrices are defined in the following manner. If c is a number and T is a matrix, then cT is the matrix whose entry in the ith row and jth column is cT_j^i. For example

$$3\begin{pmatrix} 1 & 2 \\ 2 & 6 \end{pmatrix} = \begin{pmatrix} 3 & 6 \\ 6 & 18 \end{pmatrix}$$

Once again, we remind the reader that these rules are not valid for determinants. We see from the preceding example that, if we multiply a matrix having determinant 2 by 3 we do not obtain a matrix having determinant 6.

More interesting, but somewhat more complicated, is the rule for multiplication of matrices.

If S is an $n \times k$ matrix, and T is a $k \times m$ matrix, their product $R = ST$ is the $n \times m$ matrix defined by

$$R^i_j = (ST)^i_j = \sum_{p=1}^{k} S^i_p T^p_j \tag{5.35}$$

Notice that the entry in the ith row and jth column of the product R is obtained by multiplying together and summing the entries in the ith *row* of S with those in the jth *column* of T. Once again, the mnemonic *R*oman *C*atholic may be helpful in remembering that, in computing any particular entry of ST, we pluck a *r*ow from the first matrix, S and a *c*olumn from the second matrix T. Here is a sample product:

$$\begin{pmatrix} 3 & 2 & 0 \\ 1 & 9 & 4 \\ -3 & 5 & 5 \\ 1 & 0 & -1 \end{pmatrix} \begin{pmatrix} -3 & 1 & 1 \\ 0 & 3 & 2 \\ 0 & -2 & 0 \end{pmatrix} = \begin{pmatrix} -9 & 9 & 7 \\ -3 & 20 & 19 \\ 9 & 2 & 7 \\ -3 & 3 & 1 \end{pmatrix}$$

To see how a typical entry is obtained, consider how we found $R^2_3 = 19$. We used the second row of the first matrix and the third column of the second matrix:

$$(1 \quad 9 \quad 4)\begin{pmatrix} 1 \\ 2 \\ 0 \end{pmatrix} = (19)$$

In detail, $(1)(1) + (9)(2) + (4)(0) = 19$.

The product ST is defined if and only if S has the same number of columns as T has rows. This fact need not be memorized: after you have had some practice multiplying matrices, you will see instinctively when it is possible and when it is not possible.

Row and column matrices are treated just like other matrices. If w, T, and v are as defined earlier in this section, we have

$$wT = (-3 \quad 1 \quad 14) \qquad Tv = \begin{pmatrix} 59 \\ 26 \\ 54 \\ 59 \end{pmatrix} \qquad vw = \begin{pmatrix} 9 & 27 & 18 & -36 \\ 8 & 24 & 16 & -32 \\ 2 & 6 & 4 & -8 \end{pmatrix}$$

but the products Tw, wv, vT are not defined.

A curious aspect of matrix multiplication is that it may be possible to multiply two matrices of different sizes, but it may not be possible to multiply two matrices having the same size. It is possible that ST is defined but that TS is not defined.

At this point, the reader is advised to work through the first dozen exercises at the end of this section.

A *square* matrix is one that has the same number of rows as it has columns, i.e., it is an $n \times n$ matrix. Let us now consider square matrices in greater detail.

For any positive integer n, let 0_n denote the $n \times n$ matrix, all of whose entries are zero. Thus 0_3 is the matrix, called the 3×3 zero matrix,

$$0_3 = \begin{pmatrix} 0 & 0 & 0 \\ 0 & 0 & 0 \\ 0 & 0 & 0 \end{pmatrix}$$

For any positive integer n, the "Kronecker delta" symbol is defined by

$$\delta^i_j = \begin{cases} 1 & \text{if } i = j \\ 0 & \text{if } i \neq j \end{cases}$$

($i = 1, 2, \ldots, n$; $j = 1, 2, \ldots, n$.) The matrix $I_n = (\delta^i_j)$ is called the $n \times n$ *identity matrix*. For example,

$$I_3 = \begin{pmatrix} 1 & 0 & 0 \\ 0 & 1 & 0 \\ 0 & 0 & 1 \end{pmatrix}$$

is the 3×3 identity matrix.

For any *fixed n*, $n = 2, 3, 4, \ldots$, the class of all $n \times n$ real matrices in an algebraic system for which many of the ordinary rules of algebra are valid. For example, addition is commutative and associative,

$$T + S = S + T \qquad T + (S + P) = (T + S) + P \tag{5.36}$$

the zero matrix plays a role similar to what one might expect,

$$0_n + T = T + 0_n = T \qquad \text{(for every } T \text{ in the system)} \tag{5.37}$$

the negative of a matrix is defined in the obvious manner, $-T = (-1)T$, and subtraction is defined by adding negatives, $T - S = T + (-S)$, so $T - T = 0_n$ for every T. Scalar multiples have the properties

$$c(S + T) = cS + cT \qquad (c + d)T = cT + dT \qquad (cd)T = c(dT) \tag{5.38}$$

whenever c and d are numbers and S and T are $n \times n$ matrices. Obviously $0T = 0_n$ and $1T = T$.

The product of two $n \times n$ matrices is again an $n \times n$ matrix, and multiplication is associative,

$$(ST)P = S(TP) \tag{5.39}$$

but not, in general, commutative. The identity matrix plays a role similar to that played by the number *one*,

$$I_nT = TI_n = T \tag{5.40}$$

for every $n \times n$ matrix T. Other properties are

$$S(T+P) = ST + SP \qquad (S+T)P = SP + TP \tag{5.41}$$

$$S(cT) = c(ST) = (cS)T \tag{5.42}$$

$$0_n T = T 0_n = 0_n \tag{5.43}$$

whenever S, T, and P are $n \times n$ matrices and c is a number.

As a consequence of these properties $(S+T)(S+T) = SS + ST + TS + TT$, but this cannot in general be written $SS + 2ST + TT$ since ST need not equal TS. [There is no harm in using exponents, and writing this $(S+T)^2 = S^2 + ST + TS + T^2$, provided we do not mistakenly suppose that the other superscripts used in this section refer to exponents.]

Each of the properties listed above is also valid for matrices that are *not* square whenever the rule makes sense. For example, (5.42) is valid for every number c and for every pair of matrices S and T for which the product ST is defined.

The transpose T' of a matrix T is the matrix whose rows correspond to the columns of T and whose columns correspond to the rows of T. Thus the transpose of a row matrix is a column matrix, and the transpose of a column matrix is a row matrix. Here is a specific example of a matrix and its transpose:

$$T = \begin{pmatrix} 4 & 7 & 9 \\ 3 & 2 & 1 \end{pmatrix} \qquad T' = \begin{pmatrix} 4 & 3 \\ 7 & 2 \\ 9 & 1 \end{pmatrix}$$

The transpose of an $n \times m$ matrix will be an $m \times n$ matrix. The following properties are valid whenever they make sense:

$$(T+S)' = T' + S' \tag{5.44}$$

$$(cT)' = cT' \tag{5.45}$$

$$(TS)' = S'T' \tag{5.46}$$

$$(T')' = T \tag{5.47}$$

Notice that the transpose of a product equals the product of the transposes in the opposite order.

Throughout this book we have assumed that the reader has some familiarity with determinants, at least in the 2×2 and the 3×3 case. For any square matrix T, the determinant of T will be denoted $\det(T)$, and is a number obtained from the entries of T by a somewhat complicated process. Only for 2×2 matrices can the determinant be found with hardly more than a glance:

$$\det \begin{pmatrix} a & b \\ c & d \end{pmatrix} = ad - bc \tag{5.48}$$

Here, the formula for the determinant involves only two terms, in which each term is the product of two entries. The formula for the determinant of a 3×3 matrix involves six terms, in which each term is the product of three matrix entries. In general, the formula for the determinant of an $n \times n$ matrix involves factorial n terms, in which each term is the product of n matrix entries.

For our later endeavors, we will need a certain formula for the determinant of a 3×3 matrix. The formula is

$$\det(T) = \sum_{i=1}^{3} \sum_{j=1}^{3} \sum_{k=1}^{3} \varepsilon_{ijk} T_1^i T_2^j T_3^k \tag{5.49}$$

where the symbol ε_{ijk} is defined to be equal to one if i, j, k, in that order, constitute an even permutation of 1, 2, and 3, and equal to minus one if they constitute an odd permutation of 1, 2, and 3. We let ε_{ijk} equal zero if two or more of the subscripts are equal. Thus

$$\begin{array}{lllll} \varepsilon_{123} = 1 & \varepsilon_{231} = 1 & \varepsilon_{312} = 1 & & \\ \varepsilon_{213} = -1 & \varepsilon_{132} = -1 & \varepsilon_{321} = -1 & & \\ \varepsilon_{111} = 0 & \varepsilon_{222} = 0 & \varepsilon_{333} = 0 & \varepsilon_{112} = 0 & \text{etc.} \end{array}$$

The reader can readily verify that (5.49) yields the usual formula for the determinant. Notice that, because of the way ε_{ijk} is defined, at most six of the twenty-seven terms on the right side of (5.49) can be nonzero, so this triple sum is really fairly simple.

We wish to relate (5.49) to the usual expansion of a determinant by cofactors. For any pair of indices (i,j), let ${}_j^iT$ denote the matrix obtained from T by deleting its ith row and jth column. Define the (i,j) *cofactor* of T to be the determinant of this 2×2 matrix multiplied by $(-1)^{i+j}$,

$$\mathrm{cof}_j^i(T) = (-1)^{i+j} \det({}_j^iT) \tag{5.50}$$

Using the ε symbols, we can write the cofactors of the first column of T in the form

$$\mathrm{cof}_1^i(T) = \sum_{j=1}^{3} \sum_{k=1}^{3} \varepsilon_{ijk} T_2^j T_3^k \qquad (i = 1, 2, \text{ or } 3) \tag{5.51}$$

and therefore, by (5.49),

$$\det(T) = \sum_{i=1}^{3} T_1^i \, \mathrm{cof}_1^i(T) \tag{5.52}$$

which is the expansion of $\det(T)$ by cofactors of its first column.

We can easily see that

$$\sum_{i=1}^{3} T_2^i \, \mathrm{cof}_1^i(T) = 0 \tag{5.53}$$

Indeed, the left side of (5.53) is just the right side of (5.52) in which each T_1^i has been replaced by T_2^i. Therefore this sum represents the determinant of the matrix obtained from T by deleting its first column and replacing it by a replica of its second column. The resulting matrix has two identical columns, and therefore its determinant is zero, which explains (5.53).

By similar arguments, one can show that the following formula is valid. It generalizes (5.52) and (5.53) and includes both of them as special cases:

$$\sum_{i=1}^{3} T_k^i \operatorname{cof}_j^i (T) = \delta_k^j \det (T) \tag{5.54}$$

where δ_k^j is the Kronecker index. This reduces to (5.52) when $j = k = 1$. When $j = k = 2$, this gives the expansion of det (T) by cofactors of its second column. When $j = k = 3$, this is the expansion in the third column. When $j \neq k$, this is the determinant of a matrix with two identical columns, and hence is zero [the case $j = 1$, $k = 2$, reduces to (5.53)].

Throughout this entire discussion, we have emphasized expansion by columns rather than expansion by rows. Had we emphasized rows instead, we might have written (5.49) in the form

$$\det (T) = \sum_{i=1}^{3} \sum_{j=1}^{3} \sum_{k=1}^{3} e^{ijk} T_i^1 T_j^2 T_k^3 \tag{5.55}$$

where the symbols ε^{ijk} are defined in exactly the same way as the symbols ε_{ijk}. Instead of (5.54) we would have obtained

$$\sum_{i=1}^{3} T_i^k \operatorname{cof}_i^j (T) = \delta_k^j \det (T) \tag{5.56}$$

With these messy calculations out of the way, we are in a position to discuss the *inverse* of a 3×3 real matrix. (Most of what we say applies equally well to $n \times n$ matrices.)

Since matrix multiplication is not commutative, we do not ordinarily speak of the "division" of matrices. For example, the symbol A/B is not used, because it has two possible meanings: it could denote that matrix X with the property that $XB = A$, or it could denote that matrix Y with the property that $BY = A$. We will see later that, if $\det (B) \neq 0$, matrices X and Y will exist, but they are not necessarily equal. (Throughout this discussion, all matrices are 3×3 with real entries.)

Suppose that S and T are 3×3 real matrices. If it happens that $ST = I_3$, we will call S a *left inverse* of T. If $TS = I_3$, we will call S a *right inverse* of T. If we are lucky, and both ST and TS are equal to the identity matrix, we will call S a two-sided inverse, or simply an *inverse* of T

We will show that, if $\det (T) \neq 0$, then T has an inverse. We will do this by constructing a matrix S with the property $ST = TS = I_3$. Thus, S will be both a left inverse and a right inverse of T. Once we have shown this, we can forget about the possibility that T may have other left inverses or right inverses, for the following reasons. Suppose T has another *left* inverse, say Q. Then $QT = I_3$. Then $Q = QI_3$ [by (5.40)] $= Q(TS)$ (since S is an inverse of T) $= (QT)S$ [by (5.39)] $= I_3 S$ (by hypothesis) $= S$ [by (5.40)]. This shows that $Q = S$ after all. Similarly, the only *right* inverse of T is S, since if $TR = I_3$ then $R = I_3 R = (ST)R = S(TR) = SI_3 = S$.

Suppose that $\det(T) \neq 0$. For each pair of indices (i,j) define S_i^j by

$$S_i^j = \frac{\operatorname{cof}_j^i(T)}{\det(T)} \tag{5.57}$$

To see that S is a left inverse of T, we simply compute:

$$(ST)_k^j = \sum_{i=1}^{3} S_i^j T_k^i = \frac{1}{\det(T)} \sum_{i=1}^{3} T_k^i \operatorname{cof}_j^i(T) = \delta_k^j$$

by (5.54). Therefore $ST = I_3$, showing that S is a left inverse of T.

A similar calculation, using (5.56), shows that S is also a right inverse of T. Therefore S is an inverse of T, and, from what we have said, we can say that S is *the* inverse of T. This is usually written $S = T^{-1}$.

We will leave to the exercises the proof that, if $\det(T) = 0$, T has no left inverses and also no right inverses. Therefore we are in a position to conclude that, if we have found either a left inverse or a right inverse for a 3×3 matrix, its determinant is necessarily nonzero and what we have found is *the* inverse.

A few books, fortunately in the minority, dwell at length on (5.57), pointing out that it provides a three-step process for finding the inverse of a matrix T that has nonzero determinant. First, we replace each entry in T by its cofactor. Then we take the transpose of the resulting matrix. Finally, we divide each entry by the determinant of T. The resulting matrix is T^{-1}. A more practical procedure, less conducive to error, is given in the exercises. [A common mistake in using (5.57) is to forget to take the transpose. It is also easy to make a sign error in computing a cofactor.]

Now we can see how to solve the equations $XB = A$ and $BY = A$, given that $\det(B) \neq 0$. For the first of these, we have $X = X(BB^{-1}) = (XB)B^{-1} = AB^{-1}$. By a similar argument, $Y = B^{-1}A$. We see quite clearly why the symbol A/B is not used in matrix algebra: it has two possible interpretations, as AB^{-1} and as $B^{-1}A$.

EXERCISES

In the first twelve exercises, let

$$w = (1 \quad 2 \quad 3 \quad 4) \qquad v = \begin{pmatrix} 4 \\ 3 \\ 2 \\ 1 \end{pmatrix}$$

$$T = \begin{pmatrix} 0 & 1 & -1 & 1 \\ 1 & 2 & -1 & 2 \\ 5 & 0 & 0 & 3 \end{pmatrix} \qquad S = \begin{pmatrix} 2 & 2 & 2 & 2 \\ 1 & -1 & 1 & -1 \\ 0 & 1 & 2 & 3 \\ 3 & 2 & 1 & 0 \end{pmatrix}$$

1. Compute TS.

2. Is ST defined?

3. Compute wv.

4. Compute vw.

5. What is T_4^3? What is v^2? What is w_1?

6. Compute Tv.

7. Is vT defined? If so, compute it.

8. Compute wS.

9. Compute $(wS)v$ and $w(Sv)$. Are they equal?

10. Let

$$R = \begin{pmatrix} 2 & 1 \\ 0 & 6 \end{pmatrix} \quad \text{and} \quad P = \begin{pmatrix} 4 & 4 \\ 7 & 7 \end{pmatrix}$$

Compute RP and PR. Are they equal?

11. Is $S + T$ defined? If so, compute it.

12. With R and P defined as in Exercise 10, compute $2R - P$.

In the remaining exercises, let

$$\underset{1}{e} = \begin{pmatrix} 1 \\ 0 \\ 0 \end{pmatrix} \quad \underset{2}{e} = \begin{pmatrix} 0 \\ 1 \\ 0 \end{pmatrix} \quad \underset{3}{e} = \begin{pmatrix} 0 \\ 0 \\ 1 \end{pmatrix} \quad \theta = \begin{pmatrix} 0 \\ 0 \\ 0 \end{pmatrix} \quad v = \begin{pmatrix} v^1 \\ v^2 \\ v^3 \end{pmatrix}$$

(The subscripts are placed directly beneath the *e*'s so that they will not be confused with the subscript notation used in this section.)

13. What is $\underset{1}{e}^1$? What is $\underset{2}{e}^2$? What is $\underset{3}{e}^3$?

14. Using the Kronecker index, write an expression for $\underset{i}{e}^j$.

15. If T is a 3×3 matrix, show that $T\underset{i}{e}$ is a 3×1 column matrix and explain how this matrix is related to T.

16. Show that, if $Tv = Pv$ for every possible column matrix v, where T and P are 3×3 matrices, then $T = P$.

17. (a) Show that, if $\det(T) \neq 0$, $Tv = \theta$ if and only if $v = \theta$. (T is a 3×3 matrix.)
(b) If $\det(T) = 0$, does there necessarily exist a v such that $v \neq \theta$ but $Tv = \theta$?

18. (a) Show that, if T is a 3×3 real matrix and $\det T = 0$, T has no left inverse.
(b) Under these circumstances, how would you show that T has no right inverse either?

19. Show that $u = Tv$ is a single matrix equation equivalent to three simultaneous linear equations.

20. (a) When is it possible to solve the equations in Exercise 19 for the v^i in terms of the u^j?
(b) Show that, when this is possible, the resulting matrix of coefficients is the inverse of T.

21. Use the idea suggested in the preceding two exercises to find the inverse of the matrix

$$\begin{pmatrix} 1 & -1 & 0 \\ 1 & 1 & 0 \\ 0 & 0 & 2 \end{pmatrix}$$

22. By solving the system of equations

$$\begin{aligned} 2v^1 + 4v^2 &= u^1 \\ v^1 - v^2 &= u^2 \end{aligned}$$

for the v's in terms of the u's, find the inverse of the matrix $\begin{pmatrix} 2 & 4 \\ 1 & -1 \end{pmatrix}$.

23. Show that, if

$$T = \begin{pmatrix} a & b \\ c & d \end{pmatrix} \qquad \text{then} \qquad T^{-1} = \begin{pmatrix} \dfrac{d}{ad-bc} & -\dfrac{b}{ad-bc} \\ -\dfrac{c}{ad-bc} & \dfrac{a}{ad-bc} \end{pmatrix}$$

provided $\det(T) \neq 0$.

24. Find the inverse of the matrix

$$\begin{pmatrix} 1 & -1 & 1 \\ 2 & 0 & 1 \\ 1 & 1 & 2 \end{pmatrix}$$

(a) by using (5.57),
(b) by the method suggested in earlier exercises.

25. Find the inverse of

$$\begin{pmatrix} a & 0 & 0 \\ 0 & b & 0 \\ 0 & 0 & c \end{pmatrix}$$

given that $abc \neq 0$.

5.5 BASES

The purpose of this section is to relate the matrix algebra of the preceding section with the vector algebra presented earlier. At the same time, this will motivate the apparently arbitrary rules for matrix addition and multiplication.

A set of three vectors $\underset{1}{\mathbf{e}}$, $\underset{2}{\mathbf{e}}$, and $\underset{3}{\mathbf{e}}$ is called a *basis* for space vectors provided that their triple scalar product is nonzero:

$$\underset{1}{\mathbf{e}} \cdot \underset{2}{\mathbf{e}} \times \underset{3}{\mathbf{e}} \neq 0 \tag{5.58}$$

For example, **i**, **j**, and **k**, the unit vectors determined by a cartesian coordinate system (introduced in Sec. 1.5) provide a basis for space vectors. In general, however, the vectors in a basis need not be unit vectors, nor need they be perpendicular to each other.

We shall always consider a basis as an ordered set. That is, we will take the vectors $\mathbf{e}_1$, $\mathbf{e}_2$, $\mathbf{e}_3$ in a definite order, and consider the same vectors in a different order as constituting a distinct basis. With this convention, it makes sense to speak of the kth base vector of the basis: it is $\mathbf{e}_k$.

As a consequence of (5.58), the vectors in a basis are nonzero vectors and are *not* coplanar. By a geometrical argument similar to that in Sec. 1.13, it can be shown that every vector **v** in space can be written as a linear combination of the base vectors,

$$\mathbf{v} = v^1\mathbf{e}_1 + v^2\mathbf{e}_2 + v^3\mathbf{e}_3 \tag{5.59}$$

(As in the preceding section, the superscripts here are *not* exponents.)

The coefficients in (5.59) are uniquely determined. Indeed, we can give explicit formulas for them:

$$v^1 = \frac{\mathbf{v} \cdot \mathbf{e}_2 \times \mathbf{e}_3}{\mathbf{e}_1 \cdot \mathbf{e}_2 \times \mathbf{e}_3} \qquad v^2 = \frac{\mathbf{v} \cdot \mathbf{e}_3 \times \mathbf{e}_1}{\mathbf{e}_1 \cdot \mathbf{e}_2 \times \mathbf{e}_3} \qquad v^3 = \frac{\mathbf{v} \cdot \mathbf{e}_1 \times \mathbf{e}_2}{\mathbf{e}_1 \cdot \mathbf{e}_2 \times \mathbf{e}_3} \tag{5.60}$$

(See Exercise 10, Sec. 1.13.)

We can take the numbers v^1, v^2, and v^3 as the entries in a column matrix v. We say that this is the column matrix *representing* **v** *relative to the basis* $\mathbf{e}_1$, $\mathbf{e}_2$, $\mathbf{e}_3$.

Example 5.8 Let $\mathbf{e}_1 = \mathbf{i} + \mathbf{j}$, $\mathbf{e}_2 = \mathbf{i} - \mathbf{j}$, and $\mathbf{e}_3 = 2\mathbf{k}$. Since $\mathbf{e}_1 \cdot \mathbf{e}_2 \times \mathbf{e}_3 = -4 \neq 0$, these vectors form a basis. Let $\mathbf{v} = 3\mathbf{i} + \mathbf{j} + 6\mathbf{k}$. Then by using (5.60) or, more easily, by simple algebraic juggling, we see that $\mathbf{v} = 2\mathbf{e}_1 + \mathbf{e}_2 + 3\mathbf{e}_3$. Therefore, $v = \begin{pmatrix} 2 \\ 1 \\ 3 \end{pmatrix}$ is the column matrix representing **v** relative to the basis $\mathbf{e}_1$, $\mathbf{e}_2$, $\mathbf{e}_3$.

It is easy to see that if **v** is represented by v and **u** is represented by u, relative to the same basis, then $\mathbf{u} + \mathbf{v}$ is represented by the sum $u + v$ of the column matrices. Also, if $c\mathbf{v}$ is any scalar multiple of the vector **v**, it is represented by the scalar multiple cv of the column matrix v.

Since the base vectors need not be unit vectors and need not be mutually perpendicular, it is not immediately obvious how we can compute the dot product $\mathbf{u} \cdot \mathbf{v}$ of two vectors **u** and **v**, in terms of the matrices u and v. To do this, we first introduce the numbers g_{ij} defined by

$$g_{ij} = \mathbf{e}_i \cdot \mathbf{e}_j \tag{5.61}$$

We will compute $\mathbf{u} \cdot \mathbf{v}$ making use of these numbers. We have

$$\mathbf{u} \cdot \mathbf{v} = \left(\sum_{i=1}^{3} u^i \mathbf{e}_i\right) \cdot \left(\sum_{j=1}^{3} v^j \mathbf{e}_j\right) = \sum_{i=1}^{3} \sum_{j=1}^{3} u^i v^j (\mathbf{e}_i \cdot \mathbf{e}_j) \tag{5.62}$$

and therefore

$$\mathbf{u} \cdot \mathbf{v} = \sum_{i=1}^{3} \sum_{j=1}^{3} g_{ij} u^i v^j \tag{5.63}$$

If we let u' denote the transpose of u (notice that u' is a row matrix) and let $G = (g_{ij})$, this can be written in matrix form,

$$\mathbf{u} \cdot \mathbf{v} = u'Gv \tag{5.64}$$

Example 5.9 Obtain a formula for the dot product relative to the basis given in Example 5.8.

Solution We first compute the entries g_{ij} in the matrix G. Note that $g_{11} = \mathbf{e}_1 \cdot \mathbf{e}_1 = (\mathbf{i} + \mathbf{j}) \cdot (\mathbf{i} + \mathbf{j}) = 2$, $g_{12} = \mathbf{e}_1 \cdot \mathbf{e}_2 = (\mathbf{i} + \mathbf{j}) \cdot (\mathbf{i} - \mathbf{j}) = 0$, etc. We find that

$$G = \begin{pmatrix} 2 & 0 & 0 \\ 0 & 2 & 0 \\ 0 & 0 & 4 \end{pmatrix}$$

and therefore

$$\mathbf{u} \cdot \mathbf{v} = 2u^1v^1 + 2u^2v^2 + 4u^3v^3$$

Formulas such as (5.60) occur so often in advanced work that it is convenient to have a way of writing them in simpler form. Let us introduce three vectors, denoted $\mathbf{e}^1$, $\mathbf{e}^2$, and $\mathbf{e}^3$, by the definitions

$$\mathbf{e}^1 = \frac{\mathbf{e}_2 \times \mathbf{e}_3}{\mathbf{e}_1 \cdot \mathbf{e}_2 \times \mathbf{e}_3} \qquad \mathbf{e}^2 = \frac{\mathbf{e}_3 \times \mathbf{e}_1}{\mathbf{e}_1 \cdot \mathbf{e}_2 \times \mathbf{e}_3} \qquad \mathbf{e}^3 = \frac{\mathbf{e}_1 \times \mathbf{e}_2}{\mathbf{e}_1 \cdot \mathbf{e}_2 \times \mathbf{e}_3} \tag{5.65}$$

We will show that these three vectors also constitute a basis, which is said to be *reciprocal* or *dual* to the basis $\mathbf{e}_1$, $\mathbf{e}_2$, $\mathbf{e}_3$.

If we consider $\mathbf{e}_1 \times \mathbf{e}_2$ as a single vector, then $(\mathbf{e}_3 \times \mathbf{e}_1) \times (\mathbf{e}_1 \times \mathbf{e}_2)$ is a triple vector product, and by (5.60), Sec. 1.14, it is equal to $(\mathbf{e}_3 \cdot \mathbf{e}_1 \times \mathbf{e}_2)\mathbf{e}_1$. Hence

$$(\mathbf{e}_2 \times \mathbf{e}_3) \cdot (\mathbf{e}_3 \times \mathbf{e}_1) \times (\mathbf{e}_1 \times \mathbf{e}_2) = (\mathbf{e}_3 \cdot \mathbf{e}_1 \times \mathbf{e}_2)(\mathbf{e}_2 \times \mathbf{e}_3 \cdot \mathbf{e}_1) = (\mathbf{e}_1 \cdot \mathbf{e}_2 \times \mathbf{e}_3)^2 \tag{5.66}$$

This is the same as the triple scalar product of the three vectors in (5.65), except for the denominators that occur there. It follows that

$$\mathbf{e}^1 \cdot \mathbf{e}^2 \times \mathbf{e}^3 = \frac{1}{\mathbf{e}_1 \cdot \mathbf{e}_2 \times \mathbf{e}_3} \tag{5.67}$$

Since $\mathbf{e}_1 \cdot \mathbf{e}_2 \times \mathbf{e}_3 \neq 0$ by (5.58), this is defined and is also nonzero, which shows that the vectors $\mathbf{e}^1$, $\mathbf{e}^2$, and $\mathbf{e}^3$ also constitute a basis.

Directly from the definitions, we see that $\overset{1}{\mathbf{e}}$ is perpendicular to $\underset{2}{\mathbf{e}}$ and $\underset{3}{\mathbf{e}}$. Indeed, each vector in one basis is perpendicular to two vectors in the other basis. We can say even more: from Eqs. (5.65)

$$\underset{i}{\mathbf{e}} \cdot \overset{j}{\mathbf{e}} = \delta_i^j \tag{5.68}$$

where δ_i^j is the Kronecker delta.

We can now write (5.60) in the simple form

$$v^i = \mathbf{v} \cdot \overset{i}{\mathbf{e}} \qquad (i = 1,2,3) \tag{5.69}$$

which is one of the reasons for introducing the dual basis.

There is a more important reason for introducing the notion of a basis and its dual basis. Later on, we will attach to each point in space a basis $\underset{1}{\mathbf{e}}, \underset{2}{\mathbf{e}}, \underset{3}{\mathbf{e}}$ consisting of vectors that are tangent to coordinate curves passing through that point. If the coordinate system is not orthogonal, these vectors will not be mutually perpendicular; since the scales may be different on the coordinate curves, the vectors may have different lengths. The dual basis at a point will consist of three vectors $\overset{1}{\mathbf{e}}, \overset{2}{\mathbf{e}}, \overset{3}{\mathbf{e}}$ that are perpendicular to the coordinate surfaces; they are the gradients of the functions that define the coordinate system. These matters will be discussed later. In this section, we are only concerned with algebraic matters.

There is complete duality between a basis and its dual basis. Whatever we can do with one, we can do equally well with the other. For example, we can write any vector v as a linear combination of the dual base vectors,

$$\mathbf{v} = v_1 \overset{1}{\mathbf{e}} + v_2 \overset{2}{\mathbf{e}} + v_3 \overset{3}{\mathbf{e}} \tag{5.70}$$

Because of (5.68), we have

$$v_i = \mathbf{v} \cdot \underset{i}{\mathbf{e}} \qquad (i = 1,2, \text{ or } 3) \tag{5.71}$$

We then say that the *row* matrix (v_1, v_2, v_3) represents $\mathbf{v}$ relative to the *dual* basis.

The numbers v_1, v_2, and v_3, which are the dot products of $\mathbf{v}$ with the base vectors $\underset{1}{\mathbf{e}}$, $\underset{2}{\mathbf{e}}$, and $\underset{3}{\mathbf{e}}$ respectively, are called the *covariant components* of $\mathbf{v}$, relative to the basis $\underset{1}{\mathbf{e}}, \underset{2}{\mathbf{e}}, \underset{3}{\mathbf{e}}$. This is to distinguish them from the numbers v^1, v^2, and v^3, which are the dot products of $\mathbf{v}$ with the dual base vectors, and which are then called the *contravariant components* of $\mathbf{v}$.

The reason for the occurrence of "variant" in these words is that, when we change from one basis to another (and hence change from one dual basis to another) the components of $\mathbf{v}$ will change, and the covariant components "vary" in a different manner than do the contravariant components. This will be discussed in a later section.

It might appear from these definitions that the covariant components are more fundamental than the contravariant components. Actually, the opposite is the case. The contravariant components are the more fundamental. To see this, imagine for the moment that we knew of vectors only as classes of directed line segments, but knew nothing about the concept of the magnitude of a vector and, hence, nothing about the dot products of vectors. (Physically, this might mean that we have not decided whether to use inches or centimeters.) It would still be possible to define the contravariant components of $\mathbf{v}$, relative to $\underset{1}{\mathbf{e}}$, $\underset{2}{\mathbf{e}}$, and $\underset{3}{\mathbf{e}}$, purely geometrically, using (5.59) as the definition. It is impossible to define the covariant components, however, without introducing metric concepts, such as *magnitude* and the *dot product*. (In this connection, see Example 5.10 and also Exercise 1.)

We mention in passing that the contravariant components of $\mathbf{v}$ relative to $\underset{1}{\mathbf{e}}/|\underset{1}{\mathbf{e}}|$, $\underset{2}{\mathbf{e}}/|\underset{2}{\mathbf{e}}|$, $\underset{3}{\mathbf{e}}/|\underset{3}{\mathbf{e}}|$ are called the *physical* components of $\mathbf{v}$, relative to $\underset{1}{\mathbf{e}}$, $\underset{2}{\mathbf{e}}$, and $\underset{3}{\mathbf{e}}$.

Here is an expression that gives the covariant components of v in terms of the contravariant components:

$$v_i = \sum_{j=1}^{3} v^j g_{ji} \tag{5.72}$$

This is derived quite simply: $v_i = \mathbf{v} \cdot \underset{i}{\mathbf{e}}$ [by (5.71)] $= \left(\sum_{j=1}^{3} v^j \underset{j}{\mathbf{e}}\right) \cdot \underset{i}{\mathbf{e}}$ [by (5.59)] $= \sum_{j=1}^{3} v^j(\underset{j}{\mathbf{e}} \cdot \underset{i}{\mathbf{e}}) = \sum_{j=1}^{3} v^j g_{ji}$ [by (5.61)].

If we define another matrix by

$$g^{ij} = \overset{i}{\mathbf{e}} \cdot \overset{j}{\mathbf{e}} \tag{5.73}$$

then we have

$$v^i = \sum_{j=1}^{3} v_j g^{ji} \tag{5.74}$$

The derivation of (5.74) is *exactly* the same as the derivation of (5.72); simply replace all subscripts by superscripts and vice versa.

It follows from (5.72) and (5.74) that the matrix with entries given in (5.73) is the inverse of $G = (g_{ij})$, so that $G^{-1} = (g^{ij})$. However, a direct proof may be instructive. Substituting (5.72) into (5.59) we have

$$\mathbf{v} = \sum_{j=1}^{3} (\mathbf{v} \cdot \overset{j}{\mathbf{e}})\underset{j}{\mathbf{e}} \tag{5.75}$$

This is valid for *every* vector $\mathbf{v}$. Therefore, it is valid in particular for $\mathbf{v} = \overset{i}{\mathbf{e}}$:

$$\overset{i}{\mathbf{e}} = \sum_{j=1}^{3} (\overset{i}{\mathbf{e}} \cdot \overset{j}{\mathbf{e}})\underset{j}{\mathbf{e}} \tag{5.76}$$

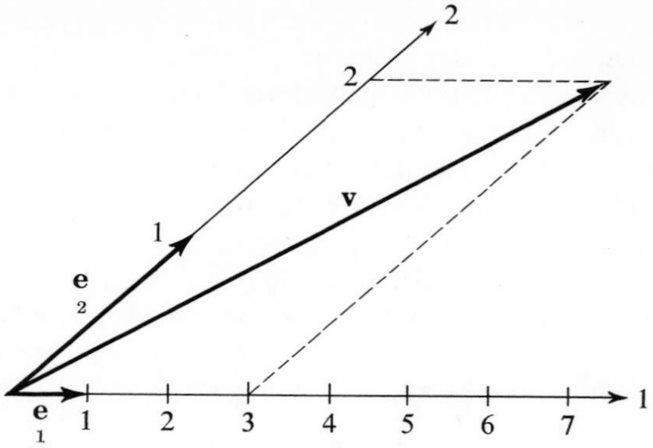

FIGURE 5.1

Now take the dot product of both sides of (5.76) with $\underset{k}{\mathbf{e}}$ and use (5.68).

$$\delta^i_k = \left[\sum_{j=1}^{3} (\overset{i}{\mathbf{e}} \cdot \overset{j}{\mathbf{e}})\underset{j}{\mathbf{e}}\right] \cdot \underset{k}{\mathbf{e}} = \sum_{j=1}^{3} (\overset{i}{\mathbf{e}} \cdot \overset{j}{\mathbf{e}})(\underset{j}{\mathbf{e}} \cdot \underset{k}{\mathbf{e}}) \tag{5.77}$$

So by (5.61) and (5.73) we have

$$\delta^i_k = \sum_{j=1}^{3} g^{ij} g_{jk} \tag{5.78}$$

showing that the product of these two matrices is the identity matrix.

What has been done in this section for vectors in euclidean space can also be done for vectors in the euclidean *plane*. We will not dwell on this, but will be content with a simple example.

Example 5.10 In the plane, let $\underset{1}{\mathbf{e}}$ and $\underset{2}{\mathbf{e}}$ be any two vectors, neither of which is a scalar multiple of the other. Then both vectors are nonzero and every vector in the plane can be written as a linear combination of these two vectors. The geometrical construction is shown in Fig. 5.1. We call $\underset{1}{\mathbf{e}}$ and $\underset{2}{\mathbf{e}}$ a *basis* for vectors in the plane. In the figure, we have $\mathbf{v} = 3\underset{1}{\mathbf{e}} + 2\underset{2}{\mathbf{e}}$, so the column matrix representing $\mathbf{v}$ relative to this basis is $\begin{pmatrix} 3 \\ 2 \end{pmatrix}$.

EXERCISES

1. Give a geometrical definition of *basis* that is equivalent to (5.58) but does not make use of scalar products.
2. Do the three vectors $\mathbf{i} + \mathbf{j} + \mathbf{k}$, $\mathbf{i} + \mathbf{j} - \mathbf{k}$, and $3\mathbf{i} + 3\mathbf{j}$ constitute a basis for space vectors?

3. (a) Show that the vectors $\underset{1}{\mathbf{e}} = \mathbf{i} + \mathbf{j} + \mathbf{k}$, $\underset{2}{\mathbf{e}} = \mathbf{j} - \mathbf{k}$, $\underset{3}{\mathbf{e}} = \mathbf{i} - \mathbf{j} + 5\mathbf{k}$ constitute a basis for space vectors.
(b) Find the contravariant components of $\mathbf{v} = 4\mathbf{i} + 4\mathbf{j} + 8\mathbf{k}$ relative to this basis.

4. Find the matrix $G = (g_{ij})$, given the basis in the preceding exercise.

5. Find the covariant components of $\mathbf{v} = 2\mathbf{i} - \mathbf{j}$ relative to the basis in Exercise 3.

6. Write $\underset{1}{\mathbf{e}}$ in terms of $\overset{1}{\mathbf{e}}$, $\overset{2}{\mathbf{e}}$, and $\overset{3}{\mathbf{e}}$. If the subscripts in (5.65) are changed to superscripts, and vice versa, do the formulas remain valid?

7. (a) Would the right side of (5.72) take on a different meaning if, wherever it occurs, the letter j were replaced by the letter k?
(b) What if j were replaced by i?

8. By imitating the derivation of (5.78), give a direct derivation of

$$\delta_i^k = \sum_{j=1}^{3} g_{ij} g^{jk} \tag{5.79}$$

9. The two matrices $G = (g_{ij})$ and $G^{-1} = (g^{ij})$ possess a special property that makes it easy to derive (5.79) directly from (5.78). State this property and give the derivation.

10. For any nonzero vector $\mathbf{v}$, $\sum_{i=1}^{3} \sum_{j=1}^{3} g_{ij} v^i v^j$ is a positive real number. Without engaging in any calculations, explain why you would expect it to be positive, and not zero or negative. [*Caution*: This is a consequence of the definition (5.61) and is not a property shared by all matrices.]

11. What column matrix represents $4\mathbf{i} + 6\mathbf{j}$ relative to the basis $\underset{1}{\mathbf{e}} = \mathbf{i} + \mathbf{j}$ and $\underset{2}{\mathbf{e}} = \mathbf{i} - \mathbf{j}$ in the plane?

12. What geometrical properties must be possessed by a basis in order that $G = (g_{ij})$ be the indentity matrix?

5.6 TENSORS OF RANK TWO

Readers with no interest in physics can skip over the introductory paragraphs of this section.

A student of elementary physics, on learning that a *scalar* quantity is characterized by magnitude alone, whereas a *vector* quantity has both magnitude and direction, might assume that all of the quantities of physics are either scalars or vectors. This is not the case. Many of the "quantities" of physics are neither scalars nor vectors. An important class of them are *tensors*.

The *tensor* concept is much broader than the notion of a *scalar* or a *vector* and constitutes both a generalization and a refinement of these notions. It is a *generalization* because it includes scalars and vectors as special cases (we will see later that a *scalar* is a *tensor of rank zero*, and a *vector* is a *tensor of rank one*). It is a *refinement* because it includes a classification scheme for scalars and vectors (for example, *temperature* and *mass density* are both scalar quantities, but they are not the same kind of scalar quantity).

Let us consider a typical example of a tensor of rank two. What we have in mind is the so-called *stress tensor*, which describes the force per unit area within a solid. We do not assume that the reader has any prior knowledge of stress; however, the reader must be somewhat familiar with the notion of "pressure": most books on calculus have at least one section of dreary exercises in calculating the force on one face of a dam due to water pressure. Pressure is, by definition, the magnitude of force per unit area, and is commonly considered a scalar quantity.

To avoid an exercise in integral calculus, let us assume that the pressure does not vary with position in space. Then if the pressure is p and the area of a plane surface is A, the magnitude of the force exerted on one face of the surface is pA. In elementary physics, and hence also in books on elementary calculus, it is assumed that this force is exerted in a direction perpendicular to the surface.

However valid this assumption may be for forces within a fluid, it is obviously not valid for the forces within a solid body. A solid body not only resists compression and expansion, but also tends to resist shear; it takes a strong man to tear a telephone book in two. When a shearing force is applied to a solid body, the force exerted on a surface within the body need *not* be perpendicular to the surface.

Consider a plane surface having area A, located entirely within the solid body, and let $\mathbf{A}$ denote a vector of magnitude A perpendicular to the surface. Let $\mathbf{F}$ denote the force exerted on one face of the plane surface. (To be more precise, let $\mathbf{F}$ denote the force exerted *by* the particles on the negative side of the surface *on* the particles located on the positive side of the surface, where "positive" and "negative" are defined, as in Sec. 1.11, by the choice of the direction of $\mathbf{A}$. We imagine that the solid body is composed of particles, i.e., atoms, and that the force is due to some kind of interatomic binding.) To avoid integral calculus, we will assume that A is sufficiently small that we can neglect variations in strain over different parts of the surface (just as we assumed, in an earlier paragraph, that the pressure was constant). We will also assume that the components of $\mathbf{F}$ are linearly related to the components of $\mathbf{A}$ (so that, e.g., doubling the area results in doubling the force).

If we were dealing with a fluid, we might be able to write $\mathbf{F} = p\mathbf{A}$, where p is a scalar, and characterize the stress simply by giving the pressure p. In a solid, however, the direction of $\mathbf{F}$ may not be the same as the direction of $\mathbf{A}$; as we have already noted, it may actually be perpendicular to $\mathbf{A}$, or very nearly perpendicular (think of that telephone book). *Stress is a physical quantity that is neither a scalar nor a vector*. It is a tensor of rank two. We will see that it can be represented, relative to a basis, by a 3×3 matrix whose entries are called the *components* of the stress (relative to the basis).

Let $\underset{1}{\mathbf{e}}, \underset{2}{\mathbf{e}}, \underset{3}{\mathbf{e}}$ be a basis, let A_1, A_2, and A_3 be the covariant components of **A** relative to this basis, and let F^1, F^2, and F^3 be the contravariant components of **F** relative to the same basis. Then we have

$$F^i = \sum_{j=1}^{3} p^{ij}A_j \qquad (i = 1,2, \text{ or } 3) \tag{5.80}$$

for a suitable choice of numbers p^{ij} $(i = 1,2,3;\ j = 1,2,3)$. These nine numbers are called the *contravariant components* of the stress tensor, relative to the basis.

If we had used the contravariant components of **A** and the covariant components of **F** we would have

$$F_i = \sum_{j=1}^{3} p_{ij}A^j \tag{5.81}$$

and the nine numbers (p_{ij}) are called the *covariant components* of the stress tensor, relative to the basis.

To see the significance of the contravariant components of the stress tensor, let us suppose that the plane surface is parallel to the 12 plane, so that **A** is a scalar multiple of $\overset{3}{\mathbf{e}}$. Then $A_1 = A_2 = 0$ and (5.80) reduces to $F^i = p^{i3}A_3$ $(i = 1,2,3)$. If $\overset{3}{\mathbf{e}}$ is a unit vector, then $\mathbf{A} = A\overset{3}{\mathbf{e}}$ and $A_3 = A$. If it happens that $A = 1$, then $F^i = p^{i3}$ so that p^{i3} is the ith contravariant component of **F**.

Quite generally, if the dual base vectors are unit vectors, p^{ij} is the ith contravariant component of the force exerted on a unit area of a surface that is perpendicular to the jth dual base vector. A similar interpretation can be given the nine components p_{ij} (see Exercise 1).

These components not only depend on the state of stress in the solid body, but also on the choice of basis. If we consider any particular solid body, in some specific state of stress, and make the simplifying assumptions above, then **F** is a function of **A**. This functional relationship can be described equally well by either (5.80) or (5.81). If we use another basis, all of the numbers represented by the symbols in (5.80) and (5.81) may be different, but will nevertheless express the same functional relationship. When we speak of stress we are referring to this *function* that gives **F** in terms of **A** When we give nine components (either the p^{ij}'s or the p_{ij}'s) we are simply *describing* this function relative to a particular choice of basis.

Although it is not obvious from what we have said, it is interesting to note that the stress tensor can be regarded as a scalar valued function of two vector variables. To see this, consider the double sum

$$\sum_{i=1}^{3} \sum_{j=1}^{3} p^{ij}A_j B_i \tag{5.82}$$

where A and B are arbitrary vectors. With a little calculation this can be shown to be the scalar product $\mathbf{F} \cdot \mathbf{B}$ (see Exercise 2; the detailed calculation will be found in the Answers and Notes). Although the numbers that appear in (5.82), i.e., the covariant components of vectors **A** and **B** and the contravariant components of the stress tensor, depend on the particular choice of basis, the numerical value of (5.82) is the scalar product $\mathbf{F} \cdot \mathbf{B}$, no matter what basis is used. In other words, the numerical value of (5.82) is independent of the choice of basis.

The double sum

$$\sum_{i=1}^{3} \sum_{j=1}^{3} p_{ij} A^j B^i \tag{5.83}$$

defines the same function. The numerical value of (5.83) is exactly the same as the value of (5.82) for any choice of vectors **A** and **B**.

These preliminaries are intended to motivate the following definition: *A tensor of rank two is a scalar-valued function of two vector variables that is linear in each variable.*

In greater detail, to say that ϕ is a tensor of rank two means that a numerical value $\phi(\mathbf{u},\mathbf{v})$ is assigned to each pair of vectors **u** and **v** and this value must be independent of the choice of basis. Moreover, $\phi(\mathbf{u},\mathbf{v})$ must be linear in its first variable, which means that

$$\phi(\alpha\mathbf{u} + \beta\mathbf{w}, \mathbf{v}) = \alpha\phi(\mathbf{u},\mathbf{v}) + \beta\phi(\mathbf{w},\mathbf{v}) \tag{5.84}$$

whenever α, β are numbers and **u**, **v**, and **w** are vectors. Also, $\phi(\mathbf{u},\mathbf{v})$ must be linear in its second variable,

$$\phi(\mathbf{u}, \alpha\mathbf{v} + \beta\mathbf{w}) = \alpha\phi(\mathbf{u},\mathbf{v}) + \beta\phi(\mathbf{u},\mathbf{w}) \tag{5.85}$$

By the *covariant components* of the tensor ϕ relative to a basis $\underset{1}{\mathbf{e}}, \underset{2}{\mathbf{e}}, \underset{3}{\mathbf{e}}$ we mean the nine numbers ϕ_{ij} defined by

$$\phi_{ij} = \phi(\underset{i}{\mathbf{e}},\underset{j}{\mathbf{e}}) \qquad (i,j = 1,2,3) \tag{5.86}$$

Because of the linearity conditions (5.84) and (5.85) we have, for any pair of vectors **u** and **v**,

$$\phi(\mathbf{u},\mathbf{v}) = \phi\left(\sum_{i=1}^{3} u^i \underset{i}{\mathbf{e}}, \sum_{j=1}^{3} v^j \underset{j}{\mathbf{e}}\right) = \sum_{i=1}^{3} \sum_{j=1}^{3} u^i v^j \phi(\underset{i}{\mathbf{e}},\underset{j}{\mathbf{e}}) \tag{5.87}$$

which becomes, on using the notation introduced in (5.86),

$$\phi(\mathbf{u},\mathbf{v}) = \sum_{i=1}^{3} \sum_{j=1}^{3} \phi_{ij} u^i v^j \tag{5.88}$$

By the *contravariant components* of ϕ relative to a basis $\underset{1}{\mathbf{e}}, \underset{2}{\mathbf{e}}, \underset{3}{\mathbf{e}}$ we mean the nine numbers ϕ^{ij} defined similarly but using the dual basis instead,

$$\phi^{ij} = \phi(\overset{i}{\mathbf{e}},\overset{j}{\mathbf{e}}) \qquad (i,j = 1,2,3) \tag{5.89}$$

and by a similar calculation we have

$$\phi(\mathbf{u},\mathbf{v}) = \sum_{i=1}^{3} \sum_{j=1}^{3} \phi^{ij} u_i v_j \tag{5.90}$$

A tensor of rank two is said to be *symmetric* if it satisfies the extra condition $\phi(\mathbf{u},\mathbf{v}) = \phi(\mathbf{v},\mathbf{u})$. If ϕ is symmetric, then $\phi_{ij} = \phi_{ji}$ and $\phi^{ij} = \phi^{ji}$ for every pair of indices i and j.

Although we introduced this section with a discussion of the stress tensor, a much simpler example can be given. This is the *metric tensor* g, defined by the scalar product

$$g(\mathbf{u},\mathbf{v}) = \mathbf{u} \cdot \mathbf{v} \tag{5.91}$$

We know from earlier work (Sec. 1.9) that the scalar product is linear in both factors and, hence, g satisfies both (5.84) and (5.85). Its covariant components g_{ij} and its contravariant components g^{ij} were discussed in the preceding section. [*Caution*: In later sections, the single letter g will be used with an entirely different meaning, to denote the determinant of the matrix $G = (g_{ij})$.]

Since the scalar product is independent of the order of its factors, the metric tensor is symmetric: $g_{ij} = g_{ji}$ and $g^{ij} = g^{ji}$. As a consequence, equations involving the metric tensor can usually be written in at least two ways. For example, (5.72) can be written either as

$$v_i = \sum_{j=1}^{3} v^j g_{ji} \qquad \text{or as} \qquad v_i = \sum_{j=1}^{3} v^j g_{ij}$$

Many of the tensors that occur in physics are symmetric. In many cases this is a consequence of Newton's third law (to every action there is opposed an equal reaction) but the detailed proofs may be difficult. For example, the stress tensor for a body in equilibrium is symmetric, but this is not obvious and will not be proved in this book. In some books the term *tensor* is reserved exclusively for symmetric tensors, and the others are called *affinors*

The next section will be devoted to tensors in general and to the formal algebra of tensors. We will conclude this section with a number of informal remarks of no great consequence.

Our first remark concerns terminology. In order to avoid circumlocution, it is customary to say "the tensor g_{ij}" instead of "the tensor whose covariant components, relative to a basis, will be denoted by g_{ij}, $i,j = 1, 2, 3$". One can object to this for much the same reason that one can object to the expression "the function $f(x)$". (This was discussed briefly in Sec. 3.5.)

Our next remark concerns the definition of *tensor*. Many definitions are possible, and it is not obvious that they are equivalent. From reading some physics texts, one might get the impression that tensors have no identity of their own, but are simply collections of numbers which must be changed every time the coordinate system in space is changed. The trend in modern mathematics is towards a more abstract approach in which components are not mentioned at all. In this book, the authors steer a middle-of-the-road course, taking advantage of the simplifications that are possible when working entirely in three-dimensional euclidean space.

Finally, we wish to note that the nine components of a tensor of rank two, relative to a basis, can be used as the entries of a 3×3 matrix. We can use either the covariant components or the contravariant components, so the same tensor can be described, relative to a basis, by two different matrices. (There are additional possibilities as well; one can also use "mixed components", not yet discussed in this book.) Unfortunately, tensor notation clashes with matrix notation to some extent. For example, Eq. (5.81) suggests that we are multiplying a 3×3 matrix with a column matrix and thereby obtaining a row matrix, which is impossible. This can be remedied by a judicious use of the notion of the "transpose" of a matrix; for our purposes, however, this is rather pointless. The reader is not advised to spend him time rewriting these equations in matrix form. A more convenient way of abbreviating them, using the Einstein summation convention, will be introduced in the next section.

EXERCISES

1. Give an interpretation for the nine components p_{ij} of the stress tensor, parallel to that given in the text for the components p^{ij}.
2. Show in detail that (5.82) gives formula for $\mathbf{F} \cdot \mathbf{B}$.
3. Show that (5.82) and (5.83) are equal.
4. For any pair of vectors $\mathbf{u} = u^1\mathbf{i} + u^2\mathbf{j} + u^3\mathbf{k}$ and $\mathbf{v} = v^1\mathbf{i} + v^2\mathbf{j} + v^3\mathbf{k}$, define the tensor ϕ by

$$\phi(\mathbf{u},\mathbf{v}) = u^1v^1 + 2u^2v^3 - 6u^3v^2 \tag{5.92}$$

   (a) What are the components ϕ_{ij} relative to the basis $\mathbf{i}, \mathbf{j}, \mathbf{k}$? Write them in the form of a 3×3 matrix.
   (b) Do the same for ϕ^{ij}.
5. Find the nine components ϕ_{ij} of the tensor defined in the preceding exercise, relative to the basis $\underset{1}{\mathbf{e}}, \underset{2}{\mathbf{e}}, \underset{3}{\mathbf{e}}$ given in Exercise 3 of the preceding section.
6. Derive a formula giving the contravariant components of a tensor of rank two in terms of its covariant components and the components of the metric tensor relative to the same basis. [*Hint*: One way is to substitute (5.76) into (5.89).]

5.7 TENSOR ALGEBRA

We will now adopt the following modified version of the *summation convention* described in the optional Sec. 1.16: a summation is implied whenever the same index occurs twice, once as a subscript and once as a superscript. By making use of this convention, we can drop summation symbols from most of our equations.

For example, instead of writing

$$\mathbf{v} = v^1\underset{1}{\mathbf{e}} + v^2\underset{2}{\mathbf{e}} + v^3\underset{3}{\mathbf{e}} \tag{5.93}$$

or even

$$\mathbf{v} = \sum_{i=1}^{3} v^i\underset{i}{\mathbf{e}} \tag{5.94}$$

we will simply write

$$\mathbf{v} = v^i\underset{i}{\mathbf{e}} \tag{5.95}$$

Since i occurs both as a subscript and as a superscript, it is understood that this expression is to be summed from $i = 1$ to 3.

This convention is used whether the subscript is placed directly beneath a letter (we use this to distinguish between different vectors) or placed below and to the right (which we use to distinguish between various covariant components of the same vector or tensor). The same is true of superscripts:

$$\mathbf{v} = v_i\overset{i}{\mathbf{e}} \tag{5.96}$$

is an abbreviated version of (5.70).

Double sums can also be simplified. For example, (5.63) now is written

$$\mathbf{u} \cdot \mathbf{v} = g_{ij}u^i v^j \tag{5.97}$$

An equation such as (5.72) can now be written

$$v_i = v^j g_{ji} \tag{5.98}$$

In this equation, j occurs both as a subscript and a superscript, so as summation over j is intended, but no summation over i is involved. We say that j is a *dummy index* because j could be replaced by any other letter (provided it is not being used elsewhere) without changing the meaning. For example,

$$v_i = v^k g_{ki} \tag{5.99}$$

has exactly the same meaning as (5.98), because there is no difference between the two sums

$$\sum_{j=1}^{3} v^j g_{ji} \qquad \text{and} \qquad \sum_{k=1}^{3} v^k g_{ki}$$

since both sums are equally good ways of writing

$$v^1 g_{1i} + v^2 g_{2i} + v^3 g_{3i}$$

and, hence, both sums really represent an expression that does not contain either j or k. Notice that neither j nor k occurs on the left side of (5.98) or (5.99). On the other hand, i does occur on both sides of both (5.98) and (5.99). We call i a *free* index, to indicate that no summation over i is intended, but that i can freely take on any one of the three values 1, 2, or 3. As a consequence of this, (5.98) is actually an abbreviation for *three* equations. There is a separate equation for each value of i:

$$v_1 = v^j g_{j1} \qquad v_2 = v^j g_{j2} \qquad \text{and} \qquad v_3 = v^j g_{j3}$$

We must not use a dummy index that is being used freely elsewhere, or accidentally use the same letter for two different dummies. For example, $v^j g_{jj}$ would stand for $v^1 g_{11} + v^2 g_{22} + v^3 g_{33}$, which is not at all the same as $v^j g_{ji}$. As another example, it would hardly do to write the right side of (5.97) as $g_{ii} u^i v^i$, because this sum would involve only three terms and we would lose the other six terms [the right side of (5.97) includes nine terms].

The summation convention is somewhat dangerous in the hands of novices, because they often forget that any summation is involved. For example, it would be ridiculous to "solve" (5.99) for g_{ki} to obtain $g_{ki} = v_i/v^k$. If the reader does not see why this is ridiculous, he should go back to the first sentence and reread this section more slowly.

For pedagogical reasons, the author does not like the summation convention. Students have some difficulty getting used to summation signs, and then have double the difficulty when they are omitted. The student is strongly advised to work the first ten exercises at the end of this section *without* looking at the answers in advance.

The definition given in the preceding section is easily generalized. *A tensor of rank r is a scalar-valued function of r vector variables that is linear in each variable.*

Thus, if ϕ is a tensor of rank three, it assigns a scalar $\phi(\mathbf{u},\mathbf{v},\mathbf{w})$ to any ordered triple of vectors **u**, **v**, and **w**. By the linearity property, if we have

$$\mathbf{u} = u^i \underset{i}{\mathbf{e}} \qquad \mathbf{v} = v^j \underset{j}{\mathbf{e}} \qquad \mathbf{w} = w^k \underset{k}{\mathbf{e}} \tag{5.100}$$

then

$$\phi(\mathbf{u},\mathbf{v},\mathbf{w}) = \phi(u^i \underset{i}{\mathbf{e}}, v^j \underset{j}{\mathbf{e}}, w^k \underset{k}{\mathbf{e}}) = u^i v^j w^k \phi(\underset{i}{\mathbf{e}},\underset{j}{\mathbf{e}},\underset{k}{\mathbf{e}}) \tag{5.101}$$

Notice that we are using the summation convention: this is a triple sum. If we introduce the notation

$$\phi_{ijk} = \phi(\underset{i}{\mathbf{e}},\underset{j}{\mathbf{e}},\underset{k}{\mathbf{e}}) \tag{5.102}$$

for the covariant components of ϕ relative to the basis $\underset{1}{\mathbf{e}}, \underset{2}{\mathbf{e}}, \underset{3}{\mathbf{e}}$ we can write (5.101) in the form

$$\phi(\mathbf{u},\mathbf{v},\mathbf{w}) = \phi_{ijk} u^i v^j w^k \tag{5.103}$$

In the manner already discussed in connection with tensors of rank two, one can also define contravariant components by

$$\phi^{ijk} = \phi(\overset{i}{\mathbf{e}},\overset{j}{\mathbf{e}},\overset{k}{\mathbf{e}}) \tag{5.104}$$

and obtain

$$\phi(\mathbf{u},\mathbf{v},\mathbf{w}) = \phi^{ijk} u_i v_j w_k \tag{5.105}$$

As an interesting exercise in tensor algebra, let us derive a formula giving the contravariant components in terms of the covariant components. We will make use of (5.76), which can be written

$$\overset{i}{\mathbf{e}} = g^{ij}\underset{j}{\mathbf{e}} \tag{5.106}$$

We will substitute this into (5.104), being careful to use dummy indices that do not clash with the other indices:

$$\phi^{ijk} = \phi(\overset{i}{\mathbf{e}},\overset{j}{\mathbf{e}},\overset{k}{\mathbf{e}}) = \phi(g^{ip}\underset{p}{\mathbf{e}},g^{jr}\underset{r}{\mathbf{e}},g^{ks}\underset{s}{\mathbf{e}}) = g^{ip}g^{jr}g^{ks}\phi(\underset{p}{\mathbf{e}},\underset{r}{\mathbf{e}},\underset{s}{\mathbf{e}}) \tag{5.107}$$

so the desired formula is

$$\phi^{ijk} = g^{ip}g^{jr}g^{ks}\phi_{prs} \tag{5.108}$$

which is a triple sum over the dummy indices p, r, and s.

A tensor of rank two or more is said to be *alternating* if its sign changes whenever two of its vector arguments are interchanged. Thus, a tensor of rank two is alternating, provided $\phi(\mathbf{u},\mathbf{v}) = -\phi(\mathbf{v},\mathbf{u})$ for any pair of vectors $\mathbf{u}$ and $\mathbf{v}$. A tensor of rank three is alternating, provided that

$$\begin{aligned} \phi(\mathbf{u},\mathbf{v},\mathbf{w}) &= -\phi(\mathbf{v},\mathbf{u},\mathbf{w}) = \phi(\mathbf{v},\mathbf{w},\mathbf{u}) = -\phi(\mathbf{w},\mathbf{v},\mathbf{u}) \\ &= \phi(\mathbf{w},\mathbf{u},\mathbf{v}) = -\phi(\mathbf{u},\mathbf{w},\mathbf{v}) \end{aligned} \tag{5.109}$$

If we let $\mathbf{u} = \mathbf{v}$ in the first equality, we have $\phi(\mathbf{u},\mathbf{u},\mathbf{w}) = -\phi(\mathbf{u},\mathbf{u},\mathbf{w})$, and therefore $\phi(\mathbf{u},\mathbf{u},\mathbf{w}) = 0$. Quite generally, if two of the vector arguments of an alternating tensor are equal, the value of ϕ is zero.

It follows that the covariant components of an alternating tensor of rank three are completely known once we have determined ϕ_{123}, since $\phi_{123} = -\phi_{213} = \phi_{231} = -\phi_{321} = \phi_{312} = -\phi_{132}$ and the other twenty-one components must be zero. Of course, a similar assertion can be made about the contravariant components.

Using the symbol ε_{ijk}, introduced in Sec. 5.4, this can be summarized in the simple expression

$$\phi(\underset{i}{\mathbf{e}},\underset{j}{\mathbf{e}},\underset{k}{\mathbf{e}}) = \varepsilon_{ijk}\phi(\underset{1}{\mathbf{e}},\underset{2}{\mathbf{e}},\underset{3}{\mathbf{e}}) \qquad (i,j,k = 1,2,3) \tag{5.110}$$

valid whenever ϕ is an alternating tensor of rank three. It is tempting to let $K = \phi(\underset{1}{\mathbf{e}},\underset{2}{\mathbf{e}},\underset{3}{\mathbf{e}})$ and write (5.110) in the form

$$\phi_{ijk} = K\varepsilon_{ijk} \tag{5.111}$$

but if we do this, we must keep clearly in mind that *the value of K depends on the choice of basis.*

Having discussed tensors of rank two and tensors of rank three, it should be fairly obvious to the reader how to proceed with tensors of rank greater than three. In general, a tensor of rank r will have 3^r components relative to any given basis.

It is not completely obvious that a tensor of rank one is a vector, as we asserted at the beginning of Sec. 5.6. It would be more accurate to say that a tensor of rank one can be *identified* with a vector. Corresponding to any tensor of rank one there is a unique vector having the same components relative to any given basis. Conversely, given any vector $\mathbf{v}$ there is a unique tensor ϕ of rank one, and relative to any basis we have $v_i = \phi_i$ and $v^i = \phi^i$ $(i = 1,2,3)$. Therefore, for all practical purposes, we can consider the two objects to be identical.

To see this, let us suppose that ϕ is a tensor of rank one. By the definition, ϕ is a scalar-valued function of a single vector variable, so it assigns a scalar $\phi(\mathbf{u})$ to every vector $\mathbf{u}$. The definition requires that it be linear in its single vector variable,

$$\phi(\alpha\mathbf{u} + \beta\mathbf{w}) = \alpha\phi(\mathbf{u}) + \beta\phi(\mathbf{w}) \tag{5.112}$$

which implies that, if $\mathbf{u} = u^i \underset{i}{\mathbf{e}}$,

$$\phi(\mathbf{u}) = \phi(u^i \underset{i}{\mathbf{e}}) = u^i \phi(\underset{i}{\mathbf{e}}) = u^i \phi_i \tag{5.113}$$

where ϕ_i is defined to be $\phi(\underset{i}{\mathbf{e}})$. Let $\mathbf{v}$ be defined to be the vector $\phi_i \overset{i}{\mathbf{e}}$. Then since $\mathbf{u} \cdot \overset{i}{\mathbf{e}} = u^i$ the scalar product of $\mathbf{u}$ with $\mathbf{v}$ is

$$\mathbf{u} \cdot \mathbf{v} = \mathbf{u} \cdot (\phi_i \overset{i}{\mathbf{e}}) = \phi_i \mathbf{u} \cdot \overset{i}{\mathbf{e}} = \phi_i u^i \tag{5.114}$$

Comparing this with (5.113) we see that

$$\phi(\mathbf{u}) = \mathbf{u} \cdot \mathbf{v} \qquad \text{(for every vector } \mathbf{u}\text{)} \tag{5.115}$$

In words: *Every linear scalar-valued function of a single vector variable can be obtained by taking the scalar product of that variable with a fixed vector* $\mathbf{v}$.

Conversely, given any vector $\mathbf{v}$, we can use (5.115) to define a tensor ϕ of rank one. The covariant components of ϕ are then, by definition,

$$\phi_i = \phi(\underset{i}{\mathbf{e}}) = \underset{i}{\mathbf{e}} \cdot \mathbf{v} = v_i \tag{5.116}$$

and one shows similarly that $\phi^i = v^i$ $(i = 1,2,3)$.

Notice that (5.115), which relates ϕ and $\mathbf{v}$, is completely independent of the choice of basis. If we had determined $\mathbf{v}$ by using another basis, we would have arrived at the same vector. Indeed, it would be impossible for another vector $\mathbf{v}'$ to be associated in this manner with the same function ϕ, because in that case we would have

$$\phi(\mathbf{u}) = \mathbf{u} \cdot \mathbf{v} = \mathbf{u} \cdot \mathbf{v}' \qquad \text{(for every vector } \mathbf{u}\text{)}$$

and hence $$\mathbf{u} \cdot (\mathbf{v} - \mathbf{v}') = 0 \qquad \text{(for every vector } \mathbf{u}\text{)}$$

In particular, taking $\mathbf{u} = \mathbf{v} - \mathbf{v}'$, this would give

$$|\mathbf{v} - \mathbf{v}'|^2 = 0$$

which is only possible when $\mathbf{v} = \mathbf{v}'$.

We now conclude this section with a brief discussion of scalars and with some examples.

A tensor of rank zero is a scalar that does not depend on any vector variables at all. Therefore, it is simply a scalar. In tensor algebra, a scalar is defined to be *a number that does not in any way depend on the choice of basis.* [The authors can (and probably will) be criticized for postponing this definition for so long. It seems to the authors that the definition would not have meant much if it had been given earlier.]

We are now in an excellent position to look at numbers that qualify to be called scalars and some that do not.

The most obvious example of a scalar is the scalar product $\mathbf{u} \cdot \mathbf{v}$ of two vectors $\mathbf{u}$ and $\mathbf{v}$. We have seen that the scalar product can be computed, relative to some given basis, by the formula $g_{ij}u^i v^j$, and when the base vectors are of unit length and mutually perpendicular this simplifies to $u^1v^1 + u^2v^2 + u^3v^3$ (which is the formula that was used throughout the first four chapters). In fact, having defined the contravariant components of a vector, we then defined the covariant components g_{ij} of the metric tensor in order that the expression $g_{ij}u^i v^j$ would give the scalar product $\mathbf{u} \cdot \mathbf{v}$. If we used a different basis, the contravariant vector components and the covariant components of the metric tensor would be different, but the numerical value $g_{ij}u^i v^j$ would be the same, simply by the way things were defined. To summarize: for any two given vectors $\mathbf{u}$ and $\mathbf{v}$, the scalar product $\mathbf{u} \cdot \mathbf{v}$ is a scalar.

Similarly, for any three vectors $\mathbf{u}$, $\mathbf{v}$, and $\mathbf{w}$, the triple scalar product $\mathbf{u} \cdot \mathbf{v} \times \mathbf{w}$ is a scalar.

The magnitude $|\mathbf{v}|$ of a vector $\mathbf{v}$ is a scalar. The scalar component $(\mathbf{u} \cdot \mathbf{v})/|\mathbf{v}|$ of a vector $\mathbf{u}$ in the direction of a nonzero vector $\mathbf{v}$ is a scalar.

On the other hand, the components v^i of a nonzero vector $\mathbf{v}$ are not scalars, since they depend on the choice of basis. The number K in equation (5.111) is not a scalar, since it depends on the basis.

Example 5.11 Since,for any three vectors $\mathbf{u}$, $\mathbf{v}$, and $\mathbf{w}$, the triple scalar product $\mathbf{u} \cdot \mathbf{v} \times \mathbf{w}$ is a scalar, we can define a tensor of order three by

$$\phi(\mathbf{u},\mathbf{v},\mathbf{w}) = \mathbf{u} \cdot \mathbf{v} \times \mathbf{w} \tag{5.117}$$

By virtue of Eq. 1.24, this is an *alternating* tensor. Therefore its components ϕ_{ijk} are completely determined once we know $\phi_{123} = \underset{1}{\mathbf{e}} \cdot \underset{2}{\mathbf{e}} \times \underset{3}{\mathbf{e}}$. It is conventional to denote this number by the letter J (because it is a jacobian; we will discuss jacobians later).

$$J = \underset{1}{\mathbf{e}} \cdot \underset{2}{\mathbf{e}} \times \underset{3}{\mathbf{e}} \tag{5.118}$$

In this case, (5.111) is written

$$\phi_{ijk} = J\varepsilon_{ijk} \tag{5.119}$$

We have seen that the usual formula for the dot product is not valid in general, but must be replaced by (5.97). Similarly, the usual formula for the triple scalar product is not valid, but must be replaced by

$$\mathbf{u} \cdot \mathbf{v} \times \mathbf{w} = J\varepsilon_{ijk} u^i v^j w^k \tag{5.120}$$

[This follows at once from (5.103) and (5.119).] This can also be written

$$\mathbf{u} \cdot \mathbf{v} \times \mathbf{w} = \frac{1}{J} \varepsilon^{ijk} u_i v_j w_k \tag{5.121}$$

since, by (5.67) $\overset{1}{\mathbf{e}} \cdot \overset{2}{\mathbf{e}} \times \overset{3}{\mathbf{e}} = 1/J$.

Both (5.120) and (5.121) can be written using determinants:

$$\mathbf{u} \cdot \mathbf{v} \times \mathbf{w} = J \begin{vmatrix} u^1 & u^2 & u^3 \\ v^1 & v^2 & v^3 \\ w^1 & w^2 & w^3 \end{vmatrix} = \frac{1}{J} \begin{vmatrix} u_1 & u_2 & u_3 \\ v_1 & v_2 & v_3 \\ w_1 & w_2 & w_3 \end{vmatrix} \tag{5.122}$$

In the special case that the basis is a right-handed system of mutually perpendicular unit vectors, $J = 1$, the covariant and contravariant components of any vector are identical, and (5.122) reduces to the usual formula for the triple scalar product.

For later purposes, it will be convenient to have an expression relating J to the determinant of the matrix $G = (g_{ij})$. It is customary to denote this determinant by g.

$$g = \det G = \varepsilon^{ijk} g_{1i} g_{2j} g_{3k} \tag{5.123}$$

We will make use of

$$\underset{i}{\mathbf{e}} = g_{ij} \overset{j}{\mathbf{e}} \tag{5.124}$$

which is derived in the same manner as (5.106). We wish to show that $J^2 = g$. Here is one way to do it:

$$\begin{aligned} J = \underset{1}{\mathbf{e}} \cdot \underset{2}{\mathbf{e}} \times \underset{3}{\mathbf{e}} &= (g_{1i} \overset{i}{\mathbf{e}}) \cdot (g_{2j} \overset{j}{\mathbf{e}}) \times (g_{3k} \overset{k}{\mathbf{e}}) \\ &= g_{1i} g_{2j} g_{3k} (\overset{i}{\mathbf{e}} \cdot \overset{j}{\mathbf{e}} \times \overset{k}{\mathbf{e}}) \\ &= \varepsilon^{ijk} g_{1i} g_{2j} g_{3k} (\overset{1}{\mathbf{e}} \cdot \overset{2}{\mathbf{e}} \times \overset{3}{\mathbf{e}}) = g \cdot \frac{1}{J} \end{aligned} \tag{5.125}$$

and therefore

$$J^2 = g \tag{5.126}$$

Example 5.12 The determinant of the product of two square matrices equals the product of their determinants. A computational proof is by no means the best proof. Nevertheless, we will now give a computational proof of the special case of 3×3 matrices, as an interesting exercise in using the summation convention. At one point in this calculation, no fewer than six summations are involved. The student who can follow this calculation and reproduce it from memory, understanding each step, cannot possibly have further difficulty with the summation convention or with determinants. Do not attempt it before working the first ten exercises at the end of this section.

Let $S=(S^i_j)$ and $T=(T^i_j)$ be 3×3 matrices and let $R=ST$. Then $R^i_k = S^i_j T^j_k$ and

$$\begin{aligned}\det(R^i_k) &= \varepsilon_{ijk} R^i_1 R^j_2 R^k_3 \\ &= \varepsilon_{ijk}(S^i_m T^m_1)(S^j_p T^p_2)(S^k_r T^r_3) \\ &= \varepsilon_{ijk} S^i_m S^j_p S^k_r T^m_1 T^p_2 T^r_3\end{aligned} \tag{5.127}$$

The sum $\varepsilon_{ijk} S^i_m S^j_p S^k_r$ is the determinant of a matrix whose first, second, and third columns are the mth, pth, and rth columns of S, respectively. Using the facts that the interchange of two columns of a matrix changes the sign of the determinant, and that if two columns are equal the determinant is zero, we see that

$$\varepsilon_{ijk} S^i_m S^j_p S^k_r = \varepsilon_{mpr}\,\varepsilon_{ijk} S^i_1 S^j_2 S^k_3 \tag{5.128}$$

Substituting this into (5.127) we obtain

$$\begin{aligned}\det(R^i_k) &= \varepsilon_{mpr}\,\varepsilon_{ijk} S^i_1 S^j_2 S^k_3 T^m_1 T^p_2 T^r_3 \\ &= (\varepsilon_{ijk} S^i_1 S^j_2 S^k_3)(\varepsilon_{mpr} T^m_1 T^p_2 T^r_3) \\ &= \det(S^i_j)\det(T^i_j)\end{aligned} \tag{5.129}$$

In more modern notation, $\det R = (\det S)(\det T)$, which is what we desired to prove.

EXERCISES

In these exercises, all summations are understood to run from 1 to 3, as in the text.

1. Write (5.81) using the summation convention.

2. Is there any difference between $u_i v^i$ and $u_j v^j$?

3. Write out in full the expression $p^{ij} A_i B_j$.

4. Is there any difference between $p^{ij} A_j B_i$ and $p^{ij} B_i A_j$?

5. How many terms are involved in the sum $\phi_{ijk} g^{ip} g^{jr} g^{ks}$?

6. How many simultaneous equations are represented by $\phi_{ij} = \phi_{ijrs} u^r v^s$?

7. Which indices in (5.127) are dummies?

8. Is there any difference between $A^j_i B^i_j$ and $A^i_j B^j_i$? Write out these sums in full.

9. What is the numerical value of the sum δ^j_j?

10. You are given that $u_i = \phi_{ij} v^j$. Show how you would substitute this into the expression $C = u_j w^j$ to obtain C in terms of the components of ϕ, v, and w. (Notice that $C = \phi_{jj} v^j w^j$ is *not* correct.)

11. Write out in full, and simplify if possible:

$$\delta_{ij} u^i v^j$$

(*Note*: δ_{ij} is just another version of the Kronecker delta.)

12. Write out in full the three equations represented by

$$w_i = \varepsilon_{ijk} u^j v^k$$

13. Find the numerical value of the triple sum

$$\varepsilon_{ijk} \varepsilon^{ijk}$$

14. Review the derivation of (5.97) by writing (5.62) and (5.63), using the summation convention.

15. Simplify: $(\overset{k}{\mathbf{e}} \cdot \overset{s}{\mathbf{e}})\underset{s}{\mathbf{e}}$

16. Simplify: $g^{ik} g_{kj}$

17. Given w_i as in Exercise 12, write out and simplify

$$p^{jk} = \varepsilon^{ijk} w_i$$

to obtain p^{jk} in terms of the components of u and v.

18. Let ϕ be an alternating tensor of rank two. Letting $w_i = \varepsilon_{ijk}\phi^{jk}$ write w_1, w_2, and w_3 in terms of ϕ^{23}, ϕ^{31}, and ϕ^{12}.

19. Simplify the expression $\varepsilon^{ijk} w_i$, where w_i was given in Exercise 18, and hence obtain an expression giving ϕ^{jk} in terms of w_i.

20. One might suppose from the notation ε_{ijk} that there exists a tensor of rank three whose covariant components relative to every basis $\underset{1}{\mathbf{e}}, \underset{2}{\mathbf{e}}, \underset{3}{\mathbf{e}}$ are ε_{ijk}. Show this is not the case. (*Hint*: If $\underset{1}{\mathbf{e}}, \underset{2}{\mathbf{e}}, \underset{3}{\mathbf{e}}$ is a basis, so also is $2\underset{1}{\mathbf{e}}, \underset{2}{\mathbf{e}}, \underset{3}{\mathbf{e}}$.)

5.8 GENERAL CURVILINEAR COORDINATES

One purpose of this section is to derive the expressions given in Sec. 4.13 for the various differential operators in curvilinear coordinates. This will also provide background material for further work on tensors on the next section.

Although a brief review of Sec. 4.13 may be helpful at this point, we will not use any of the formulas in that section and the notation will be quite different. In particular, we will not use x, y, and z to denote cartesian coordinates in euclidean space, but will use x^1, x^2, and x^3 instead. This will make it easier to use the summation convention.

We will use u^1, u^2, and u^3 to denote curvilinear coordinates in space, instead of u_1, u_2, and u_3, since this is standard in most treatments of tensor analysis. Also, for added generality, we will not require that these curvilinear coordinates be orthogonal coordinates: the coordinate curves need not have mutually perpendicular tangents.

We will work within a region of euclidean space in which the cartesian coordinates x^1, x^2, and x^3 can be expressed as functions of the curvilinear coordinates u^1, u^2, and u^3, and the gradients of these functions, which we will denote ∇u^1, ∇u^2, and ∇u^3, will be assumed to exist, be nonzero, have continuously differentiable components, and be linearly independent throughout the region.

The requirement that these gradients be linearly independent is equivalent to the requirement that their triple scalar product be nonzero throughout the region:

$$\nabla u^1 \cdot \nabla u^2 \times \nabla u^3 \neq 0 \tag{5.130}$$

We will denote these gradients by $\overset{i}{\mathbf{e}}$ so we have

$$\overset{i}{\mathbf{e}} = \nabla u^i = \frac{\partial u^i}{\partial x^1}\mathbf{i} + \frac{\partial u^i}{\partial x^2}\mathbf{j} + \frac{\partial u^i}{\partial x^3}\mathbf{k} \tag{5.131}$$

The three vectors $\overset{1}{\mathbf{e}}$, $\overset{2}{\mathbf{e}}$, $\overset{3}{\mathbf{e}}$ vary with position in space. Because of (5.130), they determine, at each point in the region, a *basis* (see Sec. 5.5).

The conditions stated ensure that through each point P in the region, having curvilinear coordinates (c^1,c^2,c^3), there will pass three isotimic surfaces $u^1 = c^1$, $u^2 = c^2$, $u^3 = c^3$. These surfaces intersect at P and intersect in pairs to give three curves passing through P, which we call *coordinate curves* at P. The isotimic surfaces are called *coordinate surfaces*. Notice that, at P, $\overset{1}{\mathbf{e}}$ is normal (i.e., perpendicular) to the surface $u^1 = c^1$ (which is sometimes called the u^2u^3 surface, since only u^2 and u^3 vary on this surface). Similarly, $\overset{2}{\mathbf{e}}$ is normal to the u^3u^1 surface, and $\overset{3}{\mathbf{e}}$ is normal to the u^1u^2 surface, at any point P. (They need not be unit vectors, even if the coordinate system is orthogonal, although in that case they will be tangent to the coordinate curves.)

Since $\overset{1}{\mathbf{e}}$, $\overset{2}{\mathbf{e}}$, and $\overset{3}{\mathbf{e}}$ are gradients, it is natural that other gradients be written as linear combinations of them. By the chain rule for partial derivatives we have

$$\frac{\partial f}{\partial x^i} = \frac{\partial f}{\partial u^j}\frac{\partial u^j}{\partial x^i} \tag{5.132}$$

where the summation convention implies a sum over j. (In using the summation convention, a superscript in a denominator is regarded as a subscript.) Therefore

$$\begin{aligned}
\nabla f &= \frac{\partial f}{\partial x^1}\mathbf{i} + \frac{\partial f}{\partial x^2}\mathbf{j} + \frac{\partial f}{\partial x^3}\mathbf{k} \\
&= \frac{\partial f}{\partial u^i}\frac{\partial u^i}{\partial x^1}\mathbf{i} + \frac{\partial f}{\partial u^i}\frac{\partial u^i}{\partial x^2}\mathbf{j} + \frac{\partial f}{\partial u^i}\frac{\partial u^i}{\partial x^3}\mathbf{k} \\
&= \frac{\partial f}{\partial u^i}\nabla u^i = \frac{\partial f}{\partial u^i}\overset{i}{\mathbf{e}}
\end{aligned} \tag{5.133}$$

which expresses the gradient as a linear combination of the three vectors $\overset{1}{\mathbf{e}}$, $\overset{2}{\mathbf{e}}$, and $\overset{3}{\mathbf{e}}$.

Notice that the del operator can be written in symbolic form

$$\nabla = \overset{i}{\mathbf{e}} \frac{\partial}{\partial u^i} \tag{5.134}$$

which generalizes our earlier notation $\nabla = \mathbf{i}\frac{\partial}{\partial x} + \mathbf{j}\frac{\partial}{\partial y} + \mathbf{k}\frac{\partial}{\partial z}$.

Do not attempt at this point to match (5.133) above with Eq. (4.78), where a completely different basis was used. They will be matched later in this section.

Recall from our earlier work that, if the position vector $\mathbf{R}$ is a function of a single parameter t along a curve, then $d\mathbf{R}/dt$ is a vector that is tangent to the curve (in some special cases it is the velocity vector of a moving particle). Along a coordinate curve, $\mathbf{R}$ is a function of a single curvilinear coordinate u^i, with the other two coordinates fixed, and therefore $\partial \mathbf{R}/\partial u^i$ is tangent to a coordinate curve. We introduce the notation

$$\underset{i}{\mathbf{e}} = \frac{\partial \mathbf{R}}{\partial u^i} \tag{5.135}$$

to denote vectors $\underset{1}{\mathbf{e}}$, $\underset{2}{\mathbf{e}}$, and $\underset{3}{\mathbf{e}}$ that are tangent to the three coordinate curves. Since $\mathbf{R} = x^1\mathbf{i} + x^2\mathbf{j} + x^3\mathbf{k}$ we have

$$\underset{i}{\mathbf{e}} = \frac{\partial x^1}{\partial u^i}\mathbf{i} + \frac{\partial x^2}{\partial u^i}\mathbf{j} + \frac{\partial x^3}{\partial u^i}\mathbf{k} \tag{5.136}$$

If f is a suitably smooth scalar field, the chain rule for partial derivatives gives

$$\frac{\partial f}{\partial u^i} = \frac{\partial f}{\partial x^j}\frac{\partial x^j}{\partial u^i} = \nabla f \cdot \underset{i}{\mathbf{e}} \tag{5.137}$$

In operator notation, this can be written

$$\frac{\partial}{\partial u^i} = \underset{i}{\mathbf{e}} \cdot \nabla \tag{5.138}$$

In (5.137), we are regarding f as a function of position, and hence as a function of u^1, u^2, and u^3. If we take f to be identically equal to one of the coordinates u^j, then $\partial f/\partial u^j = 1$ and $\partial f/\partial u^i = 0$ when $i \neq j$. That is,

$$\frac{\partial u^j}{\partial u^i} = \delta_i^j \tag{5.139}$$

where δ_i^j is the Kronecker delta. Letting $f = u^j$ in (5.137) and using (5.139) we have

$$\delta_i^j = \nabla u^j \cdot \underset{i}{\mathbf{e}} = \overset{j}{\mathbf{e}} \cdot \underset{i}{\mathbf{e}} \tag{5.140}$$

From (5.140) one can easily show that $\mathbf{e}_1, \mathbf{e}_2, \mathbf{e}_3$ and $\mathbf{e}^1, \mathbf{e}^2, \mathbf{e}^3$ are *dual bases* as described in Sec. 5.5, and therefore we can make use of the formulas derived in that section.

The vectors $\mathbf{e}_1$, $\mathbf{e}_2$, and $\mathbf{e}_3$ vary with position in space. At any point P, we call $\mathbf{e}_1, \mathbf{e}_2, \mathbf{e}_3$ the *tangent basis* at P. We call $\mathbf{e}^1, \mathbf{e}^2, \mathbf{e}^3$ the *normal basis*.

We let J denote the triple scalar product $\mathbf{e}_1 \cdot \mathbf{e}_2 \times \mathbf{e}_3$, which is a determinant of partial derivatives called the *jacobian* of x^1, x^2, x^3 with respect to u^1, u^2, u^3 and denoted, in advanced calculus, $\partial(x^1,x^2,x^3)/\partial(u^1,u^2,u^3)$

$$J = \mathbf{e}_1 \cdot \mathbf{e}_2 \times \mathbf{e}_3 = \frac{\partial(x^1,x^2,x^3)}{\partial(u^1,u^2,u^3)} = \begin{vmatrix} \dfrac{\partial x^1}{\partial u^1} & \dfrac{\partial x^1}{\partial u^2} & \dfrac{\partial x^1}{\partial u^3} \\ \dfrac{\partial x^2}{\partial u^1} & \dfrac{\partial x^2}{\partial u^2} & \dfrac{\partial x^2}{\partial u^3} \\ \dfrac{\partial x^3}{\partial u^1} & \dfrac{\partial x^3}{\partial u^2} & \dfrac{\partial x^3}{\partial u^3} \end{vmatrix} \tag{5.141}$$

By (5.67) we have $\mathbf{e}^1 \cdot \mathbf{e}^2 \times \mathbf{e}^3 = 1/J$ and hence

$$\frac{1}{J} = \mathbf{e}^1 \cdot \mathbf{e}^2 \times \mathbf{e}^3 = \frac{\partial(u^1,u^2,u^3)}{\partial(x^1,x^2,x^3)} = \begin{vmatrix} \dfrac{\partial u^1}{\partial x^1} & \dfrac{\partial u^1}{\partial x^2} & \dfrac{\partial u^1}{\partial x^3} \\ \dfrac{\partial u^2}{\partial x^1} & \dfrac{\partial u^2}{\partial x^2} & \dfrac{\partial u^2}{\partial x^3} \\ \dfrac{\partial u^3}{\partial x^1} & \dfrac{\partial u^3}{\partial x^2} & \dfrac{\partial u^3}{\partial x^3} \end{vmatrix} \tag{5.142}$$

By (5.65), Sec. 5.5, we have

$$\mathbf{e}_2 \times \mathbf{e}_3 = J\mathbf{e}^1 \qquad \mathbf{e}_3 \times \mathbf{e}_1 = J\mathbf{e}^2 \qquad \mathbf{e}_1 \times \mathbf{e}_2 = J\mathbf{e}^3 \tag{5.143}$$

and similarly

$$\mathbf{e}^2 \times \mathbf{e}^3 = \frac{\mathbf{e}_1}{J} \qquad \mathbf{e}^3 \times \mathbf{e}^1 = \frac{\mathbf{e}_2}{J} \qquad \mathbf{e}^1 \times \mathbf{e}^2 = \frac{\mathbf{e}_3}{J} \tag{5.144}$$

In a later derivation, it will be useful to know that the three vector fields in (5.144) are *curls*. For example,

$$\mathbf{curl}\,(u^2\nabla u^3) = \nabla \times (u^2\nabla u^3) = \nabla u^2 \times \nabla u^3 = \frac{\mathbf{e}_1}{J} \tag{5.145}$$

where we made use of the list of vector identities in Sec. 1.14.

A *tensor field* is a tensor-valued function of position in space. Since the base vectors are now vector fields, the metric tensor is now a tensor field. We will make use of the contravariant components $g^{ij} = \overset{i}{\mathbf{e}} \cdot \overset{j}{\mathbf{e}}$ keeping in mind, when we differentiate, that they are not constants. The number J in (5.141) also varies with position in space, so it is tempting to call J a scalar field. However, J is not a scalar, since it depends on the coordinate system; therefore we call it a *relative scalar field* or a *scalar density field.*

In physical applications, it is common to work with the *physical components* of a vector **F**. These are the components of **F** relative to a basis of *unit* vectors obtained by dividing each of the base vectors $\underset{1}{\mathbf{e}}$, $\underset{2}{\mathbf{e}}$, and $\underset{3}{\mathbf{e}}$ by their own length. Letting $h_i = |\mathbf{e}|$ the "physical basis" is

$$\underset{1}{\mathbf{u}} = \frac{\underset{1}{\mathbf{e}}}{h_1} \qquad \underset{2}{\mathbf{u}} = \frac{\underset{2}{\mathbf{e}}}{h_2} \qquad \underset{3}{\mathbf{u}} = \frac{\underset{3}{\mathbf{e}}}{h_3} \tag{5.146}$$

Although of unit magnitude, the **u**'s need not be mutually perpendicular, since the **e**'s may not be. A vector **F** can be written as a linear combination of the **u**'s,

$$\mathbf{F} = \dot{F}^1\underset{1}{\mathbf{u}} + \dot{F}^2\underset{2}{\mathbf{u}} + \dot{F}^3\underset{3}{\mathbf{u}} = \dot{F}^i\underset{i}{\mathbf{u}} \tag{5.147}$$

where the dots directly above the letter serve to remind us that these are not contravariant components of **F** but are the physical components of **F**. Of course, the physical components are simply related to the contravariant components:

$$\dot{F}^i = F^i h^i \tag{5.148}$$

No summation is implied on the right side of (5.148) since i occurs only as a superscript.

The use of these scale factors h_i does not fit in very well with tensor notation. That is one reason why we did not abbreviate (5.146) by writing $\underset{i}{\mathbf{u}} = \underset{i}{\mathbf{e}}/h_i$. Strictly speaking, a subscript in the denominator of a fraction is regarded as a superscript insofar as the summation convention is concerned, so the summation convention demands a sum over i on the right side of this equality, which renders the equation incorrect. In the equations that come later, the reader is advised to ignore h_i insofar as the summation convention is concerned: any summations will be adequately implied by indices occurring elsewhere, or explicitly stated.

Making use of (5.76), we have

$$\overset{i}{\mathbf{e}} = g^{ij}\underset{j}{\mathbf{e}} \tag{5.149}$$

Substituting this into (5.133) we have

$$\nabla f = \frac{\partial f}{\partial u^i}\overset{i}{\mathbf{e}} = \frac{\partial f}{\partial u^i}g^{ij}\underset{j}{\mathbf{e}} = \frac{\partial f}{\partial u^i}g^{ij}h_j\underset{j}{\mathbf{u}} \tag{5.150}$$

From (5.150) we can read off the covariant, contravariant, and physical components of $\mathbf{F} = \mathbf{grad}\, f$:

$$F_i = \frac{\partial f}{\partial u^i} \qquad F^j = g^{ij}\frac{\partial f}{\partial u^i} \qquad \dot{F}^j = g^{ij}h_j\frac{\partial f}{\partial u^i} \tag{5.151}$$

The coordinate system is *orthogonal* if $\underset{i}{\mathbf{e}} \cdot \underset{j}{\mathbf{e}} = 0$ whenever $i \neq j$. In that case, $g_{ij} = 0$ when $i \neq j$ and $g_{ii} = \underset{i}{\mathbf{e}} \cdot \underset{i}{\mathbf{e}} = |\underset{i}{\mathbf{e}}|^2 = h_i^2$ (the 2 is an exponent here). The metric tensor and its inverse are then represented by the matrices

$$G = (g_{ij}) = \begin{pmatrix} h_1^2 & 0 & 0 \\ 0 & h_2^2 & 0 \\ 0 & 0 & h_3^2 \end{pmatrix} \qquad G^{-1} = (g^{ij}) = \begin{pmatrix} 1/h_1^2 & 0 & 0 \\ 0 & 1/h_2^2 & 0 \\ 0 & 0 & 1/h_3^2 \end{pmatrix} \tag{5.152}$$

Ignoring the terms in (5.150) for which $i \neq j$ and writing $g^{jj} = 1/h_j^2$ we obtain

$$\nabla f = \frac{1}{h_j}\frac{\partial f}{\partial u^j}\underset{j}{\mathbf{u}} \qquad \text{(summed over } j) \tag{5.153}$$

which is valid, provided we have an *orthogonal* system of curvilinear coordinates. Thus, at long last, we have derived Eq. (4.78).

Now let us derive a general formula for the divergence of a vector field $\mathbf{F} = F^j\underset{j}{\mathbf{e}}$. Since the divergence of any curl vanishes, we will make use of the vectors $\underset{j}{\mathbf{e}}/J$ that are shown by (5.145) to be curls. We have

$$\nabla \cdot \mathbf{F} = \nabla \cdot (F^j\underset{j}{\mathbf{e}}) = \nabla \cdot \left(JF^j\frac{\underset{j}{\mathbf{e}}}{J}\right) = \nabla(JF^j) \cdot \frac{\underset{j}{\mathbf{e}}}{J} \tag{5.154}$$

where we have used (3.20). Now we will make use of (5.137)

$$\nabla \cdot \mathbf{F} = \frac{1}{J}\,[\nabla(JF^j) \cdot \underset{j}{\mathbf{e}}] = \frac{1}{J}\frac{\partial}{\partial u^j}(JF^j) \tag{5.155}$$

In physical components, the formula becomes

$$\nabla \cdot \mathbf{F} = \frac{1}{J}\frac{\partial}{\partial u^j}\left(\frac{J\dot{F}^j}{h_j}\right) \qquad \text{(summed over } j) \tag{5.156}$$

According to (5.126), $J^2 = g$ where g is the determinant of $G = (g_{ij})$. Therefore $|J| = \sqrt{g}$. Notice that (5.156) does not change if J is replaced by $|J|$ since any sign change that might occur in the numerator as a result of this replacement would be balanced by one occurring in the denominator. Therefore, (5.156) can also be written

$$\nabla \cdot \mathbf{F} = \frac{1}{\sqrt{g}}\frac{\partial}{\partial u^j}\left(\frac{\sqrt{g}\,\dot{F}^j}{h_j}\right) \qquad \text{(summed over } j) \tag{5.157}$$

In *orthogonal* curvilinear coordinates, G is given by (5.152) and we see that $\sqrt{g} = h_1 h_2 h_3$ so (5.157) takes the form

$$\nabla \cdot \mathbf{F} = \frac{1}{h_1 h_2 h_3} \frac{\partial}{\partial u^j} \left(\frac{h_1 h_2 h_3 \dot{F}^j}{h_j} \right) \qquad \text{(summed over } j\text{)} \tag{5.158}$$

which matches the form in Sec. 4.13, previously "derived" by a simple plausibility argument.

To obtain the laplacian, which is the divergence of the gradient, substitute for $\dot{F}^j$ in (5.157) the coefficients of $\underset{j}{\mathbf{u}}$ in (5.150); the h_j's disappear and we obtain the double sum

$$\nabla^2 f = \frac{1}{\sqrt{g}} \frac{\partial}{\partial u^j} \left(\sqrt{g}\, g^{ij} \frac{\partial f}{\partial u^i} \right) \tag{5.159}$$

In orthogonal curvilinear coordinates this becomes

$$\nabla^2 f = \frac{1}{h_1 h_2 h_3} \frac{\partial}{\partial u^j} \left(\frac{h_1 h_2 h_3}{h_j^2} \frac{\partial f}{\partial u^j} \right) \qquad \text{(summed over } j\text{)} \tag{5.160}$$

which matches the form in Sec. 4.13.

Finally, we will derive an expression for the curl. Since the curl of any gradient is zero, we express $\mathbf{F}$ in terms of the $\overset{i}{\mathbf{e}}$'s, which are gradients, so that one term will vanish when we apply (3.20). In the derivation we will use (5.144), which can be written in the form

$$\overset{i}{\mathbf{e}} \times \overset{j}{\mathbf{e}} = \varepsilon^{ijk} \frac{\underset{k}{\mathbf{e}}}{J} \tag{5.161}$$

Here goes:

$$\begin{aligned} \nabla \times \mathbf{F} &= \nabla \times F_j \overset{j}{\mathbf{e}} = F_j (\nabla \times \overset{j}{\mathbf{e}}) + \nabla F_j \times \overset{j}{\mathbf{e}} = \nabla F_j \times \overset{j}{\mathbf{e}} \\ &= \frac{\partial F_j}{\partial u^i} \overset{i}{\mathbf{e}} \times \overset{j}{\mathbf{e}} \quad \text{by (5.133)} \end{aligned} \tag{5.162}$$

so by (5.161) we have

$$\nabla \times \mathbf{F} = \frac{1}{J} \varepsilon^{ijk} \frac{\partial F_j}{\partial u^i} \underset{k}{\mathbf{e}} \tag{5.163}$$

which can also be written

$$\nabla \times \mathbf{F} = \frac{1}{J} \varepsilon^{ijk} \underset{k}{\mathbf{e}} \frac{\partial}{\partial u^i} (g_{js} F^s) \tag{5.164}$$

or, in physical components,

$$\nabla \times \mathbf{F} = \frac{1}{J} \varepsilon^{ijk} h_k \underset{k}{\mathbf{u}} \frac{\partial}{\partial u^i} \left(\frac{\dot{F}^s g_{js}}{h_s} \right) \tag{5.165}$$

involving no fewer than four summations! This can be written in the form of a symbolic determinant:

$$\nabla \times \mathbf{F} = \frac{1}{J} \begin{vmatrix} h_1 \underset{1}{\mathbf{u}} & h_2 \underset{2}{\mathbf{u}} & h_3 \underset{3}{\mathbf{u}} \\ \dfrac{\partial}{\partial u^1} & \dfrac{\partial}{\partial u^2} & \dfrac{\partial}{\partial u^3} \\ \dfrac{\dot{F}^s g_{1s}}{h_s} & \dfrac{\dot{F}^s g_{2s}}{h_s} & \dfrac{\dot{F}^s g_{3s}}{h_s} \end{vmatrix} \tag{5.166}$$

In right-handed orthogonal curvilinear coordinates, the sum over s in $\dot{F}^s g_{js}/h_s$ reduces to $\dot{F}^j h_j^2/h_j = \dot{F}^j h_j$ and (5.166) becomes

$$\nabla \times \mathbf{F} = \frac{1}{h_1 h_2 h_3} \begin{vmatrix} h_1 \underset{1}{\mathbf{u}} & h_2 \underset{2}{\mathbf{u}} & h_3 \underset{3}{\mathbf{u}} \\ \dfrac{\partial}{\partial u^1} & \dfrac{\partial}{\partial u^2} & \dfrac{\partial}{\partial u^3} \\ \dot{F}^1 h_1 & \dot{F}^2 h_2 & \dot{F}^3 h_3 \end{vmatrix} \tag{5.167}$$

which completes the derivation of the formula in Sec. 4.13.

In left-handed orthogonal curvilinear coordinates, $J = \underset{1}{\mathbf{e}} \times \underset{2}{\mathbf{e}} \cdot \underset{3}{\mathbf{e}} = -h_1 h_2 h_3$ and a minus sign must be prefixed to the right side of (5.167). No such change is needed in the expressions for the gradient, divergence, or the laplacian. In the language of Sec. 5.3, we would say that the gradient, divergence, and laplacian are independent of the *orientation* of the region, whereas to define the curl it is necessary that the region be endowed with a screw sense.

It should be remarked that in some books the curl is defined in a slightly different manner, with the result that J must be replaced by $|J|$ in the preceding equations and (5.167) is valid, as it stands, whether the coordinate system is right-handed or left-handed. What this means, essentially, is that these authors are not sticking to the right-hand rule in defining the vector cross product, but use this rule only when the basis is right-handed. When the basis is a left-handed system, they demand that all definitions be changed to a left-handed convention, so that vector cross products and curls become oppositely directed. This is the "when in Rome do as the Romans do" convention, and is quite appealing because $|J|$ can always be replaced by $\sqrt{g}$ whereas $J = \pm\sqrt{g}$: $J = \sqrt{g}$ in a right-handed system of coordinates, $J = -\sqrt{g}$ in a left-handed system.

As a consequence of this approach, a vector cross product cannot be regarded as a vector, but is a *pseudovector*. Curls also become pseudovectors (more precisely, pseudovector fields). However, there is relatively little ambiguity: it is only a matter of a prefixed minus sign when the basis is left-handed.

In this book, which is concerned with three-dimensional euclidean space equipped with a screw sense (a "right-hand rule"), vector cross products and curls are true vectors. That is because we assume we are given a definite concept of "magnitude" and that it makes sense to speak of a "right-hand rule". From a classical geometrophysical sense, we are playing it cool, but it may be worthwhile to record two objections.

First of all, suppose that **u** and **v** are vectors and that $\mathbf{u} \times \mathbf{v} = \mathbf{w}$. Then the magnitude of **w** is the area of the parallelogram with **u** and **v** as coterminal edges. Suppose we have been measuring magnitude in inches and we suddenly decide that the magnitude of a vector should be measured in feet instead. Then all vector magnitudes must be modified by a factor of $\frac{1}{12}$. Since **u**, **v**, and **w** are vectors, the magnitudes of all three must now be multiplied by $\frac{1}{12}$. As a result the magnitude of **w** is no longer the area of the parallelogram, since the area is now modified by a factor of $\frac{1}{144}$. So if we change from inches to feet, **w** is no longer the vector cross product of **u** and **v**. How can one possibly claim that the vector cross product is a vector, when it depends on the choice of the unit of measurement?

The second objection is somewhat more interesting and involves mirrors. Mirrors are interesting things: they convert left hands into right hands, for example. If I hold a printed page before a mirror, right and left are interchanged, so the reflected image of the printing is hard to read. Now suppose there is a clock on the wall before me, and a mirror on the wall at my left. Any directed line segment *parallel* to the mirror is identical in both magnitude and direction to its reflected image. The angular velocity vector representing the angular velocity of the second hand on the clock is directed away from me, towards the wall in front of me. However, the second hand of the reflected image is rotating in a counter-clockwise sense, and therefore its angular velocity vector points in the opposite direction. It appears that the usual laws of optics do not apply to a directed line segment representing an angular velocity!

The situation is the same with curls. Hold Fig. 3.9 so that the page is perpendicular to a mirror. The curl of the vector field shown in the figure is directed outward from the page, but the curl of the reflected image is directed inward towards the page. How can a vector parallel to a mirror, as the curl is in this case, be directed oppositely to its reflected image?

From a superficial viewpoint, both these "objections" can be dismissed by emphasizing that both the vector cross product and the curl are defined only *after* one has settled on a *metric* and an *orientation*. If, after defining the vector cross product and curl, we change the metric (for instance, by changing from inches to feet) or the orientation (as we certainly do when we consider reflected images) we can expect to run into trouble.

There is a somewhat deeper viewpoint, however, in which we actively seek to define the vector cross product and the curl in a manner that does not depend on either the metric or the orientation. This is impossible, strictly speaking, but it is possible to come very close. It is possible to define entities that are closely related to the vector product and the curl but are independent of either metric or orientation, and which are interesting objects in their own right. We will have more to say about this later.

EXERCISES

1. In cylindrical coordinates, $u^1 = \rho$, $u^2 = \theta$, and $u^3 = z$, as shown in Fig. 4.38.
   (a) Write down $\mathbf{e}^1$, $\mathbf{e}^2$, and $\mathbf{e}^3$ in terms of $\mathbf{i}$, $\mathbf{j}$, and $\mathbf{k}$.
   (b) Do the same for $\mathbf{e}_1$, $\mathbf{e}_2$, and $\mathbf{e}_3$.
   (c) Do the same for $\mathbf{u}_1$, $\mathbf{u}_2$, and $\mathbf{u}_3$.
2. Letting ds be the element of arc length in general curvilinear coordinates, show that $ds^2 = g_{ij}\, du^i\, du^j$.
3. Write down the element of arc length in cylindrical coordinates. Then, by comparing ds^2 with $g_{ij}\, du^i\, du^j$ determine the covariant components g_{ij} of the metric tensor in cylindrical coordinates.
4. Let a coordinate system be defined by

$$u^1 = x + y$$
$$u^2 = 3y$$
$$u^3 = y + z$$

   Find the nine vectors $\mathbf{e}_1$, $\mathbf{e}_2$, $\mathbf{e}_3$, $\mathbf{e}^1$, $\mathbf{e}^2$, $\mathbf{e}^3$, $\mathbf{u}_1$, $\mathbf{u}_2$, and $\mathbf{u}_3$ as in Exercise 1.
5. For the coordinate system described in Exercise 4, find the jacobian $J = \mathbf{e}_1 \cdot \mathbf{e}_2 \times \mathbf{e}_3$. Can you think of more than one way of doing this?
6. What types of coordinate systems have jacobians that are constants, i.e., do not vary with position in space? (The coordinate system described in Exercise 4 is an example.)
7. Is the coordinate system described in Exercise 4 an orthogonal coordinate system?
8. For the coordinate system described in Exercise 4, the covariant components of a vector are $v_1 = 1$, $v_2 = 3$, and $v_3 = 8$. Find the contravariant components relative to the same system of coordinates. What is this vector in terms of $\mathbf{i}$, $\mathbf{j}$, and $\mathbf{k}$?
9. By making use of (5.161), show that, if $\mathbf{w} = \mathbf{u} \times \mathbf{v}$, then

$$w^k = \frac{1}{J}\, \varepsilon^{ijk} u_i v_j \tag{5.168}$$

10. By suitably modifying (5.168) above, obtain a rather complicated expression for the vector cross product in general coordinates in terms of the physical components of all of the vectors involved. In other words, write $\dot{w}^k$ in terms of the components $\dot{u}^p$ and $\dot{v}^s$.

11. (a) What are the contravariant components of the velocity vector $v = dx/dt$ in cylindrical coordinates? (Give v^1, v^2, and v^3 in terms of ρ, θ, and z).
(b) What are the covariant components of velocity in cylindrical coordinates?
(c) What are the physical components of velocity in cylindrical coordinates?

12. Write down an expression relating h_i to one of the components of the metric tensor.

13. Show that the *matrices* whose determinants are given in (5.141) and (5.142) are inverses of one another. Can this be used to give an alternative proof of (5.67)?

14. Use the result of the preceding exercise together with (5.57), to give an alternative proof of $\underset{2}{\mathbf{e}} \times \underset{3}{\mathbf{e}} = J\overset{1}{\mathbf{e}}$. [*Hint*: The components of the vector product $\underset{2}{\mathbf{e}} \times \underset{3}{\mathbf{e}}$ of the vectors in the second and third column of the matrix $(\partial x^i/\partial u^j)$ are co-factors of the elements in the first column.]

15. On purely geometrical grounds one can see that both $\underset{2}{\mathbf{e}} \times \underset{3}{\mathbf{e}}$ and $\overset{1}{\mathbf{e}}$ are normal to the surface $u^1 = \text{constant}$ at any point P. Hence $\underset{2}{\mathbf{e}} \times \underset{3}{\mathbf{e}}$ is a scalar multiple of $\overset{1}{\mathbf{e}}$. Now use (5.140) to show that the multiplying factor is J and, hence, give yet another derivation of the expression in the preceding exercise.

16. Analyze in some detail the coordinate system defined by

$$u^1 = x + yz$$
$$u^2 = y + xz$$
$$u^3 = z + xy$$

(Find the bases, the components of the metric tensor, the various differential operators in terms of these coordinates, and so on.)

17. What is wrong with the following calculation, which makes use of (5.134):

$$\nabla \cdot \mathbf{F} = \left(\overset{i}{\mathbf{e}} \frac{\partial}{\partial u^i}\right) \cdot (F^j \underset{j}{\mathbf{e}}) = \frac{\partial F^j}{\partial u^i} \overset{i}{\mathbf{e}} \cdot \underset{j}{\mathbf{e}} = \frac{\partial F^j}{\partial u^i} \delta^i_j = \frac{\partial F^i}{\partial u^i}$$

(a sum over i is intended). This appears to show that the formula for the divergence given in Sec. 3.3 can be used in any system of curvilinear coordinates.

18. Find an expression for the divergence of $\underset{1}{\mathbf{e}}$ in terms of J and its derivatives.

19. Show that the divergence of $\overset{2}{\mathbf{e}} \times \overset{3}{\mathbf{e}}$ is zero,
(a) by showing that it is a curl,
(b) by writing both vectors as gradients and using another identity from the list in Sec. 3.7.

20. Explain each step in the following derivation:

$$\nabla \cdot \underset{1}{\mathbf{e}} = \nabla \cdot J(\overset{2}{\mathbf{e}} \times \overset{3}{\mathbf{e}}) = \nabla J \cdot \overset{2}{\mathbf{e}} \times \overset{3}{\mathbf{e}} + J\nabla \cdot (\overset{2}{\mathbf{e}} \times \overset{3}{\mathbf{e}})$$

$$= \left(\frac{\partial J}{\partial u^i} \overset{i}{\mathbf{e}}\right) \cdot \overset{2}{\mathbf{e}} \times \overset{3}{\mathbf{e}} = \frac{1}{J} \frac{\partial J}{\partial u^1}$$

(Compare with your own solution of Exercise 18).

5.9 TENSOR ANALYSIS IN THREE DIMENSIONS

Tensor analysis is the differential and integral calculus of tensor fields. Since *scalar* fields and *vector* fields are tensor fields of rank *zero* and *one* respectively, tensor analysis includes vector analysis as a special case. A general discussion of tensor analysis is beyond the scope of this book. We will restrict our attention entirely to three-dimensional euclidean space.

One of the central ideas of tensor analysis (and hence of vector analysis as well) is to describe geometrical and physical situations in a manner that is independent of the coordinate system, and (if possible) solve problems without making use of any coordinates or components. When possible, this not only lends greater mathematical elegance, but often contributes to an increased understanding.

In Sec. 1.7 a couple of geometrical problems were solved in a manner that was completely free of coordinates or components. In these solutions, we did not make use of the x, y, z components of the vectors involved. In Sec. 1.9, the scalar product $\mathbf{A} \cdot \mathbf{B}$ was defined in a coordinate-free manner, by Eq. (1.9) in that section, but notice that Eq. (1.10) is given in terms of coordinates and is not a valid equation in all coordinate systems. To be valid in general coordinates it must be replaced by $\mathbf{A} \cdot \mathbf{B} = g_{ij} A^i B^j$ or some equivalent, but we were in no position at that early stage to discuss such matters. Similar considerations hold for the vector product.

Furthermore, we have given a coordinate-free definition of a tensor; the old-fashioned definition in terms of components relative to various coordinate systems is not discussed in this book.

Continuing in this vein, let us now distinguish between three types of equations.

(*i*) There is the type of equation that does not exhibit any coordinates or components and that is valid independently of the particular choice of coordinate system simply because no coordinates are involved, either directly or indirectly.

(*ii*) There is the kind of equation that is written in terms of coordinates or components, but that is valid in every system of curvilinear coordinates.

(*iii*) There is the equation in which coordinates or components occur, that is only valid for particular coordinate systems.

For example, Newton's second law can be written $\mathbf{F} = m\mathbf{a}$ or $\mathbf{F} = m(d^2\mathbf{R}/dt^2)$; both equations are of the first type. It can also be written $F^i = ma^i$, which is of the second type. When written in the form $F^i = m(d^2x^i/dt^2)$ the equation is not always valid, and this equation is therefore of the third type. [This last equation is valid in cartesian coordinates but not, say, in cylindrical coordinates (where the radial component of acceleration is *not* simply d^2r/dt^2, as we saw in Sec. 2.4).]

An equation of either of the first two types is called a *tensor* equation, or is said to be *invariant*. One of the first type is said to be *coordinate-free*. There is an increasing trend in pure mathematics to write all invariant equations in a coordinate-free style. However, for purposes of calculation, such equations are not always desirable, and many applied mathematicians prefer to see tensor equations written out in terms of components. Equations of the third type must be used with caution.

There is another aspect of tensor analysis that has not yet been mentioned. Tensor analysis provides a useful tool for studying the geometry of spaces that are *not* euclidean spaces. One purpose of this section is to provide an introduction to this subject, and for that purpose it will be desirable to review the derivations in the preceding section from a slightly different viewpoint.

In the preceding section, we let x^1, x^2, x^3 denote a system of cartesian coordinates in euclidean space, and used u^1, u^2, u^3 to denote a system of curvilinear coordinates. In tensor analysis it is desirable to avoid any distinction between coordinate systems, since (as already mentioned) we desire all coordinates to be on an equal footing. In this section, x^1, x^2, x^3 will be used for any system of coordinates, instead of u^1, u^2, u^3 as in the preceding section. So instead of (5.135) we have

$$\underset{i}{\mathbf{e}} = \frac{\partial \mathbf{R}}{\partial x^i} \tag{5.169}$$

Subject to the usual restrictions on the existence and continuity of the partial derivatives involved, we have

$$\frac{\partial^2 \mathbf{R}}{\partial x^i \partial x^j} = \frac{\partial^2 \mathbf{R}}{\partial x^j \partial x^i} \tag{5.170}$$

from which it follows that

$$\frac{\partial \underset{j}{\mathbf{e}}}{\partial x^i} = \frac{\partial \underset{i}{\mathbf{e}}}{\partial x^j} \tag{5.171}$$

Let the kth contravariant component of $\partial \underset{i}{\mathbf{e}}/\partial x^j$ be denoted by Γ^k_{ij} so that

$$\frac{\partial \underset{i}{\mathbf{e}}}{\partial x^j} = \Gamma^k_{ij} \underset{k}{\mathbf{e}} \tag{5.172}$$

It follows from (5.171) that

$$\Gamma^k_{ji} = \Gamma^k_{ij} \tag{5.173}$$

We will rewrite some of the equations in the preceding section in terms of these symbols Γ^k_{ij}, which are called *Christoffel symbols*. Each of these symbols is a real-valued function of position in space, but since this function depends on the coordinate system it cannot be called a scalar field. Students who have been carried away by the novelty of the summation convention might guess, at this point, that $\phi(\mathbf{u},\mathbf{v},\mathbf{w}) = \Gamma^k_{ij}u^i v^j w_k$ would define a scalar-valued function ϕ and hence a tensor of order three, but this is not the case; in different coordinate systems this expression yields different values, and this lack of invariance (from the viewpoint of tensor analysis) makes this definition of $\phi(\mathbf{u},\mathbf{v},\mathbf{w})$ complete nonsense. Nevertheless, it is possible to write some invariant equations in terms of the Christoffel symbols, as we will soon see.

Since the kth contravariant component of any vector $\mathbf{v}$ equals $\mathbf{v} \cdot \overset{k}{\mathbf{e}}$, and the kth contravariant component of $\partial \underset{i}{\mathbf{e}}/\partial x^j$ is Γ^k_{ij}, we have (letting $\mathbf{v} = \partial \underset{i}{\mathbf{e}}/\partial x^j$)

$$\Gamma^k_{ij} = \frac{\partial \underset{i}{\mathbf{e}}}{\partial x^j} \cdot \overset{k}{\mathbf{e}} \tag{5.174}$$

which can be used as an alternative definition of the Christoffel symbols.

Similarly, if $\mathbf{F}$ is a vector field, and we denote the kth contravariant component of $\partial \mathbf{F}/\partial x^j$ by $F^k_{,j}$ we have

$$\begin{aligned} F^k_{,j} &= \frac{\partial \mathbf{F}}{\partial x^j} \cdot \overset{k}{\mathbf{e}} = \overset{k}{\mathbf{e}} \cdot \frac{\partial}{\partial x^j}(F^i \underset{i}{\mathbf{e}}) \\ &= \frac{\partial F^i}{\partial x^j}(\overset{k}{\mathbf{e}} \cdot \underset{i}{\mathbf{e}}) + F^i \overset{k}{\mathbf{e}} \cdot \frac{\partial \underset{i}{\mathbf{e}}}{\partial x^j} \\ &= \frac{\partial F^k}{\partial x^j} + \Gamma^k_{ij} F^i \end{aligned} \tag{5.175}$$

This is an interesting result. In cartesian coordinates, the base vectors (our old friends **i**, **j**, **k**) are constants, so their derivatives vanish and all the Christoffel symbols are identically equal to zero. In this case, the kth contravariant component of $\partial \mathbf{F}/\partial x^i$ is simply $\partial F^k/\partial x^i$, and there is no need to introduce the notation $F^k_{,j}$. In curvilinear coordinates there is an extra correction term, involving the Christoffel symbols. When the base vectors vary from point to point, the components of the derivatives of a vector field are *not* generally equal to the derivatives of the components.

Please notice the placement of the comma in $F^k_{,j}$. In tensor analysis, a comma preceding an index j usually denotes differentiation with respect to the curvilinear coordinate x^j. For example, the kth *covariant* component of $\partial \mathbf{F}/\partial x^j$ is denoted $F_{k,j}$. As usual, the fact that this is the kth covariant component is indicated by placing the k as a subscript (contravariant components are distinguished by superscripts instead). As an exercise, we suggest that the reader derive

$$F_{k,j} = \frac{\partial F_k}{\partial x^j} - \Gamma^i_{kj} F_i \tag{5.176}$$

which he can do easily by imitating the derivation of (5.175), except that instead of making use of (5.174) he should use

$$\frac{\partial \overset{i}{\mathbf{e}}}{\partial x^j} \cdot \underset{k}{\mathbf{e}} = -\Gamma^i_{jk} = -\Gamma^i_{kj} \tag{5.177}$$

whose derivation is also left as an exercise (and therefore will be found in the Answers and Notes section).

There are instances in which the comma does not set apart indices that refer to differentiation. For example, there is another class of Christoffel symbols denoted $\Gamma_{ij,k}$. As the reader might guess by analogy with (5.174) they are defined by

$$\Gamma_{ij,k} = \frac{\partial \underset{i}{\mathbf{e}}}{\partial x^j} \cdot \underset{k}{\mathbf{e}} \tag{5.178}$$

Since $\underset{k}{\mathbf{e}} = g_{sk} \overset{s}{\mathbf{e}}$

$$\Gamma_{ij,k} = \frac{\partial \underset{i}{\mathbf{e}}}{\partial x^j} \cdot \overset{s}{\mathbf{e}} g_{sk} = \Gamma^s_{ij} g_{sk} \tag{5.179}$$

which relates the two kinds of Christoffel symbols and by virtue of (5.173) shows that

$$\Gamma_{ij,k} = \Gamma_{ji,k} \tag{5.180}$$

As an exercise, the reader can show that

$$\Gamma^k_{ij} = \Gamma_{ij,s} g^{sk} \tag{5.181}$$

Let us relate the Christoffel symbols to the metric tensor. On differentiating $g_{ij} = \underset{i}{\mathbf{e}} \cdot \underset{j}{\mathbf{e}}$ we obtain

$$\frac{\partial g_{ij}}{\partial x^k} = \frac{\partial \underset{i}{\mathbf{e}}}{\partial x^k} \cdot \underset{j}{\mathbf{e}} + \underset{i}{\mathbf{e}} \cdot \frac{\partial \underset{j}{\mathbf{e}}}{\partial x^k} = \Gamma_{ik,j} + \Gamma_{jk,i} \tag{5.182}$$

Adding $2\Gamma_{ij,k}$ to both sides of (5.182), and then using (5.182) twice again, we obtain

$$\begin{aligned} \frac{\partial g_{ij}}{\partial x^k} + 2\Gamma_{ij,k} &= (\Gamma_{ij,k} + \Gamma_{ik,j}) + (\Gamma_{jk,i} + \Gamma_{ij,k}) \\ &= (\Gamma_{ji,k} + \Gamma_{ki,j}) + (\Gamma_{kj,i} + \Gamma_{ij,k}) \\ &= \frac{\partial g_{jk}}{\partial x^i} + \frac{\partial g_{ki}}{\partial x^j} \end{aligned} \tag{5.183}$$

Solving (5.183) for $\Gamma_{ij,k}$ we obtain

$$\Gamma_{ij,k} = \frac{1}{2}\left(\frac{\partial g_{jk}}{\partial x^i} + \frac{\partial g_{ki}}{\partial x^j} - \frac{\partial g_{ij}}{\partial x^k}\right) \tag{5.184}$$

and using (5.181)

$$\Gamma^k_{ij} = \frac{1}{2} g^{sk}\left(\frac{\partial g_{js}}{\partial x^i} + \frac{\partial g_{si}}{\partial x^j} - \frac{\partial g_{ij}}{\partial x^s}\right) \tag{5.185}$$

In more advanced work these two equations are used to *define* the Christoffel symbols.

In matrix algebra, an important role is played by the trace M^j_j of a matrix $M = (M^j_i)$, which is the sum of the entries on the principal diagonal. Similar sums can be formed with other objects occurring in tensor analysis, and they are called *contractions*. For example, the contracted Christoffel symbol is the sum Γ^j_{ij}. There is an interesting chain of equalities concerning this sum:

$$\Gamma^j_{ij} = \frac{1}{2g}\frac{\partial g}{\partial x^i} = \frac{1}{\sqrt{g}}\frac{\partial \sqrt{g}}{\partial x^i} = \frac{1}{J}\frac{\partial J}{\partial x^i} = \frac{\partial \underset{i}{\mathbf{e}}}{\partial x^j}\cdot \overset{j}{\mathbf{e}} = \nabla \cdot \underset{i}{\mathbf{e}} \tag{5.186}$$

These equalities can be derived many ways. For example, the first equality in

$$\nabla \cdot \underset{i}{\mathbf{e}} = \frac{1}{J}\frac{\partial J}{\partial x^i} = \frac{1}{\sqrt{g}}\frac{\partial \sqrt{g}}{\partial x^i} = \frac{1}{2g}\frac{\partial g}{\partial x^i} \tag{5.187}$$

follows from (5.155) by observing that, if $\mathbf{F} = \underset{i}{\mathbf{e}}$, then $F^j = 0$ except when $j = i$ and $F^i = 1$. (An alternative method is given in Exercise 20 of the preceding section.) The second equality follows from $J = \pm\sqrt{g}$ which was derived in Sec. 5.7, and the third equality in (5.187) is standard elementary calculus. One can then complete the chain (5.186) by the calculation

$$\begin{aligned}
\frac{1}{J}\frac{\partial J}{\partial x^i} &= \frac{1}{J}\frac{\partial}{\partial x^i}(\underset{1}{\mathbf{e}} \cdot \underset{2}{\mathbf{e}} \times \underset{3}{\mathbf{e}}) \\
&= \frac{1}{J}\left(\frac{\partial \underset{1}{\mathbf{e}}}{\partial x^i}\cdot \underset{2}{\mathbf{e}} \times \underset{3}{\mathbf{e}} + \frac{\partial \underset{2}{\mathbf{e}}}{\partial x^i}\cdot \underset{3}{\mathbf{e}} \times \underset{1}{\mathbf{e}} + \frac{\partial \underset{3}{\mathbf{e}}}{\partial x^i}\cdot \underset{1}{\mathbf{e}} \times \underset{2}{\mathbf{e}}\right) \\
&= \frac{1}{J}\left(\frac{\partial \underset{1}{\mathbf{e}}}{\partial x^i}\cdot J\overset{1}{\mathbf{e}} + \frac{\partial \underset{2}{\mathbf{e}}}{\partial x^i}\cdot J\overset{2}{\mathbf{e}} + \frac{\partial \underset{3}{\mathbf{e}}}{\partial x^i}\cdot J\overset{3}{\mathbf{e}}\right) \\
&= \frac{\partial \underset{i}{\mathbf{e}}}{\partial x^j}\cdot \overset{j}{\mathbf{e}} = \Gamma^j_{ij}
\end{aligned} \tag{5.188}$$

where the last equality comes from (5.174).

Working with vectors in this manner sometimes obscures the generality of the methods being used (quite an admission on the part of the author of a book on vector analysis). For example, in (5.188) we are differentiating $J = \underset{1}{\mathbf{e}} \cdot \underset{2}{\mathbf{e}} \times \underset{3}{\mathbf{e}}$; hence, we are basically differentiating a determinant. In general, the derivative of a determinant is the sum of the derivatives of each of its entries multiplied by the corresponding cofactor. Let us prove this for 3×3 determinants, and at the same time illustrate it for $g = \det G$. We have

$$g = \varepsilon^{ijk} g_{i1} g_{j2} g_{k3} \tag{5.189}$$

$$\frac{\partial g}{\partial x^s} = \varepsilon^{ijk} \frac{\partial g_{i1}}{\partial x^s} g_{j2} g_{k3} + \varepsilon^{ijk} g_{i1} \frac{\partial g_{j2}}{\partial x^s} g_{k3} + \varepsilon^{ijk} g_{i1} g_{j2} \frac{\partial g_{k3}}{\partial x^s}$$

$$= \frac{\partial g_{i1}}{\partial x^s} \operatorname{cof}^{i1}(G) + \frac{\partial g_{j2}}{\partial x^s} \operatorname{cof}^{j2}(G) + \frac{\partial g_{k3}}{\partial x^s} \operatorname{cof}^{k3}(G) \tag{5.190}$$

The dummies j and k can be changed to i and the entire sum written as

$$\frac{\partial g}{\partial x^s} = \frac{\partial g_{ip}}{\partial x^s} \operatorname{cof}^{ip}(G) \tag{5.191}$$

which proves the assertion.

Since $G^{-1} = (g^{ij})$, we have

$$\operatorname{cof}^{ip}(G) = g g^{pi} \tag{5.192}$$

$$\frac{1}{g} \frac{\partial g}{\partial x^s} = \frac{\partial g_{ip}}{\partial x^s} g^{pi} = (\Gamma_{is,p} + \Gamma_{ps,i}) g^{pi}$$

$$= \Gamma^i_{is} + \Gamma^p_{ps} = 2\Gamma^j_{js} = 2\Gamma^j_{sj} \tag{5.193}$$

which provides another way of obtaining the crucial first equality in (5.186).

Now let us briefly review the gradient, divergence, laplacian, and curl.

In tensor analysis, the covariant and contravariant components of the gradient of a scalar field f are often denoted f_i and f^i, so by (5.133)

$$f_i = \frac{\partial f}{\partial x^i} \tag{5.194}$$

and hence

$$f^i = g^{ij} \frac{\partial f}{\partial x^j} \tag{5.195}$$

The divergence of a vector field F can be found by using (5.186).

$$\nabla \cdot \mathbf{F} = \nabla \cdot (F^i \underset{i}{\mathbf{e}}) = \nabla F^i \cdot \underset{i}{\mathbf{e}} + F^i \nabla \cdot \underset{i}{\mathbf{e}}$$

$$= \frac{\partial F^i}{\partial x^j} \overset{j}{\mathbf{e}} \cdot \underset{i}{\mathbf{e}} + F^i \Gamma^j_{ij} = \frac{\partial F^i}{\partial x^j} \delta^j_i + \Gamma^j_{ij} F^i \tag{5.196}$$

hence, by (5.175),

$$\nabla \cdot \mathbf{F} = \frac{\partial F^i}{\partial x^i} + \Gamma^j_{ij} F^i = F^i_{,i} \tag{5.197}$$

In the calculation (5.196), if $\nabla \cdot \underset{i}{\mathbf{e}}$ is replaced by the third or fourth links in (5.186) instead of the first link, we obtain, respectively,

$$\nabla \cdot \mathbf{F} = \frac{1}{J}\frac{\partial}{\partial x^i}(JF^i) \tag{5.198}$$

or

$$\nabla \cdot \mathbf{F} = \frac{1}{\sqrt{g}}\frac{\partial}{\partial x^i}(\sqrt{g}\,F^i) \tag{5.199}$$

[Compare (5.155) and (5.157).]

The laplacian of a scalar field can now be obtained as the divergence of the gradient, using (5.199) and (5.195),

$$\nabla^2 f = f_{,i}^{\,i} = \frac{1}{\sqrt{g}}\frac{\partial}{\partial x^i}\left(\sqrt{g}g^{ij}\frac{\partial f}{\partial x^j}\right) \tag{5.200}$$

In tensor analysis it is customary to define the curl of a vector field **F** as an alternating tensor T of rank two whose covariant components are

$$T_{jk} = F_{k,j} - F_{j,k} \tag{5.201}$$

That these are the components of a tensor will be shown in Exercise 20 and, by a different method, in the next section. It is interesting to notice that the Christoffel symbols need not be used in calculating these components: they occur in the expressions for $F_{k,j}$ and $F_{j,k}$ but disappear when these expressions are subtracted.

$$\begin{aligned} T_{jk} &= F_{k,j} - F_{j,k} \\ &= \frac{\partial F_k}{\partial x^j} - \Gamma^i_{kj}F_i - \frac{\partial F_j}{\partial x^k} + \Gamma^i_{jk}F_i \\ &= \frac{\partial F_k}{\partial x^j} - \frac{\partial F_j}{\partial x^k} \end{aligned} \tag{5.202}$$

To see how the tensor curl is related to the vector curl, we will write (5.163) in two equivalent forms

$$(\nabla \times \mathbf{F})^i = \frac{1}{J}\varepsilon^{ijk}\frac{\partial F_k}{\partial x^j} = -\frac{1}{J}\varepsilon^{ijk}\frac{\partial F_j}{\partial x^k} \tag{5.203}$$

(The equivalence is proved in the Answers and Notes section.) Adding these two expressions and dividing by two we obtain yet a third expression,

$$(\nabla \times \mathbf{F}) = \frac{1}{2J}\varepsilon^{ijk}\left(\frac{\partial F_k}{\partial x^j} - \frac{\partial F_j}{\partial x^k}\right) = \frac{1}{2J}\varepsilon^{ijk}T_{jk} \tag{5.204}$$

giving the contravariant components of **curl F** in terms of the covariant components of the tensor curl of **F**. As an exercise, the reader should show that

$$T_{jk} = J\varepsilon_{ijk}(\nabla \times \mathbf{F})^i \tag{5.205}$$

In this welter of equations it is easy for an author to err with misplaced subscripts and superscripts, and for a reader to lose sight of all the essential ideas. Let us now consider some of these ideas.

In the earlier chapters, such things as the vector product, gradient, divergence, laplacian, and curl were defined by equations relative to a particular set of cartesian coordinates x, y, z. A particular basis **i**, **j**, **k** was used throughout. These cartesian coordinates are rather special, since the associated bases $\underset{1}{\mathbf{e}}$, $\underset{2}{\mathbf{e}}$, $\underset{3}{\mathbf{e}}$ and $\overset{1}{\mathbf{e}}$, $\overset{2}{\mathbf{e}}$, $\overset{3}{\mathbf{e}}$ are identical in such coordinates, and no distinction need be made between contravariant, covariant, or physical components, when such a basis is used. This is the reason that the tensor theory presented in the early optional sections was so much less complicated than what we have seen in this chapter. In the context of these earlier discussions, an important logical matter was never discussed in detail. This arises from the obvious fact that, in euclidean geometry, even when we assume it makes sense to speak of a right-handed system, there is nothing *unique* about the choice of the vectors we denote by **i**, **j**, and **k**. (There are infinitely many ways in which we can choose a right-handed system consisting of three mutually orthogonal unit vectors.)

Having chosen a particular right-handed cartesian coordinate system, and therefore a particular **i**, **j**, **k**, we are perfectly within our rights to define (say) the divergence of a vector field **F** by $\partial F_x/\partial x + \partial F_y/\partial y + \partial F_z/\partial z$. In this way, we associate to a vector-valued function **F** of position in space, a numerically-valued function, div **F**, of position in space. We are even within our rights to decree that this function, div **F**, will be a scalar function: we decree that, at any point P, the value of div **F** will be the number assigned by this numerically-valued function to the point P, regardless of the coordinate system. Having done this, we are *not* at liberty to assume div $\mathbf{F} = \partial F_u/\partial u + \partial F_v/\partial v + \partial F_w/\partial w$ when u, v, w is another coordinate system.

This is true even if u, v, w is a right-handed system of cartesian coordinates whose base vectors qualify equally well to be denoted **i**, **j**, and **k**. Thus it appears we have given undue preference to a particular system of cartesian coordinates.

Now that we have derived expressions for the gradient, divergence, laplacian, and curl, in general coordinates, we see that this is not the case. In earlier chapters we did show a preference for cartesian coordinates, but not for any particular system of cartesian coordinates. In all systems of cartesian coordinates, the Christoffel symbols are identically zero, the metric tensor can be represented by the identity matrix, and $\sqrt{g} = 1$. Thus the formulas for the gradient, divergence, and laplacian reduce to the formulas used earlier in this book, in any cartesian coordinate system. However, the coordinate system must be right-handed (so that $J = 1$ and not -1) in order that the curl formula reduce to the one used earlier, and the same is true of the vector cross product (whose discussion is left to the exercises).

We now have a confession to make to the reader. We must admit that an object which was called a vector earlier in this book is not a vector at all. We are referring to the position vector $\mathbf{R} = x\mathbf{i} + y\mathbf{j} + z\mathbf{k}$. "The position vector of a point in space is the vector extending from the origin to the point", and which vector we mean by this depends not only on the point, but on the origin. There is no reason why two different systems of cartesian coordinates need have the same origin. The position "vector" of a point P might be a nonzero vector in one coordinate system, but the zero vector relative to another (by taking P itself to be the origin). Therefore, from the viewpoint of tensor analysis, the position "vector" is not really a vector.

However, the time derivative of the position vector of a moving particle is a vector. It is the velocity vector, with contravariant components dx^i/dt. If we differentiate again, we obtain the acceleration vector:

$$\frac{d}{dt}\left(\frac{dx^i}{dt}\underset{i}{\mathbf{e}}\right) = \frac{d^2x^i}{dt^2}\underset{i}{\mathbf{e}} + \frac{dx^i}{dt}\frac{d\underset{i}{\mathbf{e}}}{dt} \tag{5.206}$$

Since, by the chain rule,

$$\frac{d\underset{i}{\mathbf{e}}}{dt} = \frac{\partial \underset{i}{\mathbf{e}}}{\partial x^j}\frac{dx^j}{dt} = \Gamma^k_{ij}\underset{k}{\mathbf{e}}\frac{dx^j}{dt} \tag{5.207}$$

the acceleration vector is

$$\frac{d^2x^k}{dt^2}\underset{k}{\mathbf{e}} + \Gamma^k_{ij}\frac{dx^i}{dt}\frac{dx^j}{dt}\underset{k}{\mathbf{e}} \tag{5.208}$$

so Newton's second law, in general coordinates, is

$$F^k = m\left[\frac{d^2x^k}{dt^2} + \Gamma^k_{ij}\frac{dx^i}{dt}\frac{dx^j}{dt}\right] \tag{5.209}$$

Suppose that a particle is moving with constant nonzero speed $ds/dt = C$ along a straight line. Then its acceleration is zero. We have (see Exercise 13) in this case

$$\frac{dx^i}{dt} = C\frac{dx^i}{ds} \qquad \frac{d^2x^i}{dt^2} = C^2\frac{d^2x^i}{ds^2} \tag{5.210}$$

Introducing these into the expression for acceleration we obtain

$$\frac{d^2x^k}{ds^2} + \Gamma^k_{ij}\frac{dx^i}{ds}\frac{dx^j}{ds} = 0 \qquad (k = 1,2,3) \tag{5.211}$$

These are called the *geodesic equations*.

The three equations $x^k = x^k(s)$ are the equations of a line in parametric form if and only if the functions $x^k(s)$ satisfy these three equations. Notice that, because of the implied summation, each of the functions $x^k(s)$ enters into all three of these equations.

For some purposes it is not necessary to take the parameter to be arc length s. Suppose we replace s in (5.211) by t, wherever it occurs. Then if three functions $x^k(t)$ satisfy these equations, they must be equations of a line in parametric form. However, it is possible for three functions $x^k(t)$ to fail to satisfy these equations, and still be parametric equations of a line. [Perhaps $x^k(t)$ give the position of a particle that is moving along a line with nonzero acceleration.]

In cartesian coordinates, the Christoffel symbols become identically zero, and the geodesic equations reduce to $d^2x^k/dt^2 = 0$. Solving these equations yields expressions for the x^k of the form of (1.5), with which we are already familiar.

At the risk of seeming repetitious, we wish to reemphasize that when the base vectors vary from point to point, the components of the derivatives of a vector field are not generally equal to the derivatives of the components. That is the reason for introducing the Christoffel symbols. We conclude this section with an example which illustrates this point very well.

Example 5.13 Let $x^k = x^k(t)$ be parametric equations of a curve in space, passing through a region in which there is defined a vector field **F**. Along the curve, **F** can be regarded as a function of the parameter t. Find an expression for the contravariant components of $d\mathbf{F}/dt$.

Solution We must be careful to distinguish between $(d\mathbf{F}/dt)^k$ and dF^k/dt. We are asked for $(d\mathbf{F}/dt)^k$. First let us find $d\mathbf{F}/dt$.

$$\begin{aligned}\frac{d\mathbf{F}}{dt} = \frac{d}{dt}(F^k\underset{k}{\mathbf{e}}) &= \frac{dF^k}{dt}\underset{k}{\mathbf{e}} + F^k\frac{d}{dt}(\underset{k}{\mathbf{e}})\\ &= \frac{dF^k}{dt}\underset{k}{\mathbf{e}} + F^k\frac{\partial}{\partial x^i}(\underset{k}{\mathbf{e}})\frac{dx^i}{dt}\\ &= \frac{dF^k}{dt}\underset{k}{\mathbf{e}} + F^k\Gamma^j_{ki}\underset{j}{\mathbf{e}}\frac{dx^i}{dt}\\ &= \frac{dF^k}{dt}\underset{k}{\mathbf{e}} + F^i\Gamma^k_{ij}\underset{k}{\mathbf{e}}\frac{dx^j}{dt}\end{aligned}$$

From this, we can read off the answer:

$$\left(\frac{d\mathbf{F}}{dt}\right)^k = \frac{dF^k}{dt} + \Gamma^k_{ij}F^i\frac{dx^j}{dt} \tag{5.212}$$

This is sometimes called the *intrinsic derivative* of **F** along the curve $x^k = x^k(t)$.

EXERCISES

1. Derive (5.177). [*Hint*: $(\partial/\partial x^j)\,(\overset{i}{\mathbf{e}}\cdot\underset{k}{\mathbf{e}})$ is identically zero for every choice of indices i, j, and k.]
2. Derive (5.176) by making use of (5.177).

3. Derive (5.181) by substituting $g^{sk}\underset{s}{\mathbf{e}}$ for $\overset{k}{\mathbf{e}}$ in (5.174).

4. Copy down (5.182), then close the book and reproduce its derivation.

5. Which of the exercises at the end of Sec. 5.7 shows that trace of the product of two matrices does not depend on the order in which they are multiplied?

6. Show that the two expressions for the curl in (5.203) are equivalent to (5.163). (This provides an excellent exercise on the notation.)

7. Show that $\varepsilon_{ijk}\,\varepsilon^{ips} = 1$ when $p = j$ and $s = k$, equals -1 when $p = k$ and $s = j$, and equals zero otherwise. (Don't refer to Sec. 1.16!)

8. Derive (5.205) by making use of the result of the preceding problem.

9. Derive an expression for the vector cross product in general coordinates by showing that, if $w = u \times v$,

$$w_k = J\varepsilon_{ijk}\,u^i v^j \tag{5.213}$$

10. (a) Show that, if $\mathbf{w} = \mathbf{A} \times \mathbf{F}$,

$$w^k = \frac{1}{J}\,\varepsilon^{ijk}\,A_i\,F_j \tag{5.214}$$

(b) Write this as a symbolic determinant.
(c) Formally replace A in this determinant by $\boldsymbol{\nabla}$, where $\boldsymbol{\nabla}$ is given by (5.134).
(d) Do you obtain the same result if (5.163) is written as a symbolic determinant?

11. A coordinate system for which the Christoffel symbols are identically zero is called an *affine* coordinate system.
(a) Give a purely geometrical description of an affine coordinate system. What can you say about the coordinate curves? The coordinate surfaces?
(b) In an affine coordinate system, the *relative volume* of a parallelepiped with coterminal edges u, v, and w, oriented by taking the edges in that order, is defined to be $\varepsilon_{ijk}\,u^i\,v^j w^k$. How is this related to the actual volume of the parallelepiped?
(c) The formula for the divergence of a vector field is the same in affine coordinates as it is in cartesian coordinates (which are affine coordinates of a special kind). By interpreting divergence as the time rate of change of volume per unit volume, explain why this should be so.

12. In most coordinate systems the "origin" has coordinates (0,0,0). Give an an example of a coordinate system defined throughout space for which no point has a coordinate $x^k = 0$.

13. Derive the two expressions given in (5.210).

14. Show that the solutions of the geodesic equations in cartesian coordinates yield the familiar expressions for straight lines in parametric form.

15. By imitating the derivation of (5.212), find an expression for $(d\mathbf{F}/dt)_k$, the kth covariant component of $d\mathbf{F}/dt$.

16. A vector field $\mathbf{F}$ is said to *move parallel* along a curve if its intrinsic derivative along the curve is identically zero. What does this mean in everyday language?

17. The definition of the intrinsic derivative of a vector field along a curve makes perfectly good sense for a vector field that is *only* defined at points on the curve.

Such a field is the field of unit tangents $\mathbf{T}$ to the curve, $T^k = dx^k/ds$. Derive the geodesic equations by using the fact that a curve $x^k = x^k(s)$ is a line if and only if the intrinsic derivative of $\mathbf{T}$ along the curve is identically zero. (In other words, the unit tangent moves parallel along the curve.)

18. (a) Show that the element of volume in general curvilinear coordinates is $dV = |J|\, dx^1\, dx^2\, dx^3$.
(b) Show what this reduces to in orthogonal curvilinear coordinates and, hence, derive the formula in Sec. 4.13.

19. (a) An observer moves with velocity $\mathbf{v}$ through a region in which there is defined a vector field $\mathbf{F}$. Find $d\mathbf{F}/dt$ as seen by this observer, in terms of $F_{k,j}$ and the contravariant components of $\mathbf{v}$. (This is similar to Exercise 15.)
(b) Use this result to write $F_{k,j}\, u^k v^j$ in a coordinate-free form.
(c) What does this show about the function

$$\phi(\mathbf{u}, \mathbf{v}) = F_{k,j}\, u^k\, v^j\,?$$

20. Show that the tensor curl of a vector field is a tensor field of rank two.

Exercises calling for explicit calculations in specified coordinate systems will be found at the end of this chapter.

5.10 COORDINATE TRANSFORMATIONS

Let x^1, x^2, x^3 be a system of curvilinear coordinates defined throughout a region of space, and let $\bar{x}^1, \bar{x}^2, \bar{x}^3$ be another system of curvilinear coordinates, which for simplicity will be assumed to be defined throughout the same region. Let $\underset{1}{\mathbf{e}}, \underset{2}{\mathbf{e}}, \underset{3}{\mathbf{e}}$ denote the tangent basis relative to the coordinates x^1, x^2, x^3, and let $\overset{1}{\mathbf{e}}, \overset{2}{\mathbf{e}}, \overset{3}{\mathbf{e}}$ denote the dual basis, as in earlier sections. Then, as already noted, for any vector field $\mathbf{v}$ defined throughout the region we have

$$\mathbf{v} = (\mathbf{v} \cdot \underset{k}{\mathbf{e}})\overset{k}{\mathbf{e}} \qquad \text{i.e., } v_k = \mathbf{v} \cdot \underset{k}{\mathbf{e}} \tag{5.215}$$

and also

$$\mathbf{v} = (\mathbf{v} \cdot \overset{j}{\mathbf{e}})\underset{j}{\mathbf{e}} \qquad \text{i.e., } v^j = \mathbf{v} \cdot \overset{j}{\mathbf{e}} \tag{5.216}$$

Let $\underset{1}{\mathbf{f}}, \underset{2}{\mathbf{f}}, \underset{3}{\mathbf{f}}$ denote the tangent basis relative to the coordinates $\bar{x}^1, \bar{x}^2, \bar{x}^3$, and let $\overset{1}{\mathbf{f}}, \overset{2}{\mathbf{f}}, \overset{3}{\mathbf{f}}$ denote its dual basis. Then

$$\mathbf{v} = (\mathbf{v} \cdot \underset{k}{\mathbf{f}})\overset{k}{\mathbf{f}} \qquad \text{i.e., } \bar{v}_k = \mathbf{v} \cdot \underset{k}{\mathbf{f}} \tag{5.217}$$

and

$$\mathbf{v} = (\mathbf{v} \cdot \overset{j}{\mathbf{f}})\underset{j}{\mathbf{f}} \qquad \text{i.e., } \bar{v}^j = \mathbf{v} \cdot \overset{j}{\mathbf{f}} \tag{5.218}$$

The bars above letters serve to distinguish coordinates and components in one system from those in the other.

We now introduce two matrix fields (i.e., matrix-valued functions of position in space) as follows:

$$A^j_k = \underset{k}{\mathbf{e}} \cdot \overset{j}{\mathbf{f}} \qquad B^j_k = \underset{k}{\mathbf{f}} \cdot \overset{j}{\mathbf{e}} \tag{5.219}$$

This notation is not standard and will only be used for a few paragraphs, until we find a better notation.

Using this notation and taking $\mathbf{v} = \overset{j}{\mathbf{f}}$ in (5.215) we obtain

$$\overset{j}{\mathbf{f}} = A^j_k \overset{k}{\mathbf{e}} \tag{5.220}$$

Taking $\mathbf{v} = \underset{k}{\mathbf{f}}$ in (5.216) we obtain

$$\underset{k}{\mathbf{f}} = B^j_k \underset{j}{\mathbf{e}} \tag{5.221}$$

and taking $\mathbf{v} = \overset{j}{\mathbf{e}}$ in (5.217),

$$\overset{j}{\mathbf{e}} = B^j_k \overset{k}{\mathbf{f}} \tag{5.222}$$

and replacing $\mathbf{v}$ by $\underset{k}{\mathbf{e}}$ in (5.218) we have

$$\underset{k}{\mathbf{e}} = A^j_k \underset{j}{\mathbf{f}} \tag{5.223}$$

Since (5.220) gives $\overset{1}{\mathbf{f}}$, $\overset{2}{\mathbf{f}}$, and $\overset{3}{\mathbf{f}}$ in terms of $\overset{1}{\mathbf{e}}$, $\overset{2}{\mathbf{e}}$, and $\overset{3}{\mathbf{e}}$, and (5.222) gives $\overset{1}{\mathbf{e}}$, $\overset{2}{\mathbf{e}}$, and $\overset{3}{\mathbf{e}}$ in terms of $\overset{1}{\mathbf{f}}$, $\overset{2}{\mathbf{f}}$, and $\overset{3}{\mathbf{f}}$, we see that the matrices $A = (A^j_k)$ and $B = (B^j_k)$ are inverses of each other. (Notice that we say "matrices" although, to be absolutely correct, we should say "matrix fields", since these matrices vary from point to point in space.)

That A and B are inverses can be seen just as well from the pair of equations (5.221) and (5.223). It can also be shown directly, by calculating the matrix product AB as follows:

$$A^i_j B^j_k = (\underset{j}{\mathbf{e}} \cdot \overset{i}{\mathbf{f}}) B^j_k = (B^j_k \underset{j}{\mathbf{e}}) \cdot \overset{i}{\mathbf{f}} = \underset{k}{\mathbf{f}} \cdot \overset{i}{\mathbf{f}} = \delta^i_k$$

The gradient of a scalar field can be written relative to either of the dual bases:

$$\nabla\phi = \frac{\partial\phi}{\partial x^j} \overset{j}{\mathbf{e}} = \frac{\partial\phi}{\partial \bar{x}^k} \overset{k}{\mathbf{f}} \tag{5.224}$$

On substituting $\phi = x^j$, we have, since $\nabla x^j = \overset{j}{\mathbf{e}}$,

$$\nabla x^j = \overset{j}{\mathbf{e}} = \frac{\partial x^j}{\partial \bar{x}^k} \overset{k}{\mathbf{f}} \tag{5.225}$$

Comparing this with (5.222), we see that

$$B_k^j = \frac{\partial x^j}{\partial \bar{x}^k} \tag{5.226}$$

and a similar calculation yields

$$A_k^j = \frac{\partial \bar{x}^j}{\partial x^k} \tag{5.227}$$

Let us compare the covariant components of $\mathbf{v}$ in the two coordinate systems.

$$\bar{v}_k = \mathbf{v} \cdot \underset{k}{\mathbf{f}} = \mathbf{v} \cdot (B_k^j \underset{j}{\mathbf{e}}) = B_k^j \mathbf{v} \cdot \underset{j}{\mathbf{e}} = B_k^j v_j = \frac{\partial x^j}{\partial \bar{x}^k} v_j$$

The system of equations

$$\bar{v}_k = \frac{\partial x^j}{\partial \bar{x}^k} v_j \tag{5.228}$$

is called the *transformation law for covariant components of a vector field.*

In essentially the same manner we can derive

$$\bar{v}^k = \frac{\partial \bar{x}^k}{\partial x^j} v^j \tag{5.229}$$

which is the *transformation law for contravariant components of a vector field.*

The transformation laws for the components of a tensor field are now easy to derive. For example, if ϕ is a tensor of rank two, we have

$$\bar{\phi}_{ij} = \phi(\underset{i}{\mathbf{f}},\underset{j}{\mathbf{f}}) = \phi(B_i^r \underset{r}{\mathbf{e}}, B_j^s \underset{s}{\mathbf{e}}) = B_i^r B_j^s \phi(\underset{r}{\mathbf{e}},\underset{s}{\mathbf{e}}) = B_i^r B_j^s \phi_{rs}$$

So, the *transformation law for covariant components of a tensor field of rank two* is

$$\bar{\phi}_{ij} = \frac{\partial x^r}{\partial \bar{x}^i} \frac{\partial x^s}{\partial \bar{x}^j} \phi_{rs} \tag{5.230}$$

Similarly,

$$\bar{\phi}^{ij} = \frac{\partial \bar{x}^i}{\partial x^r} \frac{\partial \bar{x}^j}{\partial x^s} \phi^{rs} \tag{5.231}$$

is the *transformation law for contravariant components of a tensor field of rank two.*

And so it goes. The reader should have no difficulty writing down transformation laws for the components of tensor fields of higher rank.

These transformation laws provide a computational means for determining whether or not a given "object" is a tensor. A tensor of rank r can be described, relative to a coordinate system, by 3^r components. It may happen that, in some manner, one can associate with each coordinate system a set of 3^r numbers, and still not be certain whether or not these numbers are the components of some tensor.

To fix ideas, let us restrict our attention to tensors of rank two, and let us suppose that we have a way of associating with each coordinate system x^1, x^2, x^3 a set of nine numbers ψ_{ij}. We may wonder whether or not there exists a tensor ψ with the property that, in each coordinate system, the numbers ψ_{ij} are the covariant components of ψ.

If, on changing from one coordinate system to another, the numbers ψ_{ij} do *not* change in accordance with (5.230), then of course we know that these numbers are not the covariant components of any tensor of rank two. (Once again, we remind the reader that instead of "numbers" we should say "numerically-valued functions" since, in general, everything we are talking about varies from point to point in space. Similarly, we should say "tensor field" instead of "tensor".)

If, however, these numbers ψ_{ij} *do* always transform in accordance with (5.230), then they *must* be the covariant components of a tensor of rank two. This is proved as follows. Let us select a *particular* coordinate system x^1, x^2, x^3 and let ϕ denote the tensor whose covariant components ϕ_{ij} relative to *this* coordinate system are equal to the numbers ψ_{ij} that we have associated with this coordinate system. In other words, in this particular coordinate system, $\phi(u,v) = \phi_{ij}u^iv^j = \psi_{ij}u^iv^j$. Since ϕ is a tensor, in *any other* coordinate system $\bar{x}^1, \bar{x}^2, \bar{x}^3$ the coordinates of ϕ will be $\bar{\phi}_{ij}$ as given (5.230). But since, by hypothesis, the ψ_{ij} also transform according to the same law, $\bar{\psi}_{ij}$ will be the same as $\bar{\phi}_{ij}$. In other words, the numbers we have associated with each coordinate system are the covariant components of a tensor ϕ (which, in view of these developments, we might as well denote ψ).

We will illustrate this by two examples. In the first, the numbers ψ_{ij} are not the components of a tensor, and in the second they are.

Example 5.14 Let **F** be a vector field. Associate with any coordinate system x^1, x^2, x^3 the nine numbers $\psi_{ij} = \partial F_i/\partial x^j$. The position of the index j is completely reasonable (a superscript in the denominator is generally equivalent to a subscript indicating covariance, as we have seen repeatedly). Therefore, it might be reasonable to suppose that the numbers ψ_{ij} are the covariant components of a tensor of rank two.

Let us see if they are. Relative to coordinates $\bar{x}^1$, $\bar{x}^2$, $\bar{x}^3$ the numbers are

$$\bar{\psi}_{ij} = \frac{\partial \bar{F}_i}{\partial \bar{x}^j} = \frac{\partial}{\partial \bar{x}^j}\left(\frac{\partial x^r}{\partial \bar{x}^i} F_r\right) = \frac{\partial^2 x^r}{\partial \bar{x}^j \partial \bar{x}^i} F_r + \frac{\partial x^r}{\partial \bar{x}^i}\frac{\partial F_r}{\partial x^s}\frac{\partial x^s}{\partial \bar{x}^j}$$

$$= \frac{\partial x^r}{\partial \bar{x}^i}\frac{\partial x^s}{\partial \bar{x}^j}\psi_{rs} + \frac{\partial^2 x^r}{\partial \bar{x}^j \partial \bar{x}^i} F_r \tag{5.232}$$

Since the second term is not necessarily zero, except in the trivial case where F is the zero vector, we conclude that these numbers are not the components of a tensor. (Not any kind of components of any kind of tensor: see Exercise 4.)

Example 5.15 Let **F** be a vector field. Associate with any coordinate system x^1, x^2, x^3 the nine numbers

$$T_{ij} = \frac{\partial F_j}{\partial x^i} - \frac{\partial F_i}{\partial x^j} \tag{5.233}$$

This is the difference of two expressions that we know, from the preceding example, do not represent tensor components, so it would not appear *a priori* very likely that the nine numbers T_{ij} are components of a tensor. It turns out that they are! Making use of the notation and calculation in the preceding example, we have

$$\overline{T}_{ij} = \overline{\psi}_{ji} - \overline{\psi}_{ij} = \frac{\partial x^r}{\partial \overline{x}^j}\frac{\partial x^s}{\partial \overline{x}^i}\psi_{rs} - \frac{\partial x^s}{\partial \overline{x}^i}\frac{\partial x^r}{\partial \overline{x}^j}\psi_{sr} \tag{5.234}$$

(Since the crossed partial derivatives are equal, they vanish in the subtraction process.)

$$\overline{T}_{ij} = \frac{\partial x^r}{\partial \overline{x}^j}\frac{\partial x^s}{\partial \overline{x}^i}(\psi_{rs} - \psi_{sr}) = \frac{\partial x^r}{\partial \overline{x}^j}\frac{\partial x^s}{\partial \overline{x}^i}T_{sr}$$

This shows that the T_{ij}'s are indeed the covariant components of a tensor. As mentioned in the preceding section, this is the "tensor curl" of the vector field **F**.

It follows from this that $T(\mathbf{u},\mathbf{v}) = T_{ij}u^i v^j = \overline{T}_{ij}\overline{u}^i\overline{v}^j$ for any pair of vector fields **u** and **v**, i.e., that $T(\mathbf{u},\mathbf{v})$ at any point in space is a scalar. If the magnitudes of **u** and **v** are sufficiently small, this is approximately the circulation of **F** about a parallelogram with coterminal edges **u** and **v** (see Exercise 5).

Before we proceed, it may be well to mention that there also exist "mixed components" of a tensor. We will discuss this in connection with tensors of rank two. If ϕ is a tensor of rank two, we define its mixed components $\phi_j^{\cdot i}$ and $\phi^i_{\cdot j}$ relative to a system of coordinates by

$$\phi_j^{\cdot i} = \phi(\underset{j}{\mathbf{e}},\overset{i}{\mathbf{e}}) \qquad \phi^i_{\cdot j} = \phi(\overset{i}{\mathbf{e}},\underset{j}{\mathbf{e}}) \tag{5.235}$$

We leave the derivation of the laws of transformation of mixed components to the reader, simply remarking for the record that the transformation law for the $\phi_j^{\cdot i}$ is

$$\overline{\phi}_j^{\cdot i} = \frac{\partial \overline{x}^i}{\partial x^r}\frac{\partial x^s}{\partial \overline{x}^j}\phi_s^{\cdot r} \tag{5.236}$$

and, surprisingly enough, the transformation law for the $\phi^i_{\cdot j}$ is exactly the same.

It is interesting to notice that the matrix of mixed components of the metric tensor is the identity matrix,

$$g_j^{\cdot i} = \underset{j}{\mathbf{e}} \cdot \overset{i}{\mathbf{e}} = \delta^i_j \tag{5.237}$$

Similarly, $g^i_{\cdot j} = \delta^i_j$. Indeed, for any *symmetric* tensor ϕ, the mixed components obviously must be equal: $\phi^i_{\cdot j} = \phi_j^{\cdot i}$.

If, in any coordinate system, the covariant components of two tensors ϕ and ψ are equal, $\phi_{ij} = \psi_{ij}$ (for every pair of indices i, j), then the tensors are identical. The same statement is valid if "covariant" is replaced by "contravariant", or even by "mixed", provided the mixed components are of the same kind: $\phi^{i}_{.j} = \psi_{j}^{.i}$ simply implies that $\phi(\mathbf{u},\mathbf{v}) = \psi(\mathbf{v},\mathbf{u})$ for any pair of vectors $\mathbf{u}$ and $\mathbf{v}$, so that ϕ and ψ are not really identical (although they are obviously close relatives). See Exercise 7.

This shows that the Kronecker index is not a tensor, since if it were (5.237) would imply its identity with the metric tensor, and we know that the covariant components g_{ij} and contravariant components g^{ij} of the metric tensor are *not* in general the same as δ_{ij} and δ^{ij}, respectively.

Some students have difficulty memorizing the various transformation laws for the different types of components of a tensor. Here is a clever and nearly foolproof device that makes it impossible to make mistakes, provided one is thoroughly versatile with the use of the summation convention: wherever a horizontal bar occurs over an indexed letter, forget about it and replace it by priming (stroking) all of the indices. For example, (5.230) then reads

$$\phi_{i'j'} = \frac{\partial x^r}{\partial x^{i'}}\frac{\partial x^s}{\partial x^{j'}}\phi_{rs}$$

and (5.236) becomes

$$\phi_{j'}^{\cdot i'} = \frac{\partial x^{i'}}{\partial x^r}\frac{\partial x^s}{\partial x^{j'}}\phi_s^{\cdot r}$$

A mistake, such as writing

$$\bar{\phi}_j^{\cdot i} = \frac{\partial x^i}{\partial \bar{x}^r}\frac{\partial \bar{x}^s}{\partial x^j}\phi_s^{\cdot r} \qquad \textit{this is incorrect}$$

becomes more obvious in the form

$$\phi_{j'}^{\cdot i'} = \frac{\partial x^i}{\partial x^{r'}}\frac{\partial x^{s'}}{\partial x^j}\phi_s^{\cdot r} \qquad \textit{this is incorrect}$$

since stroked indices are matched with indices without strokes, something that does not happen when this notation is used consistently.

This notation is used by many mathematicians for a very good reason. It is sensible to use a single letter (called the *kernel*) to denote a particular object, such as a vector, and then use offset subscripts or superscripts to denote the components of the object. Thus, if we let $\mathbf{v}$ denote a vector, v is the kernel letter, and v^i or v_j denote various kinds of components of the same vector. An index placed directly beneath or above a letter becomes part of the kernel, thus $\underset{1}{\mathbf{v}}$ and $\underset{2}{\mathbf{v}}$ denote different vectors, not different components of the same vector. The notation $\bar{v}^i$ suggests that we are now talking about a component of an altogether different vector $\bar{\mathbf{v}}$, whereas the notation $v^{i'}$ shows we are still talking about the same vector $\mathbf{v}$, but in a different coordinate system.

Despite the advantages, there are some pedagogical disadvantages, so we will continue to use horizontal bars instead of primed indices.

Example 5.16 Find a formula relating the value of J in one coordinate system x^1, x^2, x^3 to the value $\bar{J}$ relative to another system $\bar{x}^1$, $\bar{x}^2$, $\bar{x}^3$.

Solution By definition,

$$J = \underset{1}{\mathbf{e}} \cdot \underset{2}{\mathbf{e}} \times \underset{3}{\mathbf{e}} \tag{5.238}$$

Since this is a triple scalar product, this would be a scalar, but for the fact that what we mean by $\underset{1}{\mathbf{e}}$, $\underset{2}{\mathbf{e}}$, and $\underset{3}{\mathbf{e}}$ depends on the coordinate system. By the properties of the triple scalar product,

$$\underset{i}{\mathbf{e}} \cdot \underset{j}{\mathbf{e}} \times \underset{k}{\mathbf{e}} = J\varepsilon_{ijk} \tag{5.239}$$

In the other coordinate system,

$$\begin{aligned} \bar{J}\bar{\varepsilon}_{ijk} &= \underset{i}{\mathbf{f}} \cdot \underset{j}{\mathbf{f}} \times \underset{k}{\mathbf{f}} \\ &= \left(\frac{\partial x^p}{\partial \bar{x}^i} \underset{p}{\mathbf{e}}\right) \cdot \left(\frac{\partial x^r}{\partial \bar{x}^j} \underset{r}{\mathbf{e}}\right) \times \left(\frac{\partial x^s}{\partial \bar{x}^k} \underset{s}{\mathbf{e}}\right) \\ &= J\varepsilon_{prs} \frac{\partial x^p}{\partial \bar{x}^i} \frac{\partial x^r}{\partial \bar{x}^j} \frac{\partial x^s}{\partial \bar{x}^k} \end{aligned} \tag{5.240}$$

Taking $i = 1$, $j = 2$, and $k = 3$, $\varepsilon_{ijk} = \varepsilon_{123} = 1$, hence

$$\bar{J} = J\varepsilon_{prs} \frac{\partial x^p}{\partial \bar{x}^1} \frac{\partial x^r}{\partial \bar{x}^2} \frac{\partial x^s}{\partial \bar{x}^3} = J \left| \frac{\partial x}{\partial \bar{x}} \right| \tag{5.241}$$

where by $|\partial x/\partial \bar{x}|$ we mean the determinant of the matrix whose entries are $\partial x^i/\partial \bar{x}^j$. In advanced calculus this determinant is denoted by the symbol $\partial(x^1,x^2,x^3)/\partial(\bar{x}^1,\bar{x}^2,\bar{x}^3)$ and is called the *jacobian of* x^1, x^2, and x^3 *with respect to* $\bar{x}^1$, $\bar{x}^2$, *and* $\bar{x}^3$.

If, to each coordinate system, there is an associated number K, transforming according to the law

$$\bar{K} = \left| \frac{\partial x}{\partial \bar{x}} \right|^w K \tag{5.242}$$

we call K a *relative scalar of weight* w. If $w = 0$, K is a *scalar*. When $w = 1$, we call K a *scalar density*. We see from the preceding example that J is a scalar density.

There is a natural correspondence between scalar densities and alternating tensors of rank three. If K is a scalar density, $\phi_{ijk} = K\varepsilon_{ijk}$ gives the covariant components of an alternating tensor of rank three. If ϕ is an alternating tensor of rank three, then $\phi_{ijk} = K\varepsilon_{ijk}$ where K is a scalar density. In the special case where ϕ is defined by $\phi(\mathbf{u},\mathbf{v},\mathbf{w}) = \mathbf{u} \cdot \mathbf{v} \times \mathbf{w}$, the associated scalar density is J. (Every alternating tensor of rank three is simply a scalar multiple of this special ϕ.)

$|\mathbf{u} \cdot \mathbf{v} \times \mathbf{w}|$ is the volume of a parallelepiped with coterminal edges $\mathbf{u}$, $\mathbf{v}$, and $\mathbf{w}$. Let the parallelepiped be oriented by taking the edges $\mathbf{u}$, $\mathbf{v}$, and $\mathbf{w}$ in that order, and let $\mathbf{u} \cdot \mathbf{v} \times \mathbf{w}$ be called the volume of the oriented parallelepiped.

This notion of *oriented volume* coincides with the ordinary notion of volume insofar as its magnitude is concerned, but it may be negative (ordinary volume is never a negative quantity). In component form, this is

$$\mathbf{u} \cdot \mathbf{v} \times \mathbf{w} = J\varepsilon_{ijk} u^i v^j w^k \tag{5.243}$$

By the *relative volume* of the parallelepiped is meant the number

$$\varepsilon_{ijk} u^i v^j w^k \tag{5.244}$$

which differs from (5.243) in lacking the factor J. So long as J is a constant, independent of position in space, these expressions are also constant, for any fixed choice of **u**, **v**, and **w**. It can be shown that (5.244) defines a relative scalar of weight -1.

The relative volume of an extended region D in space is defined by a triple integral in much the same way that ordinary volume can be defined by a triple integral. We cover D by a number of small parallelepipeds whose coterminal edges are $dx^1 \underset{1}{\mathbf{e}}$, $dx^2 \underset{2}{\mathbf{e}}$, and $dx^3 \underset{3}{\mathbf{e}}$. The oriented volume of these parallelepipeds is approximately

$$dV = (dx^1 \underset{1}{\mathbf{e}}) \cdot (dx^2 \underset{2}{\mathbf{e}}) \times (dx^3 \underset{3}{\mathbf{e}}) = J\, dx^1\, dx^2\, dx^3 \tag{5.245}$$

and their relative volume is approximately

$$dV_r = dx^1\, dx^2\, dx^3 \tag{5.246}$$

If we sum these values over all of the covering parallelepipeds, and take the limit as the number of parallelepipeds is increased (and the maximum value of the dx^i's tends to zero), we obtain the integrals

$$V = \iiint_D J\, dx^1\, dx^2\, dx^3 \qquad \text{(oriented volume)} \tag{5.247}$$

and

$$V_r = \iiint_D dx^1\, dx^2\, dx^3 \qquad \text{(relative volume)} \tag{5.248}$$

for the oriented volume V and the relative volume V_r of the region D. This is the procedure normally used in calculus, except that the volume element would be taken as $|J|\, dx^1\, dx^2\, dx^3$ to avoid the possibility of a negative volume, and the resulting expression is

$$\iiint_D |J|\, dx^1\, dx^2\, dx^3 \qquad \text{(nonoriented volume)} \tag{5.249}$$

Since dV in (5.245) was defined relative to a basis, it is not a scalar. Indeed, because of the factor J, it might be called a scalar density. When a scalar density is integrated over a region, as in (5.247), one *almost* obtains a scalar V: V would be a scalar but for the fact that its sign changes if we pass from a right-handed coordinate to a left-handed coordinate system (its absolute value $|V|$ is a true scalar). That is the reason J is replaced by $|J|$ in most books on advanced calculus.

If, to each coordinate system, there is an associated number L, such that $|L|$ is a scalar but L changes sign whenever we change from a right-handed system to a left-handed system (or vice versa), we say that L is a *pseudoscalar*. Oriented volume is a pseudoscalar. More generally, if f is a scalar field and D is a region in space,

$$\iiint_D f(x^1,x^2,x^3)J\, dx^1\, dx^2\, dx^3 \tag{5.250}$$

is a pseudoscalar, whereas

$$\iiint_D f(x^1,x^2,x^3)\,|J|\, dx^1\, dx^2\, dx^3 \tag{5.251}$$

is a scalar.

The fact that (5.251) is a scalar has far-reaching consequences. In another coordinate system $\bar{x}^1$, $\bar{x}^2$, $\bar{x}^3$ the integral

$$\iiint_D f(\bar{x}^1, \bar{x}^2,\bar{x}^3)\,|\bar{J}|\, d\bar{x}^1\, d\bar{x}^2\, d\bar{x}^3 \tag{5.252}$$

taken over the same domain D must have exactly the same numerical value as (5.251). In (5.252), $f(\bar{x}^1,\bar{x}^2,\bar{x}^3)$ denotes the same scalar field as $f(x^1,x^2,x^3)$ except that we have changed variables, expressing f as a function of the new variables $\bar{x}^1$, $\bar{x}^2$, and $\bar{x}^3$. Although the domain D is understood to be the same in both (5.251) and (5.252), if we actually calculate them by iterated integration the limits of integration will be different.

Note: We should actually distinguish between three different objects, a scalar field ψ and two functions f and $\bar{f}$. The two functions simply serve to describe the same scalar field ψ in the two different coordinate systems. Thus, if P is a point with coordinates (x^1,x^2,x^3) in one system and $(\bar{x}^1,\bar{x}^2,\bar{x}^3)$ in the other, we have $\psi(P) = f(x^1,x^2,x^3) = \bar{f}(\bar{x}^1,\bar{x}^2,\bar{x}^3)$. The functions f and $\bar{f}$ are really quite different. For example, if $f(x,y,z) = x^2 + y^2 + z^2$ in cartesian coordinates, the corresponding function in spherical coordinates must be written $\bar{f}(r,\phi,\theta) = r^2$ if it is to represent the same scalar field. In pure mathematics, $f(r,\phi,\theta)$ and $f(x,y,z)$ must be identical except for the replacement of x by r, y by ϕ, and z by θ, so we would have $f(r,\phi,\theta) = r^2 + \phi^2 + \theta^2$. This does not represent the same scalar field, and in fact is almost meaningless. (What can be meant by the square of an angle? As angles, $\pi = 3\pi$, but their squares π^2 and $9\pi^2$ are not equal.)

Despite this remark, it is quite common in physics and engineering to use the same symbol for completely different functions, provided they refer to the same physical quantity. For example, if f denotes electrostatic potential, a physicist or engineer might well write $f(x,y,z) = x^2 + y^2 + z^2$ and later in the same discussion write $f(r,\phi,\theta) = r^2$. For him, f means "potential" and not "function". This difference in convention makes it difficult for pure mathematicians to read research papers in physics. The elaborate notation used by some pure mathematicians to achieve great precision also makes *their* papers inaccessible to some physicists. Authors of undergraduate textbooks must strike a middle ground somewhere between the two extremes; they seldom manage to impress the extremists. It is not our duty to impress; we leave that to the people who write reviews of our books.

Let us return to the consequences of the equality of (5.251) and (5.252). Imagine for the moment that x^1, x^2, x^3 is a *cartesian* coordinate system, so that $J = 1$. Then by (5.241) $\bar{J} = J\,|\partial x/\partial \bar{x}| = \partial(x^1,x^2,x^3)/\partial(\bar{x}^1,\bar{x}^2,\bar{x}^3)$ and since (5.251) and (5.252) are equal we know that

$$\iiint_D f(x^1,x^2,x^3)\,dx^1\,dx^2\,dx^3$$

$$= \iiint_D \bar{f}(\bar{x}^1,\bar{x}^2,\bar{x}^3)\left|\frac{\partial(x^1,x^2,x^3)}{\partial(\bar{x}^1,\bar{x}^2,\bar{x}^3)}\right| d\bar{x}^1\,d\bar{x}^2\,d\bar{x}^3 \qquad (5.253)$$

Although derived by using the assumption that x^1, x^2, and x^3 are cartesian coordinates, this is a purely analytic equality that is independent of this assumption. (One might say that the integral signs have no way of knowing whether or not x^1, x^2, and x^3 denote cartesian coordinates in space.) It is valid for any two systems of curvilinear coordinates x^1, x^2, x^3 and $\bar{x}^1$, $\bar{x}^2$, $\bar{x}^3$ defined throughout D.

We see from this that the jacobian gives a measure of the local magnification factor by which the relative volume (in the vicinity of each point) must be multiplied when we pass from one coordinate system to another, in order that an integral remain unchanged. In general, $\iiint f(x^1,x^2,x^3)\,dx^1\,dx^2\,dx^3$ is not related in any simple manner to $\iiint \bar{f}(\bar{x}^1,\bar{x}^2,\bar{x}^3)\,d\bar{x}^1\,d\bar{x}^2\,d\bar{x}^3$.

Notice that we have not given a transformation law for the relative volume V_r. *If the jacobian is a constant* it is true that

$$V_r = \left|\frac{\partial(x^1,x^2,x^3)}{\partial(\bar{x}^1,\bar{x}^2,\bar{x}^3)}\right| \bar{V}_r \qquad (5.254)$$

as we see by taking f (and hence $\bar{f}$) identically equal to unity in (5.253). If the jacobian is not constant, this will be approximately true for sufficiently small regions D. For extended regions one can only make rather qualitative remarks, such as that in Exercise 11.

Example 5.17 Let x, y, z denote cartesian coordinates and ρ, θ, z cylindrical coordinates. Then

$$x = \rho\cos\theta \qquad y = \rho\sin\theta \qquad z = z \qquad (5.255)$$

and

$$\frac{\partial(x,y,z)}{\partial(r,\theta,z)} = \begin{vmatrix} \partial x/\partial\rho & \partial x/\partial\theta & \partial x/\partial z \\ \partial y/\partial\rho & \partial y/\partial\theta & \partial y/\partial z \\ \partial z/\partial\rho & \partial z/\partial\theta & \partial z/\partial z \end{vmatrix}$$

$$= \begin{vmatrix} \cos\theta & -\rho\sin\theta & 0 \\ \sin\theta & \rho\cos\theta & 0 \\ 0 & 0 & 1 \end{vmatrix} = \rho \qquad (5.256)$$

and, therefore, when we integrate a function $g(\rho,\theta,z)$ over a domain D we must use the volume element $\rho\, d\rho\, d\theta\, dz$:

$$\iiint_D g(\rho,\theta,z)\rho\, d\rho\, d\theta\, dz \tag{5.257}$$

Of course, such integrals are usually evaluated by iterated integration. For example, the volume of a right circular cylinder of radius R and altitude H is

$$\int_0^H \int_0^{2\pi} \int_0^R \rho\, d\rho\, d\theta\, dz = \pi R^2 H \tag{5.258}$$

Example 5.18 Expressions such as $dV = dx\, dy\, dz$ cannot be taken too literally. For example, if x, y, and z are given by (5.255) and we actually compute $dx\, dy\, dz$ we obtain

$$(\cos\theta\, d\rho - \rho \sin\theta\, d\theta)(\sin\theta\, d\rho + \rho\cos\theta\, d\theta)(dz) \tag{5.259}$$

which is *not* equal to $\rho\, d\rho\, d\theta\, dz$.

Students who have read Sec. 5.2 will observe that if we multiply in (5.259) by using the *wedge* product then we *do* get $\rho\, d\rho\, d\theta\, dz$.

Example 5.19 The two-dimensional analog of (5.253) is

$$\iint_S f(x^1,x^2)dx^1\, dx^2 = \iint_S \bar{f}(\bar{x}^1, \bar{x}^2) \left| \frac{\partial(x^1,x^2)}{\partial(\bar{x}^1,\bar{x}^2)} \right| d\bar{x}^1\, d\bar{x}^2 \tag{5.260}$$

If this is applied to polar coordinates in the plane we obtain the well-known expression

$$\iint_S f(x,y)\, dx\, dy = \iint_S \bar{f}(r,\theta) r\, dr\, d\theta \tag{5.261}$$

since the jacobian $\partial(x,y)/\partial(r,\theta)$ is equal to r.

In elementary books in which jacobians are not introduced this is obtained geometrically, by drawing an "itty bitty" element of area whose sides are coordinate curves. One side is straight and has length dr, the other side is curved (a circular arc) with length $r\, d\theta$. Ergo: the element of area is $r\, dr\, d\theta$ in polar coordinates.

Some of the shenanigans earlier in this book were intended to avoid lengthy digressions to discuss jacobians. An example was the *area cosine principle.* It is instructive to review this principle from the viewpoint of jacobians. The purpose of the discussion accompanying Figs. 4.16 and 4.17 was to show that the *local area magnification factor*, when a surface is projected onto a plane, is $\cos\theta$, where θ is the angle between the surface and the plane. Since $\cos\theta$ never exceeds unity, the term *reduction factor* might seem more appropriate, but it is not considered to be good mathematical usage. The angle θ is defined to be the angle between a normal to the plane and the normal $\mathbf{n}$ to the surface. Since $\mathbf{n}$ varies from point to point on the surface, the angle θ and hence $\cos\theta$ varies from point to point, which is the reason for the word "local".

By analogy with the three-dimensional case, we immediately suspect that $\cos\theta$ is a jacobian. This is true, and to fix ideas let us make further use of Fig. 4.14. In that figure we see a surface that is projected on the xy plane. The angle between the surface and the plane is denoted γ.

For simplicity, let us suppose that the surface is equipped with *orthogonal* coordinates u and v, and that both u and v measure *arc length* along any coordinate curve. (This is not required in the discussion there.) As a consequence, the element of area on the surface is $du\,dv$. In greater detail: since u and v measure arc length, both $\partial\mathbf{R}/\partial u$ and $\partial\mathbf{R}/\partial v$ are unit vectors, and since the coordinates are orthogonal, these vectors are perpendicular and the unit normal to the surface is

$$\mathbf{n} = \frac{\partial\mathbf{R}}{\partial u} \times \frac{\partial\mathbf{R}}{\partial v} \tag{5.262}$$

Now we compute $\cos\gamma$.

$$\cos\gamma = \mathbf{k}\cdot\mathbf{n} = \mathbf{k}\cdot\frac{\partial\mathbf{R}}{du}\times\frac{\partial\mathbf{R}}{dv}$$

$$= \begin{vmatrix} 0 & 0 & 1 \\ \dfrac{\partial x}{\partial u} & \dfrac{\partial y}{\partial u} & \dfrac{\partial z}{\partial u} \\ \dfrac{\partial x}{\partial v} & \dfrac{\partial y}{\partial v} & \dfrac{\partial z}{\partial v} \end{vmatrix} = \frac{\partial(x,y)}{\partial(u,v)} \tag{5.263}$$

This shows that $\cos\gamma$ is in fact a jacobian.

In Sec. 4.6 we were actually concerned with integrals on the surface that we wished to express as integrals in the xy plane, so the relevant formula is

$$\iint_S f(u,v)\,du\,dv = \iint_S \bar{f}(x,y)\left|\frac{\partial(u,v)}{\partial(x,y)}\right| dx\,dy \tag{5.264}$$

and the relevant jacobian is

$$\frac{\partial(u,v)}{\partial(x,y)} = \left(\frac{\partial(x,y)}{\partial(u,v)}\right)^{-1} = \frac{1}{\cos\gamma} \tag{5.265}$$

The verification of (5.265) is left as an exercise.

Equation (5.264) is a purely analytical expression that is valid even if the coordinates u, v are *not* orthogonal and do *not* measure arc length. However, if u and v are general coordinates on the surface S, the element of area on the surface is not $du\,dv$ and the left side of (5.264) does not represent $\iint_S f(u,v)\,dS$.

In connection with Eq. (5.253) we made the quaint remark that the integral sign knows nothing about the geometrical meaning of the variables in the integrand. A similar remark can be made about the geometrical interpretation of the region over which we are integrating. This is well illustrated in the two-dimensional case by Fig. 4.14, where we are integrating over a surface S. Let the projection of this surface on the xy plane be denoted S'. Ask the question: Should the S on the right side of (5.264) have been replaced by S'?

The answer is, that it really makes no difference. As written, (5.264) suggests that we are considering u and v to be functions of x and y, so that x and y now provide a coordinate system on the surface S. We are, so to speak, lifting the xy coordinates in the xy plane up to the surface S, and on this surface we are integrating a function $\bar{f}(x,y) = f(u(x,y), v(x,y))$. If we wrote the right side of (5.264) as $\iint_{S'} \bar{f}(x,y) \left|\frac{\partial(u,v)}{\partial(x,y)}\right| dx\, dy$ we would have an alternative viewpoint, that we are "lowering" a function f that is defined on the surface S to obtain a function $\bar{f}$ that is defined for points in S' and integrating over S'. In either case we need the jacobian as a factor in the integrand in order to match the value of the left side of (5.264). When it comes to computing the integral, it makes no whit of difference whether we use one interpretation or the other.

Example 5.20 This example concerns fluid flow. We are given a fixed velocity field $\mathbf{F}$, assumed independent of the time. At time $t = 0$ an identifiable portion of the mass of the fluid is contained within a domain D. A particle of fluid that is within D at time $t = 0$ may not be within D at a later time t, since the particles are moving. Let x^1, x^2, x^3 be a cartesian coordinate system and relative to this coordinate system let $\bar{x}^k = \bar{x}^k(x^1,x^2,x^3,t)$ be the kth coordinate at time t of a particle whose coordinates at time $t = 0$ were (x^1,x^2,x^3). (We can also regard $\bar{x}^1$, $\bar{x}^2$, $\bar{x}^3$ as a new coordinate system, defined in the domain D, but varying with the time t.)

The volume of D is simply

$$V_0 = \iiint_D dx^1\, dx^2\, dx^3 \tag{5.266}$$

and this is the volume occupied by the portion of fluid at time $t = 0$. At a later time t, the same portion of fluid occupies some domain $\bar{D}$ whose volume is

$$V(t) = \iiint_{\bar{D}} d\bar{x}^1\, d\bar{x}^2\, d\bar{x}^3 \tag{5.267}$$

which is a simple expression since we are using cartesian coordinates. However, if we consider the $\bar{x}^k$ as a new coordinate system defined throughout D, we can no longer regard them as cartesian coordinates. (Compare the situation when the coordinate system x,y is lifted from the xy plane to a surface S. As a coordinate system defined on S, it need not be orthogonal.)

On changing variables in (5.267) we have

$$V(t) = \iiint_D \left|\frac{\partial(\bar{x}^1,\bar{x}^2,\bar{x}^3)}{\partial(x^1,x^2,x^3)}\right| dx^1\, dx^2\, dx^3 \tag{5.268}$$

where we now regard $\bar{x}^1, \bar{x}^2, \bar{x}^3$ as a system of curvilinear coordinates defined throughout D, rather than a cartesian coordinate system defined in $\bar{D}$. Since x^1, x^2, x^3 is a cartesian coordinate system in D for which $J = 1$, we have

$$\frac{1}{\bar{J}} = \frac{\partial(\bar{x}^1,\bar{x}^2,\bar{x}^3)}{\partial(x^1,x^2,x^3)} \tag{5.269}$$

since, by (5.241)

$$\bar{J} = \frac{\partial(x^1,x^2,x^3)}{\partial(\bar{x}^1,\bar{x}^2,\bar{x}^3)} \tag{5.270}$$

Since the coordinates $\bar{x}^k$ vary with time t, $1/\bar{J}$ depends on t. Since $\bar{J} = J = 1$ at time $t = 0$, and we assume $\bar{J}$ is never equal to zero, both $\bar{J}$ and $1/\bar{J}$ are always positive, so we can ignore the absolute value signs in (5.268) and write

$$V(t) = \iiint_D \bar{J}^{-1}\, dx^1\, dx^2\, dx^3 \tag{5.271}$$

The time rate of change of V is

$$\begin{aligned} \frac{dV}{dt} &= \int\int\int_D \frac{d}{dt}(\bar{J}^{-1})\, dx^1\, dx^2\, dx^3 \\ &= \int\int\int_D -\frac{1}{\bar{J}^2}\frac{d\bar{J}}{dt}\, dx^1\, dx^2\, dx^3 \end{aligned} \tag{5.272}$$

At time $t = 0$ this is

$$V'(0) = -\iiint_D \bar{J}'(0)\, dx^1\, dx^2\, dx^3 \tag{5.273}$$

We wish to calculate the value of

$$\lim_{V\to 0} \frac{1}{V}\frac{dV}{dt} \tag{5.274}$$

at time $t = 0$. If D is a sufficiently small domain, so that $\bar{J}'(t)$ at any fixed time t is approximately constant throughout D, (5.273) is approximately equal to $-\bar{J}'(0)V(0)$ so that

$$\lim_{V\to 0} \frac{1}{V}\frac{dV}{dt} = -\bar{J}'(0) \tag{5.275}$$

at time $t = 0$.

At any instant t we have

$$\bar{J} = \underset{1}{\mathbf{f}} \cdot \underset{2}{\mathbf{f}} \times \underset{3}{\mathbf{f}} \tag{5.276}$$

and therefore

$$\frac{d\bar{J}}{dt} = \left(\frac{d}{dt}\underset{1}{(\mathbf{f})}\right) \cdot \underset{2}{\mathbf{f}} \times \underset{3}{\mathbf{f}} + \underset{1}{\mathbf{f}} \cdot \left(\frac{d}{dt}\underset{2}{(\mathbf{f})}\right) \times \underset{3}{\mathbf{f}} + \underset{1}{\mathbf{f}} \cdot \underset{2}{\mathbf{f}} \times \left(\frac{d}{dt}\underset{3}{(\mathbf{f})}\right) \tag{5.277}$$

Just as $\bar{x}^1, \bar{x}^2, \bar{x}^3$ can be regarded as functions of x^1, x^2, x^3 and the time t, so also can x^1, x^2, x^3 be regarded as functions of $\bar{x}^1, \bar{x}^2, \bar{x}^3$, and t. Then the position vector $\mathbf{R} = x^1\underset{1}{\mathbf{e}} + x^2\underset{2}{\mathbf{e}} + x^3\mathbf{e}$ can be considered to be a vector-valued function of

$\bar{x}^1, \bar{x}^2, \bar{x}^3$, and t. (Keep in mind that the vectors $\underset{1}{\mathbf{e}}, \underset{2}{\mathbf{e}}$, and $\underset{3}{\mathbf{e}}$ are constants, they are our old friends **i**, **j**, and **k**.) By definition we have

$$\frac{\partial \mathbf{R}}{\partial \bar{x}^k} = \underset{k}{\mathbf{f}} \tag{5.278}$$

We also have

$$\frac{\partial \mathbf{R}}{\partial t} = -\mathbf{F} \tag{5.279}$$

The reason for the minus sign in (5.279) is that x^k gives the kth coordinate at time $-t$ of a particle whose position at time $t = 0$ is $(\bar{x}^1, \bar{x}^2, \bar{x}^3)$, so that as t increases, $R = x^1\underset{1}{\mathbf{e}} + x^2\underset{2}{\mathbf{e}} + x^3\underset{3}{\mathbf{e}}$ is actually moving along a streamline in a direction *opposite* to the flow of the particles, for any fixed $\bar{x}^1, \bar{x}^2, \bar{x}^3$.

Now we can evaluate (5.277). First we observe that the time derivatives in (5.277) are actually partial derivatives, since $\underset{1}{\mathbf{f}}, \underset{2}{\mathbf{f}}$, and $\underset{3}{\mathbf{f}}$ vary with position in space as well as with the time t. By (5.278) and (5.279),

$$\frac{\partial}{\partial t}(\underset{k}{\mathbf{f}}) = \frac{\partial}{\partial t}\left(\frac{\partial \mathbf{R}}{\partial \bar{x}^k}\right) = \frac{\partial^2 \mathbf{R}}{\partial t \partial \bar{x}^k} = \frac{\partial^2 \mathbf{R}}{\partial \bar{x}^k \partial t} = -\frac{\partial \mathbf{F}}{\partial \bar{x}^k} \tag{5.280}$$

At time $t = 0$, $\bar{x}^k$ equals x^k, and the vectors $\underset{1}{\mathbf{f}}, \underset{2}{\mathbf{f}}$, and $\underset{3}{\mathbf{f}}$ are equal to $\underset{1}{\mathbf{e}}, \underset{2}{\mathbf{e}}$, and $\underset{3}{\mathbf{e}}$, respectively. So we have, substituting into (5.277),

$$\begin{aligned} \bar{J}'(0) &= -\frac{\partial \mathbf{F}}{\partial x^1} \cdot \underset{2}{\mathbf{e}} \times \underset{3}{\mathbf{e}} - \frac{\partial \mathbf{F}}{\partial x^2} \cdot \underset{3}{\mathbf{e}} \times \underset{1}{\mathbf{e}} - \frac{\partial \mathbf{F}}{\partial x^3} \cdot \underset{1}{\mathbf{e}} \times \underset{2}{\mathbf{e}} \\ &= -\frac{\partial F^1}{\partial x^1} - \frac{\partial F^2}{\partial x^2} - \frac{\partial F^3}{\partial x^3} = -\operatorname{div} \mathbf{F} \end{aligned} \tag{5.281}$$

and (5.275) becomes

$$\lim_{V \to 0} \frac{1}{V}\frac{dV}{dt} = \operatorname{div} \mathbf{F} \tag{5.282}$$

at time $t = 0$.

(Recall Exercise 11, Sec. 3.3.)

EXERCISES

1. (a) Derive (5.227) by imitating the derivation of (5.226).
   (b) By using the chain rule for partial derivatives, give a direct proof that (5.227) is the matrix inverse of (5.226).
2. Just to be sure you understand the derivation of (5.230), derive the transformation laws for the covariant components ϕ_{ijk} of a tensor field of rank three.
3. Suppose that **F** is a constant vector field, i.e, **F** does not vary from point to point in space. Is it necessarily true that the components F_r will be constants?

4. (a) Give an example of a vector field **F** with the property that the numbers $\psi_{ij} = \partial F_i/\partial x^j$ are zero in one coordinate system, but not zero in all coordinate systems.
   (b) Hence, show that these numbers cannot possibly be the components of a tensor.
5. Show that, if the tensor T is defined by (5.233), $T(\mathbf{u},\mathbf{v})$ is related to the circulation of **F**.
6. Show that, if ϕ and ψ are tensors of rank two, and $\phi_{ij} = \psi_{ij}(i,j = 1,2,3)$ in one coordinate system, then $\phi_{ij} = \psi_{ij}$ in every coordinate system.
7. Show that, if $\phi^i_{.j} = \psi_j^{\ i}$, then $\phi(\mathbf{u},\mathbf{v}) = \psi(\mathbf{v},\mathbf{u})$ for any pair of vector fields **u** and **v**.
8. Show that, if ϕ is an alternating tensor of rank three, $\phi_{ijk} = K\varepsilon_{ijk}$ where K is a scalar density. [*Hint*: Imitate (5.240).]
9. Show that, if ϕ is an alternating tensor of rank three, $\phi^{ijk} = \phi_{ijk}/J^2$.
10. Show that $1/J$ is a relative scalar of weight -1.
11. With V_r defined as in (5.248), show that $V_r > \bar{V}_r$ if

$$\frac{\partial(x^1,x^2,x^3)}{\partial(\bar{x}^1,\bar{x}^2,\bar{x}^3)} > 1$$

12. By computing a suitable jacobian, find the element of volume in spherical coordinates.
13. Show that

$$\frac{\partial(u,v)}{\partial(x,y)} = \left(\frac{\partial(x,y)}{\partial(u,v)}\right)^{-1}$$

14. Using the notation of Example 5.20 in the text, what is $\partial\mathbf{R}/\partial t$ if $\mathbf{R} = \bar{x}^1\underset{1}{\mathbf{e}} + \bar{x}^2\underset{2}{\mathbf{e}} + \bar{x}^3\underset{3}{\mathbf{e}}$?
15. Show that, if div **F** is a constant, and $V(t)$ is defined by (5.268), $V(t) = V(0)$ $e^{(\text{div}\,\mathbf{F}\,t)}$.

5.11 HISTORICAL NOTES

It is not really possible to appreciate the history of vector analysis without knowing something of the history of mathematics in general, and this is too broad a topic for us to discuss here. We shall confine our remarks to certain specific topics, and let the interested reader pursue the subject further elsewhere.

The word "vector" comes from a Latin word meaning "to carry" and is still sometimes used to mean "that which carries". For example, one says "the mosquito is the vector of malaria." The word entered mathematics via astronomy, where it was originally used with a somewhat different meaning. The notion of vector addition was arrived at independently by Möbius and others in the early part of the nineteenth century, thus giving rise to vector *algebra.* Vector *analysis* is somewhat more recent. For example, the notion of *curl* apparently was introduced by J. C. Maxwell in his *Treatise on Electricity and Magnetism* (1873).

The notation used in this book is essentially due to J. Willard Gibbs, whose book on vector analysis was printed privately in the early 1880's, and Oliver Heaviside, whose book on *Electromagnetic Theory* (1893) makes hilarious reading because of his jibes at mathematicians.

One of the most interesting events in the history of vector analysis is the controversy that once existed between exponents of vector analysis and a few other mathematicians who felt that *quaternions* were more suitable for solving problems in physics. Before proceeding, let us briefly discuss the algebra of quarternions. Quarternions are formally similar to complex numbers, so let us first consider the background of the idea of a complex number.

As long ago as 1545 a mathematician (Cardan) "solved" a problem in algebra that has no real solutions. The problem is to find two numbers whose sum is 10 and whose product is 40. Cardan gave a formal solution, involving the square root of a negative number, and verified by substitution that these "fictitious numbers" have the required properties. As early as 1629, Girard suggested that such "impossible solutions" should be considered for three reasons: one can give a general rule for finding roots of certain equations, these solutions supply the lack of other solutions, and they may in any event have their own usefulness. In 1673, Wallis pointed out that numbers such as $\sqrt{-1}$ should be just as legitimate in mathematics as negative numbers. One cannot have $\sqrt{-1}$ eggs in a basket, but then neither can one have -7 eggs in a basket. Wallis came very close to giving the usual geometrical interpretation of complex numbers. It remained for a Norwegian surveyor Wessel to do this in 1797. (Argand did it independently in 1806, which is why the term Argand diagram is used. Wessel published his work in an obscure journal and did not receive credit during his lifetime.)

It was not until 1831 that Gauss put complex numbers on a respectable basis. Since some readers of this book may have learned complex numbers from a viewpoint that predates 1831, let us briefly review complex numbers. A complex number is an ordered pair (x,y) of real numbers. They are added and multiplied by (real) scalars as if they were row matrices. However, the product $(x_1,y_1)(x_2,y_2)$ of two row matrices is not defined in matrix algebra. We define the product of two complex numbers according to

$$(x_1,y_1)(x_2,y_2) = (x_1x_2 - y_1y_2, x_1y_2 + x_2y_1) \tag{5.283}$$

If we identify (1,0) with the real number 1, and let i denote (0,1), then

$$(x,y) = (x,0) + (0,y) = x(1,0) + y(0,1) = x + yi$$

which is the usual notation for a complex number (except for electrical engineers, who use j instead of i). Moreover, we have $i^2 = (0,1)(0,1) = (-1,0) = -1$, so it is now possible to square a number and obtain a negative number.

Now we recall that multiplication by $\cos\theta + i\sin\theta$ has the effect of rotating a complex number through an angle θ. Hence, rotations in a plane can be obtained by identifying the plane with the Argand diagram and the rotation with the operation of multiplying by $\cos\theta + i\sin\theta$. This suggested to W. R. Hamilton that rotations in space might be similarly obtained, if there were some way to multiply *triples* of numbers to obtain a system of "hypercomplex" numbers that would provide a three-dimensional analog of the complex number system. Apparently this problem troubled him for a period of fifteen years. This is not too surprising when one considers that, up to the time of Hamilton, it was generally assumed that the commutative law $xy = yx$ was a necessary condition for the consistency of the rules of algebra. Hamilton is credited with the realization that this is not the case; actually, Gauss had the same idea earlier but did not publish his work.

The realization that a noncommutative algebra is needed is still not enough. Hamilton was still trying to do the impossible. It was proved later, by Frobenius in 1878, that it is impossible to multiply ordered triples in such a manner that the resulting algebraic system will have all of the properties Hamilton desired. Evidently Hamilton suspected this himself. It was on a famous day, October 16, 1843, when he was out walking with his wife, that Hamilton, in a great flash of insight, conceived of the quaternions. It is said that he carved the fundamental formulas of this new algebra in the stone of Brougham Bridge, on which he happened to be at the moment. He immediately recognized the importance of his discovery (some might say invention) and devoted the remainder of his life to quaternions.

At first glance, a quaternion looks like a cross between a complex number and a vector. The usual form for writing quaternion is

$$x = x_0 + x_1 i + x_2 j + x_3 k \tag{5.284}$$

Quaternions are added and multiplied by real numbers in the obvious manner. The product of two quaternions is defined by formally multiplying them out. according to the usual rules of algebra (except that we must be careful to preserve the order) and then simplifying the resulting expression by using the following rules:

$$i^2 = -1 \qquad j^2 = -1 \qquad k^2 = -1 \tag{5.285}$$

$$ij = k \qquad jk = i \qquad ki = j \tag{5.286}$$

$$ji = -k \qquad kj = -i \qquad ik = -j \tag{5.287}$$

An example will illustrate the procedure. If, for instance, $x = 3 - i + 2j + k$ and $y = 3j - 2k$, we have

$$\begin{aligned} xy &= (3 - i + 2j + k)(3j - 2k) \\ &= 9j - 6k - 3ij + 2ik + 6j^2 - 4jk + 3kj - 2k^2 \\ &= 9j - 6k - 3k - 2j - 6 - 4i - 3i + 2 \\ &= -4 - 7i + 7j - 9k \end{aligned}$$

It can be shown that the quaternions constitute a division algebra. That is, to each quaternion $x \neq 0$, there is a quaternion x^{-1} such that $xx^{-1} = x^{-1}x = 1$. We shall not digress to show how an inverse is computed. It is important to note, however, that we cannot write y/x, since this would be ambiguous. We must write either $x^{-1}y$ or yx^{-1} and, since multiplication of quaternions is not commutative, these two expressions may not be equal.

The *real part* of a quaternion $x_0 + x_1 i + x_2 j + x_3 k$ is the number x_0. If the real part of a quaternion is zero, the quaternion is called a *pure quaternion*. In applying quaternions to problems in physics or geometry, pure quaternions are identified with ordinary vectors in three-dimensional space, as the notation suggests.

If x and y are pure quaternions, the real part of xy turns out to be the negative of the scalar product $x \cdot y$ (computed by the usual formula), and the pure quaternionic part represents the vector product $x \times y$. Thus it is possible to do with quaternions many of the things one ordinarily does in vector analysis by using scalar and vector products.

Although the quaternions comprise a four-dimensional division algebra, rather than a three-dimensional one, it turned out that quaternions fulfilled the needs envisaged by Hamilton. It is possible to represent rotations by the use of quaternions, although not so simply as one might have wished, and in general there is a certain awkwardness in the use of quaternions. After working for ten years, Hamilton published his *Lectures on Quaternions* (1853); his *Elements of Quaternions* appeared in 1866, the year after his death. Incidentally, the earliest use of the word *vector* (in the mathematical sense), according to the Oxford dictionary, is in this work.

Hamilton had one devoted disciple, P. G. Tait, who mastered all the tricks of quaternions, and devoted himself to the cause of convincing one and all that quaternions were the ultimate tool for geometers and physicists. There were others who disagreed.

At about the same time that Hamilton made his remarkable discovery, H. G. Grassmann published a work called the *Ausdehnungslehre*, or the *Theory of Extension*. In this remarkable book, both matrix theory and tensor algebra are developed implicitly, but because he filled the book with philosophical abstractions, and because of its difficulty, the book was essentially ignored by mathematicians. A second edition was published in 1862, but the work was not much appreciated until the twentieth century.

The vector analysis of Gibbs and Heaviside, and the various generalities in this chapter, are more closely related to the *Ausdehnungslehre* than to anything Hamilton did. Grassmann introduced various types of "products" of vectors, and set things up for Gibbs to invent dyadics (not discussed in this book) and discussed linear transformations in general. The notion of a linear associative algebra was developed by Benjamin Peirce in the 1860's. The only other name we shall mention is that of Cayley, who was eminent for (among other things) conceiving of n-dimensional space (as did Grassmann) and who published a *Memoir on the Theory of Matrices* in 1858.

A delightful controversy took place between Gibbs and Tait concerning the merits of the use of quaternions in solving problems in geometry and physics. There is a certain beauty and mathematical elegance in the quaternions, but they are not very well adapted to practical use. Tait viewed vector analysis as a "hermaphroditic monster" and did not hesitate to express this view in print. The replies of Gibbs can be found in his collected works, available in any library, and they are both entertaining and instructive to read. By the beginning of the twentieth century, vector analysis was well established, and it was amply demonstrated that Hamilton and Tait were overly optimistic in their thought that quaternions would be as revolutionary to mathematics as was the invention of calculus. The revolutionary idea contributed by Hamilton was simply that it is possible to have a self-consistent algebra in which multiplication is not commutative.

EXERCISES

1. Show that, if u and v are pure quaternions,

$$uv = -\mathbf{u} \cdot \mathbf{v} + \mathbf{u} \times \mathbf{v} \tag{5.288}$$

2. Show that if the vectors **u** and **v** are identified with pure quarternions,

$$\mathbf{u} \cdot \mathbf{v} = -\frac{uv + vu}{2} \tag{5.289}$$

and

$$\mathbf{u} \times \mathbf{v} = \frac{uv - vu}{2} \tag{5.290}$$

3. (a) Let **n** denote a unit vector that is perpendicular to a plane P. Thinking of P as a mirror, show that the reflected image of a vector **v** in the mirror is given by

$$\mathbf{v}' = \mathbf{v} - 2(\mathbf{v} \cdot \mathbf{n})\mathbf{n} \tag{5.291}$$

(b) Show that this can be written in quaternionic form as

$$v' = nvn \tag{5.292}$$

4. Let P and P' be two planes intersecting in a line L and let $\theta/2$ be the angle between the two planes. Choose unit normals **n** and **n′** respectively so that the angle between **n** and **n′** is $\theta/2$ and let **u** be a unit vector along L so chosen that $\mathbf{n} \times \mathbf{n}' = \sin(\theta/2)\,\mathbf{u}$.

(a) Letting **v′** denote the reflected image of **v** in P and **v″** denote the reflected image of **v′** in P', show that **v″** is the vector obtained by rotating **v** through an angle θ about the axis L. (The positive sense of rotation is related to the direction of **u** by the right-hand rule.)

(b) Derive the quaternionic relation

$$v'' = n'nvnn' \tag{5.293}$$

(c) Writing (5.293) in the form $v'' = (-n'n)v(-nn')$ derive the relation

$$v'' = (\cos \tfrac{1}{2}\theta + \sin \tfrac{1}{2}\theta\, u)v(\cos \tfrac{1}{2}\theta - \sin \tfrac{1}{2}\theta\, u) \tag{5.294}$$

5. If z is a complex number, the exponential e^z is defined by the infinite series

$$e^z = \sum_{n=0}^{\infty} \frac{z^n}{n!} \tag{5.295}$$

Using the same expression to define e^z when z is a quaternion, let $z = \phi u$ where u is a pure quaternion representing a unit vector and ϕ is an angle, and derive

$$e^{\phi u} = -\cos \phi + \sin \phi\, u \tag{5.296}$$

6. Rewrite (5.294) in exponential notation. (This is the formula for rotations that Hamilton was seeking when he developed the algebra of quaternions.)

Review Problems

1. Vectors from the origin O to four points A, B, C, D are given as follows:

$$\mathbf{A} = 2\mathbf{i} \qquad \mathbf{B} = 3\mathbf{j} \qquad \mathbf{C} = 4\mathbf{k} \qquad \mathbf{D} = \mathbf{i} + \mathbf{j} + 2\mathbf{k}$$

   (a) Find the length of the perpendicular drawn from A to the plane BCD.
   (b) Find the length of the common perpendicular to the lines AB and CD.
   (c) Find a vector parallel to this perpendicular.
2. The vertices of a regular tetrahedron are $OABC$. Prove that the vector $OA + OB + OC$ is perpendicular to the plane ABC.
3. Find the angle which the plane OAB makes with the z axis, if A is the point (1,3,2) and B is (2,1,1).
4. Given the points $O(0,0,0)$, $A(1,2,3)$, $B(0,-1,1)$, $C(2,0,2)$.
   (a) Find a vector perpendicular to the plane OAB.
   (b) Find the distance from C to the plane OAB.
5. Determine the shortest distance from the point (3,4,5) to the line through the origin parallel to the vector $2\mathbf{i} - \mathbf{j} + 2\mathbf{k}$.
6. Write the scalar equations of the line parallel to the intersection of the planes $3x + y + z = 5$, $x - 2y + 3z = 1$ and passing through the point (4,2,1).
7. Given the points $P_1(2,-1,4)$, $P_2(-1,0,3)$, $P_3(4,3,1)$, and $P_4(3,-5,0)$, determine
   (a) the volume of the tetrahedron $P_1P_2P_3P_4$;
   (b) the equation of the plane containing the points P_1, P_2, and P_3;
   (c) the cosine of the angle between the line segments P_1P_2 and P_1P_3.

8. Write an expression for a vector 5 units long, parallel to the plane $3x + 4y + 5z = 10$ and perpendicular to the vector $\mathbf{i} + 2\mathbf{j} + 2\mathbf{k}$.
9. Let **A**, **B**, **C**, and **D** be position vectors of the points $A(1,3,-2)$, $B(3,5,-3)$, $C(-5,9,-5)$, and $D(4,-1,10)$, respectively. Find
   (a) $|\mathbf{A} - \mathbf{D}|$
   (b) $\mathbf{A} \times \mathbf{B}$
   (c) $(\mathbf{A} - \mathbf{C}) \cdot (\mathbf{A} - \mathbf{B})$
   (d) $\mathbf{A} \cdot \mathbf{B} \times \mathbf{C}$.
10. Given the four points specified in Exercise 9, determine
    (a) the area of the triangle OAB;
    (b) the volume of the tetrahedron $OABC$;
    (c) the angle CAB.
11. By vector methods, prove that the angle subtended at the circumference by a diameter of a circle is a right angle.
12. Let PQR be a triangle. By vector methods, show there exists a triangle whose sides are parallel and equal in length to the medians of PQR.
13. (a) How many unit vectors make equal angles with the vectors $\mathbf{a} = 2\mathbf{i} + 2\mathbf{j} + \mathbf{k}$ and $\mathbf{b} = 3\mathbf{i} + 4\mathbf{k}$?
    (b) Find the unit vector **u** that bisects the angle between **a** and **b**.
14. Write $(\mathbf{u} \times \mathbf{v}) \cdot (\mathbf{u} \times \mathbf{v})$ as a determinant involving only scalar products.
15. If **u**, **v**, and **w** are vectors, is it necessarily true that $(\mathbf{u} \times \mathbf{v}) \times \mathbf{w} = \mathbf{u} \times (\mathbf{v} \times \mathbf{w})$?
16. Given that **u**, **v**, and **w** are nonzero vectors having the same magnitude and $(\mathbf{u} \times \mathbf{v}) \times \mathbf{w} = \mathbf{u} \times (\mathbf{v} \times \mathbf{w})$, what can you say about **u**, **v**, and **w**?
17. Find the distance from the point $A(3,7,2)$ to the plane passing through $B(5,10,8)$ that is perpendicular to the line AB.
18. Find the distance from the origin to the plane passing through (3,2,6) that is perpendicular to the z axis.
19. Find the distance from the origin to the plane passing through (3,4,2) that is perpendicular to the line joining (1,2,3) and (3,5,9).
20. A plane has intercepts (4,0,0), (0,6,0), and (0,0,12). Find the equations of another plane through $(6,-2,4)$ that is parallel to this plane.
21. Show that the curve $x = t$, $y = 2t^2$, $z = t^3$ intersects the plane $x + 8y + 12z = 162$ at right angles.
22. Find the point on the sphere $x^2 + y^2 + z^2 = 84$ that is nearest the plane $x + 2y + 4z = 77$.
23. Find the point on the ellipsoid $x^2 + 2y^2 + 3z^2 = 6$ that is nearest to the plane $x + 2y + 3z = 8$.
24. By vector methods, find the point on the curve $x = t$, $y = t^2$, $z = 2$ at which the temperature $\phi(x,y,z) = x^2 - 6x + y^2$ takes its minimum value.
25. What point on the curve $x = t$, $y = t^2$, $z = 2$ is closest to the surface $x^2 - 6x + y^2 + 7 = 0$?

26. At what angle does the curve $x = t$, $y = 2t - t^2$, $z = 2t^4$ intersect the surface $x^2 + y^3 + 3z^2 = 14$ at the point (1,1,2)?
27. The velocity field of a fluid is described by Fig. 3.6. A quantity of fluid occupies a spherical region centered at P at time $t = 0$. Describe the region occupied by the same particles a short time thereafter. Will the region be spherical?
28. Let $\mathbf{R} = R_1\mathbf{i} + R_2\mathbf{j} + R_3\mathbf{k}$ be a vector function of the time t, and let

$$\left.\frac{d\mathbf{R}}{dt}\right|_m = \frac{dR_1}{dt}\mathbf{i} + \frac{dR_2}{dt}\mathbf{j} + \frac{dR_3}{dt}\mathbf{k}$$

be the time rate of change of $\mathbf{R}$ computed on the assumption that $\mathbf{i}$, $\mathbf{j}$, and $\mathbf{k}$ do not vary with time. Now suppose that $\mathbf{i}$, $\mathbf{j}$, and $\mathbf{k}$ do vary with the time t, but only as a rigid system (they remain mutually perpendicular unit vectors). Show that, at any instant of time t, there exists a vector $\boldsymbol{\omega}$ such that the actual rate of change of R is

$$\frac{d\mathbf{R}}{dt} = \left.\frac{d\mathbf{R}}{dt}\right|_m + \boldsymbol{\omega} \times \mathbf{R}$$

(The letter m denotes *moving*; $(d\mathbf{R}/dt)|_m$ is the rate of change relative to the "moving frame" $\mathbf{i}$, $\mathbf{j}$, $\mathbf{k}$.)
29. If $\mathbf{R}_1$ denotes the position vector of a point P relative to an origin 0_1 in the xy plane and $\mathbf{R}_2$ denotes the position vector of the same point relative to another origin 0_2, then $|\mathbf{R}_1| + |\mathbf{R}_2| =$ constant is the equation of an ellipse with foci 0_1 and 0_2. Use this observation to prove that lines 0_1P and 0_2P make equal angles with the tangent to the ellipse at P. [*Hint*: $\mathbf{grad}(|\mathbf{R}_1| + |\mathbf{R}_2|)$ is normal to the ellipse.]
30. Find the angle between the surfaces $z = x^2 + y^2$ and $x^2 + y^2 + (z-3)^2 = 9$ at the point $(2, -1, 5)$.
31. Given $f(x,y,z) = 2x^2 + y$ and $\mathbf{R} = x\mathbf{i} + y\mathbf{j} + z\mathbf{k}$, find (a) ∇f, (b) $\nabla \cdot \mathbf{R}$, (c) $\nabla^2 f$, (d) $\nabla \times (f\mathbf{R})$.
32. If $\mathbf{F} = x^2\mathbf{i} + xy\mathbf{j} + z\mathbf{k}$, evaluate each of the following at the point $(-1,2,3)$: (a) $\nabla^2\mathbf{F}$, (b) $\nabla \times \mathbf{F}$, (c) $\nabla \cdot \mathbf{F}$.
33. Evaluate $\nabla^2[(\mathbf{i} + \mathbf{j} + \mathbf{k}) \times \nabla(\mathbf{R} \cdot \mathbf{R})^2]$, where $\mathbf{R} = x\mathbf{i} + y\mathbf{j} + z\mathbf{k}$.
34. Evaluate $\nabla \ln(xyz + 5)$ at the point $(-1,2,3)$.
35. Evaluate $\mathbf{A} \cdot \nabla\mathbf{R} + \nabla(\mathbf{A} \cdot \mathbf{R}) + \mathbf{A} \cdot \nabla \times \mathbf{R}$, where $\mathbf{A}$ is a constant vector field and $\mathbf{R} = x\mathbf{i} + y\mathbf{j} + z\mathbf{k}$.
36. If $r^2 = x^2 + y^2 + z^2$, $\mathbf{R} = x\mathbf{i} + y\mathbf{j} + z\mathbf{k}$, and $\mathbf{A}$ is a constant vector field, find
    (a) $\nabla \cdot (r^2\mathbf{A})$
    (b) $\nabla \times (r^2\mathbf{A})$
    (c) $\mathbf{R} \cdot \nabla(r^2\mathbf{A})$
    (d) $\nabla(\mathbf{A} \cdot \mathbf{R})^4$
    (e) $\nabla \cdot (r\mathbf{A})$
    (f) $\mathbf{R} \cdot \nabla(\mathbf{A} \cdot \mathbf{R}\mathbf{A})$
    (g) $\nabla \cdot (\mathbf{A} \times \mathbf{R})$
    (h) $\nabla \times (\mathbf{A} \times \mathbf{R})$
    (i) $\nabla^2(\mathbf{R} \cdot \mathbf{R})$

37. Consider the potential $\phi(x,y,z) = xyz$.
   (a) Find a vector normal to the equipotential surface through the point (1,2,3).
   (b) Find $d\phi/ds$ at the same point, if s is measured in the direction of the vector $6\mathbf{i} + 3\mathbf{j} + 2\mathbf{k}$.
38. Given $\phi(x,y,z) = z^2 - x - y$, determine
   (a) an equation of the plane tangent to the surface $\phi = 2$ at the point $(-2,4,2)$;
   (b) equations of the line normal to the surface $\phi = 2$ at the point $(-2,4,2)$;
   (c) the derivative of ϕ at $(-2,4,2)$ in the direction of the vector $3\mathbf{i} - 2\mathbf{j} + 6\mathbf{k}$.
39. What angle does the vector $3\mathbf{i} + 4\mathbf{j} + 5\mathbf{k}$ make with the surface $xy - z^2 = 3$ at the point (3,4,3)?
40. If r is the distance from the origin to the point (x,y,z) and $\mathbf{A}$ is a constant vector, evaluate

$$\nabla\left(\mathbf{A} \cdot \nabla \frac{1}{r}\right) + \nabla \times \left(\mathbf{A} \times \nabla \frac{1}{r}\right)$$

41. For what value of the constant C is the vector field $\mathbf{V} = (x + 4y)\mathbf{i} + (y - 3z)\mathbf{j} + Cz\mathbf{k}$ the curl of some vector field $\mathbf{F}$?
42. Find **curl** $[f(r)\mathbf{R}]$ where $\mathbf{R} = x\mathbf{i} + y\mathbf{j} + z\mathbf{k}$, $r = |\mathbf{R}|$, and f is a differentiable function,
   (a) by direct calculation,
   (b) by geometrical interpretation.
43. Given Maxwell's equations in free space,

$$\nabla \cdot \mathbf{E} = 0 \qquad \nabla \cdot \mathbf{H} = 0 \qquad \nabla \times \mathbf{E} = -\frac{\partial \mathbf{H}}{\partial t} \qquad \nabla \times \mathbf{H} = \frac{\partial \mathbf{E}}{\partial t}$$

show that $\mathbf{E}$ and $\mathbf{H}$ both satisfy the wave equation

$$\nabla^2 \mathbf{u} = \frac{\partial^2 \mathbf{u}}{\partial t^2}$$

44. Given $\phi = \tan^{-1} x + \tan^{-1} y$ and $\psi = \dfrac{x + y}{1 - xy}$, show that $\nabla\phi \times \nabla\psi = 0$.
45. Do the preceding exercise without explicitly calculating $\nabla\phi$ or $\nabla\psi$.
46. If $\nabla\phi \times \nabla\psi = 0$ throughout space, but neither $\nabla\phi$ nor $\nabla\psi$ is zero anywhere, what can you conclude about the isotimic surfaces ϕ = constant and ψ = constant?
47. Given $w = uv$, where u and v are scalar fields, show that $\nabla w \cdot \nabla u \times \nabla v = 0$,
   (a) by direct calculation,
   (b) without calculation.
48. Generalize the result of the preceding exercise.

49. If $\mathbf{F}$ and $\mathbf{G}$ are conservative fields, is $\mathbf{F} \times \mathbf{G}$ necessarily conservative? If not, what *can* you say about $\mathbf{F} \times \mathbf{G}$?
50. Find the surface integral $\iint \mathbf{F} \cdot d\mathbf{S}$ over the surface of the cylinder $x^2 + y^2 = 9$ included in the first octant between $z = 0$ and $z = 4$, given that $\mathbf{F} = y\mathbf{i} + (x + 2)\mathbf{j} + (x^3 \sin yz)\mathbf{k}$. (By using the divergence theorem this can be reduced to a simple problem in arithmetic.)
51. By a symmetry argument, or otherwise, show that $\int (x^2 - y^2)\, ds = 0$, when the line integral is taken around a circle $x^2 + y^2 = a^2$ in the xy plane.
52. Evaluate $\iint_S (\nabla \times \mathbf{F}) \cdot d\mathbf{S}$ where $\mathbf{F} = y\mathbf{i} + (x - 2x^3 z)\mathbf{j} + xy^3\mathbf{k}$ and S is the surface of a sphere $x^2 + y^2 + z^2 = a^2$ above the xy plane.
53. Use Green's theorem to derive the formula $A = \pi ab$ for the area of an ellipse. [*Hint*: If $\mathbf{F} = \frac{1}{2}(-y\mathbf{i} + x\mathbf{j})$, $\mathbf{curl}\ \mathbf{F} = \mathbf{k}$.]
54. Evaluate $\int_{(0,0)}^{(1,2)} (15x^4 - 3x^2y^2)\, dx - 2x^3 y\, dy$ along the path $2x^4 - 6xy^3 + 23y = 0$.
55. Surface and volume integrals of vector-valued functions are defined as for numerically valued functions. Alternatively, they can be defined by simply integrating the x,y, and z components (which are numerical) separately. Show formally that $\iiint_D \nabla\phi\, dV = \iint_S \phi\mathbf{n}\, dS$ by applying the divergence theorem to $\mathbf{F} = \phi\mathbf{C}$ where $\mathbf{C}$ is a constant vector field.
56. Similarly, derive the identity

$$\iiint_D \nabla \times \mathbf{A}\, dV = \iint_S \mathbf{n} \times \mathbf{A}\, dS$$

where $\mathbf{n}$ is the outer normal to S, the boundary of D.
57. Give a vector interpretation of each of the following. The notation is that used in Sec. 4.10.

(a) $$\lim_{V \to 0} \frac{\iint_S \mathbf{n} f\, dS}{V}$$

(b) $$\lim_{V \to 0} \frac{\iint_S \mathbf{n} \times \mathbf{F}\, dS}{V}$$

58. Parabolic cylindrical coordinates (u,v,z) are defined by $x = \frac{1}{2}(u^2 - v^2)$, $y = uv$, $z = z$ where $-\infty < u < \infty$, $v \geq 0$, $-\infty < z < \infty$. In order to make use of the formulas in Sec. 4.13, it is necessary to know the scale factors h_u, h_v, and h_z. Determine these scale factors.
59. What is the element of volume in parabolic cylindrical coordinates?
60. (a) Write div $\mathbf{A}$ in parabolic cylindrical coordinates.
(b) Write Laplace's equation $\nabla^2\phi = 0$ in parabolic cylindrical coordinates.

61. Find $J = \partial(x,y,z)/\partial(u,v,w)$ and $g = |g_{ij}|$ for the coordinate system u, v, w defined by $x = v^2 + 5$, $y = v + w$, $z = u^2 - v$.

62. Let (x,y,z) and (u,v,w) be related by

$$\begin{aligned} x &= 3u - 2v - w \\ y &= u + v + 2w \\ z &= 2u - 3v - w \end{aligned}$$

(a) Find $\underset{1}{\mathbf{e}}$, $\underset{2}{\mathbf{e}}$, $\underset{3}{\mathbf{e}}$, $\overset{1}{\mathbf{e}}$, $\overset{2}{\mathbf{e}}$, and $\overset{3}{\mathbf{e}}$ for the u, v, w coordinate system.

(b) Find J and g for this coordinate system.

(c) Consider the box bounded by $x = 0$, $x = 10$, $y = 0$, $y = 5$, $z = 0$, $z = 3$. What is its volume relative to the uvw coordinates? (Keep in mind that the uvw "relative volume" of the parallelepiped determined by $\underset{1}{\mathbf{e}}$, $\underset{2}{\mathbf{e}}$, $\underset{3}{\mathbf{e}}$ is unity.)

63. Does the Kronecker index δ_i^j give the mixed components of a tensor of rank two?

64. Determine the Christoffel symbol Γ_{32}^3 for spherical coordinates $x^1 = r$, $x^2 = \theta$, $x^3 = \phi$.

65. Find the laplacian of f in cylindrical coordinates by substituting into the expression

$$\nabla^2 f = \frac{1}{\sqrt{g}} \frac{\partial}{\partial x^k} \left(\sqrt{g} g^{kj} \frac{\partial f}{\partial x^j} \right)$$

66. Is the intrinsic derivative of the velocity of a particle, with respect to the time, equal to the acceleration of the particle?

67. Express the Maxwell equation $\nabla \times \mathbf{E} = -c^{-1}\, \partial \mathbf{B}/\partial t$ in tensor form.

68. Find the moment of inertia of the region in the first octant bounded by $x^2 - y^2 = 2$, $x^2 - y^2 = 6$, $xy = 1$, $xy = 4$, $z = 1$, and $z = 5$ with respect to the z axis, assuming the density is unity. (This is a simple exercise in the use of jacobians. Let $x^2 - y^2 = 2u$, $xy = v$.)

69. As a minor project, show that if g is a scalar field whose laplacian $\nabla^2 g$ is a constant, then

$$\bar{g}(R) - g(0) = \tfrac{1}{6} R^2 \nabla^2 g$$

where $\bar{g}(R)$ denotes the mean value of g over the surface of a sphere of radius R, and $g(0)$ denotes its value at the center.

70. Use the result of Prob. 69 to show that

$$\bar{g} - g(0) = \tfrac{1}{10} R^2 \nabla^2 g$$

where $\bar{g}$ denotes the mean value of g within a sphere of radius R, $g(0)$ its value at the center, and $\nabla^2 g$ is assumed constant.

Appendix

In this appendix we prove two theorems of advanced calculus which are important to vector analysis.

THEOREM A.1 *Let $f(x,y,z)$ be a scalar function possessing continuous first partial derivatives $\partial f/\partial x$, $\partial f/\partial y$, $\partial f/\partial z$ in some domain D. Also let* **h** *be a unit vector with components (h_1,h_2,h_3). Then the directional derivative of f in the direction* **h** *exists in D and is given by*

$$\frac{df}{ds} = \frac{\partial f}{\partial x} h_1 + \frac{\partial f}{\partial y} h_2 + \frac{\partial f}{\partial z} h_3$$

Proof The directional derivative, if its exists, is given by the limit of

$$\frac{f(x + sh_1, y + sh_2, z + sh_3) - f(x,y,z)}{s} \tag{A.1}$$

as s approaches zero.

By adding and subtracting equal terms, we rewrite (A.1) as

$$\frac{f(x + sh_1, y + sh_2, z + sh_3) - f(x + sh_1, y + sh_2, z)}{s}$$

$$+ \frac{f(x + sh_1, y + sh_2, z) - f(x + sh_1, y, z)}{s}$$

$$+ \frac{f(x + sh_1, y, z) - f(x,y,z)}{s} \tag{A.2}$$

Each of the terms of (A.2) involves differences of values of f when *only one* coordinate is changed. Hence we can use the powerful tools of the ordinary calculus of one variable; in particular, the mean value theorem applies to each term (since the partial derivatives are continuous). For the first term in (A.2), we conclude that there is a number α between 0 and 1 such that

$$f(x + sh_1, y + sh_2, z + sh_3) - f(x + sh_1, y + sh_2, z) = sh_3 \frac{\partial f}{\partial z}(x + sh_1, y + sh_2, z + \alpha sh_3)$$

Analyzing the other terms similarly, we find numbers β and γ also between 0 and 1 such that the expression (A.1) is equal to

$$\frac{sh_3 \frac{\partial f}{\partial z}(x + sh_1, y + sh_2, z + \alpha sh_3)}{s} + \frac{sh_2 \frac{\partial f}{\partial y}(x + sh_1, y + \beta sh_2, z)}{s} + \frac{sh_1 \frac{\partial f}{\partial x}(x + \gamma sh_1, y, z)}{s} \qquad \text{(A.3)}$$

Now we let s approach zero. The numbers α, β, and γ are always between 0 and 1, and since the partials are continuous, we conclude that the limit exists and is given by

$$\frac{\partial f}{\partial x} h_1 + \frac{\partial f}{\partial y} h_2 + \frac{\partial f}{\partial z} h_3$$

(Q.E.D.)

In Theorem A.2 the notation is rather confusing. We advise the reader that the following symbols mean the same thing:

$$\partial^2 f/\partial y\, \partial x = \frac{\partial^2 f}{\partial y\, \partial x} = \frac{\partial}{\partial y}\left(\frac{\partial f}{\partial x}\right)$$

THEOREM A.2 *Let $f(x,y)$ be a scalar function possessing continuous first partial derivatives $\partial f/\partial x$ and $\partial f/\partial y$ in some domain D. Furthermore let the second derivative $\partial^2 f/\partial y\, \partial x$ exist and be continuous in D. Then the second derivative $\partial^2 f/\partial x\, \partial y$ also exists in D and*

$$\frac{\partial^2 f}{\partial x\, \partial y} = \frac{\partial^2 f}{\partial y\, \partial x}$$

Proof The second derivative, $\partial^2 f/\partial x\,\partial y$, if it exists, is the limit as s goes to zero of

$$\frac{\dfrac{\partial f}{\partial y}(x+s,y)-\dfrac{\partial f}{\partial y}(x,y)}{s} \tag{A.4}$$

On the other hand, the y derivatives in (A.4) can also be expressed as limits; (A.4) is equal to

$$\frac{1}{s}\left(\lim_{t\to 0}\frac{f(x+s,y+t)-f(x+s,y)}{t}-\lim_{t\to 0}\frac{f(x,y+t)-f(x,y)}{t}\right) \tag{A.5}$$

Since limits and sums are interchangeable, we can write (A.5) as

$$\lim_{t\to 0}\frac{[f(x+s,y+t)-f(x+s,y)]-[f(x,y+t)-f(x,y)]}{st} \tag{A.6}$$

The numerator in (A.6) can be regarded as the difference between the values of a function $F(u)$ evaluated at $u = x + s$ and $u = s$; this complicated function $F(u)$ is defined by

$$F(u) = f(u, y+t) - f(u,y)$$

As a function of u, F has a continuous derivative given by

$$F'(u) = \frac{\partial f}{\partial u}(u, y+t) - \frac{\partial f}{\partial u}(u,y)$$

and is thus vulnerable to the mean value theorem of one-dimensional calculus. We conclude that there is a number α between 0 and 1 such that

$$F(x+s) - F(x) = sF'(x+\alpha s)$$

Thus the expression (A.6) is equal to

$$\lim_{t\to 0}\frac{s\left(\dfrac{\partial f}{\partial x}(x+\alpha s, y+t)-\dfrac{\partial f}{\partial x}(x+\alpha s, y)\right)}{st} \tag{A.7}$$

We can now apply the mean value theorem to the function $\partial f/\partial x$ in (A.7), since only the second argument is changing; by hypothesis, $\partial f/\partial x$ has a continuous derivative with respect to its second argument, namely, $\partial^2 f/\partial y\,\partial x$! We conclude that there is a number β between 0 and 1 such that expression (A.7) is equal to

$$\lim_{t\to 0}\frac{st\dfrac{\partial^2 f}{\partial y\,\partial x}(x+\alpha s, y+\beta t)}{st} \tag{A.8}$$

Since $\partial^2 f/\partial y\,\partial x$ is continuous, the expression (A.8) equals

$$\frac{\partial^2 f}{\partial y\,\partial x}(x + \alpha s, y) \tag{A.9}$$

We have shown that (A.4) equals (A.9). Now taking limits as s goes to zero, again invoking the continuity of $\partial^2 f/\partial y\,\partial x$, we see that (A.4) does indeed have a limit, and that it is given by

$$\frac{\partial^2 f}{\partial y\,\partial x}(x,y)$$

(Q.E.D.)

Answers and Notes

Important: Not all the notes given here will be understood by a beginner. Some are intended for graduate students or teachers who may be teaching vector analysis for the first time.

In this book, vectors are represented by bold-faced letters such as **A**, **B**, **C**, ... Since you cannot conveniently imitate this, the author suggests that you either underline the letter, $\underline{A}$, or put an arrow above it, $\vec{A}$. Be sure to distinguish between the number 0 and the vector **0**.

SECTION 1.1

Note: If the reader has studied modern algebra or logic, he will recognize that a vector is an *equivalence class* of directed line segments. Note that parallel vectors having the same length in feet will also have the same length in meters or centimeters. That is, vector equality is not a metric property; it does not depend on choice of unit of length.

SECTION 1.2

1. Arrow extending from the same initial point and forming the diagonal of the parallelogram determined by the two vectors, as shown in Fig. 1.2.
2. Notice that $\mathbf{C} - \mathbf{A} = \mathbf{C} + (-\mathbf{A}) = (-\mathbf{A}) + \mathbf{C}$.
3. Yes, the statement is correct.

4. This is easy if you observe that a regular hexagon is composed of six equilateral triangles. (a) $\mathbf{B} - \mathbf{A}$, $-\mathbf{A}$, $-\mathbf{B}$, $\mathbf{A} - \mathbf{B}$, (b) the zero vector.

5. In problems of this kind, think of the vectors as displacements. The displacement $\mathbf{C}$ can be obtained by first moving backward along $\mathbf{F}$, then moving along $\mathbf{E}$, then upward in a direction opposite to $\mathbf{D}$. Hence, $\mathbf{C} = -\mathbf{F} + \mathbf{E} - \mathbf{D}$.

6. $\mathbf{G} = -\mathbf{K} + \mathbf{C} + \mathbf{D} - \mathbf{E}$.

7. $\mathbf{x} = \mathbf{F} - \mathbf{B} = \mathbf{A}$.

8. $\mathbf{x} = \mathbf{D} - \mathbf{E} - \mathbf{H} = \mathbf{G}$.

Note: This kind of addition was called *geometrical addition* when it was first introduced by Möbius and others over a century ago. Observe that the length of $\mathbf{A} + \mathbf{B}$ does not equal the length of $\mathbf{A}$ plus the length of $\mathbf{B}$. A student of mine once announced happily that he had won a bet in a tavern by showing an instance in which three units added to four units produced five units (see Exercise 4, Sec. 1.4).

SECTION 1.3

1. No, length is never negative.

2. $|4\mathbf{A}| = 12$, $|-2\mathbf{A}| = 6$, $|s\mathbf{A}| \leq 6$.

3. $|s\mathbf{A}| = 1$, $|-s\mathbf{A}| = 1$.

Note: If s is a nonzero number and $\mathbf{A}$ is a vector, the vector $s^{-1}\mathbf{A}$ is sometimes said to be "$\mathbf{A}$ divided by s". Thus, if we divide a nonzero vector by its own length, we obtain a vector of unit magnitude. This is the point of the first part of Exercise 3.

4. Equals the magnitude of A.

5. No, $\mathbf{A}$ might be the zero vector.

6. Yes.

7. Not necessarily true, since the vectors may not point in the same direction.

8. Two. Think of the plane as the top of your desk. One of the vectors points upward and the other downward. Many students say, "There are infinitely many." This is incorrect, since we do not distinguish between vectors that are equal.

9. Infinitely many. Think of the line as perpendicular to the xy plane. The unit vector might make any angle θ with the x axis.

10. Two, pointing in opposite directions.

11. $\mathbf{C} = \frac{1}{2}(\mathbf{A} + \mathbf{B})$.

12. $|\mathbf{A}| = |\mathbf{A} - \mathbf{B} + \mathbf{B}| \leq |\mathbf{A} - \mathbf{B}| + |\mathbf{B}|$

Hence $|\mathbf{A}| - |\mathbf{B}| \leq |\mathbf{A} - \mathbf{B}|$. If you prefer a less tricky method, draw a diagram and use a well-known theorem in geometry.

13. $a = -2$, $b = c = 1$ is one possible answer. There are others.

SECTION 1.4

Note: I think the only reason some students have trouble with some of these exercises is that they think more is expected of them than simply writing down the answer. When I work one of these problems by drawing a diagram and looking at it, students sometimes say, "Oh, is that all you want?" It is not necessary for you to use any equations or formulas in giving the answer to a trivial exercise.

1. 1.

2. 0.

3. $\sqrt{2}$.

4. 5.

5. $-\mathbf{i}, -\mathbf{j}, \frac{1}{2}\sqrt{2}\mathbf{i} + \frac{1}{2}\sqrt{2}\mathbf{j}$.

6. $\mathbf{A} = \mathbf{i} - 3\mathbf{j}$.

7. $A_1 = 3\sqrt{3}, A_2 = 3$.

8. $A_1 = |\mathbf{A}| \cos\theta, A_2 = |\mathbf{A}| \sin\theta$.

9. (a) $\frac{1}{2}\mathbf{i} + \frac{1}{2}\sqrt{3}\mathbf{j}$.
(b) $\frac{1}{2}\sqrt{3}\mathbf{i} - \frac{1}{2}\mathbf{j}$.
(c) $\frac{3}{5}\mathbf{i} + \frac{4}{5}\mathbf{j}$.
(d) $\frac{1}{2}\mathbf{i} + \frac{1}{2}\sqrt{3}\mathbf{j}, \frac{1}{2}\mathbf{i} - \frac{1}{2}\sqrt{3}\mathbf{j}$.
(e) $\pm(\frac{1}{2}\sqrt{2}\mathbf{i} + \frac{1}{2}\sqrt{2}\mathbf{j})$.

10. 10, 3, $\sqrt{1 + s^2}$, 1.

11. $2\mathbf{i} + 6\mathbf{j}$.

SECTION 1.5

1. 5, 3, 5.

2. $5\mathbf{i} + 6\mathbf{j} - \mathbf{k}, 4\mathbf{j} + 4\mathbf{k}$.

3. $4\sqrt{2}$.

4. $\pm\frac{1}{3}$.

5. $\frac{3}{5}\mathbf{i} + \frac{4}{5}\mathbf{j}$.

6. (a) $4\sqrt{2}$. (b) yz plane.

7. $\cos\alpha = \frac{3}{5}$. In general, $\cos\alpha = A_1/|\mathbf{A}|$.

8. $\pm\mathbf{j}$.

9. $\sqrt{3}$.

10. $\mathbf{i} - 5\mathbf{j} - \mathbf{k}$.

11. $x\mathbf{i} + y\mathbf{j} + z\mathbf{k}$.

12. $s = 2, t = 3, r = -1$.

13. $\frac{2}{3}, -\frac{2}{3}, \frac{1}{3}$.

14. Use the pythagorean theorem.

15. Cone concentric with the positive x axis.

16. Two.

17. $-\cos\alpha, \cos\beta, \cos\gamma$.

18. $\pm\frac{1}{3}\sqrt{3}\,(\mathbf{i} + \mathbf{j} + \mathbf{k})$.

SECTION 1.6

1. $2\mathbf{i} - 5\mathbf{j} - 8\mathbf{k}$.

2. $\mathbf{i} + 2\mathbf{j} + 9\mathbf{k}$.

3. $32\mathbf{j} - 26\mathbf{k}$.

4. 10 miles.

5. 7 pounds.

SECTION 1.7

2. If $\mathbf{A} + \mathbf{B} + \mathbf{C} + \mathbf{D} = \mathbf{0}$ and $\mathbf{A} = -\mathbf{C}$ then $\mathbf{B} = -\mathbf{D}$.

3. *Hint*: Let the sides be **A**, **B**, and $\mathbf{B} - \mathbf{A}$. If parallel to **A**, the line segment is $-\frac{1}{2}\mathbf{B} + \mathbf{A} + \frac{1}{2}(\mathbf{B} - \mathbf{A}) = \frac{1}{2}\mathbf{A}$.

4. Use the technique illustrated in Example 1.3 of the text.

6. $\cos^{-1}(-\frac{2}{15})$.

7. $\cos^{-1}(\frac{1}{3}\sqrt{3})$.

8. $\cos^{-1}\frac{1}{41}\sqrt{1435}$, $\cos^{-1}\frac{1}{41}\sqrt{246}$.

9. $90° - \cos^{-1}\frac{1}{3}$.

10. $(\mathbf{i}+\mathbf{j}+\mathbf{k})\cdot(x\mathbf{i}+y\mathbf{j}+z\mathbf{k})=0$ if and only if $x+y+z=0$. Hence, $\theta=90°$ if, and only if, $x+y+z=0$.

11. True.

12. True.

13. True.

14. False (radius is 3).

15. $(x-2)^2+(y-3)^2+(z-4)^2=9$.

16. $x^2+y^2=4$.

17. Line.

18. y axis.

19. The single point (2,−3,4).

20. The three coordinate planes.

21. 5.

22. 8.

23. 1.

24. Cone of two sheets concentric with z axis.

25. Ellipsoid.

SECTION 1.8

1. $x=3t,\ y=-2t,\ z=7t$.

2. $x=1,\ y=2$.

3. $y=2,\ z=3$.

4. $\pm(\frac{3}{5}\mathbf{i}+\frac{4}{5}\mathbf{j})$.

5. $\pm(\frac{6}{7}\mathbf{i}+\frac{3}{7}\mathbf{j}+\frac{2}{7}\mathbf{k})$.

6. $\pm(\frac{3}{19}\sqrt{19}\mathbf{i}-\frac{3}{19}\sqrt{19}\mathbf{j}+\frac{1}{19}\sqrt{19}\mathbf{k})$.

7. $x=\frac{1}{4}y=-z$.

8. $x=3,\ y=4$.

9. $x-1=-\frac{1}{2}(y-4)=\frac{1}{8}(z+1)$. This may be written in other forms.

10. $\frac{1}{7}\sqrt{42}$

11. $\cos^{-1}\frac{3}{70}\sqrt{42}$, about 74°.

14. (a) $0<\lambda<\infty$; $-1<\lambda<0$; $-\infty<\lambda<-1$.

15. (a) (2,2,3).
   (b) The lines coincide.
   (c) No intersection (parallel lines).
   (d) No intersection.

SECTION 1.9

Note: In Sec. 1.5 we explained what is meant by the components of a vector in the x, y, and z directions. More generally, we can define the *scalar component* of a vector $\mathbf{A}$ in any direction to be $\mathbf{A}\cdot\mathbf{n}$ where $\mathbf{n}$ is a *unit vector* in the desired direction. The *vector component* of $\mathbf{A}$ in the direction of a unit vector $\mathbf{n}$ is $(\mathbf{A}\cdot\mathbf{n})\mathbf{n}$. Unless otherwise stated, "component" means "scalar component" in this book.

1. 19.

2. $8+27-12=23$.

3. 20.

4. $\cos^{-1}\frac{2}{15}$.

5. $\cos^{-1}\frac{3}{5}$.

6. −2.

7. $\frac{10}{3}$.

8. $\sqrt{2}$.

9. $\frac{15}{13}\sqrt{26}$.

10. $\sqrt{5}\mathbf{i} + \sqrt{5}\mathbf{j}$.

11. Nothing. But $\mathbf{A} = \mathbf{0}$.

13. (a) Circle with diameter $|\mathbf{A}|$.
(b) Sphere with diameter $|\mathbf{A}|$.

14. $|\sin \frac{1}{2}\theta|$.

17. Expand $(\mathbf{A} + \mathbf{B}) \cdot (\mathbf{A} + \mathbf{B}) + (\mathbf{A} - \mathbf{B}) \cdot (\mathbf{A} - \mathbf{B})$.

19. $-\frac{214}{49}\mathbf{i} + \frac{37}{49}\mathbf{j} - \frac{330}{49}\mathbf{k}$.

SECTION 1.10

Note: Quite often we speak of *the* equation of a plane where it would be better to speak of *an* equation, since distinct equations may represent the same plane. For example, $x + y + 2z = 3$ and $2x + 2y + 4z = 6$ both represent the same plane.

1. (a) $\pm(\frac{2}{3}\mathbf{i} + \frac{1}{3}\mathbf{j} + \frac{2}{3}\mathbf{k})$.
(b) $\pm(\frac{1}{2}\sqrt{2}\mathbf{i} - \frac{1}{2}\sqrt{2}\mathbf{k})$.
(c) $\pm(-\frac{1}{37}\sqrt{37}\mathbf{j} + \frac{6}{37}\sqrt{37}\mathbf{k})$.
(d) $\pm\mathbf{i}$.
(e) $\pm(\frac{1}{2}\sqrt{2}\mathbf{j} - \frac{1}{2}\sqrt{2}\mathbf{k})$.
(f) $\pm(\frac{1}{2}\sqrt{2}\mathbf{i} - \frac{1}{2}\sqrt{2}\mathbf{j})$.

2. $x - 4y + z = 0$.

3. $2x - 2y + z + 3 = 0$.

4. $3x + y - z = 3$.

5. No.

6. $\frac{16}{3}$.

7. (a) $\sqrt{14}$. (b) $3\sqrt{2}$. (c) 2.

8. $\frac{1}{3}\sqrt{3}$.

9. $(\mathbf{i} + \mathbf{j} + 3\mathbf{k}) \cdot (2\mathbf{i} - 8\mathbf{j} + 2\mathbf{k}) = 0$.

10. $\sin^{-1} \frac{5}{9}\sqrt{3}$, about 74°.

11. $90° - \cos^{-1} \frac{5}{9}\sqrt{3}$.

12. $3x - y = C$, $z = 0$.

13. $\frac{5}{2}\sqrt{2}$.

14. $3x + 2y = 11$, $z = 0$.

15. $2x + 2y + z = 4$.

16. $\pm\frac{1}{3}$.

17. (a) The point $(-2,1,5)$.
(b) No intersection.
(c) The line $x = y + 3 = -\frac{1}{2}z$.
(d) No intersection.

18. (a) $2\mathbf{i} - \mathbf{j} + 5\mathbf{k}$.
(b) Any scalar multiple of $(2\mathbf{i} + 3\mathbf{j} - 4\mathbf{k})$.
(c) Any scalar multiple of $(3\mathbf{i} + \mathbf{j} + 7\mathbf{k})$.
(d) $\pm(\frac{2}{3}\mathbf{i} - \frac{2}{3}\mathbf{j} + \frac{1}{3}\mathbf{k})$.
(e) $\pm(\frac{1}{37}\sqrt{37}\mathbf{i} - \frac{6}{37}\sqrt{37}\mathbf{k})$.
(f) $\pm(\frac{3}{5}\mathbf{i} + \frac{4}{5}\mathbf{j})$.

SECTION 1.11

Note to instructor: A k-dimensional vector space (or k-dimensional subspace) is oriented by selecting a linearly independent ordered set consisting of k vectors. Any other such linearly independent ordered set is said to have "positive" orientation if it can be obtained from the given set in the proper order by a linear transformation with positive determinant. If an n-dimensional space has been oriented, and if also an $(n - 1)$-dimensional subspace of the same space is oriented by an ordered set $\mathbf{A}_1, \mathbf{A}_2, \ldots, \mathbf{A}_{n-1}$, then the same orientation of the subspace can be prescribed just as well by selecting a single vector $\mathbf{C}$ not in the subspace, using the following convention: the ordered set $\mathbf{A}_1, \mathbf{A}_2, \ldots, \mathbf{A}_{n-1}, \mathbf{C}$ must have positive orientation.

1. Numerically they are equal to the areas of the projections of the area on the coordinate planes.

SECTION 1.12

1. (a) $2\mathbf{i} + 14\mathbf{j} + 4\mathbf{k}$.
   (b) $-8\mathbf{i} + 23\mathbf{j} - \mathbf{k}$.
   (c) $-11\mathbf{i} - 6\mathbf{j} + \mathbf{k}$.
   (d) $\mathbf{k}$.
   (e) $\mathbf{j} - \mathbf{i}$.
2. $\sqrt{26}$.
3. $\frac{1}{2}\sqrt{61}$.
4. $\mathbf{0}$. $\mathbf{A}$ and $\mathbf{B}$ are parallel.
5. $\pm\frac{1}{11}\sqrt{11}\mathbf{i} - \frac{3}{11}\sqrt{11}\mathbf{j} + \frac{1}{11}\sqrt{11}\mathbf{k})$.
6. $\frac{1}{8}(x-2) = -\frac{1}{13}(y-3) = -\frac{1}{3}(z-7)$.
7. $x = -\frac{1}{4}y = \frac{1}{3}z$.
8. $-64\mathbf{j} + 16\mathbf{k}$, $16\mathbf{i} - 16\mathbf{j} + 16\mathbf{k}$. No.
9. $17x - y + 9z = 43$.
10. $\pm\frac{1}{25}\sqrt{5}(5\mathbf{i} + 6\mathbf{j} - 8\mathbf{k})$.
11. $\sin(\psi - \theta) = \sin\psi\cos\theta - \cos\psi\sin\theta$.
13. $\sqrt{65}/\sqrt{26}$.
14. $r = 3$, $s = -\frac{27}{2}$.
15. One of them is zero.
16. $\pm 8\mathbf{i}$.
17. (a) No.
   (b) $\frac{1}{2}x - \frac{52}{7} = -\frac{1}{4}y + \frac{52}{21} = z - \frac{208}{21}$. (This answer can be written in many other ways, so don't be discouraged if your answer differs from this in appearance.)
   (c) $4/\sqrt{21}$.
18. $x^2 + y^2 + z^2 - xy - yz - zx = 2$; a cylinder of radius $\frac{2}{3}\sqrt{3}$ ft.

SECTION 1.13

1. (a) 30. (b) -13. (c) 5. (d) 1.
2. 5.
3. 0.
4. $\frac{2}{3}$.
5. 1.
6. $3x - 17y - 4z = 0$.
7. $3x - 7y + z = -20$.
8. (a) Their triple scalar product is zero. Alternatively, all three are perpendicular to $\mathbf{i} + \mathbf{j} + \mathbf{k}$.
   (b) $x + y + z = 0$.
9. (a) $C_3 = 2$. (c) Draw a diagram.
10. $\frac{2}{19}\sqrt{38}$.
11. Yes.
12. They are coplanar.
13. (a) Compare $\mathbf{A} \cdot \mathbf{i}$ and $\mathbf{A} \cdot \mathbf{u}$.
   (b) $\mathbf{A}$.
15. Write the coefficients in (1.28) in determinant form.
16. Only (a), (b), (c), (g), and (h) have meaning.

SECTION 1.14

5. $(\omega \cdot \mathbf{R})\omega - (\omega \cdot \omega)\mathbf{R}$.
6. No.
7. 0.

SECTION 1.15

These exercises appeared already in Sec. 1.14.

SECTION 2.1

Note: Since different rules can be used to define the same function, the definition of vector function given in the text is now regarded as old-fashioned. The more modern way is to define a function as a set of pairs determined by some rule. For further details on the "new mathematics" listen to the appropriate Tom Lehrer record; most mathematicians find the old-fashioned definition quite adequate.

1. (a) $\cos t\,\mathbf{i} - \sin t\,\mathbf{j}$.
(b) True since $\mathbf{k} \cdot \mathbf{F}'(t) = 0$.
(c) $t = n\pi$ $(n = 0, \pm 1, \pm 2, \ldots)$.
(d) Yes, $\sqrt{2}$.
(e) Yes, 1.
(f) $-\sin t\,\mathbf{i} - \cos t\,\mathbf{j}$.

2. (a) $3\mathbf{i} + 3t^2\mathbf{j}$.
(b) $\cos t\,\mathbf{i} - e^{-t}\mathbf{j}$.
(c) $-2t\mathbf{i} + (e^t + 5t^4)\mathbf{j} + (e^t - 3t^2)\mathbf{k}$.
(d) $(\cos t + 3t^2)(\mathbf{i} + \mathbf{j} + 2\mathbf{k})$.
(e) $\mathbf{0}$.

3. (a) $6t - 10t \sin t - 5t^2 \cos t$.
(b) $(8t\sqrt{8t^2 + 1})/(8t^2 + 1)$.
(c) $1 - 12t^3$.

4. Use Theorem 2.4, noting that one term vanishes in this case.

5. (a) 7.
(b) 33.
(c) $8\mathbf{i} + 5\mathbf{j} - 6\mathbf{k}$.
(d) 0.
(e) -2.
(f) $\frac{3}{5}\mathbf{i} + \frac{2}{3}\mathbf{j} + \frac{6}{5}\mathbf{k}$.
(g) $-42\mathbf{i} + 66\mathbf{j} - \mathbf{k}$.
(h) $\mathbf{B}$.
(i) $\mathbf{B} \times \mathbf{C}$.

SECTION 2.2

1. No, the tangent may be parallel to the y axis.

2. If we dropped (*iii*) then (2.15) would not make sense, since the denominator might be zero.

3. $x^2 - y^2 = 1$, $z = 0$.

4. At (0,0,0), corresponding to $t = 0$.

5. $(\mathbf{i} + 2\pi\mathbf{j})/\sqrt{1 + 4\pi^2}$.

6. Along a straight line, $\mathbf{T}$ is constant.

7. (a) $\int_0^1 \sqrt{14}\,dt = \sqrt{14}$. (b) Distance between points is $\sqrt{14}$, and the path is straight.

8. $\sqrt{2}(e - 1)$.

9. (a) $2\sqrt{5}\pi^2$.
(b) $\frac{1}{5}\sqrt{5}(\sin t\,\mathbf{i} + \cos t\,\mathbf{j} + 2\mathbf{k})$.
(c) $\frac{1}{5}\sqrt{5}(-\mathbf{j} + 2\mathbf{k})$.

10. $\mathbf{i}$.

SECTION 2.3

1. (a) $\sqrt{2}\,e^t$.
(b) $a_t = \sqrt{2}\,e^t$, $a_n = \sqrt{2}\,e^t$.
(c) $\frac{1}{2}\sqrt{2}\,[(\cos t - \sin t)\mathbf{i} + (\sin t + \cos t)\,\mathbf{j}]$.
(d) $\frac{1}{2}\sqrt{2}\,e^{-t}$.

2. (a) $\sqrt{9t^2 + 25}$.
(b) $9t/\sqrt{9t^2 + 25}$, $[9(t^2 + 4) - 81t^2/(9t^2 + 25)]^{1/2}$.
(c) $\dfrac{3(\cos t - t \sin t)\mathbf{i} + 3(\sin t + t \cos t)\,\mathbf{j} + 4\mathbf{k}}{\sqrt{9t^2 + 25}}$.
(d) $\dfrac{[9(t^2 + 4) - 81t^2/(9t^2 + 25)]^{1/2}}{9t^2 + 25}$.

3. (a) $\sqrt{3}\,e^t$.
(b) $a_t = \sqrt{3}\,e^t$, $a_n = \sqrt{2}\,e^t$.
(c) $\frac{1}{3}\sqrt{3}[(\cos t - \sin t)\mathbf{i} + (\sin t + \cos t)\,\mathbf{j} + \mathbf{k}]$.
(d) $\frac{1}{3}\sqrt{2}\,e^{-t}$.

4. (a) $10\sqrt{5}$.
(b) $a_t = 0$, $a_n = 80$.
(c) $\frac{1}{5}\sqrt{5}(2 \cos 4t\,\mathbf{i} - 2 \sin 4t\,\mathbf{j} + \mathbf{k})$.
(d) $\frac{4}{25}$.

5. (a) $v = \frac{3}{2}$.
(b) $\mathbf{a} = -\cos t(\mathbf{i} - \mathbf{j}) - \sin t(\mathbf{i} + \mathbf{j})$.
(c) $-\frac{2}{3} \sin t(\mathbf{i} - \mathbf{j}) + \frac{2}{3} \cos t(\mathbf{i} + \mathbf{j}) + \frac{1}{3}\mathbf{k}$.
(d) $k = \frac{8}{27}\sqrt{5}$.

6. $\dfrac{2(3t^4 + 2t^3 - 3t^2 - 2t + 2)^{1/2}}{3(2t^4 - 4t^3 + 10t^2 + 1)^{3/2}}$.

7. $\frac{1}{2}$; $\frac{1}{2}$.

8. 6, $\frac{1}{2}$, 0, circle of radius 2 in the plane $x = y$.

9. $\mathbf{F} \times \dfrac{d\mathbf{F}}{dt} \cdot \dfrac{d^3\mathbf{F}}{dt^3}$.

10. (a) 1.
(b) 0.
(c) $a_t = d^2s/dt^2$.
(d) 0.
(e) ds/dt.
(f) τ.
(g) 1.
(h) $\mathbf{k}$.
(i) $-\tau\mathbf{N}$.

13. (a) False. (b) False. (c) True.

SECTION 2.4

1. $$\left[\frac{d^3r}{dt^3} - 3\,\frac{dr}{dt}\left(\frac{d\theta}{dt}\right)^2 - 3r\,\frac{d\theta}{dt}\,\frac{d^2\theta}{dt^2}\right]\mathbf{u}_r$$
$$+\left[3\,\frac{d^2r}{dt^2}\,\frac{d\theta}{dt} + 3\,\frac{dr}{dt}\,\frac{d^2\theta}{dt^2} + r\,\frac{d^3\theta}{dt^3} - r\left(\frac{d\theta}{dt}\right)^3\right]\mathbf{u}_\theta.$$

2. (a) 0.

3. $\mathbf{v} = 4b[(\sin\theta)\mathbf{u}_r + (1 - \cos\theta)\mathbf{u}_\theta]$
$\mathbf{a} = 16b[(2\cos\theta - 1)\mathbf{u}_r + (2\sin\theta)\mathbf{u}_\theta]$.

4. $\mathbf{v} = b[(\cos t)\mathbf{u}_r - e^{-t}(1 + \sin t)\mathbf{u}_\theta]$
$\mathbf{a} = b([-\sin t - e^{-2t}(1 + \sin t)]\mathbf{u}_r + e^{-t}[1 + \sin t - 2\cos t]\mathbf{u}_\theta)$.

5. If the particle is moving parallel to the field no force will be exerted. (In elementary books it is sometimes stated that the force is proportional to the rate at which the particle "cuts" the lines of flow.)

6. $v/r\,|\mathbf{B}|$. [$qv\,|\mathbf{B}|$ must equal the component a_n discussed in Sec. 2.3.]

7. (a) The second term.
(b) The second and third terms.
(c) All are nonzero.
(d) Many possibilities.

8. (a) Yes, except when its velocity is zero. (b) No.

9. (a) $\pi^2 r$ cm/sec² (if r is in cm) directed towards the center. Note that 30 rev/min = π rad/sec.
(b) $4\pi\mathbf{u}_\theta$ cm/sec.

10. 24π, since $dr/dt = 3$ and $d\theta/dt = 4\pi$.

11. $E = \dfrac{m}{2}\left(\dfrac{dr}{dt}\right)^2 + \dfrac{m}{2}\left(r\,\dfrac{d\theta}{dt}\right)^2 - \displaystyle\int_0^t \left(F_r\,\frac{dr}{dt} + F_\theta\, r\,\frac{d\theta}{dt}\right)dt.$ Now differentiate and use $\dfrac{d}{dt}\displaystyle\int_0^t f(t)\,dt = f(t)$.

SECTION 3.1

1. (i) $(\cos x + ye^{xy})\mathbf{i} + xe^{xy}\mathbf{j} + \mathbf{k}$. (ii) $-1/|\mathbf{R}|^2$. (iii) $\mathbf{k}$.

2. yz plane, where $x = 0$.

3. f depends only on y.

4. $f(x,y,z) = x^2 + yz + C$.

5. Unit vector directed away from the z axis, except at points on the z axis, where it is not defined.

6. (a) 0. (b) $-\frac{4}{3}$.

7. (a) $\frac{5}{3}$. (b) $-\frac{2}{3}$. (c) $-\frac{28}{3}$. (d) $\frac{1}{42}\sqrt{14}$.

8. (a) 10.
(b) The maximum rate of increase of r^2 is in the direction of **R**, whence

$$\frac{d}{ds}(r^2) = \frac{d}{dr}(r^2) = 2r$$

which equals 10 at (3,0,4).

9. $150\sqrt{5}$. This function equals s^6, where s is the distance to the y axis. We have $(d/ds)(s^6) = 6s^5 = 150\sqrt{5}$ at this point.

10. Any scalar multiple of $4\mathbf{i} + \mathbf{j} + \mathbf{k}$.

11. $2x + 4y - z = 21$.

12. (a) From your diagram you see that any scalar multiple of $\mathbf{i} + \mathbf{k}$ will do. (b) $4\mathbf{i} + 4\mathbf{k}$.

13. $x + 2y - 8z = -28$.

14. $x = y$, $z = 0$.

15. $\pm\frac{1}{14}\sqrt{14}(3\mathbf{i} - \mathbf{j} + 2\mathbf{k})$.

16. $4x + 6y - z = 13$.

17. $\pm\frac{1}{2}\sqrt{2}(\mathbf{i} - \mathbf{j})$. In (c), let $\mathbf{R} = 2 \sin t\, \mathbf{i} + 2 \cos t\, \mathbf{j} + \sqrt{5}\,\mathbf{k}$.

18. $\cos^{-1} \frac{31}{32}$.

19. $\sin^{-1} \frac{2}{3}\sqrt{2}$.

SECTION 3.2

1. See Fig. 3.3.

2. (a) $x(z + a) = -1$, $y(z + b) = -1$.
(b) $x(z - 3) = -1$, $y(z - 3) = -1$.

3. Half lines extending from the origin.

4. The gradient is normal to these surfaces.

SECTION 3.3

1. $ye^{xy} + x \cos xy - 2x \cos zx \sin zx$.

2. 3.

3. $6y^3z + 18x^2yz$.

4. Zero except at the origin, where the field is not defined. The magnitude of this field at any point is $1/r^2$, so this field can be thought of as the electric field intensity due to a charge of suitably chosen magnitude at the origin. A physicist or electrical engineer might say that the divergence is "infinity" at the origin, since the divergence of an electrostatic field is proportional to the charge density, and the charge density at a point charge is "infinity".

6. Let $\mathbf{F} \cdot \mathbf{grad}\, \phi = 0$.
7. $\mathbf{F} = y\mathbf{i} + z\mathbf{j} + x\mathbf{k}$ is one example.
8. There are infinitely many possible answers, for example $\mathbf{F} = -x\mathbf{i}$.
9. Again there are infinitely many acceptable answers. Two of them are $e^x\mathbf{i}$ and $e^x\mathbf{i} + ye^x\mathbf{j}$.
10. False (e.g., a constant field).
11. Divergence is zero everywhere, since $\partial F_1/\partial x = 0$, $F_2 = 0$, and (we assume) $F_3 = 0$. Some of my students observe that $\mathbf{F} = Cy\mathbf{i}$ for some constant C, and then compute the answer using the formula for the divergence. This is clever, but not the point of the exercise.
12. Divergence is zero everywhere. For example, consider point P. Along the x axis, $F_1 = 0$, so $\partial F_1/\partial x = 0$ at P. As we move through P along the flow line indicated, F_2 takes on its maximum value $|\mathbf{F}|$, therefore $\partial F_2/\partial s = 0$ at P, where s is measured along the flow line. But at point P we are moving parallel to the y axis, so $\partial F_2/\partial y = \partial F_2/\partial s$ at P, hence is zero at this point. Another method: Conjecture that $\mathbf{F} = -y\mathbf{i} + x\mathbf{j}$ and use the formula.

SECTION 3.4

1. $x\mathbf{i} - y\mathbf{j} + y(1 - 2x)\mathbf{k}$.
2. $-z^2 \sin yz^2\, \mathbf{i} + (y \cos xy - xe^{xy})\mathbf{k}$.
3. $-(y^2 + z^2)\mathbf{i} + 2zx\mathbf{j}$.
4. (a) $1 + z^2 + x + y$.
   (b) $z\mathbf{i} + 2xz\mathbf{j} + y\mathbf{k}$.
5. The paddle wheel will not tend to rotate.
6. Think of the velocity field of a fluid swirling about the x axis. Assume constant angular velocity $\boldsymbol{\omega}$. Then $\mathbf{v} = \boldsymbol{\omega} \times \mathbf{R}$, and since $\mathbf{curl}\, \mathbf{F} = 2\boldsymbol{\omega}$ as stated in the text (to be proved later) we have $\boldsymbol{\omega} = \mathbf{i}$ and

$$\mathbf{v} = \mathbf{i} \times \mathbf{R} = \mathbf{i} \times (x\mathbf{i} + y\mathbf{j} + z\mathbf{k}) = y\mathbf{k} - z\mathbf{j}$$

   This is one possible answer. Another is $2y\mathbf{k}$, which represents a shearing motion parallel to the xz plane.
7. No (Fig. 3.13).
8. No. A physicist or engineer would say that in many types of problems arising in practical work it *is* possible.
9. The following answers are *barely acceptable* in my opinion. If f is a scalar field, $\mathbf{grad}\, f$ at a point is a vector pointing in the direction of maximum rate of increase of f at that point, having magnitude equal to this maximum rate of increase. If $\mathbf{F}$ is the velocity field of a fluid, div $\mathbf{F}$ at a point is the time rate of change of volume per unit volume at that point; $\mathbf{curl}\, \mathbf{F}$ at a point is a vector equal to $2\boldsymbol{\omega}$, where $\boldsymbol{\omega}$ is the angular velocity vector of the fluid at that point.

SECTION 3.5

1. 16.

2. $12\mathbf{i} + 4\mathbf{j} + \mathbf{k}$.

3. 64.

4. (a) $2xy + 1$.
(b) $-2\mathbf{i} + \mathbf{j} - x^2\mathbf{k}$.
(c) $2y\mathbf{i} + 2x\mathbf{j}$.

5. Scalar field.

6. Vector field.

7. 3, **0**.

8. $(x^2 + z^2)e^{xz}$.

9. Always **0**.

10. Always 0.

SECTION 3.6

1. $20x^3yz^3 + 6x^5yz$.

2. 0 except at the origin.

3. $-2yz^2(y^2z^2 + 3x^2z^2 + 6x^2y^2)\mathbf{k}$.

4. (a) and (b). Also (c) provided that $p^2 = q^2$.

5. (a) Vector field.
(b) Scalar field.
(c) Vector field.
(d) Scalar field.
(e) Zero vector field.
(f) Meaningless.
(g) Vector field.
(h) Vector field.
(i) Meaningless.
(j) Vector field.

6. (b) $\dfrac{\sin x \sinh y}{\sinh 5} + \dfrac{\sin 2x \sinh 2y}{\sinh 10}$.

SECTION 3.7

5. As written, the right side is symmetrical in **F** and **G**, but the left side is not, since $\mathbf{F} \times \mathbf{G} \neq \mathbf{G} \times \mathbf{F}$.

SECTION 4.1

1. (a) $\frac{1}{2}\sqrt{2}(\mathbf{i} + \mathbf{j})$.
(b) $\mathbf{i}$.
(c) $-\mathbf{j}$.

2. (a) $\sqrt{2}\, dx$ or $\sqrt{2}\, dy$.
(b) dx.
(c) $-dy$.

3. (a) $d\mathbf{R} = dx\,\mathbf{i} + dy\,\mathbf{j} = dx\,\mathbf{i} + dx\,\mathbf{j} = (\frac{1}{2}\sqrt{2}\,\mathbf{i} + \frac{1}{2}\sqrt{2}\,\mathbf{j})\sqrt{2}\,dx = \mathbf{T}\,ds$.
(b) $d\mathbf{R} = dx\,\mathbf{i} + dy\,\mathbf{j} = \mathbf{i}\,dx = \mathbf{T}\,ds$.
(c) $d\mathbf{R} = dx\,\mathbf{i} + dy\,\mathbf{j} = dy\,\mathbf{j} = \mathbf{T}\,ds$.

4. (a) Along this path, $\mathbf{F} = \sqrt{1-x^2}\,\mathbf{i} - x\mathbf{j}$ and

$$d\mathbf{R} = dx\,\mathbf{i} - \frac{x\,dx}{\sqrt{1-x^2}}\,\mathbf{j}$$

so

$$\mathbf{F}\cdot d\mathbf{R} = \frac{dx}{\sqrt{1-x^2}} \qquad \text{and} \qquad \int \mathbf{F}\cdot d\mathbf{R} = \int_{-1}^{1} \frac{dx}{\sqrt{1-x^2}} = \pi$$

(b) π.

5. $\mathbf{F}\cdot d\mathbf{R} = -d(\tan^{-1} y/x) = -d\theta$.

6. (a) 8. (b) 8.

7. 36. (*Caution:* $\mathbf{R}\cdot d\mathbf{R} = s\,ds$ in this case because the points are collinear with the origin.)

8. $\pm 8\pi$, depending on direction.

9. 40. (This can also be done by observing that $\mathbf{F}\cdot d\mathbf{R} = d\phi$ where $\phi = x^2y + zy$, so that the integral is $\phi(3,4,1) - \phi(1,0,2)$. See Sec. 4.3 for further discussion of this "trick".)

10. Zero.

11. $\frac{41}{6}$.

12. (a) 0. ($\mathbf{F}$ is perpendicular to $d\mathbf{R}$.)
(b) $\frac{4}{3}(\omega_1 - \omega_2)$.

SECTION 4.2

Note: In this book, any set of points is a *region* and a region is a *domain* if and only if it is open and connected. In some books other conventions are used; there is no standard agreement: for example, some books use *domain* to mean *domain of definition* and those domains that are open and connected are called regions.

1. Domain, not simply-connected.
2. Simply-connected domain.
3. Simply-connected domain.
4. Not a domain. (Points on the plane $z = 0$ are not interior.)
5. Simply-connected domain.
6. Domain, not simply-connected.
7. Simply-connected domain.
8. Not a domain (not connected).

SECTION 4.3

1. The integral over C equals that over C_1 minus that over C_2, so if the first of these is zero the other two are equal.
2. Many possibilities.
3. Many possibilities.

4. 2π or -2π, depending on which way the circle is oriented.

5. ϕ is a multiple-valued function, and hence not a scalar field as we have defined it.

6. $\phi = yx + \sin xz + C$.

7. $\mathbf{F} = \mathbf{grad}\,\phi$ where $\phi = x^2y + yz$.

SECTION 4.4

1. (a) Conservative, $\phi = 6x^2y + xyz + C$.
(b) Conservative, $\phi = e^{xz} + C$.
(c) Conservative, $\phi = -\cos x + \frac{1}{3}y^3 + e^z + C$.
(d) Not conservative.
(e) Conservative, $\phi = \ln(x^2 + y^2) + z^2$.

2. (e), since the domain of definition is not simply-connected. You must explicitly construct ϕ.

3. Yes. $\phi + \psi$.

4. Letting $\mathbf{F} = F_1\mathbf{i} + F_2\,\mathbf{j} + F_3\,\mathbf{k}$, we have

$$\phi(x,y,z) = \phi(x_0,y_0,z_0) + \int_{x_0}^{x} F_1(x,y_0,z_0)\,dx + \int_{y_0}^{y} F_2(x,y,z_0)\,dy + \int_{z_0}^{z} F_3(x,y,z)\,dz$$

Since (x_0,y_0,z_0) is a fixed point, the first of these integrals yields a function of x alone, the second yields a function of x and y only, and the third integral yields a function of x, y, and z. It follows from the fundamental theorem of calculus that

$$\frac{\partial\phi}{\partial z} = F_3(x,y,z)$$

Also, we have

$$\frac{\partial\phi}{\partial y} = F_2(x,y,z_0) + \frac{\partial}{\partial y}\int_{z_0}^{z} F_3(x,y,z)\,dz$$

Since F_3 is continuous and has a continuous derivative $\partial F_3/\partial y$ in the sphere, we can interchange the order of differentiation and integration. (We omit the proof; this is a special case of "Leibnitz's rule" which the interested reader can look up elsewhere.)

$$\frac{\partial\phi}{\partial y} = F_2(x,y,z_0) + \int_{z_0}^{z} \frac{\partial F_3(x,y,z)}{\partial y}\,dz$$

Since we assume that $\mathbf{curl}\,\mathbf{F} = \mathbf{0}$, we have by (4.11)

$$\frac{\partial\phi}{\partial y} = F_2(x,y,z_0) + \int_{z_0}^{z} \frac{\partial F_2(x,y,z)}{\partial z}\,dz$$

$$= F_2(x,y,z_0) + F_2(x,y,z)\Big|_{z_0}^{z} = F_2(x,y,z)$$

In a similar manner, we see that

$$\begin{aligned}\frac{\partial\phi}{\partial x} &= F_1(x,y_0,z_0) + \int_{y_0}^{y}\frac{\partial F_2(x,y,z_0)}{\partial x}\,dy + \int_{z_0}^{z}\frac{\partial F_3(x,y,z)}{\partial x}\,dz \\ &= F_1(x,y_0,z_0) + \int_{y_0}^{y}\frac{\partial F_1(x,y,z_0)}{\partial y}\,dy + \int_{z_0}^{z}\frac{\partial F_1(x,y,z)}{\partial z}\,dz \\ &= F_1(x,y_0,z_0) + F_1(x,y,z_0)\Big|_{y_0}^{y} + F_1(x,y,z)\Big|_{z_0}^{z} \\ &= F_1(x,y,z)\end{aligned}$$

Hence

$$\mathbf{grad}\ \phi = \frac{\partial\phi}{\partial x}\mathbf{i} + \frac{\partial\phi}{\partial y}\mathbf{j} + \frac{\partial\phi}{\partial z}\mathbf{k} = F_1\mathbf{i} + F_2\,\mathbf{j} + F_3\,\mathbf{k}$$

5. (b) $\phi = -1/r$ in spherical coordinates. Hence, the maximum rate of increase of ϕ is in a direction away from the origin. Compare the example at the end of Sec. 3.7.

6. $\phi(1,2,3) = -\frac{1}{14}\sqrt{14}$ and $\phi(2,3,5) = -\frac{1}{38}\sqrt{38}$; hence the work done is

$$\phi(2,3,5) - \phi(1,2,3) = \tfrac{1}{14}\sqrt{14} - \tfrac{1}{38}\sqrt{38}$$

7. No, provided the path avoids the origin.

Note: Conservative fields are sometimes called *potential fields.* The term *irrotational* is also used. It is not possible for a flow line of such a field to be a closed curve, for the integral of a field about a closed flow line is nonzero, and this would contradict (*ii*). Therefore the flow lines either have no endpoints (i.e., if they "extend to infinity" in both directions) or perhaps they start at a point (called the "source") and perhaps end at another point (called the "sink"). For this reason, such fields are also called *source fields.* A simple example is the electrostatic field due to a positive point charge at the origin. The origin is the "source" and the flow lines extend radially away from the origin.

SECTION 4.5

2. $-\frac{1}{2}x^2\mathbf{k}$.

3. If $\mathbf{F} = \nabla\phi$, a vector potential is given by $\phi\mathbf{G}$.

SECTION 4.6

This section makes no pretense to rigor.

2. (a) $\frac{1}{3}\sqrt{3}(\mathbf{i}+\mathbf{j}+\mathbf{k})$.

(b) $\mathbf{k}\cdot\mathbf{n} = \frac{1}{3}\sqrt{3}$.

(c) $\displaystyle\int_0^1\int_0^{1-y}\frac{dx\,dy}{|\cos\gamma|}$.

(d) $\frac{1}{2}\sqrt{3}$.

4. $\sqrt{4x^2+4y^2+1}\,dx\,dy$.

5. 11.

SECTION 4.7

1. 18π.

2. (a) 8.
(b) 16.
(c) 24.
(d) 0.
(e) 0.
(f) 0.
(g) 0.

3. $\int_0^1 \int_0^{2-2x} \frac{7}{2} \cdot \frac{6}{7}\, x\, dy\, dx = 1$.

4. $|\mathbf{E}| = \lambda/2\pi\varepsilon_0 r$.

6. (a) $T_r = T_a + \dfrac{1/r - 1/a}{1/b - 1/a}(T_b - T_a)$.
(b) No.

7. Zero.

8. $3\pi a^2$.

9. -1.

10. (a) No.
(b) Yes.
(c) 4.

11. $13\frac{7}{8}$.

12. The term *source* is used rather than *sink* in Exercise 12 because in electrostatics it is conventional to take the electric field to be the *negative* of the potential.
(a) By Gauss's law and symmetry, $\mathbf{F} = \mathbf{0}$ within the sphere so ϕ is constant within the sphere, and at the center $r = a$ is a constant so $\phi = q/a = 4\pi a^2\sigma/a$.
(b) By Gauss's law and symmetry, the electric field outside the sphere is the same as that due to a point charge of magnitude $4\pi a^2\sigma$ located at the center.

13. (a) 8π. (Point is within sphere.)
(b) $\frac{16}{3}\pi$. (Point is outside sphere.)

14. 20π.

SECTION 4.8

3.

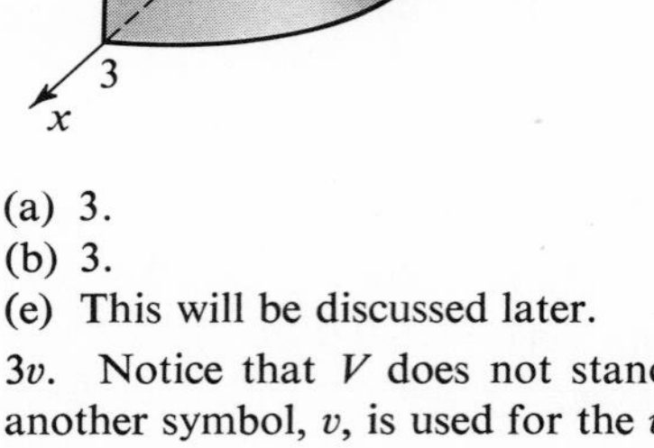

4. (a) 3.
(b) 3.
(e) This will be discussed later.

5. $3v$. Notice that V does not stand for a number but for a domain. Hence another symbol, v, is used for the *volume* of V, which is a *number*.

6. $\pi(1 - e^{-1})$.

7. $\nabla \cdot \mathbf{E} = \rho/\varepsilon_0$ at each point in space. Here we assume charge to be distributed continuously, i.e., no point charges in the domain.

8. (a) $\frac{22}{3}\pi$. (b) $\frac{32}{9}\pi$.

9. $\frac{32}{255}\sqrt{85}\,\pi$.

SECTION 4.9

6. (a) 0.
(b) -2.
(c) 4.
(d) 0.
(e) -1.

7. The divergence is identically zero, so the desired integral equals the negative of the integral over the missing top, which, in this case, is trivial to compute.

8. The field is $\frac{1}{3}x^3\mathbf{i} + \frac{1}{3}y^3\mathbf{j}$.

10. $\pm 2\pi$, depending on direction of integration.

11. (a) 16.8 if volume is proportional to the cube of the minimal diameter.
(b) Yes.

12. $5\varepsilon_0$.

13. (a) $4\pi b^4$.
(b) To avoid a triple integral, take $dV = 4\pi r^2\, dr$, so that the integral is

$$\int_0^b 16\pi r^3\, dr$$

14. 8π.

15. 0.

16. (a) Use (3.19).
(b) $\frac{928}{3}\pi$.

17. (a) 108π.
(b) 1944π.

[Exercise 16(a) does not apply in part (b) since this function is not harmonic.]

SECTION 4.10

1. In applying the fundamental theorem of calculus.

2. To ensure that the volume integral of div **F** over the bounded domain D exists.

5. $\cos\gamma = 0$, so the expression $dx\, dy/|\cos\gamma|$ is meaningless.

6. 30.

7. $5v$.

8. Yes.

9. (a) An outer sphere with **n** pointing away from the origin and an inner sphere with **n** pointing towards the origin.
(b) Sum of two integrals.
(c) They are equal.
(d) No.
(e) 4π.

10. Note that $\mathbf{F} \cdot \mathbf{n} = \partial f / \partial n$ and $\nabla \cdot \mathbf{F} = \nabla^2 \phi$.

11. (b) The lumpiness equals the negative of the laplacian. Use Exercise 6 to see this.
(c) The lumpiness is zero.

12. *Second hint:* In steady state, rate of heat flow out of a domain equals the rate of heat flow into the domain; otherwise the temperature would be changing. Hence,

$$\iint \frac{\partial \phi}{\partial n}\, dS = 0$$

over arbitrary closed surfaces. Also note that the limit, as $V \to 0$, of

$$\frac{1}{V} \iiint_D \nabla^2 \phi \, dV$$

as the domain D shrinks down to a point, is the value of $\nabla^2 \phi$ at that point, if $\nabla^2 \phi$ is continuous.

13. $c\rho(\partial \phi / \partial t) = k \nabla^2 \phi$.
Note: These derivations can be placed on a more rigorous level by making use of the theorem that if f is continuous and

$$\iiint f(x, y, z)\, dV = 0$$

for every domain D, then f is identically zero. For instance, in Exercise 13 this theorem is used, taking

$$f = c\rho \frac{\partial \phi}{\partial t} - k \nabla^2 \phi$$

14. $-4\pi\phi(P)$.

15. They are equal.

17. $4\pi\phi(0,0,0) = 20\pi$.

18. (a) $-4\pi\phi(0,1,0) = -20\pi$.
(b) $-4\pi\phi(2,1,3) = 0$.

19. Zero.

SECTION 4.11

6. Zero.

7. -36π, since $\textbf{curl}\ \mathbf{F} \cdot \mathbf{k} = -4$ and area enclosed by C is 9π.

8. (a) 6π. (b) 6π.

9. (a) -16. (b) -16. (c) Second term.

10. 28π.

11. What is the title of Sec. 1.11?

SECTION 4.12

1. The curl of a vector field **F** points in the direction of maximum swirl and its magnitude equals this maximum swirl.

2. (a) Zero.
(b) Zero.

(c) Zero. More rigorously, use the theorem mentioned in the answer to Exercise 13, Sec. 4.10, to avoid having to speak of "very small" laundry bags.

(d) div **curl F** = 0.

Note: The divergence of a vector field at a point is sometimes called the *source density* of the field at that point. This is because the divergence of the electric intensity of an electrostatic field is equal (within a factor) to the charge density, and electric charge is the "source" or "cause" of the field. The statement "a field has zero divergence in any region that is free of sources" has an intuitive appeal to many students. The above exercise can be worded: the curl of a vector field is another vector field that is free of sources.

3. (a) Zero.
(b) Zero.
(c) Zero.

4. (a) Zero.
(b) Zero.
(c) Zero vector.
(d) **curl grad** $\phi = \mathbf{0}$.

Note: The curl of a vector field at a point is sometimes called the *vortex density* of the field at that point. This is because, in some sense, the curl describes the "eddy" or "whirlpool" nature of the field. Note that vortex density is a vector quantity. Just as engineers sometimes think of a point source as a point where the divergence is "infinite", so also do they think of a *vortex filament* as a curve in space along which the magnitude of the curl is "infinite". The central part of a tornado provides an approximate idea. We leave to the reader the precise formulation of the definition. The intuitive content of Exercise 4 is that any field that can be derived from a scalar potential must be vortex-free. It should be noted, however, that if we allow the scalar potential to be a multiple-valued function, it is sometimes possible to find a scalar potential for the velocity field of fluid swirling about a vortex filament. We heartily recommend the chapter on vector analysis in *Mathematics of Circuit Analysis*, by E. A. Guillemin (Wiley, 1949), in which these matters are taken up in greater detail.

Let us now briefly review and extend some of the earlier ideas. We consider only continuously differentiable vector fields.

If a vector field defined in a domain D has any one of the following properties, it has all of them:

(i) Its curl is zero at every point.
(ii) Its integral around any closed contour is zero, provided that there is a surface enclosed by the contour entirely within D.
(iii) It is the gradient of a scalar function, but this function may possibly be multiple-valued.

If the domain D is simply-connected, we can omit the clauses starting "provided that . . ." and "but this . . ." from these properties. When D is simply-connected, the following terms are used for these fields: conservative field, irrotational field, potential field, source field.

Similarly, any one of the following properties of a continuously differentiable vector field implies the others:

(i) Its divergence is zero at every point in D.
(ii) Its integral over every surface is zero, provided that we consider only closed surfaces enclosing points all of which are in D.
(iii) It is the curl of another (possibly multiple-valued) vector field.

These statements are not precise and should not be taken very seriously. Terms sometimes used for such fields are: solenoidal field, rotational field, turbulent field, source-free field, vortex field. The terminology is not standardized; in modern usage, the term "turbulent" has an altogether different meaning. In applications, vector fields that are discontinuous along a surface are of considerable importance. We have not discussed such fields because they arise more naturally in courses dealing with applications, where the motivation for studying them is more apparent. The above statements are utterly false for such fields.

6. (a) $2z$. (c) -20π.
(b) $-5\mathbf{k}$.

7. (a) 27π. (b) 0.

SECTION 4.13

2. $\partial f/\partial n$ in the u_1 direction is $\partial f/h_1\, \partial u_1$ and its surface integral over *abcd* is $h_2 h_3\, du_2\, du_3$ times this, and so the surface integral over this face and the opposite face is

$$\frac{\partial}{\partial u_1}\left(\frac{h_2 h_3}{h_1}\frac{\partial f}{\partial u_1}\right) du_1\, du_2\, du_3$$

and similarly for the other pairs of faces. The laplacian is the overall sum divided by the volume $h_1 h_2 h_3\, du_1\, du_2\, du_3$.

4. $n(n+1)r^{n-2}$.

6. Both zero.

7. (a) No. (b) The element of volume in spherical coordinates is different in shape and position from that in cartesian coordinates.

8. (a) Yes.
(b) $x = (u_1 + u_2)/2$, $y = (u_1 - u_2)/2$, $z = u_3/2$.
(c) $h_1 = \frac{1}{2}\sqrt{2}$, $h_2 = \frac{1}{2}\sqrt{2}$, $h_3 = \frac{1}{2}$.

(d) $\nabla^2 f = 2\dfrac{\partial^2 f}{\partial {u_1}^2} + 2\dfrac{\partial^2 f}{\partial {u_2}^2} + 4\dfrac{\partial^2 f}{\partial {u_3}^2}$.

(e) $\sqrt{2}\,\mathbf{u}_1 + \sqrt{2}\,\mathbf{u}_2 + 4\mathbf{u}_3$.

9. (a) $x = \frac{1}{3}(2u_1 + u_2)$, $y = \frac{1}{3}(u_1 - u_2)$, $z = \frac{1}{2}u_3$.
(c) This coordinate system is not orthogonal.

10. $(1/u_1)\, du_1\, du_2\, du_3$.

11. This coordinate system is not right-handed, hence the usual formula for curl does not apply.

12. $\mathbf{F} = \mathbf{u}_r/r^2$. (a) Use the formula given above for divergence in spherical coordinates. (b) $\mathbf{u}_r \cdot \mathbf{n} = 1$, so the integral is trivial. (c) The divergence theorem applies to fields that are continuously differentiable throughout the given domain, but this field is not defined at the origin. (d) Zero.

13. $\frac{16}{3}\pi$.

14. (a) $1/uv$.
(b) $2w/uv$.

SECTION 5.2

1. (a) 0. (b) $(15z^3 + 2xy)\, dx \wedge dy \wedge dz$. (c) 0.

2. (a) $y^2z^3\, dx + 2xyz^3\, dy + 3xy^2z^2\, dz$.
(b) 0.
(c) $(2yz^3 - 2x^2y^2z)\, dy \wedge dz + xy\, dz \wedge dx + (2xy^2z^2 - xz)\, dx \wedge dy$.
(d) $(1 + 2yz + 3xz^2)\, dx \wedge dy \wedge dz$.

3. $dx \wedge dy = r\, dr \wedge d\theta$. (Element of area in polar coordinates.)

4. $dx \wedge dy \wedge dz = r^2 \sin \phi\, dr \wedge d\phi \wedge d\theta$. (Element of volume in spherical coordinates.)

5. No. $dx \wedge dx + dy \wedge dy + dz \wedge dz = 0$.

6. (a) In cylindrical coordinates, $h_1 = 1$, $h_2 = r$, $h_3 = 1$. Simply substitute into (5.10), (5.11), and (5.12).
(b) $3\, dr + 5r\, d\theta + 7r\, dz$ and $3r\, d\theta \wedge dz + 5\, dz \wedge dr + 7r^2\, dr \wedge d\theta$.
(c) $1/r$. (The two-form associated with $\mathbf{u}_r$ is $r\, d\theta \wedge dz$ with differential $dr \wedge d\theta \wedge dz$ which in standard order is $(1/r)r\, dr \wedge d\theta \wedge dz$ so the divergence is $1/r$.)
(d) $\mathbf{u}_r + (1/r)\mathbf{u}_\theta$.
(e) $(1/r)\mathbf{u}_r + 3\mathbf{u}_\theta$.

7. (a) $r^2 \sin \phi F_r\, d\phi \wedge d\theta + r \sin \phi F_\phi\, d\theta \wedge dr + rF_\theta\, dr \wedge d\phi$.
(b) $fr^2 \sin \phi\, dr \wedge d\phi \wedge d\theta$.
(c) $3\mathbf{u}_r + 8\mathbf{u}_\phi + r^4\mathbf{u}_\theta$.

(d) $\dfrac{\partial f}{\partial r}\mathbf{u}_r + \dfrac{1}{r}\dfrac{\partial f}{\partial \phi}\mathbf{u}_\phi + \dfrac{1}{r \sin \phi}\dfrac{\partial f}{\partial \theta}\mathbf{u}_\theta$.

8. Taking $df = \dfrac{\partial f}{\partial u_1}\partial u_1 + \dfrac{\partial f}{\partial u_2} du_2 + \dfrac{\partial f}{\partial u_3} du_3$ to be (5.10), (5.9) must be

$$\frac{1}{h_1}\frac{\partial f}{\partial u_1}\mathbf{u}_1 + \frac{1}{h_2}\frac{\partial f}{\partial u_2}\mathbf{u}_2 + \frac{1}{h_3}\frac{\partial f}{\partial u_3}\mathbf{u}_3 .$$

9. Imitate Example 5.6, expect that you find the differential of (5.10) instead of (5.11). For the answer, see Sec. 4.13. Notice that the differential of (5.10) is, symbolically,

$$\begin{vmatrix} du_2 \wedge du_3 & du_3 \wedge du_1 & du_1 \wedge du_2 \\ \dfrac{\partial}{\partial u_1} & \dfrac{\partial}{\partial u_2} & \dfrac{\partial}{\partial u_3} \\ F_1 h_1 & F_2 h_2 & F_3 h_3 \end{vmatrix}$$

10. (a) $\dfrac{h_2 h_3}{h_1}\dfrac{f}{u_1}\, du_2 \wedge du_3 + \text{etc.}$

(b) Same as (4.80) with $du_1 \wedge du_2 \wedge du_3$ tacked to the end.

SECTION 5.3

Note: The statement made in the text, that a curve is one-dimensional, is prefaced by "roughly speaking" because it is only true for the rather simple curves considered in elementary work. It is possible, by a rather ingenious construction, to have a continuous curve that passes through every point in a square exactly once, and such a curve might properly be regarded as two-dimensional.

1. For any three-form $\alpha = f(x,y,z)\, dx \wedge dy \wedge dz$, $d\alpha = 0$.
2. Compare (3.32).
3. Compare (3.33).
4. $\beta(PQR) =$ oriented boundary of an oriented triangle $=$ three directed line segments QR, RP, PQ. Draw a picture to check the consistency of the orientation.
5. Draw a picture of the tetrahedron to see that, if $\mathbf{n}$ is the outward normal, the oriented faces (they are oriented by $\mathbf{n}$) are QRS, RPS, PQS, QPR. Hence, a right-handed screw sense orientation in a tetrahedron demands an outward-normal orientation for the faces.
6. (a) If $\mathbf{curl\ F} = \mathbf{0}$, $\mathbf{F} = \nabla\phi$ for some ϕ.
   (b) Not generally, but true with additional hypotheses (simply-connected region, etc.)
7. -24.
8. $\mathbf{F} = 4\mathbf{i} - 3\mathbf{j} + 2\mathbf{k}$.
9. (a) Yes, one is the negative of the other.
   (b) The first integral.

SECTION 5.4

1. $\begin{pmatrix} 4 & 0 & 0 & -4 \\ 10 & 3 & 4 & -3 \\ 19 & 16 & 13 & 10 \end{pmatrix}$.

2. No.

3. (20).

   Half the students taking an examination on this will claim that vw is not defined.

4. $\begin{pmatrix} 4 & 8 & 12 & 16 \\ 3 & 6 & 9 & 12 \\ 2 & 4 & 6 & 8 \\ 1 & 2 & 3 & 4 \end{pmatrix}$.

5. $T^3_4 = 3$, $v^2 = 3$, $w_1 = 1$.

6. $\begin{pmatrix} 2 \\ 10 \\ 23 \end{pmatrix}$.

7. Not defined.

8. (16,11,14,9).

9. (134). Yes.

10. $RP = \begin{pmatrix} 15 & 15 \\ 42 & 42 \end{pmatrix}$, $PR = \begin{pmatrix} 8 & 28 \\ 14 & 49 \end{pmatrix}$. Not equal.

11. Not defined.

12. $\begin{pmatrix} 0 & -2 \\ -7 & 5 \end{pmatrix}$.

13. 1, 0, 1.

14. δ_i^j.

15. It is the ith column of T.

16. If $Tv = Pv$ for every v, then $T\underset{i}{e} = P\underset{i}{e}$ for every i, so the columns of T are identical to the columns of P.

17. (a) If $v = \theta$ it is easy to see that $Tv = \theta$. If $Tv = \theta$ and $\det(T) \neq 0$ then T^{-1} exists and $T^{-1}Tv = T^{-1}\theta = \theta$ so $v = \theta$.
(b) Yes, since the three simultaneous equations $\sum_{i=1}^{3} T_i^j v^i = 0$ have a solution v^1, v^2, v^3 (not all zero) when $\det(T) \neq 0$, a standard fact in the theory of determinants.

18. (a) By 17(b) there exists $v \neq \theta$ with $Tv = \theta$. If $ST = I_3$ we would have $STv = v$, but $STv = S\theta = \theta$, a contradiction.
(b) *Hint*: Consider the transpose of T.

19. $u^j = \sum_{i=1}^{3} T_i^j v^i$.

20. Whenever $\det(T) \neq 0$.

21. $\begin{pmatrix} \frac{1}{2} & \frac{1}{2} & 0 \\ -\frac{1}{2} & \frac{1}{2} & 0 \\ 0 & 0 & \frac{1}{2} \end{pmatrix}$.

22. $\begin{pmatrix} \frac{1}{6} & \frac{2}{3} \\ \frac{1}{6} & -\frac{1}{3} \end{pmatrix}$.

23. Multiply to show $TT^{-1} = I_2$.

24. $\begin{pmatrix} -\frac{1}{4} & \frac{3}{4} & -\frac{1}{4} \\ -\frac{3}{4} & \frac{1}{4} & \frac{1}{4} \\ \frac{1}{2} & -\frac{1}{2} & \frac{1}{2} \end{pmatrix}$.

25. $\begin{pmatrix} a^{-1} & 0 & 0 \\ 0 & b^{-1} & 0 \\ 0 & 0 & c^{-1} \end{pmatrix}$.

SECTION 5.5

1. A basis $\underset{1}{\mathbf{e}}, \underset{2}{\mathbf{e}}, \underset{3}{\mathbf{e}}$ for space vectors is an ordered set of three nonzero vectors that are not coplanar.

2. No; they are coplanar.

3. (a) Their triple scalar product is nonzero.
(b) $v^1 = 2$, $v^2 = 4$, $v^3 = 2$.

4. $\begin{pmatrix} 3 & 0 & 5 \\ 0 & 2 & -6 \\ 5 & -6 & 27 \end{pmatrix}$.

5. $v_1 = 6$, $v_2 = -2$, $v_3 = 16$. [Use (5.72).]

6. $\overset{1}{\mathbf{e}} = \dfrac{\underset{2}{\mathbf{e}} \times \underset{3}{\mathbf{e}}}{\underset{1}{\mathbf{e}} \cdot \underset{2}{\mathbf{e}} \times \underset{3}{\mathbf{e}}}$. Yes.

7. (a) Yes. (b) No.

9. $\sum_{j=1}^{3} g_{ij} g^{jk} = \sum_{j=1}^{3} g^{jk} g_{ij} = \sum_{j=1}^{3} g^{kj} g_{ji} = \delta_i^k$ by (5.78). The property used is symmetry of the matrices: $g^{kj} = g^{jk}$, $g_{ij} = g_{ji}$.

10. $\mathbf{v} \cdot \mathbf{v} > 0$ when $\mathbf{v} \neq \mathbf{0}$.

11. $\begin{pmatrix} 5 \\ -1 \end{pmatrix}$.

12. The basis must consist of mutually perpendicular unit vectors.

SECTION 5.6

Note: The metric tensor is so called because it describes the metric notions of length and angle. In the theory of relativity, the metric tensor varies with position in space; it is related to the gravitational field potential. It follows that the shortest path between two points is not necessarily straight, so that space is "curved". These remarks must not be taken too literally, since the space of relativity is four-dimensional with a metric tensor defined in a different manner. When the reader has finished this chapter, he will be in a good position to read elementary books on relativity.

1. p_{ij} is the ith covariant component of the force per unit area on a surface perpendicular to the jth base vector.

2. $\mathbf{F} \cdot \mathbf{B} = \sum_{i=1}^{3} \sum_{k=1}^{3} g_{ik} F^i B^k = \sum_{i=1}^{3} F^i B_i = \sum_{i=1}^{3} \sum_{j=1}^{3} p^{ij} A_i B_j$.

3. $\mathbf{F} \cdot \mathbf{B} = \sum_{i=1}^{3} \sum_{k=1}^{3} g^{ik} F_i B_k = \sum_{i=1}^{3} F_i B^i = \sum_{i=1}^{3} \sum_{j=1}^{3} p_i^j A^j B^i$.

4. $\begin{pmatrix} 1 & 0 & 0 \\ 0 & 0 & 2 \\ 0 & -6 & 0 \end{pmatrix}$. For example, $\phi_{32} = \phi(\underset{3}{\mathbf{e}},\underset{2}{\mathbf{e}}) = \phi(\mathbf{k},\mathbf{j}) = -6$, since for $\mathbf{u} = \mathbf{k}$ we have $u^1 = 0$, $u^2 = 0$, $u^3 = 1$ and for $\mathbf{v} = \mathbf{j}$ we have $v^1 = 0$, $v^2 = 1$, $v^3 = 0$.

5. $\begin{pmatrix} -3 & -8 & 17 \\ 8 & 4 & 4 \\ -31 & -28 & 19 \end{pmatrix}$.

6. $\phi^{ij} = g^{ip} g^{js} \phi_{ps}$.

SECTION 5.7

1. $F_i = p_{ij} A^j$.

2. No.

3. $p^{11}A_1B_1 + p^{12}A_1B_2 + p^{13}A_1B_3 + p^{21}A_2B_1 + p^{22}A_2B_2 + p^{23}A_2B_3 + p^{31}A_3B_1 + p^{32}A_3B_2 + p^{33}A_3B_3$.

4. No.

5. 27.

6. 9.

7. i, j, k, m, p, r. Note that $\det(R^i_k)$ simply means $\det R$. The i and k on the left side are meaningless.

8. $\sum_{i=1}^{3}\sum_{j=1}^{3} A^j_i B^i_j = \sum_{j=1}^{3}\sum_{i=1}^{3} A^i_j B^j_i.$

There is no difference between them.

9. 3.

10. $C = u_j w^j = \phi_{jk} v^k w^j.$

11. $u^1v^1 + u^2v^2 + u^3v^3.$

12. $w_1 = u^2v^3 - u^3v^2,\ w_2 = u^3v^1 - u^1v^3,\ w_3 = u^1v^2 - u^2v^1.$

13. 6.

15. $\overset{k}{\mathbf{e}}.$

16. $\delta^i_j.$

17. $p^{jk} = u^jv^k - u^kv^j.$

18. $w_1 = 2\phi^{23},\ w_2 = 2\phi^{31},\ w_3 = 2\phi^{12}.$

19. $\phi^{jk} = \frac{1}{2}\varepsilon^{ijk} w_i.$

20. If ϕ were a tensor of rank three with $\phi(\underset{i}{\mathbf{e}},\underset{j}{\mathbf{e}},\underset{k}{\mathbf{e}}) = \varepsilon_{ijk}$ for every basis, $\phi(\underset{1}{\mathbf{e}},\underset{2}{\mathbf{e}},\underset{3}{\mathbf{e}}) = 1$ and also $\phi(2\underset{1}{\mathbf{e}},\underset{2}{\mathbf{e}},\underset{3}{\mathbf{e}}) = 1$, contradicting the linearity of ϕ.

SECTION 5.8

1. $\overset{1}{\mathbf{e}} = \nabla\rho = \cos\theta\,\mathbf{i} + \sin\theta\,\mathbf{j} = \underset{1}{\mathbf{e}} = \underset{1}{\mathbf{u}}$

$\overset{2}{\mathbf{e}} = \nabla\theta = -\dfrac{\sin\theta}{\rho}\,\mathbf{i} + \dfrac{\cos\theta}{\rho}\,\mathbf{j}$

$\overset{3}{\mathbf{e}} = \nabla z = \mathbf{k} = \underset{3}{\mathbf{e}} = \underset{3}{\mathbf{u}}$

$\underset{2}{\mathbf{e}} = -\rho\sin\theta\,\mathbf{i} + \rho\cos\theta\,\mathbf{j}$

$\underset{2}{\mathbf{u}} = -\sin\theta\,\mathbf{i} + \cos\theta\,\mathbf{j}.$

2. $d\mathbf{R}\cdot d\mathbf{R} = \left(\sum du^i \underset{i}{\mathbf{e}}\right)\cdot\left(\sum du^j \underset{j}{\mathbf{e}}\right)$ etc.

3. $ds^2 = d\rho^2 + \rho^2\, d\theta^2 + dz^2$

$$G = \begin{pmatrix} 1 & 0 & 0 \\ 0 & \rho^2 & 0 \\ 0 & 0 & 1 \end{pmatrix}.$$

4. $\underset{1}{\mathbf{e}} = \mathbf{i},\ \underset{2}{\mathbf{e}} = -\tfrac{1}{3}\mathbf{i} + \tfrac{1}{3}\mathbf{j} - \tfrac{1}{3}\mathbf{k},\ \underset{3}{\mathbf{e}} = \mathbf{k}$

$\overset{1}{\mathbf{e}} = \mathbf{i} + \mathbf{j},\ \overset{2}{\mathbf{e}} = 3\mathbf{j},\ \overset{3}{\mathbf{e}} = \mathbf{j} + \mathbf{k}$

$\underset{1}{\mathbf{u}} = \mathbf{i},\ \underset{2}{\mathbf{u}} = -\tfrac{1}{3}\sqrt{3}\mathbf{i} + \tfrac{1}{3}\sqrt{3}\mathbf{j} - \tfrac{1}{3}\sqrt{3}\mathbf{k},\ \underset{3}{\mathbf{u}} = \mathbf{k}.$

5. $J = \frac{1}{3}.$

6. $u^i = A^i_j x^j + C^i$ where A^i_j are constant and x^1, x^2, x^3 are cartesian coordinates.

7. No.

8. $\mathbf{v} = v_i \overset{i}{\mathbf{e}} = \mathbf{i} + 18\mathbf{j} + 8\mathbf{k}$

$v^1 = 19,\ v^2 = 54,\ v^3 = 26$

$\dot{v}^1 = 19,\ \dot{v}^2 = 18\sqrt{3},\ \dot{v}^3 = 26.$

9. *Hint*: $\mathbf{w} = (u_i \overset{i}{\mathbf{e}}) \times (v_j \overset{j}{\mathbf{e}}) = u_i v_j \varepsilon^{ijk} \underset{k}{\mathbf{e}}/J$.

10. $$\dot{w}^k = \frac{h^k}{J} \varepsilon^{ijk} g_{ip} g_{js} \frac{\dot{u}^p}{h_p} \frac{\dot{v}^s}{h_s}.$$

11. (a) $v^1 = d\rho/dt,\ v^2 = d\theta/dt,\ v^3 = dz/dt$.
    (b) $v_1 = d\rho/dt,\ v_2 = \rho^2\, d\theta/dt,\ v_3 = dz/dt$.
    (c) $\dot{v}_1 = d\rho/dt,\ \dot{v}_2 = \rho\, d\theta/dt,\ \dot{v}_3 = dz/dt$.

12. $h_i = \sqrt{g_{ii}}$.

13. $$\delta^i_j = \frac{\partial u^i}{\partial u^j} = \frac{\partial u^i}{\partial x^k} \frac{\partial x^k}{\partial u^j} \text{ (a matrix product).}$$

14. When these cofactors are divided by the determinant $J = \underset{1}{\mathbf{e}} \cdot \underset{2}{\mathbf{e}} \times \underset{3}{\mathbf{e}}$ we obtain the entries of the first row $\nabla u^1 = \overset{1}{\mathbf{e}}$ of the inverse matrix $(\partial u/\partial x)$.

15. $\underset{2}{\mathbf{e}} \times \underset{3}{\mathbf{e}} = C\overset{1}{\mathbf{e}}$ so $J = \underset{2}{\mathbf{e}} \times \underset{3}{\mathbf{e}} \cdot \underset{1}{\mathbf{e}} = C\overset{1}{\mathbf{e}} \cdot \underset{1}{\mathbf{e}} = C$.

16. $\overset{1}{\mathbf{e}} = \mathbf{i} + z\mathbf{j} + y\mathbf{k}$

$$\underset{1}{\mathbf{e}} = \frac{(1 - x)\mathbf{i} + (xy - z)\mathbf{j} + (xz - y)\mathbf{k}}{1 + 2xyz - x^2 - y^2 - z^2}$$

$g^{12} = 2z + xy$, etc.

17. The differentiation is incorrect, since $\underset{j}{\mathbf{e}}$ need not be constant.

18. $(1/J)\ \partial J/\partial u^1$.

19. (a) $\overset{2}{\mathbf{e}} \times \overset{3}{\mathbf{e}} = \mathbf{curl}\,(u^2 \nabla u^3)$.
    (b) Find div $(\nabla u^2 \times \nabla u^3)$ using Sec. 3.7.

SECTION 5.9

Note: It is a fairly common practice in tensor analysis to say *vector* or *tensor* where it would be better to say *vector field* or *tensor field*.

In comparing this section with Sec. 5.8, keep in mind that general coordinates are now denoted by x^1, x^2, x^3 rather than u^1, u^2, u^3.

1. $$0 = \frac{\partial}{\partial x^j}(\overset{i}{\mathbf{e}} \cdot \underset{k}{\mathbf{e}}) = \frac{\partial \overset{i}{\mathbf{e}}}{\partial x^j} \cdot \underset{k}{\mathbf{e}} + \overset{i}{\mathbf{e}} \cdot \frac{\partial \underset{k}{\mathbf{e}}}{\partial x^j} = \frac{\partial \overset{i}{\mathbf{e}}}{\partial x^j} \cdot \underset{k}{\mathbf{e}} + \Gamma^i_{kj}.$$

2. $F_{k,j} = \dfrac{\partial \mathbf{F}}{\partial x^j} \cdot \underset{k}{\mathbf{e}}$. Now proceed as in (5.175).

3. This is routine. An alternate method for deriving (5.181) is to explicitly calculate $\Gamma^j_{i,s} g^{sk}$ using (5.179) and the fact that $(g^{ij}) = G^{-1}$ so that $g_{ij} g^{jk} = \delta^k_i$.

5. Exercise 8, Sec. 5.7, shows that trace $(AB) = $ trace (BA).

6. By (5.163), $(\nabla \times \mathbf{F})^k = \dfrac{1}{J}\varepsilon^{ijk}\dfrac{\partial F_j}{\partial x^i}$. Changing the role of the indices (k to i, i to j, j to k) gives

$$(\nabla \times \mathbf{F})^i = \frac{1}{J}\varepsilon^{jki}\frac{\partial F_k}{\partial x^j} = \frac{1}{J}\varepsilon^{ijk}\frac{\partial F_k}{\partial x^i} = -\frac{1}{J}\varepsilon^{ikj}\frac{\partial F_k}{\partial x^i}$$

Now interchange the role of the dummies k and j to obtain the second expression in (5.164).

7. It helps to observe that, for any *fixed* j and k, if $j \neq k$, for only one index i will ε_{ijk} be nonzero, and for this index i, the only ε^{ips} that do not vanish are ε^{ijk} and ε^{ikj}.

8. $$J\varepsilon_{ijk}\left(\frac{1}{2J}\varepsilon^{ips}T_{ps}\right) = \tfrac{1}{2}\varepsilon_{ijk}\varepsilon^{ips}T_{ps} = \tfrac{1}{2}(2T_{jk}) = T_{jk}$$

Notice that we have made use of the fact that $T_{ps} = -T_{sp}$.

9. $$\mathbf{w} = (u^i\underset{i}{\mathbf{e}}) \times (v^j\underset{j}{\mathbf{e}}) = u^iv^j(\underset{i}{\mathbf{e}} \times \underset{j}{\mathbf{e}}) = u^iv^jJ\varepsilon_{ijk}\overset{k}{\mathbf{e}}$$

10. (a) Similar to Exercise 9.

(b) $$w = \frac{1}{J}\begin{vmatrix} \underset{1}{\mathbf{e}} & \underset{2}{\mathbf{e}} & \underset{3}{\mathbf{e}} \\ A_1 & A_2 & A_3 \\ F_1 & F_2 & F_3 \end{vmatrix}.$$

(c) $$w = \frac{1}{J}\begin{vmatrix} \underset{1}{\mathbf{e}} & \underset{2}{\mathbf{e}} & \underset{3}{\mathbf{e}} \\ \dfrac{\partial}{\partial x^1} & \dfrac{\partial}{\partial x^2} & \dfrac{\partial}{\partial x^3} \\ F_1 & F_2 & F_3 \end{vmatrix}.$$

(d) Yes.

11. (a) The coordinate curves are lines, the coordinate surfaces are planes. The same as a cartesian coordinate system except that the three axes are not necessarily mutually perpendicular and the scale factors for these axes need not be unity nor need they be equal to one another.

(b) Volume $= J$(relative volume). Notice that the relative volume of the oriented parallelepiped determined by $\underset{1}{\mathbf{e}}$, $\underset{2}{\mathbf{e}}$, and $\underset{3}{\mathbf{e}}$ is unity. Notice also that relative volume can be negative.

(c) The constant factor J cancels out of the expression $(1/V)\,dV/dt$.

12. One example is: $x^1 = e^x$, $x^2 = e^y$, $x^3 = e^z$ where x, y, z are cartesian coordinates.

13. $$\frac{dx^i}{dt} = \frac{dx^i}{ds}\frac{ds}{dt} = C\frac{dx^i}{ds}$$

$$\frac{d^2x^i}{dt^2} = \frac{d}{ds}\left(C\frac{dx^i}{ds}\right)\frac{ds}{dt} = C^2\frac{d^2x^i}{dt^2}.$$

14. Simply use the fact that $d^2f/dt^2 = 0$ has solutions $f(t) = a + bt$ where a and b are constants.

15. $$\left(\frac{d\mathbf{F}}{dt}\right)_k = \frac{dF_k}{dt} - \Gamma^i_{kj} F_i \frac{dx^j}{dt}.$$

16. $\mathbf{F}$ is constant along the curve.

17. Taking $\mathbf{F} = \mathbf{T}$ and $t = s$ in (44) we have

$$0 = \left(\frac{d\mathbf{T}}{ds}\right)^k = \frac{dT^k}{ds} + \Gamma^k_{ij} T^i \frac{dx^j}{ds} = \frac{d^2x^k}{ds^2} + \Gamma^k_{ij} \frac{dx^i}{ds}\frac{dx^j}{ds}$$

(The unit tangent is constant along a curve if and only if the curve is a line.)

18. (a) $dV = |(\underset{1}{\mathbf{e}}\, dx^1) \cdot (\underset{2}{\mathbf{e}}\, dx^2) \times (\underset{3}{\mathbf{e}}\, dx^3)| = |J|\, dx^1\, dx^2\, dx^3$.

(b) If the coordinate system is right-handed, $J = |J| = h_1 h_2 h_3$. Jacobians are discussed in greater detail in the next chapter.

19. (a) $F_{k,j} v^k \overset{j}{\mathbf{e}}$.

(b) $(d\mathbf{F}/dt) \cdot \mathbf{u}$.

(c) ϕ is a tensor of rank two with covariant components $F_{k,j}$.

20. By the preceding exercise, it is the difference of two tensor fields.

SECTION 5.10

1. $$\delta^i_j = \frac{\partial x^i}{\partial x^j} = \frac{\partial x^i}{\partial \bar{x}^k}\frac{\partial \bar{x}^k}{\partial x^j} = B^i_k A^k_j.$$

2. In other words, derive

$$\bar{\phi}_{ijk} = \frac{\partial x^r}{\partial \bar{x}^i}\frac{\partial x^s}{\partial \bar{x}^j}\frac{\partial x^t}{\partial \bar{x}^k}\phi_{rst}$$

3. No.

4. One example is $\mathbf{F} = \mathbf{i}$ for which $\partial F_i/\partial x^i$ are zero in cartesian coordinates but not in cylindrical coordinates.

5. Let $\mathbf{w} = \mathbf{curl\ F}$. Then $T_{ij} u^i v^j = \varepsilon_{ijk} w^k u^i v^j = (\mathbf{u} \times \mathbf{v}) \cdot \mathbf{w}$ is approximately the surface integral of the normal component of **curl F** over the parallelepiped. Now apply Stokes' theorem.

6. $\phi(\mathbf{u},\mathbf{v}) = \psi(\mathbf{u},\mathbf{v})$ independently of the coordinate system. (No calculations are required.)

7. $\phi(\mathbf{u},\mathbf{v}) = \phi(u_i \overset{i}{\mathbf{e}}, v^j \underset{j}{\mathbf{e}}) = u_i v^j \phi^i_{\cdot j} = u_i v^j \psi_j^{\cdot i} = \psi(v^j \underset{j}{\mathbf{e}}, u_i \overset{i}{\mathbf{e}}) = \psi(\mathbf{v},\mathbf{u})$.

9. It suffices to show $\phi^{123} = \phi_{123}/J^2$.

11. $$V_r = \iiint_D dx^1\, dx^2\, dx^3$$

$$= \iiint_D \frac{\partial(x^1,x^2,x^3)}{\partial(\bar{x}^1,\bar{x}^2,\bar{x}^3)} d\bar{x}^1\, d\bar{x}^2\, d\bar{x}^3 = \iiint_D d\bar{x}^1\, d\bar{x}^2\, d\bar{x}^3 = \bar{V}_r$$

14. F.

15. $(1/V)\,dV/dt = \operatorname{div} \mathbf{F} = \text{constant}$.
Solve the differential equation $dV/dt = (\text{constant})V$.

SECTION 5.11

1. Simply multiply $(u_1 i + u_2 j + u_3 k)(v_1 i + v_2 j + v_3 k)$.

2. (a) $uv + vu = (-u \cdot v + u \times v) + (-v \cdot u + v \times u)$ by (5.288). The cross products disappear.
(b) Use (5.288) to compute $uv - vu$.

3. (a) This is simple vector algebra (draw a picture).
(b) Use (5.289) as follows: $v' = v - 2(v \cdot n)n = v + (vn + nv)n = v + vnn + nvn$. But $n \cdot n = -nn$ by (5.289) and since n is a unit vector $nn = -1$. So $v' = v - v + nvn = nvn$.

4. As in the preceding exercise, make use of (5.288), (5.289), (5.290). For example, by (5.288), $n'n = -(n' \cdot n) + n' \times n = -\cos \tfrac{1}{2}\theta - u \sin \tfrac{1}{2}\theta$.

5. Since u is a unit vector, $u^2 = -1$ by (5.288), so $u^3 = -u$, $u^4 = 1$, $u^5 = u$, ... and

$$1 + \phi u + \phi^2 u^2/2! + \phi^3 u^3/3! + \cdots$$
$$= (1 - \phi^2/2! + \phi^4/4! - \cdots) + (\phi - \phi^3/3! + \cdots)u$$

6. $v'' = e^{(\theta/2)u} v e^{-(\theta/2)u}$.

REVIEW PROBLEMS

1. (a) $\tfrac{8}{29}\sqrt{29}$
(b) $\tfrac{8}{77}\sqrt{77}$.
(c) Any scalar multiple of $6\mathbf{i} + 4\mathbf{j} + 5\mathbf{k}$.

3. $90° - \cos^{-1} \tfrac{1}{7}\sqrt{35}$.

4. (a) Any scalar multiple of $5\mathbf{i} - \mathbf{j} - \mathbf{k}$
(b) $\tfrac{8}{27}\sqrt{27}$.

5. $\sqrt{34}$.

6. $\tfrac{1}{5}(x - 4) = -\tfrac{1}{8}(y - 2) = -\tfrac{1}{7}(z - 1)$.

7. (a) $\tfrac{1}{6}101$.
(b) $x - 11y - 14z + 43 = 0$.
(c) $\tfrac{1}{319}\sqrt{319}$.

8. $\pm\tfrac{5}{3}(2\mathbf{i} + \mathbf{j} - 2\mathbf{k})$.

9. (a) 13.
(b) $\mathbf{i} - 3\mathbf{j} - 4\mathbf{k}$.
(c) 3.
(d) -12.

10. (a) $\tfrac{1}{2}\sqrt{26}$.
(b) 2.
(c) $\cos^{-1} \tfrac{1}{9}$.

11. Let C be the center, A, B the ends of diameter, and let P be another point on the circumference. Write PA and PB in terms of PC and CA or CB; then show $PA \cdot PB = 0$. You will need to use the fact that $|CA| = |BC| = |PC|$.

12. Show that the vector sum of the medians is the zero vector.

13. (a) Infinitely many. (b) $\mathbf{u} = (19\mathbf{i} + 10\mathbf{j} + 17\mathbf{k})/\sqrt{750}$.
Note that $\mathbf{u} \cdot (\mathbf{a}/|\mathbf{a}|) = \mathbf{u} \cdot (\mathbf{b}/|\mathbf{b}|)$, $\mathbf{u} \cdot \mathbf{a} \times \mathbf{b} = 0$, and $|\mathbf{u}| = 1$ determine $\pm\mathbf{u}$. How do we know the answer just given is $\mathbf{u}$ and not $-\mathbf{u}$?

14. $(\mathbf{u} \times \mathbf{v}) \cdot (\mathbf{u} \times \mathbf{v}) = \mathbf{u} \cdot \mathbf{v} \times (\mathbf{u} \times \mathbf{v})$. Expand the triple vector product. The answer is

$$\begin{vmatrix} \mathbf{u} \cdot \mathbf{u} & \mathbf{u} \cdot \mathbf{v} \\ \mathbf{u} \cdot \mathbf{v} & \mathbf{v} \cdot \mathbf{v} \end{vmatrix}$$

15. No.

16. Either $\mathbf{u} = \pm\mathbf{v}$ or both $\mathbf{u}$ and $\mathbf{v}$ are perpendicular to $\mathbf{w}$.

17. 7. (Simply the distance $|AB|$.)

18. 6. (No calculations are required.)

19. $\frac{30}{7}$.

20. $3x + 2y + z = 18$.

21. The vector $\mathbf{i} + 8\mathbf{j} + 12\mathbf{k}$ is tangent to the curve and perpendicular to the plane at the point (2,8,8).

22. (2,4,8). (The vector extending from the center of the sphere to this point is perpendicular to the given plane.)

23. (1,1,1). [The gradient of $x^2 + 2y^2 + 3z^2$ is parallel to $\mathbf{i} + 2\mathbf{j} + 3\mathbf{k}$ at (1,1,1).]

24. (1,1,2). (At this point the tangent to the curve is perpendicular to **grad** ϕ. Of course, this can also be done without using vector methods, by observing that $\phi = t^2 - 6t + t^4$ has its minimum at $t = 1$.)

25. (1,1,2). This is the preceding exercise in a different format.

26. $90° - \cos^{-1} 98/(\sqrt{157}\,\sqrt{65})$.

27. A region to the right of P, approximately cigar-shaped, with major axis parallel to the y axis.

28. $$\frac{d\mathbf{R}}{dt} = \frac{d}{dt}(R_1\mathbf{i} + R_2\mathbf{j} + R_3\mathbf{k}) = \left.\frac{d\mathbf{R}}{dt}\right|_m + R_1\frac{d\mathbf{i}}{dt} + R_2\frac{d\mathbf{j}}{dt} + R_3\frac{d\mathbf{k}}{dt}$$

By Example 2.6, $d\mathbf{i}/dt$ is perpendicular to $\mathbf{i}$. Therefore,

$$\frac{d\mathbf{i}}{dt} = \alpha_1\mathbf{j} + \alpha_2\mathbf{k}$$

Similarly,

$$\frac{d\mathbf{j}}{dt} = \alpha_3\mathbf{k} + \alpha_4\mathbf{i}$$

$$\frac{d\mathbf{k}}{dt} = \alpha_5\mathbf{i} + \alpha_6\mathbf{j}$$

Differentiating both sides of $\mathbf{i} \cdot \mathbf{j} = 0$, we obtain $\mathbf{i} \cdot (d\mathbf{j}/dt) + (d\mathbf{i}/dt) \cdot \mathbf{j} = 0$. Hence $\alpha_4 = -\alpha_1$. Similarly, $\alpha_5 = -\alpha_2$ and $\alpha_6 = -\alpha_3$. Let $\boldsymbol{\omega} = \alpha_3\mathbf{i} - \alpha_2\mathbf{j} + \alpha_1\mathbf{k}$ and verify that $\boldsymbol{\omega} \times \mathbf{R} = R_1\, d\mathbf{i}/dt + R_2\, d\mathbf{j}/dt + R_3\, d\mathbf{k}/dt$.

29. If $\mathbf{T}$ is a unit tangent to the ellipse, $\nabla(|\mathbf{R}_1| + |\mathbf{R}_2|) \cdot \mathbf{T} = 0$ (why?). Also, $\nabla|\mathbf{R}_1|$ and $\nabla|\mathbf{R}_2|$ are unit vectors in the directions $\mathbf{R}_1$ and $\mathbf{R}_2$ respectively, so the cosine of the angle between $\nabla|\mathbf{R}_2|$ and $\mathbf{T}$ equals the cosine of the angle between $\nabla|\mathbf{R}_1|$ and $-\mathbf{T}$.

30. $\cos^{-1} \frac{8}{63}\sqrt{21}$.

31. (a) $4x\mathbf{i} + \mathbf{j}$.
(b) 3.
(c) 4.
(d) $z\mathbf{i} - 4xz\mathbf{j} + (4xy - x)\mathbf{k}$.

32. (a) $2\mathbf{i}$.
(b) $2\mathbf{k}$.
(c) -2.

33. $40[(z - y)\mathbf{i} + (x - z)\mathbf{j} + (y - x)\mathbf{k}]$.

34. $-6\mathbf{i} + 3\mathbf{j} + 2\mathbf{k}$.

35. $2\mathbf{A}$.

36. (a) $2\mathbf{R} \cdot \mathbf{A}$.
(b) $2\mathbf{R} \times \mathbf{A}$.
(c) $2r^2\mathbf{A}$.
(d) $4(\mathbf{A} \cdot \mathbf{R})^3\mathbf{A}$.
(e) $(\mathbf{A} \cdot \mathbf{R})/r$.
(f) $(\mathbf{A} \cdot \mathbf{R})\mathbf{A}$.
(g) 0.
(h) $2\mathbf{A}$.
(i) 6.

37. (a) Any scalar multiple of $6\mathbf{i} + 3\mathbf{j} + 2\mathbf{k}$.
(b) 7.

38. (a) $x + y - 4z + 6 = 0$.
(b) $x + 2 = y - 4 = -\frac{1}{4}(z - 2)$.
(c) $\frac{23}{7}$.

39. $90° - (\cos^{-1} \frac{3}{305}\sqrt{122})$.

40. Zero vector field except where $r = 0$; not defined where $r = 0$.

41. div (**curl F**) $= 0$. Hence $2 + C = 0$ and $C = -2$.

42. **0**. By symmetry, it is fairly clear that a paddle wheel in such a force field will not tend to rotate, no matter how the wheel is oriented.

43. $\nabla \times (\nabla \times \mathbf{E}) = \nabla \times (-\partial\mathbf{H}/\partial t) = -\partial/\partial t(\nabla \times \mathbf{H}) = -\partial^2 E/\partial t^2$
Also, $\nabla \times (\nabla \times \mathbf{E}) = -\nabla^2\mathbf{E} + \nabla(\nabla \cdot \mathbf{E}) = -\nabla^2\mathbf{E}$
Hence $\nabla^2\mathbf{E} = \partial^2\mathbf{E}/\partial t^2$. The derivation for $\mathbf{H}$ is similar.

45. Since $\psi = \tan\phi$, the two functions have the same isotimic surfaces, so $\nabla\psi$ and $\nabla\phi$ are parallel.

46. Since $\nabla\phi$ and $\nabla\psi$ are parallel, every isotimic surface of ϕ is also an isotimic surface of ψ and vice versa.

47. (a) $\nabla w \cdot \nabla u \times \nabla v = (u\nabla v + v\nabla u) \cdot \nabla u \times \nabla v$
$= u(\nabla v \cdot \nabla u \times \nabla v) + v(\nabla u \cdot \nabla u \times \nabla v) = 0$
(b) At any point in space, the isotimic surfaces $u =$ constant and $v =$ constant intersect in a curve along which both u and v and, hence, w are constant. $\nabla u \times \nabla v$ is tangent to this curve and, hence, perpendicular to ∇w.

48. If u, v, and w are functionally related, $\nabla w \cdot \nabla u \times \nabla v = 0$.

49. No. div $(\mathbf{F} \times \mathbf{G}) = 0$.

50. 60. The z component of $\mathbf{F}$ can be ignored, so replace $\mathbf{F}$ by $\mathbf{G} = y\mathbf{i} + (x + 2)\mathbf{j}$. Div $\mathbf{G} = 0$ so (by the divergence theorem) the desired integral is the negative of the integral of $\mathbf{G}$ over the four *flat* faces of a certain five sided closed surface. Only two faces contribute nonzero values to the integral. The average value of

$x+2$ over the face in the xz plane is $\frac{7}{2}$ and the average value of y over the face in the yz plane is $\frac{3}{2}$ so the arithmetic is $\frac{7}{2}(3)(4)+\frac{3}{2}(3)(4)=60$.

51. Interchanging the role of x and y amounts to reflecting the plane in the line $y=x$; following this by an inversion (replacing x by $-x$ and y by $-y$) we obtain an integral that "means" the same as before. But the effect of these replacements is to change the sign of the integrand. Therefore, the integral equals its own negative and must be zero. If this seems too abstruse, let $x=a\cos\theta$, $y=a\sin\theta$, $ds=a\,d\theta$, and the integral becomes $\int_0^{2\pi} a^3\cos 2\theta\,d\theta=0$.

52. 0. Use Stokes' theorem and the preceding problem.

53. $\int \mathbf{F}\cdot d\mathbf{R}=\frac{1}{2}\int x\,dy-y\,dx$. Let $x=a\cos\theta$, $y=b\sin\theta$. The integral becomes $\frac{1}{2}\int_0^{2\pi} ab\,d\theta=\pi ab$.

54. -1. The integral is independent of the path.

55. $\iiint \nabla\cdot\mathbf{F}\,dV=\iint \mathbf{F}\cdot\mathbf{n}\,dS$ leads to $\mathbf{C}\cdot\iiint\nabla\phi\,dV=C\cdot\iint\phi\mathbf{n}\,dS$ and, since this is valid for every constant vector $\mathbf{C}$, the identity follows.

56. In the divergence theorem, let $\mathbf{F}=\mathbf{A}\times\mathbf{C}$ where $\mathbf{C}$ is a constant vector field, and proceed as in the preceding problem.

57. (a) ∇f.

(b) $\nabla\times\mathbf{F}$. (Make use of the two preceding problems.)

58. $h_u=h_v=\sqrt{u^2+v^2}$, $h_z=1$.

59. $(u^2+v^2)\,du\,dv\,dz$.

60. (a) $$\frac{1}{u^2+v^2}\left(\frac{\partial}{\partial u}(\sqrt{u^2+v^2}A_u)+\frac{\partial}{\partial v}(\sqrt{u^2+v^2}A_v)\right)+\frac{\partial A_z}{\partial z}$$

(b) $$\frac{\partial^2\phi}{\partial u^2}+\frac{\partial^2\phi}{\partial v^2}+(u^2+v^2)\frac{\partial^2\phi}{\partial z^2}=0.$$

61. $J=4vu$, $g=16v^2u^2$. (Notice that $g=J^2$).

62. (a) $\underset{1}{\mathbf{e}}=3\mathbf{i}+\mathbf{j}+2\mathbf{k}$, etc. $\overset{1}{\mathbf{e}}=3\mathbf{i}-2\mathbf{j}-\mathbf{k}$, etc.

(b) $J=10$, $g=J^2=100$.

(c) 15 ("Actual volume" is 150).

Note: An alternative viewpoint is to regard the equations as defining a mapping operation from *uvw* space to *xyz* space for which the volume magnification factor is 10. Then the *actual* volume of the parallelepiped in *uvw* space (that is mapped into the given rectangular parallelepiped in *xyz* space) is 15.

63. Yes, these are the mixed components of the metric tensor $\phi(\mathbf{u},\mathbf{v})=\mathbf{u}\cdot\mathbf{v}$.

64. $$\Gamma^3_{32}=\frac{1}{2g_{33}}\frac{\partial g_{33}}{\partial x^2}=\frac{1}{2r^2\sin^2\theta}\frac{\partial}{\partial\theta}(r^2\sin^2\theta)=\cot\theta.$$

65. $g^{11}=1$, $g^{22}=\dfrac{1}{\rho^2}$, $g^{33}=1$. Substitution yields

$$\frac{1}{\rho}\left[\frac{\partial}{\partial\rho}\left(\rho\frac{\partial f}{\partial\rho}\right)+\frac{\partial}{\partial\phi}\left(\frac{1}{\rho}\frac{\partial f}{\partial\phi}\right)+\frac{\partial}{\partial z}\left(\rho\frac{\partial f}{\partial z}\right)\right]$$

66. Yes.

67. $\frac{1}{\sqrt{g}} \varepsilon^{ijk} E_{j,k} = \frac{1}{c} \frac{\partial B^i}{\partial t}$.

68. 24. $\iiint_D (x^2 + y^2)\, dx\, dy\, dz = \int_1^5 \int_1^4 \int_1^3 du\, dv\, dz = 24.$

[Note that $\partial(u,v,z)/\partial(x,y,z) = x^2 + y^2$.]

69. This is not trivial. See K. Pomeranz, Am. J. Phys. **31**, 622 (1963) or H. F. Davis, Am. J. Phys. **32**, 318 (1964). Instructors may obtain reprints by writing directly to the author of this book (please do not write to the publisher).

70. Multiply both sides by $4\pi R^2$ and integrate from 0 to R, then divide both sides by the volume of the sphere.

Index